Know Your Common Plant Names

Compiled by Brian Davis & Brian Knapp

Cover photograph: Davidia involucrata by Brian Davis.

This publication is an extension to the original 'Know Your Common Names' which was commissioned by the Horticultural Trades Association (HTA) for use by its members. We wish to thank the HTA for their help and support during the compilation and production of this version which we hope will be of further benefit to HTA members.

Compiled by Brian Davis & Brian Knapp.

Published by MDA Publications, Concept House, 10 Oxford Road, Newbury, Berkshire, RG13 1PA England.

Printed and bound by Quadgraphics, Newbury, England.

First Published August 1992.

Joint Copyright 1992 © MDA Publications and Brian Davis

ISBN 0-9 519 833-0-X

Contents & Key

Key to Plant Type

A	-	Annual
B	-	Biennial
BB	-	Bulb or Corm
C	-	Conifer
CL	-	Climber
CS	-	Cactus
FU	-	Fungi
F	-	Fruit
FN	-	Fern
G	-	Grass or Bamboo
H	-	Herbaceous Perennial
HB	-	Herb
HP	-	House Plant
MB	-	Moss
O	-	Orchid
P	-	Palm
PE	-	Parasite
R	-	Rockery or Alpine Plant
S	-	Shrub
ST	-	Shrub or Tree
SW	-	Sea Weed
T	-	Tree
TCL	-	Tropical Climber
TH	-	Tropical Herb
TS	-	Tropical Shrub
TT	-	Tropical Tree
V	-	Vegetable
WP	-	Water Plant

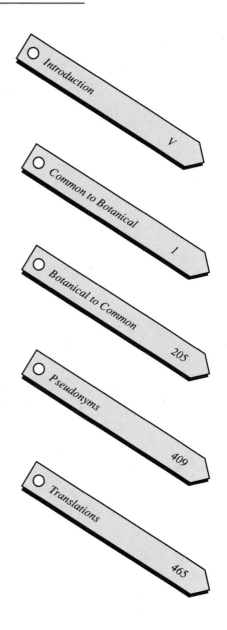

Introduction V

Common to Botanical I

Botanical to Common 205

Pseudonyms 409

Translations 465

The authors and publishers are always pleased to receive further established Common Names for inclusion within future editions of this publication. If you have any names that you would like to suggest please send details to the publishers at the address opposite.

Know Your Common Plant Names

Introduction

With so many plants having both common and botanical names, it has become apparent that for sometime there has been a need to record as many as can be researched. This book has been published as a result of such research.

Common names are colloquial by nature and only recognised nationally (after many years, even decades), so no list however carefully researched will ever be complete and the author's and researcher's of "Know Your Common Plant Names" would be only too pleased to receive further information that can then be added to future editions.

However, those that are listed in the following pages, represent one of the widest compilations of such names published to date. Not only do they work from common names to botanical, but vice-versa, making it possible for the reader to use both routes to achieve the correct naming.

Many plants have pseudonyms and these are also covered within the pages of this book. An attempt has been made to go back approximately ten years, although many are even older, and we have tried to identify the cross reference between the modern botanical name and that attributed to the plant in the past.

Plants that are introduced from Europe and other parts of the world often carry a name in the language of the country of origin. Wherever these have been found, and an English translation is available, they are listed.

A thorough attempt has been made to enter each of the botanical names in correct nomenclature style and it is envisaged that those who reproduce or write text and script regarding plants, will use this to standardize their use of plant names.

As we mention in the opening statement, a list of this type can never be complete. We have taken into account common names in Europe, U.S.A., and throughout the Northern and Southern Hemispheres, wherever it has been possible to find them.

However, knowing the botanical, common name, pseudonym or translation is only the first part. You may well have a name, but you need to know whether it is a tree, shrub or conifer etc. To this effect we have marked each of the entries with an identification code, so that it can quickly be identified as to its classification in the horticultural industry and further research carried out.

We hope that this first edition of Know Your Common Plant Names will prove useful to you no matter whether your interest is for business or pleasure.

Brian Davis   Brian Knapp

Know Your Common Plant Names

Common
to
Botanical

Know Your Common Plant Names

Common	Botanical	Type
AARON'S BEARD	Hypericum calycinum	(S)
AARON'S ROD	Sulidago	(H)
AARON'S ROD	Verbascum thapsus	(H)
ABACA	Musa textilis	(F)
ABATA COLA	Cola acuminata	(TF)
ABCESS ROOT	Polemonium reptans	(HB)
ABELE	Populus alba	(T)
ABRAHAM, ISAAC & JACOB	Trachystemon orientalis	(H)
ABSINTHE	Artemisia absinthium	(HB)
ABYSSINIAN BANANA	Enseta ventricosa	(F)
ABYSSINIAN FEATHERTOP	Pennisetum villosum	(G)
ACHOCHA	Cyclanthera pedata	(TS)
ACIDANTHERA	Gladiolus callianthus	(BB)
ACONITE	Aconitum	(H)
ACONITE-LEAVED BUTTERCUP	Ranunculus aconitifolius	(H)
ADAM'S APPLE	Tabernaemontana coronaria	(S)
ADAM'S FLANNEL	Verbascum thapsus	(H)
ADAM'S LABURNUM	+ Laburnocytisus adamii	(T)
ADAM'S NEEDLE	Yucca gloriosa	(S)
ADDER'S MOUTH	Pogonia	(O)
ADDER'S ROOT	Arum maculatum	(H)
ADDER'S TONGUE	Erythronium	(BB)
ADDER'S TONGUE	Erythronium americanum	(BB)
ADDER'S TONGUE FERN	Ophioglossum vulgatum	(FN)
ADDERS VIOLET	Goodyera pubescens	(H)
ADDERWORT	Persicaria bistorta	(H)
ADENOSTYLES	Adenostyles alliariae	(H)
ADRUE	Cyperus articulatus	(G)
ADVENTURE BAY PINE	Phyllocladus aspleniifolius	(C)
ADZUKIBEAN	Phaseolus angularis	(V)
AFARA	Terminalia superba	(TS)
AFGHAN ASH	Fraxinus xanthoxyloides	(T)
AFGHAN CHERRY	Prunus jacquemontii	(S)
AFRICAN ALMOND	Brabeium	(H)
AFRICAN BOXWEED	Myrsina africana	(T)
AFRICAN BREADFRUIT	Treculia africana	(TF)
AFRICAN CORN LILY	Ixia	(BB)
AFRICAN CYPRESS	Widdringtonia	(C)
AFRICAN DAISY	Arctotis	(A)
AFRICAN DAISY	Dimorphotheca, osteospermum	(H)
AFRICAN DAISY	Osteospermum	(H)
AFRICAN FERN PINE	Podocarpus gracilior	(C)
AFRICAN FOUNTAIN GRASS	Pennisetum setaceum	(G)
AFRICAN HAREBELL	Roella ciliata	(H)
AFRICAN HEMP	Sparmannia africana	(HP)
AFRICAN HONEYSUCKLE	Halleria lucida	(TS)
AFRICAN JUNIPER	Juniperus procera	(C)

Common	Botanical	Type
AFRICAN LILY	Agapanthus	(H)
AFRICAN MAHOGANY	Khaya	(TT)
AFRICAN MAHOGANY	Khaya spp.	(TT)
AFRICAN MARIGOLD	Tagetes erecta	(A)
AFRICAN MILKBUSH	Synadenium grantii	(TS)
AFRICAN OAK	Lophira alata	(TT)
AFRICAN OAK	Lophira lanceolata	(TT)
AFRICAN PEACH	Nauclea latifolia	(TT)
AFRICAN RAGWORT	Othonna	(H)
AFRICAN RED ALDER	Cunonia capensis	(TT)
AFRICAN TULIP TREE	Spathodea campanulata	(TT)
AFRICAN VALERIAN	Fedia	(TS)
AFRICAN VIOLET	Saintpaulia	(HP)
AFRICAN WALNUT	Coula edulis	(TT)
AFRICAN YELLOW WOOD	Podocarpus elongatus	(C)
AGAR-AGAR	Gelidium amansii	(SW)
AGRIMONY	Agrimonia eupatoria	(H)
AGUE ROOT	Aletris farinosa	(H)
AGUE TREE	Sassafras albidum	(T)
AGUE WEED	Eupatorium	(H)
AHUEHUETE	Taxodium mucronatum	(C)
AILANTO	Ailanthus glandulosa	(T)
AIR PLANT	Kalanchoe pinnatum	(HP)
AIR-PLANT	Aerides	(HP)
AIRPLANE PROPELLOR PLANT	Crassula falcata	(HP)
AKEE TREE	Blighia sapida	(TT)
ALABAMA SNOW WREATH	Neviusa alabamensis	(S)
ALAMO VINE	Ipomoea dissecta	(CL)
ALASKA CEDAR	Chamaecyparis nootkatensis	(C)
ALBANY BOTTLEBRUSH	Callistemon speciosus	(S)
ALBANY CAT'S PAW	Anigozanthus preissii	(H)
ALBERTA WHITE SPRUCE	Picea glauca albertiana	(C)
ALCOCK SPRUCE	Picea bicolor	(C)
ALDER	Alnus	(T)
ALDER BUCKTHORN	Rhamnusfrangula	(ST)
ALECOST	Balsamita major	(HB)
ALEHOOF	Glechoma hederacea	(H)
ALEPPO PINE	Pinus halepensis	(C)
ALERCE	Tetraclinis articulata	(C)
ALERCE CYPRESS	Fitzroya	(C)
ALEXANDERS	Smyrnium olusatrum	(H)
ALEXANDRA PALM	Archontophoenix alexandrae	(P)
ALEXANDRIAN LAUREL	Danae racemosa	(S)
ALEXANDRIAN SENNA	Cassia senna	(S)
ALFALFA	Medicago sativa	(V)
ALGERIAN ASH	Fraxinus xanthoxyloides dimorpha	(T)
ALGERIAN FIR	Abies numidica	(C)

Know Your Common Plant Names

Common	Botanical	Type
ALGERIAN IRIS	Iris unguicularis	(H)
ALGERIAN OAK	Quercus canariensis	(T)
ALISON	Alyssum	(R)
ALKANET	Alkanna tinctoria	(H)
ALKANET	Anchusa officinalis	(H)
ALKANET	Pentaglottis sempervirens	(H)
ALLAMANDA	Allamanda cathartica	(TS)
ALLEGHANY VINE	Adlumia fungosa	(CL)
ALLEGHENY SERVICE BERRY	Amelanchier laevis	(ST)
ALLEGHENY SPURGE	Pachysandra procumbens	(S)
ALLEGHENY VINE	Adlumia fungosa	(CL)
ALLIGATOR APPLE	Annona glabra	(TT)
ALLIGATOR APPLE	Annona palustris	(TT)
ALLIGATOR JUNIPER	Juniperus deppeana	(C)
ALLIGATOR JUNIPER	Juniperus pachyphlaea	(C)
ALLIGATOR PEAR	Persea americana	(F)
ALLSAINTS CHERRY	Prunus cerasus "Semperflorens"	(T)
ALLSEED	Radiola linoides	(H)
ALLSPICE	Calycanthus floridus	(S)
ALLSPICE TREE	Pimenta officinialis	(T)
ALMOND	Prunus dulcis	(T)
ALMOND LEAVED PEAR	Pyrus amygdaliformis	(T)
ALMOND LEAVED WILLOW	Salix triandra	(ST)
ALPENROSE	Rhododendron ferrugineum	(S)
ALPINE ASH	Eucalyptus delegatensis	(T)
ALPINE ASPHODEL	Tofieldia calyculata	(H)
ALPINE ASTER	Aster alpinus	(R)
ALPINE AVENS	Geum montanum	(H)
ALPINE AZALEA	Loiseleuria procumbens	(S)
ALPINE BASTARD TOADFLAX	Thesium alpinum	(H)
ALPINE BISTORT	Polygonum viviporum	(H)
ALPINE BUTTERCUP	Ranunculus alpestris	(R)
ALPINE CAMPION	Lychnis alpina	(R)
ALPINE CAT'S FOOT	Antennaria alpina	(R)
ALPINE CINQUEFOIL	Potentilla crantzii	(H)
ALPINE CLEMATIS	Clematis alpina	(CL)
ALPINE CLOVER	Trifolium alpinum	(H)
ALPINE COLTSFOOT	Homogyne alpina	(H)
ALPINE CURRANT	Ribes alpinum	(S)
ALPINE FIR	Abies lasiocarpa	(C)
ALPINE FLEABANE	Erigeron borealis	(H)
ALPINE FORGET-ME-NOT	Myosotis alpestris	(R)
ALPINE GUM	Eucalyptus archeri	(T)
ALPINE GYPSOPHILA	Gypsophila repens	(H)
ALPINE HONEYSUCKLE	Lonicera alpigena	(S)
ALPINE LABURNUM	Laburnum alpinum	(T)
ALPINE LADY'S MANTLE	Alchemilla alpina	(R)

Know Your Common Plant Names

Common	Botanical	Type
ALPINE LARCH	Larix lyallii	(C)
ALPINE MEADOW GRASS	Poa alpina	(G)
ALPINE MEADOW RUE	Thalictrum alpinum	(H)
ALPINE MILK-VETCH	Astragalus alpinus	(H)
ALPINE MOON-DAISY	Leucanthemopsis alpina	(H)
ALPINE MOUSE-EAR	Cerastium alpinum	(H)
ALPINE PENNY CRESS	Thlaspi aplestre	(H)
ALPINE PENNYROYAL	Teucrium montanum	(H)
ALPINE PHLOX	Phlox douglasii	(R)
ALPINE PINK	Dianthus alpinus	(R)
ALPINE POPPY	Papaver alpinum	(R)
ALPINE ROCK-CRESS	Arabis alpina	(R)
ALPINE ROSE	Rosa alpina (pendulina)	(S)
ALPINE SAINFOIN	Hedysarum obscurum	(R)
ALPINE SANDWORT	Arenaria montana	(R)
ALPINE SNOWBELL	Soldanella alpina	(R)
ALPINE SPEEDWELL	Veronica alpina	(H)
ALPINE SQUILL	Scilla bifolia	(BB)
ALPINE STRAWBERRY	Fragaria vesca	(R)
ALPINE THISTLE	Carduus defloratus	(H)
ALPINE TOTARA	Podocarpus	(C)
ALPINE WALLFLOWER	Erysimum alpinum	(R)
ALPINE WHITEBEAM	Sorbus chamaemespilus	(S)
ALPINE YARROW	Achillea tomentosa	(H)
ALSIKE CLOVER	Trifolium hybridum	(H)
ALTAI MOUNTAIN THORN	Crataegus altaica	(T)
ALUMINIUM PLANT	Pilea cadieri	(HP)
ALUMROOT	Heuchera	(H)
AMARANTH	Amaranthus	(A)
AMARANTH FEATHERS	Humea elegans	(S)
AMARYLLIS	Hippeastrum	(BB)
AMATUNGULU	Carissa macrocarpa	(TS)
AMAZON LILY	Eucharis	(BB)
AMAZON LILY	Eucharis grandiflora	(BB)
AMBARELLA	Spondias cytheria	(TT)
AMBASH	Herminiera elaphroxylon	(TT)
AMBOYNA PITCH TREE	Agathis alba	(C)
AMBROSIA	Chenopodium botrys	(HB)
AMERICAN ARBOR-VITAE	Thuya occidentalis	(C)
AMERICAN ARUM	Arum triphyllum	(H)
AMERICAN ASH	Fraxinus americana	(T)
AMERICAN ASPEN	Populus tremuloides	(T)
AMERICAN BARRENWORT	Vancouveria hexandra	(H)
AMERICAN BASSWOOD	Tilia americana	(T)
AMERICAN BEAUTY BUSH	Kolkwitzia amabilis	(S)
AMERICAN BEECH	Fagus grandifolia	(T)
AMERICAN BIRD CHERRY	Prunus serotina	(T)

Know Your Common Plant Names

Common	Botanical	Type
AMERICAN BLACKCURRANT	Ribes americanum	(S)
AMERICAN BOXWOOD	Cornus florida	(S/T)
AMERICAN BRAMBLE	Rubus odoratus	(S)
AMERICAN CENTAURY	Sabatia angularis	(HB)
AMERICAN CHESTNUT	Castanea dentata	(T)
AMERICAN COLOMBO	Frasera carolinensis	(TS)
AMERICAN COWBEAN	Cicuta maculata	(H)
AMERICAN COWSLIP	Dodecatheon	(R)
AMERICAN CRANBERRY	Vaccinium macrocarpum	(S)
AMERICAN CRANESBILL	Geranium maculatum	(H)
AMERICAN CRESS	Barbarea verna	(H)
AMERICAN ELDER	Sambucus canadensis	(C)
AMERICAN ELM	Ulmus americana	(T)
AMERICAN FUMITORY	Fumaria indica	(H)
AMERICAN GINSENG	Panax quinquifolium	(S)
AMERICAN GREEK VALERIAN	Polemonium reptans	(H)
AMERICAN GREEN ALDER	Alnus crispa	(T)
AMERICAN GREEN ALDER	Alnuscrispa mollis	(T)
AMERICAN HAZEL	Corylus americana	(T)
AMERICAN HELLEBORE	Veratrum viride	(H)
AMERICAN HEMP	Apocynum cannabinum	(H)
AMERICAN HOLLY	Ilex opaca	(S)
AMERICAN HORNBEAM	Carpinus caroliniana	(T)
AMERICAN HORSEMINT	Monarda punctata	(H)
AMERICAN IVY	Parthenocissus quingefolia	(CL)
AMERICAN JUDAS TREE	Cercis canadensis	(T)
AMERICAN LARCH	Larix laricina	(C)
AMERICAN LAUREL	Kalmia latifolia	(S)
AMERICAN LIME	Tilia americana	(T)
AMERICAN LIQUORICE	Glycyrrhiza lepidota	(H)
AMERICAN LIVERWORT	Anemone hepatica	(H)
AMERICAN MANDRAKE	Podophyllum peltatum	(H)
AMERICAN MASTIC TREE	Schinus molle	(T)
AMERICAN MISTLETOE	Phoradendron flavescens	(PE)
AMERICAN MOUNTAIN ASH	Sorbus americana	(T)
AMERICAN PERSIMMON	Diospyros virginiana	(T)
AMERICAN PLANE	Platanus occidentalis	(T)
AMERICAN PONDWEED	Potamogeton epihydrus	(WP)
AMERICAN RED PINE	Pinus resinosa	(C)
AMERICAN RED PLUM	Prunus americana	(T)
AMERICAN RED SPRUCE	Picea rubens	(C)
AMERICAN SAFFRON	Carthamus tinctorius	(H)
AMERICAN SANICLE	Sanicula marilandica	(H)
AMERICAN SARSAPARILLA	Aralia nudicaulis	(S)
AMERICAN SEA-LAVENDER	Limonium caroliniana	(H)
AMERICAN SLOE	Prunus alleghaniensis	(S)
AMERICAN SMOKETREE	Cotinus obovatus	(S)

Know Your Common Plant Names

Common	Botanical	Type
AMERICAN SNAKE ROOT	Aristolochia serpentaria	(CL)
AMERICAN SOLE	Prunus alleghaniensis	(T)
AMERICAN SPATTER DOCK	Nuphar advena	(WP)
AMERICAN SPEEDWELL	Veronica peregrina	(H)
AMERICAN SPIKENARD	Aralia racemosa	(S)
AMERICAN STORAX	Styrax americana	(T)
AMERICAN SWAMP LILY	Saururus cernuus	(BB)
AMERICAN SWAMP-LAUREL	Kalmia glauca	(S)
AMERICAN SYCAMORE	Platanus occidentalis	(T)
AMERICAN TROUT LILY	Erythronium revolutum	(BB)
AMERICAN WAKE ROBIN	Arisaema triphyllum	(H)
AMERICAN WAKE ROBIN	Arum triphyllum	(H)
AMERICAN WAYFARING TREE	Viburnum lantanoides	(S)
AMERICAN WILLOWHERB	Epilobium ciliatum	(H)
AMERICAN WINTERCRESS	Barbarea verna	(H)
AMERICAN WOOD LILY	Trillium grandiflorum	(H)
AMERICAN WORMCRESS	Chenopodium anthelminticum	(H)
AMERICAN WORMSEED	Chenopodium anthelminticum	(H)
AMERICAN WYCH HAZEL	Fothergilla	(S)
AMETHYST DECEIVER	Laccaria amethystea	(FU)
AMETHYST FESCUE	Festuca amethystina	(G)
AMMONIACUM	Dorema ammoniacum	(T)
AMSINCKIA	Amsinckia micrantha	(H)
AMUR CORK TREE	Phellodendron amurense	(T)
AMUR LILAC	Syringa amurensis	(S)
AMUR MAPLE	Acer tataricum ginnala	(ST)
AMUR PRIVET	Ligustrum amurense	(S)
AMUR SILVER GRASS	Miscanthus sacchariflorus	(G)
ANACONOA	Cordia sebestena	(TT)
ANARRHINUM	Anarrhinum bellidifolium	(H)
ANCHOR PLANT	Colletia cruciata	(S)
ANDAMAN MARBLE	Diospyros kurzii	(TT)
ANEMONE	Anemone	(H) (BB)
ANGEL WINGS	Caladium	(HP)
ANGEL'S TEARS	Billbergia nutans	(HP)
ANGEL'S TRUMPET	Brugmansia cornigera	(H)
ANGEL'S WINGS	Caladium	(HP)
ANGELICA	Angelica archangelica	(HB)
ANGELICA TREE	Aralia elata	(ST)
ANGELS FISHING ROD	Dierama	(H)
ANGELS TEARS	Narcissus triandus albus	(BB)
ANGELS TRUMPET	Brugmansia suaveolens	(S)
ANGELWING BEGONIA	Begonia coccinea	(HP)
ANGLO-JAPANESE YEW	Taxus media	(C)
ANGOLA HEMP	Sansevieria	(HP)
ANGOSTURA	Cusparia febrifuga	(TT)
ANIME RESIN	Hymenaea courbaril	(T)

Common	Botanical	Type
ANISE, ANISEED	Pimpinella anisum	(HB)
ANISE HYSSOP	Agastache anisata	(H)
ANISE HYSSOP	Agastache foeniculum	(HB)
ANISEED TREE	Illicium anisatum	(T)
ANNATTO	Bixa orellana	(T)
ANNATTO TREE	Bixa orellana	(T)
ANNUAL ANCHUSA	Anchusa capensis	(A)
ANNUAL ASTER	Callistephus	(A)
ANNUAL BEARD-GRASS	Polypogon monspeliensis	(G)
ANNUAL BORAGE	Echium	(A)
ANNUAL CANDYTUFT	Iberis umbellata	(A)
ANNUAL CLARY	Salvia horminum	(H)
ANNUAL GAILLARDIA	Gaillardia pulchella	(A)
ANNUAL GYPSOPHILA	Gypsophila muralis	(H)
ANNUAL MALLOW	Lavatera trimestris	(A)
ANNUAL MEADOW GRASS	Poa annua	(A)
ANNUAL MERCURY	Mercurialis annua	(A)
ANNUAL PHLOX	Phlox drummondii	(A)
ANNUAL PINK	Dianthus chinensis	(A)
ANNUAL RUDBECKIA	Rudbeckia hirta	(A)
ANNUAL SEA-BLITE	Suaeda maritima	(H)
ANNUAL SUNFLOWER	Helianthus annuus	(A)
ANNUAL THYMELAEA	Thymelaea passerina	(A)
ANNUAL VERNAL GRASS	Anthoxanthum aristatum	(G)
ANNUAL WALL ROCKET	Diplotaxis muralis	(A)
ANTARCTIC BEECH	Nothofagus antarctica	(T)
ANTARCTIC FORGET-ME-NOT	Myosotidium	(H)
ANTELOPE BITTERBRUSH	Purshia tridentata	(S)
ANTHONY NUT	Staphylea pinnata	(S)
APACHE BEADS	Anemopsis californica	(A)
APACHE PINE	Pinus engelmannii	(C)
APACHE PLUME	Fallugia paradoxa	(S)
APAMATA	Tabebuia serratifolia	(TT)
APOTHECARY'S ROSE	Rosa gallica 'Officinalis'	(S)
APPLE BERRY	Billardiera longiflora	(CL)
APPLE BLOSSOM CASSIA	Cassia javanica	(TT)
APPLE BLOSSOM CHERRY	Prunus 'Amanogawa'	(T)
APPLE MINT	Mentha suaveolens	(HB)
APPLE OF PERU	Nicandra physaloides	(A)
APPLE OF SODOM	Solanum carolinense	(H)
APPLE OF SODOM	Solanum sosomeum	(H)
APPLE ROSE	Rosa villosa	(S)
APPLE SCENTED GERANIUM	Pelargonium odoratissimum	(A)
APPLE-BERRY	Billardiera	(CL)
APPLE-FRUITED PASSION FLOWER	Passiflora maliformis	(CL)
APRICAN JUNIPER	Juniperus procera	(C)
APRICOT	Prunus armenaica	(F)

Know Your Common Plant Names

Common	Botanical	Type
APRICOT PLUM	Prunus simonii	(T)
ARABIAN JASMINE	Jasminum sambac	(CL)
ARABIAN THISTLE	Onopordon arabicum	(B)
ARABIAN VIOLET	Exacum affine	(HP)
ARAGUANEY	Tabebuia	(TS)
ARALIA-IVY	X Fatshedera lizei	(S)
ARAROBA	Andira araroba	(TT)
ARBOR-VITAE	Thuja	(C)
ARCHANGEL	Lamium album	(H)
ARCTIC MOUSE-EAR	Cerastium articum	(H)
ARCTIC POPPY	Papaver radicatum	(H)
ARCTIC SANDWORT	Arenaria norvegica	(R)
ARCTIC WILLOW	Salix artica	(S)
ARECA NUT	Areca catechu	(TT)
ARGYLE APPLE	Eucalyptus cinerea	(T)
ARIZONA ASH	Fraxinus velutina	(T)
ARIZONA CORK FIR	Abies lasiocarpa arizonica	(C)
ARIZONA POPPY	Kalistroemeria grand flora	(A)
ARIZONA RAINBOW HEDGEHOG	Echinocereus enneacanthus	(CS)
ARMENIAN OAK	Quercus pontica	(T)
ARMSTRONG	Polygonum ariculare	(A)
ARNICA	Arnica montana	(H)
AROLLA PINE	Pinus cembra	(C)
ARROW BAMBOO	Pseudosasa japonica	(G)
ARROW BROOM	Genista sagittalis	(S)
ARROW-ARUM	Peltandra	(H)
ARROWHEAD	Sagittaria sagittifolia	(WP)
ARROWHEAD PLANT	Syngonium podophyllum	(HP)
ARROWHEAD VINE	Syngonium angustatum	(HP)
ARROWHEAD VINE	Syngonium podophyllum	(HP)
ARROWLEAF BALSAMROOT	Balsamorhiza sagittata	(TS)
ARROWROOT	Maranta arundinacea	(HB)
ARROWWOOD	Viburnum dentatum	(S)
ARTILLERY PLANT	Pilea microphylla	(HP)
ARUM LILY	Zantedeschia	(H)
ASAFETIDA	Ferula foetida	(HB)
ASARABACCA	Asarum europaeum	(R)
ASGARA	Pterostyrax hispida	(T)
ASH	Fraxinus	(T)
ASH LEAFED MAPLE	Acer negundo	(T)
ASHWAGANDHA	Withania somnifera	(H)
ASHWEED	Aegopodium podograri	(H)
ASHY WOADWAXEN	Genista tenera 'Golden Shower'	(S)
ASIATIC LIQUORICE	Glycyrrhiza uralensis	(H)
ASIATIC POISON BULB	Crinum asiaticum	(BB)
ASIATIC SWEETLEAF	Symplocos paniculata	(T)
ASOKA TREE	Saraca indica	(TT)

Know Your Common Plant Names

Common	Botanical	Type
ASPARAGUS FERN	Asparagus plumosus	(F)
ASPARAGUS PEA	Lotus tetragonolobus	(V)
ASPEN	Populus tremula	(T)
ASPHODEL	Asphodelus alpus	(H)
ASS'S FOOT	Tussilago farfara	(H)
ASSAM TEA	Camellia sinensis assamensis	(S)
ASSEGAI WOOD	Curtisia	(TT)
ASTHMA WEED	Euphorbia hirta	(H)
ASTHMA WEED	Lobelia inflata	(H)
ATAMASCO LILY	Zephyranthes atamasco	(BB)
ATHAMANTA	Athamanta cretensis	(H)
ATLAS CEDAR	Cedrus atlantica	(C)
AUBERGINE	Solanum melongena	(V)
AUNT ELIZA	Curtonus	(H)
AURICULA	Primula auricula	(R)
AUSTRALIAN BANYAN	Ficus macrophylla	(HP)
AUSTRALIAN BEAN FLOWER	Kennedya	(HP)
AUSTRALIAN BEECH	Eucalyptus polyanthemos	(TT)
AUSTRALIAN BEEFWOOD	Casuarina equisetifolia	(TT)
AUSTRALIAN BLACKWOOD	Acacia melonoxylon	(T)
AUSTRALIAN BLUE-BELL CREEPER	Sollya fusiformis	(CL)
AUSTRALIAN BRAKE	Pteris tremula	(FN)
AUSTRALIAN BRUSH CHERRY	Eugenia myrtifolia	(S)
AUSTRALIAN CABBAGE PALM	Livistona australis	(P)
AUSTRALIAN CHERRY	Exocarpus cupressiformis	(S)
AUSTRALIAN CURRANT	Leucopogon	(S)
AUSTRALIAN CYCAD	Macrozania	(TS)
AUSTRALIAN DESERT KUMQUAT	Eremocitrus	(TS)
AUSTRALIAN DOUBAH	Leichhardtia australis	(S)
AUSTRALIAN EVERLASTING FLOWER	Helipterum	(H)
AUSTRALIAN FAN PALM	Livistona australis	(P)
AUSTRALIAN FEVER BUSH	Alstonia scholaris	(TT)
AUSTRALIAN FLEABANE	Erigeron karvinskianum	(H)
AUSTRALIAN FLYCATCHER PLANT	Cephalotus follicularis	(H)
AUSTRALIAN FUCHSIA	Correa	(S)
AUSTRALIAN GIANT LILY	Doryanthes excelsa	(BB)
AUSTRALIAN HEATH	Epacris impressa	(S)
AUSTRALIAN HONEYSUCKLE	Banksia	(S)
AUSTRALIAN HOP	Daviesia	(S)
AUSTRALIAN IVY	Muehlenbeckia adpressa	(CL)
AUSTRALIAN LAUREL	Pittosporum tobira	(ST)
AUSTRALIAN LILAC	Hardenbergia monophylla	(S)
AUSTRALIAN MAIDENHAIR FERN	Adiantum formosum	(FN)
AUSTRALIAN MINT BUSH	Prostranthera	(S)
AUSTRALIAN PEA	Lablab purpureus	(CL)
AUSTRALIAN PINE	Casuarina equisetifolia	(TT)
AUSTRALIAN PITCHER PLANT	Cephalotus	(H)

Know Your Common Plant Names

Common	Botanical	Type
AUSTRALIAN QUININE	Alstonia constricta	(S)
AUSTRALIAN ROSEMARY	Westringia	(S)
AUSTRALIAN ROSEMARY	Westringia fruticosa	(S)
AUSTRALIAN SARSAPARILLA	Hardenbergia violacea	(S)
AUSTRALIAN SASSAFRAS	Atherosperma moschatum	(CT)
AUSTRALIAN SMOKE BUSH	Conospermum stoechadis	(TS)
AUSTRALIAN SWORD LILY	Anigozanthos	(S)
AUSTRALIAN VIOLET	Viola hederacea	(H)
AUSTRIAN BRIAR	Rosa foetida	(S)
AUSTRIAN COPPER ROSE	Rosa foetida 'Bicolor'	(ST)
AUSTRIAN PINE	Pinus Nigra	(C)
AUTUMN CHERRY	Prunus subhirtella 'Autumnalis'	(T)
AUTUMN CROCUS	Colchicum	(BB)
AUTUMN FELWORT	Gentianella amarella	(H)
AUTUMN HAWKBIT	Leontodon autumnalis	(H)
AUTUMN LADY'S TRESSES	Spiranthes spiralis	(O)
AUTUMN OLIVE	Elaeagnus umbellata	(S)
AUTUMN SNOWDROP	Galanthus reginae-olgae	(BB)
AUTUMN SQUILL	Scilla autumnalis	(BB)
AUTUMN-FLOWERING SQUILL	Scilla autumnalis	(BB)
AUTUMNAL WATER-STARWORT	Callitriche hermaphroditum	(WP)
AVALANCHE LILY	Erythronium montanum	(BB)
AVALANCHE TREE	Erythronium montanum	(BB)
AVENS	Geum urbanum	(H)
AVIGNON BERRY	Rhamnus infectoria	(S)
AVOCADO	Persea americana	(F)
AWLWORT	Subularia aquatica	(WP)
AYRSHIRE ROSE	Rosa arvensis	(S)
AZADIRACHTA	Melia azadirachta	(T)
AZALEA	Rhododendron	(S)
AZAROLE	Crataegus azarolus	(T)
AZOREAN HOLLY	Ilex perado	(T)
AZTEC LILY	Sprekelia formosissima	(BB)
BABASSU	Orbignya speciosa	(P)
BABASSU PALM	Orbignya speciosa	(P)
BABOON ROOT	Babiana	(BB)
BABY BLUE EYES	Nemophila menziesii	(A)
BABY RUBBER PLANT	Peperomia obtusifolia	(HP)
BABY TEARS	Bacopa monnieri	(WP)
BABY'S TOES	Fenestraria aurantiaca	(CS)
BABYS BREATH	Gypsophila	(A/H)
BABYS TEARS	Hypoestes phyllostachya	(HP)
BABYS TEARS	Soleirolia	(R)
BACHELOR'S BUTTONS	Ranunculus acris	(H)
BACHELORS BUTTONS	Kerria japonica 'Plena'	(S)
BACHELORS BUTTONS	Ranunculus	(BB/H)
BACHELORS BUTTONS	Tanacetum parthenium	(HB)

Common	Botanical	Type
BACON AND EGGS	Lotus corniculatus	(H)
BACON WEED	Chenopudium album	(A)
BAEL FRUIT	Aegle marmelos	(F)
BALD CYPRESS	Taxodium distichum	(C)
BALD MONEY	Meum atramanticum	(H)
BALDHIP ROSE	Rosa gymnocarpa	(S)
BALEARIC BOX	Buxus balearica	(S)
BALFOUR ARALIS	Polyscias balfouriana	(HP)
BALISIER	Heliconia bihai	(H)
BALKAN BLUE GRASS	Sesleria heufleriana	(G)
BALKAN CRANE'S BILL	Geranium macrorrhizum	(H)
BALKAN MAPLE	Acer hyrcanum	(T)
BALL MUSTARD	Neslia paniculata	(H)
BALLOON FLOWER	Platycodon	(H)
BALLOON VINE	Cardiospermum halicacabum	(CL)
BALM	Melissa officinalis	(HB)
BALM OF GILEAD	Abies balsamea	(C)
BALM OF GILEAD	Cedronella triphylla	(HB)
BALM OF GILEAD	Commiphora opobalsamum	(HB)
BALM OF GILEAD	Populus candicans	(T)
BALM-LEAVED FIGWORT	Scrophularia scorodonia	(H)
BALMONY	Chelone glabra	(H)
BALSA	Ochroma lagopus	(TT)
BALSA	Ochroma pyramidale	(TT)
BALSAM	Impatiens balsamina	(A)
BALSAM APPLE	Momordica balsmina	(H)
BALSAM APPLE	Momordica charantia	(F)
BALSAM FIR	Abies balsamea	(C)
BALSAM OF GILEAD	Commiphora opobalsmum	(HB)
BALSAM OF PERU	Myroxylon pereirae	(TS)
BALSAM PEAR	Momordica charantia	(H)
BALSAM POPLAR	Populus balsamifera	(T)
BALSAM WILLOW	Salix pyrifolia	(S)
BALSAM-SCENTED GERANIUM	Pelargonium filicifolium	(A)
BALSAM-SCENTED GERANIUM	Pelargonium radula	(A)
BALSAM-WEED	Impatiens aurea	(H)
BAMBOO	Arundinaria	(G)
BAMBOO	Bambusa	(G)
BAMBOO	Chusquea	(G)
BAMBOO	Phyllostachys	(G)
BAMBOO	Sasa	(G)
BAMBOO	Shibataea	(G)
BAMBOO BRIER	Acacia nudicaulis	(T)
BAMBOO PALM	Chamaedorea erumpens	(P)
BAMBOO PALM	Rhapis excelsa	(P)
BAMBOO-LEAVED OAK	Quercus prinus	(T)
BAMENDA COLA	Cola anomala	(TF)

Common	Botanical	Type
BANANA	Musa sapientum	(F)
BANEBERRY	Actaea spicata	(H)
BANKSIAN ROSE	Rosa banksiae	(S)
BANYAN	Ficus benghalensis	(T)
BAOBAB	Adansonia digitata	(T)
BARBADOS CHERRY	Malpighia glabra	(TT)
BARBADOS GOOSEBERRY	Pereskia aculeata	(TT)
BARBADOS LILY	Hippeastrum edule	(BB)
BARBADOS LILY	Hippeastrum equestre	(BB)
BARBADOS NUT	Jatropha curcas	(TS)
BARBADOS-PRIDE	Caesalpinia pulcherrima	(TS)
BARBED-WIRE PLANT	Tylecodon reticulata	(CS)
BARBERRY	Berberis	(S)
BARBERTON DAISY	Gerbera jamesonii	(H)
BARLEY	Hordeum	(V)
BARREL CACTUS	Echinocactus grusonii	(CS)
BARREN BROME	Bromus sterilis	(G)
BARREN STRAWBERRY	Potentilla sterilis	(H)
BARREN STRAWBERRY	Waldsteinia	(H)
BARRENS CLAWFLOWER	Calothamnus validus	(S)
BARRENWORT	Epimedium	(H)
BARTRAM'S OAK	Quercus x heterophylla	(T)
BARWOOD	Baphia	(P)
BASEBALL CACTUS	Euphorbia obesa	(CS)
BASFORD WILLOW	Salix 'Basfordiana'	(S)
BASIL	Ocimum basilicum	(HB)
BASIL THYME	Acinos arvensis	(HB)
BASIN SAGEBRUSH	Artemisia tridentata	(H)
BASKET FLOWER	Centaurea americana	(H)
BASKET GRASS	Oplismenus hirtellus	(HP)
BASKET OAK	Quercus prinus	(T)
BASKET PLANT	Aeschynanthus	(HP)
BASKET WILLOW	Salix vimanalis	(S)
BASSWOOD	Tilia americana	(T)
BASTARD AGRIMONY	Aremonia agrimonoides	(H)
BASTARD BALM	Melittis melissophyllum	(HB)
BASTARD BREADNUT	Pseuolmedia	(TT)
BASTARD BULLET TREE	Houmiria floribunda	(TT)
BASTARD CABBAGE	Rapistrum rugosum	(H)
BASTARD CABBAGE TREE	Geoffraea	(TT)
BASTARD CEDAR	Guazuma ulmifolia	(TT)
BASTARD HEMP	Datisca	(H)
BASTARD INDIGO	Amorpha fruticosa	(S)
BASTARD JASMINE	Androsace chamaejasme	(R)
BASTARD JASMINE	Cestrum	(S)
BASTARD LOGWOOD	Acacia berteriana	(T)
BASTARD PENNYROYAL	Trichostema	(H)

Know Your Common Plant Names

Common	Botanical	Type
BASTARD SERVICE TREE	Sorbus thuringiaca	(T)
BASTARD TEAK	Pterocarpus marsupium	(TT)
BASTARD TOADFLAX	Thesium humifusum	(H)
BAT FLOWER	Tacca chantrieri	(H)
BAT PLANT	Tacca integrifolia	(HP)
BAT'S WING FERN	Histiopteris incisa	(FN)
BATH ASPARAGUS	Ornithogalum pyrenaicum	(BB)
BATS-IN-THE-BELFRY	Campanula trachelium	(H)
BAY	Laurus nobilis	(S)
BAY LAUREL	Laurus nobilis	(S)
BAY WILLOW	Salix pentandra	(S)
BAY-TREE	Laurus	(S/T)
BAYBERRY	Myrica pensylvanica	(S)
BAYONET PLANT	Aciphylla squarrosa	(H)
BEACH GRASS	Ammophila	(G)
BEACH HEATHER	Hudsonia tomentosa	(S)
BEACH MORNING GLORY	Ipomoea pes-caprae	(TH)
BEACH PEA	Lathyrus littoralis	(H)
BEACH PEA	Lathyrus maritimus	(H)
BEACH PINE	Pinus contorta	(C)
BEACH PLUM	Prunus maritima	(T)
BEAD PLANT	Nertera depressa	(HP)
BEAD TREE	Melia azedarach	(T)
BEAK WILLOW	Salix bebbiana	(S)
BEAKED HAWK'S BEARD	Crepis vesicaria	(B)
BEAKED HELICONIA	Heliconia rostrata	(TH)
BEAKED TASSEL PONDWEED	Ruppia maritima	(WP)
BEAR HUCKLEBERRY	Gaylussacia ursina	(S)
BEAR OAK	Quercus illicifolia	(T)
BEAR TONGUE	Clintonia	(H)
BEAR'S EAR	Primula auricula	(R)
BEAR'S FOOT	Alchemilla vulgaris	(H)
BEAR'S FOOT FERN	Humata tyermannii	(FN)
BEAR'S GARLIC	Allium ursinum	(HB)
BEAR-TONGUE	Clintonia	(H)
BEARBERRY	Arctostaphylos	(S)
BEARBERRY WILLOW	Salix uva-ursi	(S)
BEARD GRASS	Andropogon	(H)
BEARD TONGUE	Penstemon	(H)
BEARDED BELLFLOWER	Campanula barbata	(H)
BEARDED COUCH	Elymus caninus	(G)
BEARDED FESCUE	Vulpia ambigua	(G)
BEARDED IRIS	Iris germanica	(H)
BEARGRASS	Xerophyllum tenax	(G)
BEARS BREECHES	Acanthus	(H)
BEARSFOOT	Polymnia uvedalia	(H)
BEAUTY BERRY	Callicarpa	(S)

Know Your Common Plant Names

Common	Botanical	Type
BEAUTY BUSH	Kolkwitzia amabilis	(S)
BEAVER TAIL	Sedum morganianum	(H)
BECHTEL CRAB	Malus ioensis 'Plena'	(T)
BEDDING BEGONIA	Begonia semperflorens	(A)
BEDDING DAHLIA	Dahlia merckii	(A)
BEDDING GERANIUM	Pelargonium x hortorum	(A)
BEDDING LOBELIA	Lobelia erinus	(A)
BEDSTRAW	Galium	(AH)
BEE BALM	Monarda didyma	(H)
BEE NETTLE	Lamium album	(H)
BEE ORCHID	Ophrys apifera	(O)
BEECH	Fagus	(T)
BEECH FERN	Phegopteris connectilis	(FN)
BEECHWOOD	Casuarina equisetifolia	(T/S)
BEEFWOOD	Mimusops balata	(S)
BEEFSTEAK BEGONIA	Begonia xerythrophylla	(HP)
BEEFSTEAK FUNGUS	Fistulina hepatica	(FU)
BEEFSTEAK PLANT	Acalypha wilkesiana	(HP)
BEEFSTEAK PLANT	Iresine herbstii	(HP)
BEEFSTEAK PLANT	Perilla frutescens	(HP)
BEEFWOOD	Casuarina	(T)
BEEHIVE CACTUS	Coryphampha vivipara arizonica	(CS)
BEENWEED	Scytosiphon lonentaria	(SW)
BEET	Beta vulgaris	(V)
BEETROOT	Beta vulgaris	(V)
BEGGAR'S BUTTONS	Arctium lappa	(H)
BEGGAR'S TICKS	Bidens	(H)
BEGGARTICKS	Bidens frondosa	(H)
BELGIAN ELM	Ulmus x hollandica 'Belgica'	(CL)
BELGIAN GAGEA	Gagea spathacea	(H)
BELL HEATHER	Erica cinerea	(S)
BELL PEPPER	Capsicum annuum	(F)
BELL-FLOWERED CHERRY	Prunus campanulata	(T)
BELL-FRUIT TREE	Codonocarpus cotinifolius	(TT)
BELLADONNA	Atropa belladonna	(H)
BELLADONNA LILY	Amaryllis belladonna	(BB)
BELLBINE	Calystegia	(H)
BELLFLOWER	Campanula	(H)
BELLFLOWER	Wahlenbergia	(H)
BELLFLOWER HEATHER	Erica cinerea	(S)
BELLS OF IRELAND	Molucella laevis	(A)
BELLWORT	Uvularia	(H)
BELVEDERE	Kochia scoparia trichophylla	(A)
BEN OIL	Moringa oleifera	(TT)
BENGAL CLOCKVINE	Thunbergia grandiflora	(TCL
BENGAL QUINCE	Aegle marmelos	(S)
BENGAL ROOT	Zingibar cassumunar	(HB)

Common	Botanical	Type
BENGAL TRUMPET	Thunbergia grandiflora	(TCL)
BENJAMIN BUSH	Lindera benzoin	(S)
BENT GRASS	Agrostis	(G)
BENTHAM'S CORNEL	Cornus capitata	(ST)
BENZOIN	Lindera benzoin	(S)
BENZOIN	Styrax benzoin	(TT)
BERGAMOT	Citrus bergamia	(F)
BERGAMOT	Monarda didyma	(H)
BERGAMOT MINT	Mentha x piperita citrata	(HB)
BERLIN POPLAR	Populus x berolinensis	(T)
BERMUDA BUTTERCUP	Oxalis pes-caprae	(BB)
BERMUDA GRASS	Cynodon dactylon	(G)
BERMUDA JUNIPER	Juniperus bermudiana	(C)
BERMUDA LILY	Lilium longiflorum	(BB)
BERRY CATCHFLY	Cucubalus baccifer	(H)
BESOM HEATH	Erica scoparia	(S)
BETEL	Piper betel	(T)
BETEL NUT	Areca catechu	(F)
BETEL NUT	Areca sp.	(P)
BETEL PEPPER	Piper betle	(TF)
BETH ROOT	Trillium erectum	(H)
BETHLEHEM SAGE	Pulmonaria saccharata	(H)
BETHROOT	Trillium	(H)
BETONY	Stachys betonica	(H)
BETONY	Stachys officinalis	(H)
BHANG	Cannabis sativa	(HB)
BHENDI TREE	Thespesia populnea	(TT)
BHUTAN CYPRESS	Cupressus duclouxiana	(C)
BHUTAN CYPRESS	Cupressus torulosa	(C)
BHUTAN PINE	Pinus wallichiana	(C)
BIBLE LEAF	Hypericum androsaemum	(S)
BIDGEE-WIDGEE	Acaena anserinifolia	(R)
BIDI-BIDI	Acaena	(R)
BIDIDY-BID	Acaena	(R)
BIG BERRY MANZANITA	Arctostaphylos glauca	(S)
BIG BLUE LILY-TURF	Liriope muscari	(H)
BIG CONE PINE	Pinus coulteri	(C)
BIG NIPPLE CACTUS	Coryphantha runyonii	(CS)
BIG POD SEGO LILY	Calochortus nitidus	(B)
BIG TREE	Sequoiadendron	(C)
BIG-BUD HICKORY	Carya tomentosa	(T)
BIG-LEAF STORAX	Styrax obassia	(S/T)
BIG-TOOTHED ASPEN	Populus grandidentata	(T)
BIGCONE SPRUCE	Pseudotsuga macrocarpa	(C)
BILBERRY	Vaccineum myrtillus	(F)
BILIMBI	Averrhoa bilimbi	(TT)
BINDWEED	Calystegia	(H)

Common	Botanical	Type
BINDWEED	Convolvulus arvensis	(H)
BIRCH	Betula	(T)
BIRCH BRACKET	Piptoporus betulinus	(FU)
BIRCH-BARK CHERRY	Prunus serrula	(T)
BIRCH-LEAF MAPLE	Acer tetramerum	(T)
BIRD CHERRY	Prunus padus	(T)
BIRD OF PARADISE FLOWER	Strelitzia reginae	(HP)
BIRD'S EYE	Veronica chamaedrys	(H)
BIRD'S EYE	Veronica officinalis	(H)
BIRD'S EYE MAPLE	Acer saccharinum	(T)
BIRD'S EYE PRIMROSE	Primula farinosa	(H)
BIRD'S EYES	Gilia tricolor	(H)
BIRD'S FOOT	Ornithopus perpusillus	(H)
BIRD'S FOOT TREFOIL	Lotus corniculatus	(H)
BIRD'S FOOT VIOLET	Viola pedata	(H)
BIRD'S NEST FERN	Asplenium nidus	(FN)
BIRD'S NEST ORCHID	Neottia nidus-avis	(O)
BIRD'S TONGUE	Polygonum aviculare	(H)
BIRD-CATCHER TREE	Pisonia umbellifera	(HP)
BIRDPEPPER	Capsicum frutescens	(F)
BIRDS FOOT	Ornithopus perpusillus	(H)
BIRDS-FOOT SEDGE	Carex ornithopoda	(G)
BIRTH-ROOT	Trillium erectum	(H)
BIRTHROOT	Trillium	(H)
BIRTHWORT	Aristolochia clematis	(CL)
BISHOP PINE	Pinus muricata	(C)
BISHOP'S CAP	Mitella	(R)
BISHOP'S CAP CACTUS	Astrophytum myriostigma	(CS)
BISHOP'S FLOWER	Ammi majus	(H)
BISHOP'S HAT	Epimedium	(H)
BISHOP'S HOOD	Astrophytum myriostigma	(CS)
BISHOP'S WEED	Aegopodium podagraria	(H)
BISHOP'S WORT	Stachys officinalis	(H)
BISTORT	Persicaria bistorta	(H)
BITHYNIAN VETCH	Vicia bithynica	(H)
BITING PERSICARIA	Polygonum hydropiper	(H)
BITING STONECROP	Sedum acre	(R)
BITTER ALMOND	Prunus dulcis amara	(T)
BITTER ALOE	Aloe ferox	(CS)
BITTER ALOES	Aloe vera	(CS)
BITTER APPLE	Citrullus colocynthis	(TT)
BITTER ASH	Picraena excelsa	(T)
BITTER BARK	Alstonia scholaris	(TT)
BITTER BROOM	Sabatia angularis	(HB)
BITTER CASSAVA	Manihot utilissima	(F)
BITTER CHERRY	Prunus emarginata	(T)
BITTER CLOVER	Sabatia angularis	(HB)

Common	Botanical	Type
BITTER CUCUMBER	Citrullus colocynthis	(H)
BITTER DAMSON	Simaruba amara	(TT)
BITTER OAK	Quercus cerris	(T)
BITTER ORANGE	Citrus aurantium	(F)
BITTER ROOT	Apocynum androsaemifolium	(H)
BITTER ROOT	Lewisia rediviva	(R)
BITTER VETCH	Lathyrus montanus	(H)
BITTER WRACK	Fucas serratus	(SW)
BITTER-BARK	Pinckneya pubens	(TS)
BITTER-SWEET	Solanum dulcamara	(H)
BITTERBUSH	Picramnia pentandra	(S)
BITTERCRESS	Cardamine	(H)
BITTERNUT	Carya cordiformis	(T)
BITTERWOOD	Quassia amara	(TT)
BITTERWORT	Lewisia	(R)
BLACK ALDER	Alnus glutinosa	(T)
BLACK ALDER	Ilex verticilliata	(S/T)
BLACK APRICOT	Prunus dascycarpa	(S)
BLACK ASH	Fraxinus nigra	(T)
BLACK BAMBOO	Phyllostachys nigra	(G)
BLACK BEAN	Kennedia nigricans	(CL)
BLACK BEAN TREE	Castanospermum australe	(TT)
BLACK BEANBERRY	Arctous alpinus	(S)
BLACK BEECH	Nothofagus solandri	(T)
BLACK BENT	Agrostis gigantea	(G)
BLACK BINDWEED	Fallopia convolvulus	(H)
BLACK BIRCH	Betula nigra	(T)
BLACK BOY	Xanthorrhoea preissii	(T)
BLACK BROOM	Lembotropis nigricans	(S)
BLACK BRYONY	Tamus communis	(CL)
BLACK BUTT	Eucalyptus pilularis	(T)
BLACK CALLA	Arum palaestinum	(H)
BLACK CAP	Rubus occidentalis	(S)
BLACK CHERRY	Atropa belladonna	(H)
BLACK CHOKEBERRY	Aronia melanocarpa	(S)
BLACK COHOSH	Cimifuga racemosa	(H)
BLACK COSMOS	Cosmos atrosanguineus	(H)
BLACK COTTONWOOD	Populus trichocarpa	(T)
BLACK CUMIN	Nigella sativa	(A)
BLACK CYPRESS PINE	Callitris calcarata	(C)
BLACK DOGWOOD	Rhamnus frangula	(S/T)
BLACK ELDER	Sambucus nigra	(S/T)
BLACK FALSE HELLEBORE	Veratrum nigrum	(H)
BLACK FRITILLARY	Fritillaria camschatensis	(BB)
BLACK GRASS	Alopecurus myosuroides	(G)
BLACK GUM	Eucalyptus aggregata	(T)
BLACK GUM	Nyssa sylvatica	(T)

Common	Botanical	Type
BLACK HAW	Viburnum prunifolium	(S)
BLACK HAWTHORN	Crataegus douglasii	(T)
BLACK HELLEBORE	Helleborus niger	(H)
BLACK HOREHOUND	Ballota nigra	(H)
BLACK HUCKLEBERRY	Gaylussacia baccata	(S)
BLACK INDIAN HEMP	Apocynum cannabinum	(H)
BLACK IRIS	Ferraria	(BB)
BLACK IRON WOOD	Olea laurifolia	(S)
BLACK ITALIAN POPLAR	Populus serotina	(T)
BLACK JACK	Bidens pilosa	(H)
BLACK JETBEAD	Rhodotypos scandens	(S)
BLACK JUNIPER	Juniperus wallichiana	(C)
BLACK KAURI PINE	Agathis microstachys	(C)
BLACK KNAPWEED	Centaurea nigra	(H)
BLACK LARCH	Larix laricina	(C)
BLACK LILY	Fritillaria camschatensis	(BB)
BLACK LOCUST	Robinia pseudoacacia	(T)
BLACK LOVAGE	Smyrnium olusatrum	(H)
BLACK MANGROVE	Avicennia nitida	(TT)
BLACK MAPLE	Acer nigrum	(T)
BLACK MEDICK	Medicago lupulina	(H)
BLACK MULBERRY	Morus nigra	(T)
BLACK MUSTARD	Brassica nigra	(V)
BLACK NIGHTSHADE	Solanum nigrum	(A)
BLACK OAK	Quercus velutina	(T)
BLACK ORCHID	Coelogyne pandurata	(O)
BLACK PEA	Lathyrus niger	(V)
BLACK PEPPER	Piper nigrum	(F)
BLACK PINE	Pinus thunbergii	(C)
BLACK PINE OF NEW ZEALAND	Prumnopitys taxifolia	(C)
BLACK POPLAR	Populus nigra	(T)
BLACK PUSSY WILLOW	Salix melanostachys	(S)
BLACK RAMPION	Phyteuma nigrum	(H)
BLACK RASPBERRY	Rubus occidentalis	(S)
BLACK ROOT	Leptandra virginica	(H)
BLACK ROOT	Veronicastrum virginicum	(H)
BLACK SALLY	Eucalyptus stellulata	(T)
BLACK SALSIFY	Scorzonera	(B)
BLACK SAMSON	Echinacea purpurea	(H)
BLACK SARANA	Fritillaria camschatcensis	(BB)
BLACK SASSAFRAS	Atherosperma moschatum	(T)
BLACK SEDGE	Carex atrata	(G)
BLACK SNAKEROOT	Cimicifuga racemosa	(H)
BLACK SPLEENWORT	Asplenium adiantum nigrum	(FN)
BLACK SPRUCE	Picea mariana	(C)
BLACK STINKWOOD	Ocotea bullata	(TT)
BLACK VANILLA ORCHID	Nigritella nigra	(O)

Know Your Common Plant Names

Common	Botanical	Type
BLACK WALNUT	Juglans nigra	(T)
BLACK WILLOW	Salix nigra	(T)
BLACK WOOD	Dalbergia latifolia	(TT)
BLACK-BARK	Diospyros whyteana	(TT)
BLACK-BOY	Xanthorrhoea	(S)
BLACK-EYED SUSAN	Rudbeckia hirta	(H)
BLACK-EYED SUSAN	Thunbergia alata	(CL)
BLACK-GOLD PHILODENDRON	Philodendron melanochrysum	(HP)
BLACK-LEAVED PLUM	Prunus cerasifera nigra	(S.T)
BLACK-WOOD ACACIA	Acacia melanoxylon	(T)
BLACKBERRY	Rubus carpinifolius	(F)
BLACKBERRY	Rubus fruticosus	(F)
BLACKBERRY	Rubus radula	(F)
BLACKBERRY	Rubus silvaticus	(F)
BLACKBERRY	Rubus ulmifolius	(F)
BLACKBERRY	Rubus vestitus	(F)
BLACKBERRY LILY	Belamcanda	(BB)
BLACKBERRY LILY	Belamcanda chinensis	(BB)
BLACKBOY	Xanthorrhea	(S)
BLACKBUTT	Eucalyptus pilularis	(T)
BLACKCAP	Rubus leucodermis	(S)
BLACKCHERRY	Prunus serotina	(T)
BLACKCURRANT	Ribes nigrum	(F)
BLACKJACK OAK	Quercus marilandica	(T)
BLACKTHORN	Prunus spinosa	(ST)
BLADDER CAMPION	Silene vulgaris	(H)
BLADDER CHERRY	Physalis	(H)
BLADDER FERN	Cystopteris	(FN)
BLADDER GENTIAN	Gentiana utriculosa	(H)
BLADDER HERB	Physalis	(H)
BLADDER KETMIA	Hibiscus trionum	(S)
BLADDER PEA	Vesicaria	(H)
BLADDER SEDGE	Carex vesicaria	(G)
BLADDER SENNA	Colutea	(S)
BLADDER-NUT	Diospyros whyteana	(TT)
BLADDERED FUMITORY	Fumitoria vesicaria	(A)
BLADDERNUT	Staphylea	(S)
BLADDERPOD	Isomeris arborea	(H)
BLADDERSEED	Physospermum cornubiense	(H)
BLADDERWORT	Utricularia	(H)
BLADDERWRACK	Fucus vesiculosus	(SW)
BLAEBERRY	Vaccinium myrtillus	(F)
BLAK ASH	Fraxinus nigra	(T)
BLANKET FLOWER	Gaillardia	(H)
BLAZE	Prunus cerasifera 'Nigra'	(TS)
BLAZING STAR	Aletris farinosa	(H)
BLAZING STAR	Dartonia	(H)

Know Your Common Plant Names

Common	Botanical	Type
BLAZING STAR	Liatris	(H)
BLAZING STAR	Mentzelia lindleyi	(S)
BLAZING STAR	Tritonia	(BB)
BLEEDING HEART	Dicentra	(H)
BLEEDING-HEART VINE	Clerodendrum thomsoniae	(HP)
BLESSED THISTLE	Cnicus benedictus	(H)
BLEWIT	Lepista saeva	(FU)
BLIND NETTLE	Lamium album	(H)
BLINKS	Montia fontana	(H)
BLISTERCRESS	Erysimum	(H)
BLOOD FLOWER	Asclepias curassavica	(TH)
BLOOD FLOWER	Scadoxus multiflorus katherinae	(HP)
BLOOD LILY	Haemanthus	(BB)
BLOOD ORANGE	Citrus aurantium melitensis	(F)
BLOOD-BERRY	Rivina	(H)
BLOOD-DROP	Stylomecon heterophylla	(H)
BLOOD-LEAF	Iresine herbstii	(HP)
BLOOD-LEAF JAPANESE MAPLE	Acer palmatum 'Atropurpureum'	(S)
BLOOD-RED GERANIUM	Geranium sanguineum	(H)
BLOODROOT	Potentilla erecta	(H)
BLOODROOT	Sanguinaria	(H)
BLOODWOOD TREE	Haematoxylum campechianum	(TT)
BLOODWORT	Rumex sanguineus	(H)
BLOODWORT	Sanguinaria	(H)
BLOODY CRANE'S BILL	Geranium sanguineum	(H)
BLOODY DOCK	Rumex sanguineus sanguineus	(H)
BLUE ALPINE DAISY	Aster alpinus	(R)
BLUE AMARYLLIS	Worsleya	(BB)
BLUE ANEMONE	Anemone appennina	(BB)
BLUE ASH	Fraxinus quadrangulata	(T)
BLUE ATLAS CEDAR	Cedrus atlantica 'Glauca'	(C)
BLUE BARREL	Echinocereus horizinthalonius	(CS)
BLUE BEAN	Lupinus perennis	(H)
BLUE BEARD	Caryopteris	(S)
BLUE BEECH	Carpinus caroliniana	(T)
BLUE BELL	Phacelia	(A)
BLUE BELLS	Polemonium reptans	(H)
BLUE BENT GRASS	Molinia coerulea	(G)
BLUE BIRCH	Betula coerulea-grandis	(T)
BLUE BOTTLE	Centaurea cyanus	(H)
BLUE BROOM	Erinacea anthyllis	(S)
BLUE BROOM	Psoralea pinnata	(TS)
BLUE BUGLE	Ajuga genevensis	(H)
BLUE BUSH	Eucalyptus macrocarpa	(T)
BLUE BUSH	Kochia	(A)
BLUE CANDLE	Myrtillocactus geometrizans	(CS)
BLUE CEDAR	Cedrus atlantica 'Glauca'	(C)

Common	Botanical	Type
BLUE CENTURY PLANT	Agave pelmeri	(CS)
BLUE COHOSH	Caulophyllum thalictroides	(H)
BLUE COMFREY	Symphytum caucasicum	(H)
BLUE CORNFLOWER	Centaurea cyanus	(A)
BLUE COWSLIP	Pulmonaria angustifolia	(H)
BLUE CUPIDONE	Catananche	(H)
BLUE CURLS	Trichostema lanatum	(H)
BLUE DAISY	Felicia	(H)
BLUE DAWN FLOWER	Ipomoea learii	(CL)
BLUE DOUGLAS FIR	Pseudotsuga menziesii glauca	(C)
BLUE EGYPTIAN LOTUS	Nymphaea caerulea	(WP)
BLUE ELDER BERRY	Sambucus caerulea	(S)
BLUE FAN PALM	Erythea armata	(P)
BLUE FESCUE	Festuca glauca	(G)
BLUE FLAG	Iris versicolor	(H)
BLUE FLAX	Linum perenne	(H)
BLUE FLEABANE	Erigeron acre	(H)
BLUE FLOWERED TORCH	Tillandsia lindenii	(H)
BLUE GENSENG	Caulophyllum thalictroides	(H)
BLUE GRAMA	Bouteloua gracilis	(G)
BLUE GRASS LILY	Aphyllanthes monspeliensis	(H)
BLUE GUM	Eucalyptus globulus	(T)
BLUE HAZE	Pachyphytum	(H)
BLUE HAZE	Selago thunbergii	(H)
BLUE HEATH	Phyllodoce caerulea	(H)
BLUE HOLLY	Ilex x meservae	(S)
BLUE LACE FLOWER	Didiscus caeruleus	(H/A)
BLUE LIPS	Collinsia grandiflora	(H)
BLUE LOBELIA	Lobelia siphilitica	(H)
BLUE LOBELIA	Lobelia urens	(H)
BLUE LOTUS OF INDIA	Nymphaea stellata	(WP)
BLUE LOTUS OF THE NILE	Nymphaea stellata	(WP)
BLUE MAGNOLIA	Magnolia acuminata	(T)
BLUE MARGUERITE	Felicia amelloides	(H)
BLUE MOOR GRASS	Sesleria albicans	(G)
BLUE MOUNTAIN BIDI-BIDI	Acaena inermis	(R)
BLUE MOUNTAIN BIDI-BIDI	Acaena microphylla	(R)
BLUE OAK	Quercus douglasii	(T)
BLUE OXALIS	Parochetus	(H)
BLUE PALM	Erythea armata	(P)
BLUE PALMETTO	Rhapidophyllum	(TS)
BLUE PASSION FLOWER	Passiflora coerulea	(CL)
BLUE PETREA	Petrea volubilis	(TCL)
BLUE PIMPERNEL	Anagallis foemina	(H)
BLUE PINCUSHION	Brunonia australis	(H)
BLUE POPPY	Meconopsis betonicifolia	(H)
BLUE SAGE	Eranthemum	(HP)

Know Your Common Plant Names

Common	Botanical	Type
BLUE SAGE	Salvia azurea	(H)
BLUE SAGE	Salvia patens	(H)
BLUE SAILORS	Cichorium intybus	(H)
BLUE SAXIFRAGE	Saxifraga caesia	(R)
BLUE SOW-THISTLE	Lactuca aplina	(H)
BLUE SOWTHISTLE	Cicerbita	(H)
BLUE SOWTHISTLE	Cicerbita macrophylla	(H)
BLUE SPANISH FIR	Abies pinsapo glauca	(C)
BLUE SPIDERWORT	Commelina	(H)
BLUE SPIRAEA	Caryopteris	(S)
BLUE SPRUCE	Picea pungens 'Glauca' cvs	(C)
BLUE SPURGE	Euphorbia myrsinites	(H)
BLUE STAR	Chamaescilla corymbosa	(BB)
BLUE THROATWORT	Trachelium caeruleum	(H)
BLUE TRUMPET VINE	Thunbergia grandiflora	(TCL)
BLUE VERVAIN	Verbena hastata	(H)
BLUE WATER LILY	Nymphaea capensis	(WP)
BLUE WATER SPEEDWELL	Veronica anagallis-aquatica	(WP)
BLUE WATTLE	Acacia cynanophylla	(T)
BLUE WEED	Echium vulgare	(A)
BLUE WILLOW	Salix alba 'Caerulea'	(T)
BLUE WILLOW	Salix caesia	(S)
BLUE WOODRUFF	Asperula arvensis	(H)
BLUE-BERRIED HONEYSUCKLE	Lonicera caerulea	(S)
BLUE-EYED GRASS	Sisyrinchium angustifolium	(H)
BLUE-EYED MARY	Collinsia	(H)
BLUE-EYED MARY	Omphalodes Verna	(H)
BLUEBEAD-LILY	Clintonia borealis	(H)
BLUEBEARD	Caryopteris	(S)
BLUEBEARD	Salvia horminum	(H)
BLUEBELL	Hyacinthoides non-scripta	(BB)
BLUEBELL CREEPER	Sollya heterphylla	(CL)
BLUEBERRY	Vaccinium corymbosum	(F)
BLUEBERRY ASH	Elaeocarpus reticulatus	(S)
BLUEBERRY ROOT	Caulophyllum thalictroides	(H)
BLUEBIRD VINE	Petrea volubilis	(TCL)
BLUECURLS	Trichostema	(A)
BLUETS	Hedyotis caerulea	(H)
BLUNT PLANTAIN LILY	Hosta decorata	(H)
BLUNT-FRUITED WATER-STARWORT	Callitriche obtusangula	(WP)
BLUSHING BRIDE	Serruria florida	(H)
BLUSHING BROMELIAD	Neoregelia carolinae	(HP)
BLUSHING BROMELIAD	Neoregelia carolinae tricolor	(HP)
BLUSHING BROMELIAD	Nidularium fulgens	(HP)
BLUSHING PHILODENDRON	Philodendron erubescens	(HP)
BO TREE	Ficus religiosa	(HP)
BO-TREE	Ficus religios	(TT)

Common	Botanical	Type
BOAT LILY	Tradescantia stathacea	(HP)
BOG ARUM	Calla palustris	(WP)
BOG ASPHODEL	Narthecium ossifragum	(H)
BOG BEAN	Menyanthes	(H)
BOG BILBERRY	Vaccinium uliginosum	(S)
BOG HEATHER	Erica tetralix	(S)
BOG MYRTLE	Myrica gale	(S)
BOG ORCHID	Arethusa bulbosa	(O)
BOG ORCHID	Calypso bulbosa	(O)
BOG PIMPERNEL	Anagallis tenella	(H)
BOG PONDWEED	Potamogeton polygonifolius	(WP)
BOG RHUBARB	Petasites vulgaris	(H)
BOG ROSEMARY	Andromeda polifolia	(S)
BOG SEDGE	Carex limosa	(G)
BOG STITCHWORT	Stellaria alsine	(A)
BOG STITCHWORT	Stelloria uliginosa	(H)
BOG VIOLET	Viola palustris	(H)
BOG WHORTLEBERRY	Vaccineum uliginosum	(S)
BOG-RUSH	Schoenus	(G)
BOGA ARUM	Lysichiton americanum	(WP)
BOHEMIAN GAGEA	Gagea bohemica	(H)
BOLDO	Peumus boldus	(T)
BOMBARRA GROUND NUT	Voandzeia subterranea	(TS)
BONAVIST	Lablab purpurea	(S)
BONESET	Eupatorium perfoliatum	(H)
BONESET	Symphytum officinale	(H)
BOOTLACE FUNGUS	Armillariella mellea	(FU)
BOOTLACE WEED	Chorda filum	(SW)
BORAGE	Borago officinalis	(HB)
BORDER CARNATION	Dianthus caryophyllus	(A)
BORDER PINK	Dianthus plumarius	(H)
BORECOLE	Brassica fimbriata	(V)
BOSNIANPINE	Pinus leucodermis	(C)
BOSTON FERN	Nephrolepis exaltata	(FN)
BOSTON FERN	Nephrolepis exaltata bostoniensis	(FN)
BOSTON IVY	Parthenocissus veitchii	(CL)
BOTANY BAY GUM	Xanthorrhea	(S)
BOTANY BAY GUM	Xanthorrhoea arborea	(T)
BOTANY BAY TEA TREE	Correa alba	(S/T)
BOTTLE GOURD	Lagenaria siceraria	(V)
BOTTLE GOURD	Lagenaria siceraria	(F)
BOTTLE PLANT	Hatiora salicornioides	(CS)
BOTTLE TREE	Brachychiton	(TT)
BOTTLEBRUSH	Callistemon	(S)
BOTTLEWEED	Cebtaurea scabiosa	(H)
BOULE D'OR	Trollius europaeus	(H)
BOUNCING BESS	Centranthus ruber	(H)

Common	Botanical	Type
BOUNCING BETT	Saponaria officinalis	(H)
BOURBON PALM	Latania	(P)
BOURNEMOUTH PINE	Pinus pinaster	(C)
BOURTREE	Sambucus nigra	(S)
BOWER PLANT	Pandorea jasminoides	(S)
BOWER PLANT OF AUSTRALIA	Pandorea jasminioides	(TS)
BOWLE'S BLACK VIOLET	Viola nigra	(H)
BOWLE'S GOLDEN GRASS	Milium effusum 'Aureum'	(G)
BOWMAN'S ROOT	Apocynum cannabinum	(H)
BOWMAN'S ROOT	Gillenia trifoliata	(S)
BOWSTRING HEMP	Sansevieria hahnii	(HP)
BOX	Buxus	(S)
BOX BERRY	Gaultheria	(S)
BOX BERRY	Gaultheria procumbens	(S)
BOX BLUEBERRY	Vaccineum ovatum	(S)
BOX ELDER	Acer negundo	(T)
BOX HOLLY	Ruscus aculeatus	(S)
BOX HUCKLEBERRY	Gaylussacia brachycera	(S)
BOX THORN	Lycium	(S)
BOXBERRY	Gaultheria procumbens	(S)
BOXWOOD	Buxus sempervirens	(S)
BOY'S LOVE	Artemisia abrotanum	(S)
BOYSEN BERRY	Rubus loganobaccus	(F)
BRACELET HONEY MYRTLE	Melaleuca armillaris	(S/T)
BRACELET WOOD	Jacquinia armillaris	(TT)
BRACKEN	Pteridium aquilinum	(FN)
BRAKE FERN	Pteridium aquilinum	(FN)
BRAMBLE	Rubus	(F)
BRAMBLE FERN	Hyolepis punctata	(FN)
BRAMBLE OF MOUNT IDA	Rubus idaeus	(F)
BRANCHED ASPHODEL	Asphodelus ramosus	(H)
BRANCHED BUR-REED	Sparganium erectum	(WP)
BRANCHED LARKSPUR	Consolida regalis	(A)
BRANDY BOTTLE	Nuphar lutea	(WP)
BRANK-URSINE	Acanthus mollis	(H)
BRASILETTO	Caesalpinia vesicaria	(TT)
BRASS BUTTONS	Cotula coronopifolia	(R)
BRAYA	Braya lineoris	(H)
BRAZIL NUT	Bertholletia excelsa	(F)
BRAZILIAN ARAUCARIA	Araucaria angustifolia	(C)
BRAZILIAN EDELWEISS	Sinningia leucotricha	(HP)
BRAZILIAN GLOXINIA	Sinningia speciosa	(HP)
BRAZILIAN MORNING GLORY	Ipomoea setosa	(CL)
BRAZILIAN PEPPER TREE	Schinus terebinthifolius	(TT)
BRAZILIAN PINE	Araucaria angustifolia	(C)
BRAZILIAN PLUME	Jacobinia carnea	(HP)
BRAZILWOOD	Caesalpinia brasiliensis	(TS)

Know Your Common Plant Names

Common	Botanical	Type
BREAD AND CHEESE	Crataegus monogyna	(T)
BREAD TREE	Encephalartos altensteinii	(FN)
BREAD WHEAT	Triticum aestivum	(G)
BREAD-NUT	Brosimum alicastrum	(TT)
BREADFRUIT	Artocarpus altilis	(F)
BREATH OF HEAVEN	Adenandra fragrans	(S)
BRECKLAND THYME	Thymus serpyllum	(H)
BREWER'S SALTBUSH	Atriplex lentiformis breweri	(S)
BREWERS WEEPING SPRUCE	Picea brewerana	(C)
BRIANCON APRICOT	Prunus brigantina	(T)
BRIAR	Erica arborea	(S)
BRIAR ROSE	Rosa canina	(S)
BRIDAL BOUQUET	Porana paniculata	(CL)
BRIDAL WREATH	Francoa sonchifolia	(R)
BRIDAL WREATH	Spiraea x arguta	(S)
BRIDEWEED	Linaria vulgaris	(H)
BRIDEWORT	Spiraea salicifolia	(S)
BRINJAL	Solanum melongena	(V)
BRISBANE BOX	Tristania	(B)
BRISBANE BOX	Tristania conferta	(TT)
BRISBANE LILY	Eurycles	(BB)
BRISTLE BENT	Agrostis curtisii	(G)
BRISTLE CLUB-RUSH	Scirpus setaceus	(G)
BRISTLE OAT	Arena strigosa	(G)
BRISTLE-CONE PINE	Pinus aristata	(C)
BRISTLE-GRASS	Setaria	(G)
BRISTLECONE FIR	Abies bracteata	(C)
BRISTLY LOCUST	Robinia hispida	(T)
BRISTLY OX-TONGUE	Picris echioides	(H)
BRITISH COLOMBIA WILD GINGER	Asarum caudatum	(H)
BRITISH MYRRH	Myrrhis odorata	(HB)
BRITTLE BLADDER FERN	Cystopteris fragilis	(FN)
BROAD BEAN	Vicia faba	(V)
BROAD BEECH FERN	Thelypteris hexagonoptera	(FN)
BROAD BUCKLER FERN	Dryopteris dilatata	(FN)
BROAD WEDGE-PEA	Gompholobium latifolium	(H)
BROAD-LEAVED ARBORVITAE	Thujopsis	(C)
BROAD-LEAVED COCKSPUR THORN	Crataegus prunifolia	(T)
BROAD-LEAVED DOCK	Rumex obtusifolius	(H)
BROAD-LEAVED EYEBRIGHT	Euphrasia tetraquetra	(H)
BROAD-LEAVED HELLEBORINE	Epipactis helleborine	(O)
BROAD-LEAVED KINDLING BARK	Eucalyptus dalrympleana	(T)
BROAD-LEAVED MARSH ORCHID	Dactylorhiza majalis	(O)
BROAD-LEAVED RAGWORT	Senecio fluviatilis	(H)
BROAD-LEAVED SERMOUNTAIN	Laserpitium latifolium	(H)
BROAD-LEAVED SILVER HOLLY	Ilex aquifolium "argenteomarginata"	(S.T.)
BROAD-LEAVED SPINDLE	Euonymus latifolius	(S)

Common	Botanical	Type
BROAD-LEAVED SPURGE	Euphorbia platyphyllos	(H)
BROAD-LEAVED WHITEBEAM	Sorbus latifolia	(T)
BROAD-LEAVED WILLOW HERB	Epilobium montanum	(H)
BROADLEAF	Griselinia littoralis	(S)
BROCCOLI	Brassica oleracea botrytis	(V)
BROME GRASS	Bromus	(G)
BROMPTON STOCK	Matthiola incana	(B)
BRONVAUX MEDLAR	Crataegomespilus dardari	(T)
BRONZE FENNEL	Foeniculum vulgare purpureum	(H)
BROOK BEAN	Menyanthes trifoliata	(WP)
BROOK THISTLE	Cirsium rivulare	(H)
BROOKLIME	Veronica beccabunga	(H)
BROOKWEED	Samolus valerandi	(H)
BROOM	Cytisus, Genista	(S)
BROOM CYPRESS	Kochia scoparia trichophylla	(A)
BROOM PALM	Thrinax argentea	(P)
BROOM WATTLE	Acacia calamifolia	(T)
BROOM-CORN	Sorghum vulgare	(G)
BROOMCORN MILLET	Panicum millaceum	(G)
BROOMRAPE	Orobanche	(H)
BROWN BENT GRASS	Agrostis canina	(G)
BROWN CABBAGE TREE	Pisonia grandis	(TS)
BROWN CLOVER	Trifolium badium	(H)
BROWN KNAPWEED	Centaurea jacea	(H)
BROWN SEDGE	Carex disticha	(G)
BROWN STRINGY BARK	Eucalyptus baxteri	(T)
BROWN-EYED SUSAN	Rudbeckia triloba	(H)
BRUISEWORT	Symphytum officinale	(H)
BRUNELLA	Prunella	(H)
BRUSH BOX	Tristania conferta	(S)
BRUSH BUSH	Eucryphia	(S)
BRUSHBOX TREE	Tristania conferta	(TT)
BRUSSEL SPROUT	Brassica oleracea gemmifera	(V)
BRYONY	Bryonia	(CL)
BRYONY	Tamus	(CL)
BUCHU	Barosma betulina	(S)
BUCK BRUSH	Ceanothus cuneatus	(S)
BUCK'S HORN PLANTAIN	Plantago coronopus	(H)
BUCK-BEAN	Menyanthes	(H)
BUCKET ORCHID	Coryanthes	(O)
BUCKEYE	Aesculus	(S.T.)
BUCKLER FERN	Dryopteris	(FN)
BUCKLER LEAF SORREL	Rumax scutatus	(HB)
BUCKLER MUSTARD	Biscutella laevigata	(H)
BUCKTHORN	Rhamnus	(S.T.)
BUCKWHEAT	Fagopyrum esculentum	(H)
BUCKWHEAT TREE	Cliftonia monophylla	(S)

Know Your Common Plant Names

Common	Botanical	Type
BUDDHIST PINE	Podocarpus macrophyllus	(C)
BUFFALO BERRY	Shepherdia argentea	(S)
BUFFALO CURRANT	Ribes odoratum	(S)
BUFFALO GRASS	Buchloc dactyloides	(GS)
BUFFALO GRASS	Stenotaphrum secundatum	(HP)
BUFFALO HERB	Medicago Sativa	(HB)
BUFFALO THORN	Zizythis mucronata	(TS)
BUG ORCHID	Orchis coriophora	(O)
BUGBANE	Actaea spicata	(H)
BUGBANE	Cimicifuga	(H)
BUGLE	Ajuga	(H)
BUGLE LILY	Watsonia	(BB)
BUGLEWEED	Lycopus virginicus	(H)
BUGLOSS	Anchusa arvensis	(H)
BUISSON ARDENT	Pyracantha coccinea	(S)
BULBOUS BUTTERCUP	Ranunculus bulbosus	(H)
BULBOUS CHERVIL	Chaerophyllum	(H)
BULBOUS CORYDALIS	Corydalis cava	(H)
BULBOUS FOXTAIL	Alopecurus bulbosus	(G)
BULBOUS FUMITORY	Corydalis solida	(H)
BULBOUS MEADOW GRASS	Poa bulbosa	(G)
BULGARIAN FIR	Abies borisii-regis	(C)
BULL BANKSIA	Banksia grandis	(S)
BULL HOOF TREE	Bauhinia purpurea	(TT)
BULL NETTLE	Solanum carolinense	(H)
BULL'S HORN ACACIA	Acacia spadicigera	(T)
BULLACE	Prunus domestica insititia	(F)
BULLBAY	Magnolia grandiflora	(S)
BULLOCK BUSH	Templetonia retusa	(S)
BULLOCK'S EYE	Semperrivum tectorum	(R)
BULLOCK'S HEART	Annona reticulata	(S)
BULRUSH	Scirpus	(G)
BULRUSH REEDMACE	Typha latifolia	(H)
BUNCH BERRY	Cornus canadensis	(S)
BUNCH FLOWER	Melanthium	(H)
BUNCH-FLOWERED NARCISSUS	Narcissus tazetta	(WP)
BUNIAS	Bunias erucago	(H)
BUNNYEARS	Opuntia microdasys	(CS)
BUNYA-BUNYA	Araucaria bidwillii	(C)
BUR CHERVIL	Anthriscus caucalis	(H)
BUR CUCUMBER	Sicyos angulatus	(S)
BUR FORGET-NE-NOT	Lappula squarrosa	(H)
BUR MARIGOLD	Bidens tripartita	(H)
BUR MEDICK	Medicago minima	(H)
BUR REED	Sparganium	(G)
BUR-CUCUMBER	Sicyos angulatus	(F)
BUR-MARIGOLD	Bidens tripartita	(H)

Common	Botanical	Type
BUR-REED	Sparganium ramosum	(WP)
BURDOCK	Arctium lappa	(H)
BURMESE FISHTAIL PALM	Caryota mitis	(P)
BURNET	Sanguisorba officinalis	(HB)
BURNET ROSE	Rosa pimpinellifolia	(S)
BURNETT SAXIFRAGE	Pimpinella saxifraga	(HB)
BURNING BUSH	Cotinus coggygria follis purpureis	(S)
BURNING BUSH	Dictamnus	(H)
BURNING BUSH	Euonymus atropurpureus	(S)
BURNING BUSH	Kochia scoparia	(A)
BURNING BUSH	Kochia scoparia trichophylla	(A)
BURNT-TIP ORCHID	Orchis ustulata	(O)
BURR OAK	Quercus macrocarpa	(T)
BURR ROSE	Rosa roxburghii	(S)
BURRO'S TAIL	Sedum morganianum	(H)
BURSTWORT	Herniaria	(H)
BUSH BASIL	Ocimum basilicum minimum	(HB)
BUSH CHINQUAPIN	Chrysolepis sempervirens	(T)
BUSH CLOVER	Lespedeza	(S)
BUSH GRAPE	Vitis rupestris	(F)
BUSH GROUNDSEL	Baccharis halirrifolia	(S)
BUSH GWARRI	Euclea crispa	(H)
BUSH LAUREL	Rubus cissoides	(S)
BUSH MALLOW	Lavatera olbia	(S)
BUSH POMEGRANATE	Balaustion microphyllum	(TS)
BUSH VETCH	Vicia sepium	(H)
BUSH VIOLET	Browallia	(HP)
BUSH-HONEYSUCKLE	Diervilla	(S)
BUSH-PEA	Pultenaea	(S)
BUSHY MINT	Mentha x gentilis	(HB)
BUSY LIZZIE	Impatiens sultanii	(A)
BUTCHER'S BROOM	Ruscus aculeatus	(S)
BUTTER AND EGGS	Linaria vulgaris	(H)
BUTTER-DOCK	Petasites vulgaris	(H)
BUTTER-NUT	Juglans cinerea	(T)
BUTTERBEAN	Phaseolus vulgaris	(V)
BUTTERBURR	Petasites hybridus	(H)
BUTTERCUP	Ranunculus	(H)
BUTTERCUP FLOWER	Allamanda cathartica	(TS)
BUTTERCUP SHRUB	Potentilla	(S)
BUTTERCUP TREE	Cochlospermum religiosum	(TT)
BUTTERCUP TREE	Cochlospermum vitifolium	(TT)
BUTTERFLY BUSH	Buddleja davidii	(S)
BUTTERFLY FLAG	Diplarrhena moraea	(H)
BUTTERFLY FLOWER	Bauhinia monandra	(H)
BUTTERFLY FLOWER	Schizanthus	(A)
BUTTERFLY GINGER	Hedychium coronarium	(TH)

Common	Botanical	Type
BUTTERFLY IRIS	Iris spuria	(H)
BUTTERFLY IRIS	Moraea: Iris ochroleuca	(BB)
BUTTERFLY LAVENDER	Lavandula stoechas	(S)
BUTTERFLY LILY	Calochortus	(BB)
BUTTERFLY LILY	Hedychium coronarium	(BB)
BUTTERFLY ORCHID	Oncidium papilio	(O)
BUTTERFLY ORCHID	Platanthera chlorantha	(O)
BUTTERFLY PALM	Areca lutescens	(P)
BUTTERFLY PALM	Chrysalidocarpus lutescens	(P)
BUTTERFLY PEA	Clitoria ternatea	(S)
BUTTERFLY TREE	Bauhinia purpurea	(TT)
BUTTERFLY TULIP	Calochortus	(BB)
BUTTERFLY WEED	Asclepias tuberosa	(H)
BUTTERWORT	Pinguicula	(H)
BUTTON BUSH	Cephalanthus occidentalis	(S)
BUTTON CACTUS	Epithelontha bokei	(CS)
BUTTON FERN	Pellaea rotundifolia	(FN)
BUTTON SNAKEROOT	Liatris spicata	(H)
BUTTONS	Tanacetum vulgare	(H)
BUTTONWEED	Cotula coronopifolia	(H)
BUTTONWOOD	Platanus occidentalis	(T)
BUXBAUM'S SPEEDWELL	Veronica persica	(H)
CABBAGE	Brassica oleracea capitata	(V)
CABBAGE GUM	Eucalyptus pauciflora	(T)
CABBAGE LETTUCE	Lactuca sativa capitata	(V)
CABBAGE PALM	Areca aleracae	(P)
CABBAGE PALM	Cordyline australis	(H)
CABBAGE PALM	Livistona australis	(P)
CABBAGE PALM	Roystonea oleracea	(P)
CABBAGE ROSE	Rosa centifolia	(S)
CABBAGE THISTLE	Cirsium oleraceum	(H)
CABBAGE TREE	Andira	(TT)
CABBAGE TREE	Cordyline australis	(S)
CACAO	Theobroma cacao	(F)
CACTUS DAHLIA	Dahlia juarezii	(A)
CADE	Juniperus oxycedrus	(C)
CAJUPUT	Melaleuca leucadendron	(S)
CALABA TREE	Calophyllum	(TT)
CALABAR BEAN	Physostigma venenosum	(V)
CALABASH GOURD	Lagenaria siceraria	(F)
CALABASH NUTMEG	Monodora myristica	(S)
CALABASH TREE	Crescentia cujete	(T)
CALABRESSE	Brassica oleracea italica	(V)
CALAF OF PERSIA WILLOW	Salix aegyptiaca	(S/T)
CALAMINT	Calamintha	(H)
CALAMONDIN	X Citrofortunella microcarpa	(F)
CALATHIAN VIOLET	Gentiana pneumonanthe	(H)

Common	Botanical	Type
CALICO BUSH	Kalmia latifolia	(S)
CALICO FLOWER	Aristolochia elegans	(CL)
CALICO HEARTS	Adromischus maculatus	(HP)
CALIFONIAN BUCKTHORN	Rhamnus purshiana	(S)
CALIFORNIA BIG TREE	Sequoiadendron giganteum	(C)
CALIFORNIA BLUEBELL	Phacelia whitlavia	(A)
CALIFORNIA BUCKEYE	Aesculus californica	(S)
CALIFORNIA BUCKWHEAT	Eriogonum fasciculatum	(S)
CALIFORNIA BUCKWHEAT	Eriogonum fasciculatum	(H)
CALIFORNIA GOLDEN BELLS	Emmenanthe	(A)
CALIFORNIA SASSAFRAS	Umbellularia californica	(S)
CALIFORNIAN ALLSPICE	Calycanthus occidentalis	(C)
CALIFORNIAN BAY	Umbellularia californica	(S)
CALIFORNIAN BAYBERRY	Myrica californica	(S)
CALIFORNIAN BLACK CURRANT	Ribes bracteosum	(S)
CALIFORNIAN BLACK OAK	Quercus kelloggii	(T)
CALIFORNIAN BLACK WALNUT	Juglans hindsii	(T)
CALIFORNIAN BLUEBELL	Nemophila phacelia	(A)
CALIFORNIAN FUCHSIA	Zauschneria californica	(R)
CALIFORNIAN HYACINTH	Brodiaea	(BB)
CALIFORNIAN LAUREL	Umbellularia californica	(ST)
CALIFORNIAN LILAC	Ceanothus	(S)
CALIFORNIAN LIVE OAK	Quercus agrifolia	(T)
CALIFORNIAN LIVE OAK	Quercus chrysolepis	(T)
CALIFORNIAN MAYBUSH	Heteromeles arbutifolia	(S)
CALIFORNIAN MOUNTAIN PINE	Pinus monticola	(C)
CALIFORNIAN NUT MEG	Torreya californica	(C)
CALIFORNIAN PITCHER PLANT	Darlingtonia	(H)
CALIFORNIAN POPPY	Eschscholtzia	(H)
CALIFORNIAN RED FIR	Abies magnifica	(C)
CALIFORNIAN REDWOOD	Sequoia sempervirens	(C)
CALIFORNIAN SCRUB OAK	Quercus dumosa	(T)
CALIFORNIAN TREE POPPY	Romneya	(S)
CALIFORNIAN WHISPERING BELLS	Emmenanthe penduliflora	(H)
CALIFORNIAN YEW	Taxus brevifolia	(C)
CALISAYA	Cinchona calisaya	(TT)
CALLA LILY	Zantedeshia	(H)
CALOTROPIS	Calotropis procera	(TT)
CALUMBA	Jateorhiza calumba	(TT)
CALVARY CLOVER	Medicago echinus	(H)
CALVE'S SNOUT	Linaria vulgaris	(H)
CALYPSO	Calypso bulbosa	(O)
CAMBRIDGE MILK-PARSLEY	Selinum carvifolia	(H)
CAMBRIDGE OAK	Quercus warburgii	(T)
CAMEL THORN	Acacia giraffae	(T)
CAMEL THORN	Alhagi camelorum	(TT)
CAMEL'S FOOT	Bauhinia purpurea	(TT)

Know Your Common Plant Names

Common	Botanical	Type
CAMPEACHY WOOD	Haematoxylum campechianum	(TT)
CAMPERDOWN ELM	Ulmus glabra 'Camperdowmii"	(T)
CAMPHOR PLANT	Balsamita major tomentosum	(HB)
CAMPHOR TREE	Cinnamomum camphora	(T)
CAMPION	Lychnis	(A/H)
CAMPION	Silene	(A/H)
CAMWOOD	Baphia nitida	(P)
CANADA LILY	Lilium canadense	(BB)
CANADA MOONSEED	Menispermum canadense	(CL)
CANADA PITCH	Tsuga canadensis	(C)
CANADA ROOT	Asclepias tuberosa	(H)
CANADA TED	Gaultheria	(S)
CANADIAN FLEABANE	Conyza canadensis	(A)
CANADIAN GOLDEN-ROD	Solidago canadensis	(H)
CANADIAN HEMLOCK	Tsuga canadensis	(C)
CANADIAN HEMP	Apocynum cannabinum	(H)
CANADIAN JUNIPER	Juniperus communis 'Depressa'	(C)
CANADIAN MAPLE	Acer rubrum	(T)
CANADIAN MOONSEED	Menispermum canadense	(CL)
CANADIAN PONDWEED	Elodea canadensis	(WP)
CANADIAN RED PINE	Pinus resinosa	(C)
CANADIAN WILD RICE	Zizania aquatica	(WP)
CANADIAN YEW	Taxus canadensis	(C)
CANARY CREEPER	Tropaeolum peregrinum	(CL)
CANARY DATE PALM	Phoenix canariensis	(P)
CANARY GRASS	Phalaris canariensis	(G)
CANARY ISLAND BELLFLOWER	Canarina canariensis	(CL)
CANARY ISLAND DATE PALM	Phoenix canariensis	(P)
CANARY ISLAND HOLLY	Ilex platyphylla	(S)
CANARY ISLAND IVY	Hedera canariensis	(CL)
CANARY ISLAND LAUREL	Laurus azorica	(S)
CANARY ISLAND LAUREL	Laurus canariensis	(S/T)
CANARY ISLAND PINE	Pinus canariensis	(C)
CANARY ISLANDS BANANA	Musa cavendishii	(F)
CANARY MELON	Cucumis melo dudaim	(F)
CANARY-BIRD BUSH	Crotalaria agatiflora	(S)
CANCER BUSH	Sutherlandia frutescens	(S)
CANDALABRA SPRUCE	Picea montigena	(C)
CANDELABRA ALOE	Aloe arborescens	(HP)
CANDELABRA TREE	Araucaria angustifolia	(C)
CANDELABRA TREE	Euphorbia candelabrum	(TT)
CANDELILLA	Euphorbia antisyphilitica	(CS)
CANDLE BUSH	Cassia didymobotrya	(TS)
CANDLE CRANBERRY	Astroloma ciliatum	(S)
CANDLE PLANT	Kleinia articulata	(HP)
CANDLE PLANT	Plectranthus oertendahlii	(HP)
CANDLE TREE	Parmentiera cereifera	(TT)

Common	Botanical	Type
CANDLE-DARK GUM	Eucalyptus rubida	(T)
CANDLEBERRY	Myrica cerifera	(J)
CANDLEBERRY TREE	Aleurites moluccana	(TT)
CANDLENUT	Aleurites moluccana	(T)
CANDLEWICK	Verbascum thapsus	(H)
CANDLEWOOD	Fouquiera	(TS)
CANDY CARROT	Athamanta matthioli	(TS)
CANDY LILIES	X Pardancanda	(BB)
CANDY MUSTARD	Acthionema saxatile	(R)
CANDYTUFT	Iberis	(AH)
CANDYTUFT	Iberis amora	(R)
CANE CACTUS	Opuntia cylindrica	(CS)
CANE PALM	Calamus	(G)
CANE REED	Arundinaria gigantea	(G)
CANNON BALL TREE	Couroupita guianensis	(TT)
CANOE BIRCH	Betula papyrifera	(T)
CANTALA	Agave cantala	(CS)
CANTALOUPE (MELON)	Cucumis melo	(V)
CANTERBURY BELL	Campanula media	(S)
CANYON LIVE OAK	Quercus chrysolepis	(T)
CAPA DE ORO	Solandra maxima	(CL)
CAPE ALOE	Aloe ferox	(CS)
CAPE BLUE WATER LILY	Nymphaea capensis	(WP)
CAPE BOX	Buxus macowani	(TS)
CAPE CHESTNUT	Calodendron capense	(T)
CAPE COWSLIP	Lachenalia	(HP)
CAPE DAISY	Venidium fastuosum	(A)
CAPE DANDELION	Arctotheca calendula	(H)
CAPE FIGWORT	Phygelius capensis	(H)
CAPE FORGET-ME-NOT	Anchusa capensis	(A)
CAPE FUCHSIA	Phygelius capensis	(H)
CAPE GOOSEBERRY	Physalis peruviana	(H)
CAPE GUM	Acacia senegal	(T)
CAPE HEATH	Erica Hyemalis	(HP)
CAPE HIBISCUS	Hibiscus diversifolius	(S)
CAPE HONEYSUCKLE	Tecomaria capensis	(CL)
CAPE IVY	Senecio macroflossus	(HP)
CAPE JASMINE	Gardenia	(HP)
CAPE JASMINE	Gardenia jasminoides	(HP)
CAPE LEADWORT	Plumbago auriculata	(TS)
CAPE LILY	Crinum x powellii	(BB)
CAPE MARIGOLD	Dimorphotheca	(H)
CAPE MYRTLE	Myrsine africana	(S)
CAPE PONDWEED	Aponogeton distachyos	(WP)
CAPE PRIMROSE	Streptocarpus	(HP)
CAPE STOCK	Heliophila	(H)
CAPE SUNDEW	Drosera capensis	(H)

Know Your Common Plant Names

Common	Botanical	Type
CAPE TREASURE FLOWER	Gazania pavonia	(A)
CAPE VIOLET	Ionidium capense	(TS)
CAPER PLANT	Capparis spinosa	(S)
CAPER SPURGE	Euphorbia lathyrus	(H)
CAPPADOCIAN MAPLE	Acer cappadocium	(T)
CAPULIN CHERRY	Prunus salicifolia	(T)
CARAMBOLA	Averrhoa caranbola	(H)
CARAWAY	Carum carvi	(HB)
CARAWAY THYME	Thymus herba-barona	(R)
CARDAMON	Elletaria cardamomum	(HP)
CARDINAL CLIMBER	Ipomoea quamoclit	(TCL)
CARDINAL FLOWER	Lobelia cardinalis	(H)
CARDINAL FLOWER	Sinningia cardinalis	(HP)
CARDINAL SAGE	Salvia fulgens	(S)
CARDINAL SALVIA	Salvia fulgens	(A)
CARDINAL'S GUARD	Pachystachys coccinea	(HP)
CARDOON	Cynara cardunculus	(V)
CARIBBEAN PINE	Pinus caribaea	(C)
CARICATURE PLANT	Graptophyllum pictum	(CS)
CARLINE THISTLE	Carlina vulgaris	(H)
CARMEL CEANOTHUS	Ceanothus griseus	(S)
CARNANBA PALM	Copernica cerifera	(P)
CARNATION	Dianthus caryophyllus	(H)
CARNATION GRASS	Carex panicea	(G)
CARNATION SEDGE	Carex panicea	(G)
CARNAUBA PALM	Copernica cerifera	(P)
CARNAUBA WAX PALM	Copernica prunifera	(P)
CAROB	Ceratonia siliqua	(T)
CAROB TREE	Jacaranda procera	(TT)
CAROLINA ALLSPICE	Calycanthus floridus	(S)
CAROLINA HEMLOCK	Tsuga caroliniana	(C)
CAROLINA JESSAMINE	Gelsemium sempervirens	(CL)
CAROLINA LUPIN	Thermopsis caroliniana	(H)
CAROLINA MOONSEED	Cocculus carolinus	(CL)
CAROLINA POPLAR	Populus eugenei	(T)
CAROLINA SILVERBELL	Halesia carolina	(T/S)
CARPATHIAN HAREBELL	Campanula carpatica	(R)
CARPATHIAN SPRUCE	Picea abies carpathica	(C)
CARPENTER'S LEAF	Galax aphylla	(H)
CARPENTER'S SQUARE	Scrophularia nodosa	(H)
CARPENTERS HERB	Ajugareptons	(H)
CARPET PLANT	Ionopsidium acaule	(A)
CARRAGEEN	Chondrus crispus	(MS)
CARRION FLOWER	Stapelia	(H)
CARRION FLOWERS	Stapelia	(HP)
CARRION TREE	Couroupita guianensis	(TT)
CARROT	Daucus carota sativus	(V)

Common	Botanical	Type
CARROT BROOMRAPE	Orobanche maritima	(PE/H)
CARTAGENA BARK	Cinchona cordifolia	(TT)
CARTWHEEL FLOWER	Heracleum mantegazzianum	(H)
CASCARA	Picramnia antidesma	(TS)
CASCARA SAGRADA	Rhamnus purshiana	(T)
CASCARILLA	Croton eleuteria	(TS)
CASE-WEED	Capsella bursa-pastoris	(A)
CASHEW NUT	Anacardium occidentale	(V)
CASPIAN LOCUST	Cleditsia caspica	(T)
CASPIAN WILLOW	Salix acutifolia	(S)
CASSA-BANANA	Sicana odorifera	(TS)
CASSADA WOOD	Turpinia occidentalis	(TT)
CASSAVA	Manihot esculenta	(V)
CASSAVA WOOD	Turpinia occidentalis	(TT)
CASSIA	Cinnamomum cassia	(S/T)
CASSINE	Ilex vomitoria	(T)
CAST IRON PLANT	Aspidistra	(HP)
CASTOR BEAN	Ricinus communis	(A)
CASTOR OIL PLANT	Fatsia japonica	(H)
CASTOR OIL PLANT	Ricinus communis	(A)
CAT BRIER	Smilax	(CL)
CAT CLAW CACTUS	Hamatocactus uncinatus	(CS)
CAT TAIL	Phleum	(G)
CAT TAIL	Typha	(G)
CAT THYME	Teucrium marum	(H)
CAT'S CLAW	Doxantha unguis-cato	(S)
CAT'S EAR	Hypochoeris radicata	(H)
CAT'S FOOT	Antennaria dioica	(R)
CAT'S HEAD PLANT	Tacca nivea	(H)
CAT'S PAW	Anigozanthus humilis	(S)
CAT'S TAIL	Phleum pratense	(G)
CAT'S WHISKERS	Tacca chantrieri	(HP)
CATALINA CEANOTHUS	Ceanothus arboreus	(S)
CATALINA IRONWOOD	Lyonothamnus floribundus	(T)
CATCHFLY	Lychnis silene	(H)
CATHEDRAL BELLS	Cobaea	(A.CL)
CATHEDRAL WINDOWS	Calathea maxoyana	(HP)
CATJANG	Vigna sinensis cylindrica	(TS)
CATMINT	Nepeta cataria	(H)
CATNEP	Nepeta cataria	(H)
CATNIP	Nepeta cataria	(H)
CATS HAIR	Euphorbia pilulifera	(H)
CAUCASIAN ALDER	Alnus subcordata	(T)
CAUCASIAN ELM	Zelkova carpinifolia	(T)
CAUCASIAN FIR	Abies nordmanniana	(C)
CAUCASIAN LIME	Tilia x euchlora	(T)
CAUCASIAN MAPLE	Acer cappadocicum	(T)

Know Your Common Plant Names

Common	Botanical	Type
CAUCASIAN OAK	Quercus macranthera	(T)
CAUCASIAN WHORTLEBERRY	Vaccineum arctostaphylos	(S)
CAUCASIAN WING NUT	Pterocarya fraxinifolia	(T)
CAULIFLOWER	Brassica olearacea botrytis	(V)
CAYENNE PEPPER	Capsicum frutescens	(F)
CEARA RUBBER	Manihot glaziovii	(TT)
CEDAR	Cedrus	(C)
CEDAR ELM	Ulmus crassifolia	(T)
CEDAR OF GOA	Cupressus lusitanica	(C)
CEDAR OF LEBANON	Cedrus libani	(C)
CEDAR WATTLE	Acacia elata	(T)
CEDRAT LEMON	Citrus medica cedra	(F)
CEDRON	Simaba cedron	(TS)
CELANDINE	Chelidonium	(H)
CELANDINE CROCUS	Crocus korolkowii	(BB)
CELANDINE POPPY	Stylophorum diphyllum	(H)
CELERIAC	Apium graveolens rapaceum	(V)
CELERY	Apium graveolens	(V)
CELERY PINE	Phyllocladus alpinus	(C)
CELERY-LEAVED CROWFOOT	Ranunculus sceleratus	(H)
CELERY-TOP PINE	Phyllocladus aspleniifolius	(C)
CELERY-TOPPED PINE	Phyllocladus aspleniifolius	(C)
CELTUCE	Lactuca sativa angustana	(V)
CENTAURY	Centaurum erythraea	(H)
CENTURY	Blackstonia perfoliata	(H)
CENTURY PLANT	Agave americana	(V)
CEP	Boletus edulis	(FU)
CERIMAN	Monstera deliciosa	(H/P)
CEVENNES PINE	Pinus nigra cebennensis	(C)
CEYLON EBONY	Diospyros ebenum	(TT)
CEYLON MAHOGANY	Melia dubium	(TT)
CEYLON OLIVE	Elaeocarpus serratus	(TT)
CEYLON ROSEWOOD	Albizzia odoratissima	(TS)
CHACONIA	Warszewiczia coccinea	(TS)
CHAFF WEED	Anagallis minima	(H)
CHAIN CACTUS	Rhipsalis paradoxa	(CS)
CHAIN FERN	Woodwardia	(FN)
CHAIN OF LOVE	Antigonon leptopus	(TCL)
CHAIN PLANT	Tradescantia navicularis	(HP)
CHAIN-LINK CACTUS	Opuntia imbricata	(CS)
CHALICE VINE	Solandra nitida	(TCL)
CHALK MAPLE	Acer leucoderme	(T)
CHALK MILKWORT	Polygala calcarea	(H)
CHALK PLANT	Gypsophila paniculata	(H)
CHAMOIS GRASS	Hutchinsia alpina	(G)
CHAMOMILE	Chamaemelum nobile	(H)
CHAMPION'S OAK	Quercus velutina 'Rubrifolia'	(T)

Know Your Common Plant Names

Common	Botanical	Type
CHANDELIER PLANT	Kalanchoe tubiflora	(HP)
CHANNELLED WRACK	Pelvetia canaliculata	(SW)
CHANTERELLE	Cantharellus cibarius	(FU)
CHAPARRAL LILY	Lilium rubescens	(BB)
CHARD	Beta vulgaris cicla	(V)
CHARLOCK	Sinapis arvensis	(H)
CHASTE TREE	Vitex agnus-castus	(S)
CHATHAM ISLAND FORGET-ME-NOT	Brunnera	(H)
CHATHAM ISLAND LILY	Myosotidium hortensia	(H)
CHAYOTE	Sechium edule	(TS)
CHECKER BERRY	Gaultheria procumbens	(S)
CHECKERBERRY	Mitchella repens	(S)
CHEDDAR PINK	Dianthus gratianopolitanus	(R)
CHEDDAR WHITEBEAM	Sorbus anglica	(T)
CHEESEBERRY	Cyathodes glauca	(S)
CHEKEN	Eugenia cheken	(T)
CHEKEN	Luma chequen	(T)
CHENILLE PLANT	Acalypha hispida	(HP)
CHENNAR TREE	Platanus orientalis	(T)
CHEQUERED DAFFODIL	Fritillaris meleagris	(BB)
CHEQUERED LILY	Fritillaria meleagris	(BB)
CHERIMOYA	Annona cherimola	(TS)
CHEROKEE ROSE	Rosa laevigata	(CL.S)
CHERRRY	Prunus	(S.T.)
CHERRY BIRCH	Betula lenta	(T)
CHERRY ELAEAGNUS	Elaeagnus multiflora	(S)
CHERRY LAUREL	Prunus laurocerasus	(S)
CHERRY PLUM	Prunus cerasifera	(ST)
CHERRY TOMATO	Lycopersicon esculentum cerasiforme	(F)
CHERRY-BLADDER	Physalis	(H)
CHERRY-PIE	Heliotropium	(A)
CHERRYSTONE JUNIPER	Juniperus monosperma	(C)
CHERVIL	Anthriscus cerefolium	(HB)
CHERVIL	Chaerophyllum temulentum	(HB)
CHESTNUT	Castanea	(T)
CHESTNUT OAK	Quercus prinus	(T)
CHESTNUT ROSE	Rosa roxburghii	(S)
CHESTNUT RUSH	Juncus castaneus	(G)
CHESTNUT VINE	Tetrastigma voinieranum	(NP)
CHESTNUT-LEAFED OAK	Quercus castanaefolia	(T)
CHIAN TURPENTINE TREE	Pistacia terebinthus	(T)
CHICHESTER ELM	Ulmus vegeta	(T)
CHICK PEA	Cicer arietinum	(V)
CHICKASAW PLUM	Prunus angustifolia	(S)
CHICKLING PEA	Lathyrus sativus	(H)
CHICKWEED	Stellaria media	(A)
CHICKWEED WILLOWHERB	Epilobium alsinifolium	(H)

Know Your Common Plant Names

Common	Botanical	Type
CHICKWEED WINTERGREEN	Trientalis europaea	(H)
CHICLE	Achras zapota	(TT)
CHICORY	Cichorium intybus	(V/HB)
CHIHUAHUA FLOWER	Tacitus bellus	(TS)
CHILE BELLFLOWER	Lapageria rosea	(CL)
CHILE PINE	Araucaria araucana	(C)
CHILE PITCHER-FLOWER	Sarmienta repens	(S)
CHILE RHUBARB	Gunnera manicata	(H)
CHILEAN BELL-FLOWER	Lapageria	(CL)(CA)
CHILEAN BELLFLOWER	Nolana	(S)
CHILEAN BOLDO TREE	Peumus boldus	(T)
CHILEAN CEDAR	Austrocedrus chilensis	(C)
CHILEAN CROCUS	Tecophilaea cyanocrocus	(BB)
CHILEAN FIRE BUSH	Embothrium	(T)
CHILEAN GLORY FLOWER	Eccremocarpus	(CL)
CHILEAN GUAVA	Ugnia molinae	(T)
CHILEAN HAZEL	Gevuina avellana	(S)
CHILEAN INCENSE CEDAR	Austrocedrus chilensis	(C)
CHILEAN JASMINE	Mandevilla suaveolens	(CL)
CHILEAN LAUREL	Laurelia serrata	(B)
CHILEAN NUT	Gevuina avellana	(S)
CHILEAN OIL PLANT	Madia sativa	(H)
CHILEAN POTATO TREE	Solanum crispum	(CL)
CHILEAN YEW	Podocarpus andinus	(C)
CHILGHOZA PINE	Pinus gerardiana	(C)
CHILI	Capsicum frutescens	(F)
CHILI PEPPER	Capsicum frutescens	(F)
CHIMNEY BELLFLOWER	Campanula pyramidalis	(H)
CHIN CACTUS	Gymnocalycium quehlianum	(CS)
CHINA ASTER	Callistephus chinensis	(A)
CHINA BERRY	Melia azedarach	(T)
CHINA CANE	Rhapis excelsa	(P)
CHINA GRASS	Boehmeria nivea	(G)
CHINA JUTE	Abutilon avicennae	(TS)
CHINA ROOT	Smilax china	(CL)
CHINA ROSE	Rosa chinensis	(S)
CHINA TEA PLANT	Lycium chinense	(S)
CHINA TREE	Koelreuteria	(T)
CHINA-FIR	Cunninghamia lanceolata	(C)
CHINA-GRASS	Boehmeria nivea	(G)
CHINAMAN'S BREECHES	Dicentra spectabilis	(H)
CHINCHERINCHEE	Ornithogalum thyrsoides	(BB)
CHINESE ANGELICA TREE	Aralia chinensis	(S/T)
CHINESE ARBOR-VITAE	Thuya orientalis	(C)
CHINESE ARTICHOKE	Stachys affinis	(H)
CHINESE ASH	Fraxinus chinensis	(T)
CHINESE BALLOON FLOWER	Platycodon	(H)

Common	Botanical	Type
CHINESE BEECH	Fagus englerana	(T)
CHINESE BELLFLOWER	Platycodon	(H)
CHINESE BOX THORN	Lycium barbarum	(S)
CHINESE BUSH BERRY	Prunus glandulosa	(S)
CHINESE CABBAGE	Brassica pekinensis	(V)
CHINESE CAT POWDER	Actinidia polygama	(CL)
CHINESE CEDAR	Toona sinensis	(T)
CHINESE CHESTNUT	Castanea mollissima	(T)
CHINESE CHIVES	Allium tuberosum	(BB)
CHINESE CRAB	Malus spectabilis	(T)
CHINESE DATE	Zizyphus jujuba	(S)
CHINESE DOGWOOD	Cornus kousa chinensis	(S)
CHINESE DOUGLAS FIR	Pseudotsuga sinensis	(C)
CHINESE ELM	Ulmus parviflora	(T)
CHINESE FAN PALM	Livistona chinensis	(P)
CHINESE FIR	Cunninghamia lanceolata	(C)
CHINESE FLOWERING ASH	Fraxinus mariesii	(T)
CHINESE FOUNTAIN GRASS	Pennisetum alopecuroides	(G)
CHINESE FOXGLOVE	Rehmannia angulata	(H)
CHINESE FRINGE TREE	Chionanthus retusus	(T)
CHINESE GOOSEBERRY	Actinidia deliciosa	(CL)
CHINESE HAT PLANT	Holmskioldia sanguinea	(TS)
CHINESE HAWTHORN	Photinia serrulata	(T)
CHINESE HAZEL	Corylus chinensis	(T)
CHINESE HEMLOCK	Tsuga chinensis	(C)
CHINESE HIBISCUS	Hibiscus rosa-sinensis	(S)
CHINESE HILL CHERRY	Prunus serrulata huphensis	(T)
CHINESE HOLLY	Ilex cornuta	(S)
CHINESE HONEY LOCUST	Gleditsia sinensis	(T)
CHINESE JASMINE	Trachelospermum	(CL)
CHINESE JUNIPER	Juniperus chinensis	(C)
CHINESE LANTERN	Physalis	(H)
CHINESE LANTERNS	Sandersonia aurantiaca	(HP)
CHINESE LARCH	Larix potaninii	(C)
CHINESE LILAC	Syringa x chinensis	(S)
CHINESE LOOSESTRIFE	Lysimachia clethroides	(H)
CHINESE MAT GRASS	Cyperus tagetiformis	(G)
CHINESE MOONSEED	Sinomenium acutum	(CL)
CHINESE MUGWORT	Artemisia verlotiorum	(H)
CHINESE NECKLACE POPLAR	Populus lasiocarpa	(T)
CHINESE PARASOL TREE	Firmiana simplex	(T)
CHINESE PEACH	Prunus davidiana	(TS)
CHINESE PEONY	Paeonia lactiflora	(H)
CHINESE PERSIMMON	Diospyros kaki	(T)
CHINESE PINE	Pinus tabulaeformis	(C)
CHINESE PINK	Dianthus sinensis	(A)
CHINESE PISTACHIO	Pistacia chinensis	(T)

Know Your Common Plant Names

Common	Botanical	Type
CHINESE PLUM YEW	Cephalotaxus fortunei	(C)
CHINESE PRIVET	Ligustrum sinense	(S)
CHINESE QUINCE	Pseudocydonia sinensis	(T)
CHINESE RED BUD	Cercis chinensis	(T)
CHINESE RED-BARKED BIRCH	Betula albosinensis	(T)
CHINESE RHUBARB	Rheum officinale	(H)
CHINESE SACRED BAMBOO	Nandina	(S)
CHINESE SACRED LILY	Narcissus tazetta orientalis	(BB)
CHINESE SCARLET ROWAN	Sorbus commixta 'Embley'	(T)
CHINESE SILK VINE	Periploca sepium	(CL)
CHINESE SILKWORM THORN	Cudrania tricuspidata	(T)
CHINESE SILVER GRASS	Miscanthus sinensis	(G)
CHINESE SNOWBALL	Viburnum macrocephalum	(S)
CHINESE SPRUCE	Picea asperata	(C)
CHINESE STAR ANISE	Illicium vernum	(T)
CHINESE STEWARTIA	Stewartia sinensis	(S/T)
CHINESE SUGAR MAPLE	Sorghum saccharatum	(G)
CHINESE TALLOW TREE	Sapium sebiferum	(T)
CHINESE TRUMPET FLOWER	Incarvillea delavayi	(H)
CHINESE TRUMPET VINE	Campsis chinensis	(CL)
CHINESE VIRGINIA CREEPER	Parthenocissus henryana	(CL)
CHINESE WALNUT	Juglans cathayensis	(T)
CHINESE WATER CHESTNUT	Eleocharis tuberosa	(G)
CHINESE WEEPING CYPRESS	Cupressus funebris	(C)
CHINESE WING-NUT	Pterocarya stenoptera	(T)
CHINESE WISTERIA	Wisteria sinensis	(CL)
CHINESE WITCH HAZEL	Hamamelis mollis	(S)
CHINESE WOODBINE	Lonicera tragophylla	(CL)
CHINESE YAM	Dioscorea batatas	(V)
CHINESE YELLOWWOOD	Cladratis sinensis	(T)
CHINESE YEW	Taxus chinensis	(C)
CHINESE ZELKOVA	Zelkova sinica	(T)
CHINESE-LANTERN LILY	Sandersonia aurantiaca	(BB)
CHINQUAPIN	Castanea pumila	(T)
CHINQUAPIN OAK	Quercus prinoides	(T)
CHIRETTA	Swertia chirata	(HB)
CHITAM WOOD	Cotinus obovatus	(S)
CHIVES	Allium schoenoprasum	(HB)
CHOC TAW ROOT	Apocynum cannabinum	(H)
CHOCOLATE COSMOS	Cosmos atrosanguineus	(H)
CHOCOLATE TREE	Theobroma cacao	(TT)
CHOCOLATE VINE	Akebia quinata	(CL)
CHOKE CHERRY	Prunus virginiana	(T)
CHOKEBERRY	Aronia	(T)
CHOLLA	Opuntia	(CS)
CHONDRILLA	Chondrilla juncea	(H)
CHRIST'S THORN	Paliurus spina-christi	(S)

Know Your Common Plant Names

Common	Botanical	Type
CHRISTMAS BEGONIA	Begonia x cheimantha	(HP)
CHRISTMAS BELL	Blandfordia grandiflora	(H)
CHRISTMAS BERRY	Heteromeles arbutifolia	(S)
CHRISTMAS BOX	Sarcococca	(S)
CHRISTMAS BUSH	Prostranthera lasianthos	(S)
CHRISTMAS CACTUS	Schlumbergera 'Bridgesii'	(CS)
CHRISTMAS CHEER	Sedum rubrotinctum	(HP)
CHRISTMAS FERN	Polystichum acrostichoides	(FN)
CHRISTMAS JEWELS	Aechmea racineae	(HP)
CHRISTMAS PALM	Veitchia merrillii	(P)
CHRISTMAS PEPPER	Capsicum annuum	(F)
CHRISTMAS PRIDE	Ruellia macrantha	(HP)
CHRISTMAS ROSE	Helleborus niger	(H)
CHRISTMAS STAR	Euphorbia pulcherrima	(HP)
CHRISTMAS TREE	Blandfordia grandiflora	(H)
CHRISTMAS TREE	Nuytsia floribunda	(TT)
CHRISTMAS TREE	Picea abies	(C)
CHRISTMAS-HORNS	Delphinium nudicaule	(H)
CHUFA	Cyperus esculentus	(G)
CHUFFA	Cyperus esculentus	(G)
CHURCH STEEPLES	Agrimonia eupatoria	(H)
CHUSAN PALM	Trachycarpus fortunei	(P)
CIDER GUM	Eucalyptus gunnii	(T)
CIGAR PLANT	Cuphea ignea	(HP)
CILIATE HEATH	Erica ciliaris	(S)
CILICIAN FIR	Abies cilicica	(C)
CINDERELLA SLIPPERS	Sinningia regina	(HP)
CINERARIA	Senecio cruentus	(HP)
CINNAMON	Cinnamonum zeylanicum	(T)
CINNAMON CACTUS	Opuntia microdasys rufida	(CS)
CINNAMON CACTUS	Opuntia rufida	(CS)
CINNAMON FERN	Osmunda cinnamomea	(FN)
CINNAMON ROSE	Rosa majalis	(S)
CINNAMON VINE	Apios americana	(CL)
CINQUEFOIL	Potentilla	(HS)
CIRCLE FLOWER	Lysimachia punctata	(H)
CITRANGE	x Citroncirus webberi	(F)
CITRON	Citrus medica	(F)
CITRONELLA	Collinsonia	(H)
CITRONELLA	Cymbopogon nardus	(G)
CITRONELLA GRASS	Cymbopogon nardus	(G)
CLAMMY LOCUST	Robinia viscosa	(T)
CLANWILLIAM CEDAR	Widdringtonia juniperoides	(C)
CLARET ASH	Fraxinus oxycarpa 'Raywood'	(T)
CLARKIA	Clarkia unguiculata	(A)
CLARY	Salvia sclarea	(HB)
CLASSICAL FENUGREEK	Trigonella foenum-graecum	(H)

4 2

Common	Botanical	Type
CLAW CACTUS	Schlumbergera truncata	(CS)
CLEAR EYE	Salvia sclarea	(HB)
CLEAVERS	Galium aparine	(H)
CLEMENTINE	Citrus reticulata 'Clementine'	(F)
CLIFF BREAK FERN	Pellaea	(FN)
CLIFFBRAKE FERN	Pellaea	(FN)
CLIMBIMG SAILOR	Cymbalaria	(H)
CLIMBING BITTERSWEET	Celastrus	(CL)
CLIMBING BUTCHER'S BROOM	Semele androgyna	(CL)
CLIMBING CACTUS	Acanthocereus	(CS)
CLIMBING DAHLIA	Hidalgoa	(CL)
CLIMBING FERN	Lygodium	(FN)
CLIMBING FUMITORY	Adlumia	(H)
CLIMBING FUMITORY	Corydalis claviculata	(H)
CLIMBING GAZANIA	Nutisia	(CL)
CLIMBING HEATH	Pieris phillyreifolia	(S)
CLIMBING HEMPWEED	Mikania	(CL/S)
CLIMBING HYDRANGEA	Hydrangea petiolaris	(CL)
CLIMBING LILY	Gloriosa	(BB)
CLIMBING LILY	Littonia modesta	(BB)
CLIMBING PALAS	Butea superba	(TS)
CLIMBING TRIGGER PLANT	Stylidium scandens	(CL)
CLOAK FERN	Notholaena	(FN)
CLOCK VINE	Thunbergia alata	(A)
CLOCK VINE	Thunbergia grandiflora	(CL)
CLOG PLANT	Alloplectus nummularia	(HP)
CLOT-BUR	Arctium lappa	(H)
CLOTH-OF-GOLD CROCUS	Crocus angustifolius	(BB)
CLOUD GRASS	Agrostis nebulosa	(G)
CLOUD GRASS	Aichryson x domesticum	(CS)
CLOUDBERRY	Rubus chamaemorus	(S)
CLOVE PINK	Dianthus caryophyllus	(H)
CLOVE ROOT	Geum urbanum	(H)
CLOVE TREE	Eugenia caryophyllus	(F)
CLOVER	Trifolium	(H)
CLUB LILY	Kniphofia	(H)
CLUB OF HERCULES	Aralia spinosa	(S)
CLUB OF HERCULES	Xanthoxylum clava-herculis	(S)
CLUB PALM	Cordyline	(P)
CLUB SEDGE	Carex buxbaumii	(G)
CLUB-MOSS	Lycopodium selaginella	(R)
CLUB-RUSH	Scirpus	(G)
CLUSTER FIG	Ficus racemosa	(HP)
CLUSTER PINE	Pinus pinaster	(C)
CLUSTERED BELLFLOWER	Campanula glomerata	(H)
CLUSTERED BROOM	Chamaecytisus supinus	(S)
CLUSTERED CLOVER	Trifolium glomeratum	(H)

Common	Botanical	Type
COAST BANKSIA	Banksia integrifolia	(S)
COAST REDWOOD	Sequoia sempervirens	(C)
COB CACTUS	Escobaria tuberculosa	(CS)
COB CACTUS	Lobivia hertrichiana	(C)
COB-NUT	Corylus avellana	(S)
COBRA LILY	Darlingtonia californica	(HP)
COBRA PLANT	Arisaema nepenthoides	(H)
COBWEB HOUSE-LEEK	Sempervivum arachnoideum	(R)
COCA	Erythroxylon coca	(T)
COCAINE	Erythroxylum coca	(TT)
COCK'S COMB	Erythrina crista-galli	(S)
COCK'S COMB BEECH	Fagus sylvatica 'Cristata'	(T)
COCK'S FOOT GRASS	Dactylis glomerata	(G)
COCKLEBUR	Xanthium spinosum	(H)
COCKSCOMB	Celosia cristata	(A)
COCKSCOMB	Rhinanthus minor	(A)
COCKSFOOT	Dactylis glomerata	(G)
COCKSPUR	Echinochloa crus-galli	(G)
COCKSPUR CORAL TREE	Erythrina crista-galli	(S)
COCKSPUR THORN	Crataegus crus-galli	(T)
COCKY BABY	Arum maculatum	(H)
COCO PLUM	Chrysobalanus icaco	(TT)
COCO-DE-MER	Lodoicea maldarica	(P)
COCO-PLUM	Chrysobalanus icaco	(TT)
COCOA	Theobroma cacao	(FT)
COCODEMER	Lodoicea maldivica	(P)
COCONA	Solanum topiro	(TS)
COCONUT PALM	Cocos nucifera	(P)
COCONUT PALM	Cocos weddeliana	(P)
COCOYAM	Colocasia	(F)
CODLINS AND CREAM	Epilobium hirsutum	(H)
COFFEE	Coffea arabica	(FS)
COFFEE SENNA	Cassia occidentalis	(T)
COFFEE-BERRY	Rhamus californica	(S)
COFFIN JUNIPER	Juniperus recurva 'Coxii'	(C)
COHOSH	Actaea	(H)
COIGUE	Nothofagus dombeyi	(T)
COIGUE DE MAGELLANES	Nothofagus betuloides	(T)
COLA	Cola acuminata	(T)
COLE	Brassica napus oleifera	(V)
COLEWORT	Geum urbanum	(H)
COLIC ROOT	Aletris farinosa	(H)
COLLARD	Brassica oleracea acephala	(V)
COLOCYNTH	Citrullus colocynthus	(F)
COLOMBIA BUTTERCUP	Oncidium cheirophorum	(O)
COLOMBIAN BALL CACTUS	Wigginsia vorwerkiana	(CS)
COLOMBO	Cocculus palmatus	(H)

Common	Botanical	Type
COLORADA SPRUCE	Picea pungens	(C)
COLORADO FIR	Abies concolor	(C)
COLORADO GRASS	Panicum texanum	(G)
COLT'S FOOT	Tussilago farfara	(H)
COLUMBINE	Aquilegia	(H)
COLZA	Brassica napus	(V)
COMB FERN	Schizaea	(FN)
COMFREY	Symphytum officinale	(H)
COMMON ACACIA	Robinia pseudoacacia	(T)
COMMON AGRIMONY	Agrimonia eupatoria	(H)
COMMON ALDER	Alnus glutinosa	(T)
COMMON ALMOND	Prunus dulcis	(T)
COMMON AMARANTH	Amaranthus retroflexus	(H)
COMMON APPLE	Malus sylvestris	(T)
COMMON APRICOT	Prunus armeniaea	(S)
COMMON ARROWHEAD	Sagittaria sagittifolia	(WP)
COMMON ASH	Fraxinus excelsior	(T)
COMMON ASPARAGUS	Asparagus officinalis	(V)
COMMON BANEBERRY	Actaea spicata	(H)
COMMON BARBERRY	Berberis vulgaris	(S)
COMMON BEECH	Fagus sylvatica	(T)
COMMON BENT	Agrostis tenuis	(G)
COMMON BLADDERWORT	Utricularia vulgaris	(H)
COMMON BOX	Buxus sempervirens	(TS)
COMMON BRIAR	Rosa canina	(S)
COMMON BROOM	Cytisus scoparius	(S)
COMMON BROOMRAPE	Orobanche minor	(PE/H)
COMMON BUCKTHORN	Rhamnus cathartica	(S)
COMMON BUTTERWORT	Pinguicula vulgaris	(R)
COMMON CALAMINT	Calamintha ascendens	(H)
COMMON CAMELLIA	Camellia japonica	(S)
COMMON CANDYTUFT	Iberis umbellata	(R)
COMMON CAT'S EAR	Hypochoeris radicata	(H)
COMMON CENTAURY	Centaurium erythraea	(A)
COMMON CHICKWEED	Stellaria media	(H)
COMMON COMFREY	Symphytum officinale	(H)
COMMON CORAL BEAN	Erythrina corallodendron	(TT)
COMMON CORD-GRASS	Spartina anglica	(G)
COMMON COTONEASTER	Contoneaster integerrimus	(S)
COMMON COTTON-GRASS	Eriophorum angustifolium	(G)
COMMON COUCH	Elymus repens	(G)
COMMON COW-WHEAT	Melampyrum pratense	(H)
COMMON CRAB APPLE	Malus sylvestris	(T)
COMMON CYPRESS PINE	Callitris oblonga preissii	(C)
COMMON DAISY	Bellis perennis	(H)
COMMON DODDER	Cuscuta epithymum	(CL)
COMMON DOG VIOLET	Viola riviniana	(H)

Know Your Common Plant Names

Common	Botanical	Type
COMMON DOGWOOD	Cornus sangutnea	(S)
COMMON DUCKWEED	Lemna minor	(WP)
COMMON DYER'S WEED	Isatis tinctoria	(H)
COMMON EEL-GRASS	Zostera marina	(WP)
COMMON ELDER	Sambucus nigra	(S)
COMMON EYEBRIGHT	Euphrasia nemorosa	(H)
COMMON FIG	Ficus caricca	(F)
COMMON FLAX	Linum usitatissimum	(H)
COMMON FLEABANE	Pulicaria dysenterica	(H)
COMMON FUMITORY	Fumaria officinalis	(A)
COMMON GOOSEBERRY	Ribes uva-crispi	(S)
COMMON GORSE	Ulex europaeus	(S)
COMMON GRAPE HYACINTH	Muscari neglectum	(BB)
COMMON GRAPE VINE	Vitis vinifera	(F)
COMMON GRASS-WRACK	Zostera marina	(WP)
COMMON GROMWELL	Lithospermum officinale	(R)
COMMON HAWKWEED	Hieracium vulgatum	(H)
COMMON HAWTHORN	Crataegus monogyna	(ST)
COMMON HAZEL	Corylus avellana	(S)
COMMON HEMP-NETTLE	Galeopsis tetrahit	(H)
COMMON HOLLY	Ilex aquifolium	(ST)
COMMON HORNBEAM	Carpinus betulus	(T)
COMMON HORSE CHESTNUT	Aesculus hippocastanum	(T)
COMMON HOUSELEEK	Sempervivum tectorum	(H)
COMMON HYACINTH	Hyacinthus orientalis	(BB)
COMMON IMMORTELLE	Xeranthemum	(A)
COMMON IRIS	Iris germanica	(H)
COMMON IVY	Hedera helix	(CL)
COMMON JUNIPER	Juniperus communis	(C)
COMMON KNOTGRASS	Polygonum aviculare	(H)
COMMON LABURNUM	Laburnum anagyroides	(T)
COMMON LADYBELL	Adenophora lilifolia	(H)
COMMON LARCH	Larix decidua	(C)
COMMON LAUREL	Prunus laurocerasus	(S)
COMMON LAVENDER	Lavandula angustifolia	(S)
COMMON LILAC	Syringa vulgaris	(ST)
COMMON LIME	Tilia x europaea	(T)
COMMON MALLOW	Malva sylvestris	(A)
COMMON MAPLE	Acer campestre	(ST)
COMMON MEADOW RUE	Thalictrum flavum	(H)
COMMON MILKWORT	Polygala vulgaris	(H)
COMMON MILLET	Panicum miliaceum	(G)
COMMON MOREL	Morchella esculenta	(H)
COMMON MORNING GLORY	Ipomoea purpurea	(CL)
COMMON MOUNTAIN ASH	Sorbus aucuparia	(T)
COMMON MOUSE-EAR	Cerastium fontanum	(H)
COMMON MULBERRY	Morus nigra	(T)

Common	Botanical	Type
COMMON MULLEIN	Verbascum thapsus	(H)
COMMON MYRTLE	Myrtus communis	(S)
COMMON OAK	Quercus robur	(T)
COMMON ORACHE	Atriplex patula	(A)
COMMON OSIER	Salix viminalis	(T)
COMMON PAPAW	Carica papaya	(F)
COMMON PEACH	Prunus persica	(F)
COMMON PEAR	Pyrus communis	(T)
COMMON PEARLWORT	Sagina procumbens	(H)
COMMON PERSICARIA	Polygonum persicaria	(H)
COMMON POLYPODY	Polypodium vulgare	(FN)
COMMON POPPY	Papaver rhoeas	(A)
COMMON PRIVET	Ligustrum vulgare	(S)
COMMON QUAKING GRASS	Briza media	(G)
COMMON QUINCE	Cydonia oblonga	(T)'
COMMON RAMPING FUMITORY	Fumaria muralis	(H)
COMMON RED POPPY	Papaver rhoeas	(H)
COMMON REED	Phragmites australis	(G)
COMMON RHUBARB	Rheum rhaponticum	(F)
COMMON ROCKROSE	Helianthemum nummularium	(R)
COMMON ROWAN	Sorbus aucuparia	(T)
COMMON RUSH	Juncus communis	(G)
COMMON RUSH	Juncus subuliflorus	((G)
COMMON SAGE	Salvia officinalis	(HB)
COMMON SALLOW	Salix cinerea	(S)
COMMON SALLOW	Salix cinerea oleifolia	(S)
COMMON SALTMARSH GRASS	Puccinella maritima	(G)
COMMON SEA HOLLY	Eryngium maritimum	(H)
COMMON SEDGE	Carex nigra	(G)
COMMON SILVER FIR	Abies alba	(C)
COMMON SILVERBIRCH	Betula pendula	(T)
COMMON SNOWDROP	Galanthus nivalis	(BB)
COMMON SOW THISTLE	Sonchus oleraceus	(H)
COMMON SPEEDWELL	Veronica officinalis	(H)
COMMON SPIKE-RUSH	Eleocharis palustris	(G)
COMMON SPINDLE	Euonymus europaeus	(S)
COMMON SPOTTED ORCHID	Dactylorhiza fuchsii	(O)
COMMON SPRUCE	Picea abies	(C)
COMMON STORK'S-BILL	Erodium cicutarium	(R)
COMMON TEASEL	Dipsacus fullonum	(H)
COMMON THYME	Thymus vulgaris	(HB)
COMMON TOADFLAX	Linaria vulgaris	(H)
COMMON TOBACCO	Nicotiana tabacum	(H)
COMMON TWAYBLADE	Listera ovata	(O)
COMMON VETCH	Vicia sativa	(H)
COMMON VIOLET	Viola riviniana	(H)
COMMON VIRGINIA CREEPER	Parthenocissus inserta	(CL)

Common	Botanical	Type
COMMON WALNUT	Juglans regia	(T)
COMMON WATER CROWFOOT	Ranunculus aquatalis	(H)
COMMON WATER DROPWORT	Oenanthe fistulosa	(H)
COMMON WHITE BIRCH	Betula pubescens	(T)
COMMON WHITE JASMINE	Jasminum officinale	(CL)
COMMON WINTERCRESS	Barbarea vulgaris	(H)
COMMON WINTERGREEN	Pyrola minor	(H)
COMMON WITCHHAZEL	Hamamelis virginiana	(S)
COMMON WORMWOOD	Artemisia absinthium	(HB)
COMMON YELLOW AZALEA	Rhododendron luteum	(S)
COMMON YELLOW ROCKET	Barbarea vulgaris	(H)
COMMON YEW	Taxus baccata	(C)
COMPASS PLANT	Silphium laciniatum	(H)
COMPEACHY-WOOD	Haematoxylum campechianum	(TT)
CONE FLOWER	Rudbeckia	(H)
CONE PLANT	Conophytum	(A)
CONE-HEAD	Strobilanthes	(C)
CONFEDERATE ROSE	Hibiscus mutabilis	(S)
CONFEDERATE VINE	Antigonon	(CL)
CONFETTI BUSH	Coleonema pulchrum	(S)
CONKER TREE	Aesculus hippocastanum	(T)
CONNEMARA HEATH	Daboecia cantabrica	(S)
CONTORTED HAZEL	Corylus avellana 'Contorta'	(S)
CONTORTED WILLOW	Salix babylonica Pekinensis 'Tortuosa'	(ST)
COOLABAH	Eucalyptus microtheca	(T)
COOLWORT	Tiarella cordifolia	(H)
COONROOT	Sanguinaria canadensis	(H)
COOTAMUNDRA WATTLE	Acacia saileyana	(T)
COPAIBA	Copaifera langsdorffii	(CS)
COPIHUE	Lapageria rosea	(CL)
COPPER BEECH	Fagus sylvatica purpurea	(ST)
COPPER LEAF	Acalypha wilkesiana	(HP)
COPPER-POD	Peltophorum pterocarpum	(TS)
COPPERCUPS	Pileantus peduncularis	(HP)
CORAL BELLS	Heuchera	(H)
CORAL BERRY	Ardisia	(S)
CORAL BERRY	Symphoricarpos orbiculatus	(S)
CORAL BUSH	Templetonia retusa	(S)
CORAL CACTUS	Mammillaria heyderi	(CS)
CORAL DROPS	Bessera	(H)
CORAL DROPS	Bessera elegans	(H)
CORAL FLOWER	Heuchera	(H)
CORAL GUM	Eucalyptus torquata	(T)
CORAL HIBISCUS	Hibiscus schizopetalus	(TS)
CORAL LILY	Lilium pumilum	(BB)
CORAL NECKLACE	Illecebrum verticilliatum	(H)
CORAL PEA	Hardenbergia violacea	(CL)

Know Your Common Plant Names

Common	Botanical	Type
CORAL PLANT	Berberidopsis	(S)
CORAL PLANT	Russelia equisetiformis	(TS)
CORAL PLANT	Russelia juncea	(TS)
CORAL ROOT	Cardamine bulbifera	(H)
CORAL ROOT ORCHID	Corallorhiza trifida	(O)
CORAL TREE	Erythrina corallodendron	(S/T)
CORAL TREE	Erythrina crista-galli	(S)
CORAL VINE	Antigonon leptopus	(CL)
CORAL-BARK MAPLE	Acer palmatum 'senkaki'	(ST)
CORAL-BARK WILLOW	Salix alba 'Chermesina'	(ST)
CORAL-WORT	Dentaria bulbifera	(S)
CORALROOT BITTERCRESS	Cardamine bulbifera	(H)
CORD GRASS	Spartina pectinata	(G)
CORDIA	Cordia sebestana	(TT)
CORIANDER	Coriandrum sativum	(HB)
CORK ELM	Ulmus thomasii	(T)
CORK FIR	Abies lasiocarpa arizonica	(C)
CORK HOPBUSH	Kallstroemia platyptera	(TS)
CORK OAK	Quercus suber	(T)
CORK TREE	Phellodendron	(T)
CORKSCREW HAZEL	Corylus avellana 'Contorta'	(S)
CORKSCREW RUSH	Juncus effusus 'Spiralis'	(WP)
CORKSCREW WILLOW	Salix babylonica pekinensis 'Tortuosa'	(ST)
CORKWOOD	Leitneria floridana	(T)
CORKWOOD TREE	Duboisia myoporoides	(T)
CORN	Zea mays	(V)
CORN BUTTERCUP	Ranunculus arvensis	(H)
CORN CAMPION	Agrostemma githago	(A)
CORN CHAMOMILE	Anthemis arvensis	(H)
CORN COCKLE	Agrostemma githago	(A)
CORN CROWFOOT	Ranunculus arvensis	(H)
CORN GROMWELL	Buglossoides arvensis	(H)
CORN LILY	Ixia	(BB)
CORN MARIGOLD	Chrysanthemum segetum	(H)
CORN MIGNONETTE	Reseda phyteuma	(H)
CORN MINT	Mentha arvensis	(H)
CORN PARSLEY	Petroselinum segetum	(H)
CORN PINK	Agrostemma githago	(A)
CORN POPPY	Papaver rhoeas	(A)
CORN SALAD	Valerianella olitoria	(V)
CORN SILK	Zea mays	(G)
CORN SOWTHISTLE	Sonchus arvensis	(H)
CORN SPURREY	Spergula arvensis	(A)
CORN WOUNDWORT	Stachys arvensis	(H)
CORN-ON-THE-COB	Zea mays	(V)
CORNCOB CACTUS	Euphorbia mammillaris	(CS)
CORNEL	Cornus mas	(S)

Know Your Common Plant Names

Common	Botanical	Type
CORNELIAN CHERRY	Cornus mas	(S)
CORNFLOWER	Centaurea cyanus	(AH)
CORNISH ELM	Ulmus angustifolia cornubiensis	(T)
CORNISH HEATH	Erica vagans	(S)
CORNISH MONEYWORT	Sibthorpia europaea	(H)
COROMANDEL EBONY	Diospyros melanoxylon	(TT)
CORSICAN HEATH	Erica terminalis	(S)
CORSICAN MINT	Mentha requienii	(HB)
CORSICAN PINE	Pinus nigra maritina	(C)
CORSICAN SPEEDWELL	Veronica repens	(H)
COS LETTUCE	Lactuca sativa longifolia	(V)
COSMEA	Cosmos	(A)
COSTA RICAN NIGHTSHADE	Solanum wendlandii	(CL)
COSTMARY	Balsamita major	(HB)
COSTORPHINE PLANE	Acer pseudoplatanus 'Costorphinense'	(T)
COTONEASTER	Cotoneaster	(ST)
COTTAGE PINK	Dianthus caryophyllus	(H)
COTTON	Gossypium	(F)
COTTON BALL CACTUS	Espostoa lanata	(CS)
COTTON DAISY	Celmisia spectabilis	(H)
COTTON GRASS	Eriophorum	(G)
COTTON GUM	Nyssa aquatica	(T)
COTTON LAVENDER	Santolina	(S)
COTTON ROSE	Hibiscus mutabilis	(S)
COTTON THISTLE	Onopordon acanthium	(H)
COTTON TREE	Bombax	(TT)
COTTON TREE	Ceiba	(TT)
COTTON-POLE CACTUS	Opuntia vestita	(CS)
COTTON-WEED	Diotis candidissima	(H)
COTTONPOLE CACTUS	Opuntia vestita	(CS)
COTTONWOOD	Populus deltoides	(T)
COUCH GRASS	Elymus repens	(G)
COUGHWORT	Tussilago farfara	(H)
COURGETTE	Cucurbita pepo ovifera	(V)
COUVE TRONCHUDA	Brassica oleracea costata	(V)
COW BASIL	Vaccaria hispanica	(H)
COW CRESS	Veronica beccabunga	(H)
COW ITCH TREE	Lagunaria patersonii	(T)
COW PARSLEY	Anthriscus sylvestris	(H)
COW PARSLEY	Heracleum sphondylium	(H)
COW PEA	Vigna sinensis	(TS)
COW PEA	Vigna unguiculata	(H)
COW TANG	Pelvetia canaliculata	(SW)
COW TREE	Brosimum	(TT)
COW WHEAT	Melampyrum	(H)
COW-ITCH	Rhus radicans	(S)
COW-ITCH	Urera baccifera	(H)

Common	Botanical	Type
COW-ITCH CHERRY	Malpighia urens	(H)
COWBANE	Cicuta virosa	(H)
COWBERRY	Vaccinium vitis-idaea	(S)
COWHAGE	Mucuna pruriens	(H)
COWHERB	Vaccaria pyramidata	(H)
COWPEA	Vigna sinensis	(TS)
COWS TAIL PINE	Cephalotaxus	(C)
COWSLIP	Primula veris	(H)
COWSLIP BUSH	Corylopsis	(S)
COYAN	Nothofagus obliqua	(T)
COYOTE BRUSH	Baccharis pilularis	(S)
COYOTE WILLOW	Salix exigua	(S)
CRAB APPLE	Malus	(T)
CRAB CACTUS	Schlumbergera truncata	(CS)
CRAB CLAWS	Stylidium macranthum	(H)
CRAB'S EYE VINE	Abrus precatorius	(CL)
CRACK WILLOW	Salix fragilis	(T)
CRADLE ORCHID	Anguloa clowesii	(O)
CRAMPBARK	Viburnum opulus	(S)
CRANBERRY	Vaccinium oxycoccos	(F)
CRANBERRY BUSH	Viburnum trilobum	(S)
CRANBERRY COTONEASTER	Cotoneaster apiculatus	(S)
CRANBERRY GOURD	Abobra	(S)
CRANE FLOWER	Strelitzia reginae	(HP)
CRANE LILY	Strelitzia reginae	(HP)
CRANESBILL	Lagerstromia indica	(T)
CRAPE GINGER	Costus speciosus	(TH)
CRAPE JASMINE	Tabernaemontana coronaria	(S)
CRAWLEY ROOT	Corallorhiza odontorhiza	(O)
CREAM CACTUS	Mammillaria heyderi	(CS)
CREAM CUPS	Platystemon californicus	(A)
CREEPING AVENS	Geum reptans	(H)
CREEPING BARBERRY	Mahonia repens	(S)
CREEPING BELLFLOWER	Campanula rapunculoides	(H)
CREEPING BENT	Agrostis stolonifera	(G)
CREEPING BLUE BLOSSOM	Ceanothus thyrsiflorus 'Repens'	(S)
CREEPING BOOBIALLA	Mysporum parvifolium	(TS)
CREEPING BUTTERCUP	Ranunculus repens	(H)
CREEPING CHARLIE	Pilea nummulariifolia	(HP)
CREEPING CINQUEFOIL	Potentilla reptans	(H)
CREEPING DOGWOOD	Cornus canadensis	(S)
CREEPING FESCUE	Festuca rubra	(G)
CREEPING FIG	Ficus pumila	(HP)
CREEPING FORGET-ME-NOT	Omphalodes verna	(H)
CREEPING FUCHSIA	Fuchsia procumbens	(S)
CREEPING JENNY	Lysimachia nummularia	(H)
CREEPING JUNIPER	Juniperus horizontalis	(C)

Common	Botanical	Type
CREEPING JUNIPER	Juniperus procumbens	(C)
CREEPING LADY'S TRESSES	Goodyera repens	(O)
CREEPING MOUNTAIN ASH	Antirrhinum asarina	(H)
CREEPING MOUNTAIN ASH	Sorbus reducta	(S)
CREEPING SNOWBERRY	Chiogenes hispidula	(S)
CREEPING SOFT GRASS	Holcus mollis	(G)
CREEPING ST. JOHN'S WORT	Hypericum humifusum	(H)
CREEPING THISTLE	Cirsium arvense	(H)
CREEPING THYME	Thymus serpyllum	(HB)
CREEPING TWITCH	Elymus repens	(G)
CREEPING WILLOW	Salix repens	(S)
CREEPING WINTERGREEN	Gaultheria procumbens	(S)
CREEPING YELLOWCRESS	Rorippa sylvestris	(H)
CREEPING ZINNIA	Sanvitalia procumbens	(HP)
CREEPING-BENT	Agrostis stolonifera	(G)
CREOSOTE BUSH	Larrea divaricata	(S)
CREOSOTE BUSH	Larrea tridentata	(S)
CRESS	Lepidium sativum	(V)
CRESTED BUCKLER FERN	Dryopteris cristata	(FN)
CRESTED DOG'S TAIL	Cynosurus cristatus	(G)
CRESTED GENTIAN	Gentiana septemfida	(H)
CRESTED HAIR-GRASS	Koeleria macrantha	(G)
CRESTED MOSS ROSE	Rosa centifolia cristata	(S)
CRESTED POPPY	Argemone	(H)
CRESTED POPPY	Argemone platyceras	(H)
CRETAN BEAR'S TAIL	Celsia arcturus	(B)
CRETAN BRAKE	Pteris cretica	(FN)
CRETAN DITTANY	Amaracus dictamnus	(H)
CRETAN DITTANY	Origanum dictamnus	(H)
CRETAN FERN	Pteris cretica	(FN)
CRETAN MAPLE	Acer sempervirens	(T)
CRETAN MULLEIN	Celsia	(A)
CRETAN ZELKOVA	Zelkova abelicea	(T)
CRICKET BAT WILLOW	Salix alba 'Caerulea'	(T)
CRIMEAN LIME	Tilia euchlora	(T)
CRIMEAN PINE	Pinus nigra caramanica	(C)
CRIMSON CLOVER	Trifolium incarnatum	(H)
CRIMSON DWARF	Prunus 'Cistena'	(S)
CRIMSON FLAG	Schizostylis coccinea	(H)
CRIMSON-GLORY VINE	Vitis coignettiae	(CL)
CROSS GENTIAN	Gentiana cruciata	(H)
CROSS VINE	Bignonia capreolata	(CL)
CROSS-LEAVED HEATH	Erica tetralix	(S)
CROSSWORT	Crucianella ciliata	(R)
CROSSWORT	Cruciata ciliata	(H)
CROSSWORT	Cruciata laevipes	(H)
CROSSWORT	Gallium cruciata	(H)

Know Your Common Plant Names

Common	Botanical	Type
CROTON	Codiaeum variegatum pictum	(HP)
CROW FLOWER	Geranium sylvaticum	(H)
CROW GARLIC	Allium vineale	(BB)
CROWBERRY	Empetrum nigrum	(H)
CROWFOOT	Ranunculus	(H)
CROWN ANEMONE	Anemone coronaria	(H)
CROWN CACTUS	Rebutia	(CS)
CROWN DAISY	Chrysanthemum coronarium	(A)
CROWN FERN	Blechnum discolor	(FN)
CROWN IMPERIAL	Fritillaria imperialis	(BB)
CROWN OF THORNS	Euphorbia milii	(CS)
CROWN OF THORNS	Paliurus spina-christi	(S)
CROWN VETCH	Coronilla varia	(H)
CRUEL PLANT	Araujia sericofera	(CL)
CRUSADER'S SPEARS	Urginea maritima	(BB)
CRYSTAL ANTHURIUM	Anthurium crystallinum	(TH)
CRYSTAL WORT	Riccia	(H)
CUBAN BAST	Hibiscus elatus	(TT)
CUBAN LILY	Scilla peruviana	(BB)
CUBAN PINE	Pinus occidentalis	(C)
CUBAN ROYAL PALM	Roystonea regia	(P)
CUBEBS	Piper cubeba	(H)
CUCKOO FLOWER	Cardamine pratensis	(R)
CUCKOO PINT	Arum maculatum	(H)
CUCUMBER	Cucumis sativus	(V)
CUCUMBER TREE	Magnolia acuminata	(T)
CUCUMBER TREE OF SOCOTRA	Dendrosicyos socotrana	(TT)
CUCUZZI	Lagenaria siceraria	(F)
CUDWEED	Filago vulgaris	(H)
CULEU	Chusquea culeou	(G)
CULTIVATED APPLE	Malus domestica	(F)
CULTIVATED BIRD'S FOOT	Ornithopus sativus	(H)
CULTIVATED CARROT	Daucus carota sativus	(V)
CULTIVATED MUSHROOM	Agaricus bisporus	(F)
CULVER'S ROOT	Veronicastrum virginicum	(H)
CULVERKEYS	Hyacinthoides non-scripta	(BB)
CULVERWORT	Aquilegia vulgaris	(H)
CUMIN	Cuminum cyminum	(HB)
CUP AND SAUCER	Cobaea scandens	(A)
CUP AND SAUCER CANTERBURY BELL	Campanula medium calycanthema	(B)
CUP FERN	Dennstaedtia	(FN)
CUP FLOWER	Nierembergia	(H)
CUP FLOWER	Nierembergia rivularis	(R)
CUP PLANT	Silphium perfiliatum	(H)
CUP-OF-GOLD	Solandra nitida	(TCL)
CUPID'S BOWER	Achimenes	(BB)
CUPID'S DART	Catananche	(H)

Common	Botanical	Type
CUPIDONE	Catananche	(II)
CURARE	Chondrodendron tomentosum	(TS)
CURARE	Strychnos toxifera	(TS)
CURLED DOCK	Rumex crispus	(H)
CURLED MALLOW	Malva crispa	(H)
CURLED PONDWEED	Potamogeton crispus	(WP)
CURLY MINT	Mentha spicata 'Crispa'	(HB)
CURLY PALM	Howea belmoreana	(P)
CURLY SENTRY PALM	Howea belmoreana	(P)
CURLY WATER-THYME	Lagerosiphon major	(WP)
CURRANT	Ribes	(S)
CURRANT TOMATO	Lycopersicon piminellifolium	(H)
CURRY LEAF	Murraya koenigii	(S)
CURRY PLANT	Helichrysum seotinum	(S)
CURRY-LEAF	Murraya paniculata	(S)
CURVED SEDGE	Carex maritima	(G)
CUSCUS	Pennisetum glaucum	(G)
CUSHION SPURGE	Euphorbia epithymoides	(H)
CUSTARD APPLE	Annona reticulata	(F)
CUT-LEAF BEECH	Fagus syl. heterophylla	(T)
CUT-LEAF OAK	Quercus robur 'Filicifolia'	(T)
CUT-LEAF PURPLE BEECH	Fagus syl 'Rohanii'	(T)
CUT-LEAF ZELKOVA	Zelkova verschaffeltii	(T)
CUT-LEAVED BRAMBLE	Rubus laciniatus	(S)
CUT-LEAVED CRANESBILL	Geranium dissectum	(H)
CUT-LEAVED ELDER	Sambucus nigra 'Laciniata'	(S)
CUT-LEAVED HAZEL	Corylus avellana 'Heterophylla'	(S)
CUT-LEAVED MALLOW	Malva alcea	(H)
CUT-LEAVED MOUNTAIN ASH	Sorbus aucuparia 'Aspenifolia'	(T)
CUT-LEAVED WALNUT	Juglans regia 'Laciniata'	(T)
CUTCH	Catechu nigrum	(TT)
CYPERUS SEDGE	Carex pseudocyperus	(G)
CYPHEL	Minuartia sedoides	(H)
CYPRESS	Cupressus/Chamaecyparis	(C)
CYPRESS HEBE	Hebe cupressoides	(S)
CYPRESS OAK	Quercus robur 'Fastigiata'	(T)
CYPRESS PINE	Callitris	(C)
CYPRESS PINE	Wildringtonia	(C)
CYPRESS SPURGE	Euphorbia cyparissias	(H)
CYPRESS VINE	Ipomloea pennata	(CL)
CYPRESS VINE	Ipomoea quamoclit	(CL)
CYPRESS-PINE	Callitris	(C)
CYPRIAN CEDAR	Cedrus brevifolia	(C)
CYPRUS CEDAR	Cedrus brevifolia	(C)
CYPRUS STRAWBERRY TREE	Arbutus andrachne	(S)
DABBERLOCKS	Alaria esculenta	(SW)
DAFFODIL	Narcissus	(BB)

Know Your Common Plant Names

Common	Botanical	Type
DAFFODIL ORCHID	Ipsea speciosa	(O)
DAFFY-DOWN-DILLY	Narcissus	(BB)
DAGGER PLANT	Yucca aloifolia	(S)
DAHLBERG DAISY	Thymophylla tenuiloba	(H)
DAHLIA CACTUS	Wilcoxia poselgeri	CS
DAHOONHOLLY	Ilex cassine	(S)
DAHURIAN LARCH	Larix gmelinii	(C)
DAIKON	Raphanus sativus	(V)
DAIMIO OAK	Quercus dentata	(T)
DAISY	Bellis perennis	(H)
DAISY BUSH	Olearia	(S)
DALMATIAN BROOM	Genista sylvestris	(S)
DALMATIAN LABURNUM	Petteria ramentacea	(S)
DALMATIAN PELLITORY	Tanacetum cinerariifolium	(H)
DALMATIAN PYRETHRUM	Tanacetum cinerariifolium	(H)
DAMASK HORSE CHESTNUT	Aesculus 'Plantierensis'	(T)
DAMASK ROSE	Rosa damasceana	(S)
DAMASK VIOLET	Herperis matronalis	(H)
DAME'S VIOLET	Hesperis matronalis	(H)
DAMIANA	Turnera diffusa	(S)
DAMMAR	Agathis dammara	(C)
DAMMAR PINE	Agathis	(C)
DAMSON	Prunus domestica insititia	(F)
DANCING DOLL ORCHID	Oncidium flexuosum	(O)
DANCING LADY ORCHID	Oncidium	(O)
DANDELION	Taraxacum officinale	(H)
DANEWORT	Sambucus ebulus	(H)
DANGLEBERRY	Gaylussacia frondosa	(S)
DANISH SCURVY-GRASS	Cochlearia danica	(A)
DAPHNE LILAC	Syringa microphylla 'Superba'	(S)
DARK COLUMBINE	Aquilegia atrata	(H)
DARK LEAVED WILLOW	Salix nigricans	(S)
DARK MULLEIN	Verbascum nigrum	(H)
DARK OPAL BASIL	Ocimum basilicum 'Purpurascens'	(HB)
DARK RED HELLEBORINE	Epipactis atrorubans	(O)
DARK SEDGE	Carex buxbaumii	(G)
DARK-LEAVED WILLOW	Salix nigricans	(S)
DARLING RIVER PEA	Swainsonia	(H)
DARNEL	Lolium temulentum	(G)
DARNEL SEDGE	Carex loliacea	(G)
DARWIN STRINGY BARK	Eucalyptus tetradonta	(T)
DASHEEN	Colocasia esculenta	(F)
DATE PALM	Phoenix dactylifera	(P)
DATE PALM	Phoenix sp.	(P)
DATE PLUM	Diospyros lotus	(T)
DATE YUCCA	Samuela	(F)
DAVID'S HARP	Polyganatum x hybridum	(H)

Common	Botanical	Type
DAVID'S PINE	Pinus armandii	(C)
DAWN REDWOOD	Metasequoia	(C)
DAWYCK BEECH	Fagus sylvatica 'Dawyck'	(T)
DAWYCK CHERRY	Prunus x dawyckensis	(T)
DAY FLOWER	Commelina	(H)
DAY LILY	Hemerocallis	(H)
DE CAEN ANEMONE	Anemone coronaria	(BB)
DEAD MAN'S FINGERS	Orchis mascula	(O)
DEAD MEN'S BELLS	Digitalis purpurea	(H)
DEAD NETTLE	Lamium maculatum	(H)
DEADLY NIGHTSHADE	Atropa belladonna	(A)
DEAL PINE	Pinus strobus	(C)
DEATH CAMAS	Zigadenus	(S)
DEATH CAP	Amanita phalloides	(FU)
DEATHCAP	Amanita phalloides	(FU)
DECEIVER	Laccaria laccata	(FU)
DECIDUOUS CAMELLIA	Stewartia	(ST)
DECIDUOUS CYPRESS	Taxodium distichum	(C)
DEER BRUSH	Ceanothus integerrimus	(S)
DEER BUSH	Ceanothus integerrimus	(S)
DEER FERN	Blechnum spicant	(FN)
DEER GRASS	Scirpus cespitosus	(G)
DEER OAK	Quercus sadleriana	(T)
DEER WEED	Lotus scoparius	(H)
DEER'S TONGUE	Liatris odoratissima	(H)
DEER-FOOT	Achlys	(H)
DEER-GRASS	Rhexia	(G)
DEERBERRY	Vaccineum stamineum	(S)
DEERGRASS	Scirpus cespitosus	(G)
DEERSFOOT FERN	Davallia canariensis	(FN)
DEERWEED	Lotus scoparius	(H)
DELTA MAIDENHAIR FERN	Adiantum raddianum	(FN)
DENSE SILKY BENT	Apera interrupta	(G)
DENSE-FLOWERED ORCHID	Neotinea maculata	(O)
DEODAR	Cedrus deodara	(C)
DEPTFORD PINK	Dianthus armeria	(H)
DESERT CANDLE	Dasylirion leiophyllum	(CS)
DESERT CANDLE	Eremurus	(BB)
DESERT CHRISTMAS CACTUS	Optunia leptocaulis	(CS)
DESERT FAN PALM	Washingtonia filifera	(P)
DESERT GUM	Eucalyptus rudis	(T)
DESERT MARIGOLD	Baileya multiradiata	(TS)
DESERT PRIVET	Peperomia magnoliifolia	(HP)
DESERT ROD	Eremostachys	(TS)
DESERT ROSE	Adenium obesum	(TH)
DESERT TEA	Ephedera spp	(S)
DESTROYING ANGEL	Amanita virosa	(FU)

Common	Botanical	Type
DEUTZIA	Deutzia	(S)
DEVIL CACTUS	Opuntia schottii	(CS)
DEVIL FLOWER	Tacca chantrieri	(HP)
DEVIL TREE	Alstonia scholaris	(TT)
DEVILWOOD	Osmanthus americanus	(S)
DEVIL'S APPLE	Datura stramonium	(H)
DEVIL'S APPLE	Mandragora officinarum	(HB)
DEVIL'S BACKBONE	Kalanchoe daigremontanum	(HP)
DEVIL'S BIT	Alstonia scholaris	(TT)
DEVIL'S BIT SCABIOUS	Sucissa pratensis	(H)
DEVIL'S CLAW	Harpogophytum procumbens	(H)
DEVIL'S CLAW	Physoplexis comosa	(HP)
DEVIL'S CLUB	Oplopanax horridus	(T)
DEVIL'S FIG	Argemone mexicana	(TS)
DEVIL'S IVY	Epipremnum aureus	(HP)
DEVIL'S LEAF	Urtica urentissima	(H)
DEVIL'S PAINTBRUSH	Hieraceum aurantiacum	(H)
DEVIL'S TONGUE	Ferocactus latispinus	(CS)
DEVIL'S TONGUE	Sansevieria	(HP)
DEVIL'S WALKING STICK	Aralia spinosa	(S)
DEVIL'S WHISKER PLANT	Tacca nivea	(H)
DEVILS DUNG	Ferula foetida	(H)
DEWBERRY	Rubus caesius	(F)
DHOBI'S NUT	Semecarpus anacardium	(TS)
DIAMOND FLOWER	Ionopsidium acaule	(H)
DICKSON'S GOLDEN ELM	Ulmus x sarniensis 'Dicksonii'	(T)
DIELYTRA	Dicentra	(H)
DIGGER PINE	Pinus sabiniana	(C)
DIGGER'S SPEEDWELL	Veronica perfoliata	(H)
DILDO	Cereus	(CS)
DILL	Anethum graveolens	(A/HB)
DINNER PLATE ARALIA	Polyscias balfouriana	(HP)
DIOECIOUS SEDGE	Carex dioica	(G)
DIRTWEED	Chenopodium album	(H)
DISHCLOTH GOURD	Luffa cylindrica	(V)
DISTANT SEDGE	Carex distans	(G)
DISTANT-FLOWERED SEDGE	Carex remota	(G)
DITA BARK	Alstonia scholaris	(S)
DITANY	Cunila mariana	(H)
DITCHMOSS	Elodea	(WP)
DITTANDER	Lepidium latifolium	(H)
DITTANY	Dictamnus	(H)
DIVI-DIVI	Caesalpinia coriarian	(S)
DOCK	Rumex	(H)
DOCKMACKIE	Viburnum acerifolium	(S)
DODDER	Cuscuta epithymum	(H)
DODDERING DILLIES	Briza media	(G)

Common	Botanical	Type
DOG CHOLLA	Opuntia schottii	(CS)
DOG DAISY	Leucanthemum vulgare	(H)
DOG HAIR-GRASS	Deschampsia setacea	(G)
DOG HOBBLE	Leucothoe catesbaei	(S)
DOG POISON	Aethusa cynapium	(A)
DOG VIOLET	Viola canina	(R)
DOG'S CABBAGE	Thelygonum cynocrambe	(H)
DOG'S FENNEL	Anthemis cotula	(H)
DOG'S MERCURY	Mercurialis perennis	(H)
DOG'S TAIL	Cynosurus	(G)
DOG'S TOOTH VIOLET	Erythronium dens-canis	(BB)
DOG-GRASS	Elymus repens	(G)
DOGBANE	Apocymun venetum	(H)
DOGBERRY	Cornus sanguinea	(S)
DOGBERRY	Sorbus americana	(T)
DOGROSE	Rosa canina	(S)
DOGSTOOTH GRASS	Dichanthium ischaemum	(G)
DOGWOOD	Cornus	(S)
DONKEY PLANT	Onosma	(H)
DONKEY'S TAIL	Sedum morganianum	(HP)
DORSET HEATH	Erica ciliaris	(S)
DOTTED LOOSESTRIFE	Lysimachia punctata	(H)
DOTTED SEDGE	Carex punctata	(G)
DOUBLE COCONUT	Lodoicea maldivica	(P)
DOUBLE CRIMSON THORN	Crataegus laevigata 'Paul's Scarlet'	(T)
DOUBLE FLOWERED GORSE	Ulex europeaus 'Plenus'	(S)
DOUBLE GEAN	Prunus avium 'Plena'	(T)
DOUBLE PINK THORN	Crataegus laevigata 'Rosea'	(T)
DOUBLE WHITE THORN	Crataegus laevigata 'Alba Plena'	(T)
DOUGLAS FIR	Pseudotsuga	(C)
DOUGLAS MAPLE	Acer glabrum douglasii	(T)
DOUM PALM	Hyphaene thebaica	(P)
DOVE ORCHID	Peristeria	(O)
DOVE TREE	Davidia involucrata	(T)
DOVE'S FOOT CRANESBILL	Geranium columbinum	(H)
DOVEDALE MOSS	Saxifraga hypnoides	(R)
DOWN THISTLE	Onopordon acanthium	(H)
DOWNY BIRCH	Betula pubescens	(T)
DOWNY BLACK POPLAR	Populus nigra 'Betulifolia'	(T)
DOWNY CHERRY	Prunus tomentosa	(S)
DOWNY CLEMATIS	Clematis macropetala	(CL)
DOWNY HAWTHORN	Crataegus mollis	(T)
DOWNY HEMP-NETTLE	Galeopsis segetum	(H)
DOWNY JAPANESE MAPLE	Acer japonicum	(ST)
DOWNY OAK	Quercus pubescens	(T)
DOWNY OAT	Helictotrichon pubescens	(G)
DOWNY ROSE	Rosa tomentosa	(S)

Know Your Common Plant Names

Common	Botanical	Type
DOWNY ST. JOHN'S WORT	Hypericum lanuginosum	(H)
DOWNY WILLOW	Salix lapponum	(S)
DOWNY WOUNDWORT	Stachys germanica	(H)
DRAGON ARUM	Arisaema	(H)
DRAGON ARUM	Dracunculus vulgaris	(H)
DRAGON MOUTH	Horminum pyranaicum	(H)
DRAGON PLANT	Dracunculus	(H)
DRAGON ROOT	Arisaema dracontium	(H)
DRAGON ROOT	Arum triphyllum	(H)
DRAGON SPRUCE	Picea asperata	(C)
DRAGON TREE	Dracaena draco	(HP)
DRAGON'S BLOOD	Daemomorops draco	(TS)
DRAGON'S CLAW WILLOW	Salix babylonica pekinensis 'Tortuosa'	(T)
DRAGON'S HEAD	Euphorbia gorgonis	(CS)
DRAGON'S MOUTH	Helicodiceros muscivorus	(H)
DRAGON'S MOUTH	Horminum pyrenaicum	(R)
DRAGON'S TEETH	Tetragonolobus maritimus	(H)
DRAGON-ROOT	Arisaema	(H)
DRAGONHEAD	Dracocephalum	(H)
DROOPING BITTERCRESS	Cardamine enneaphyllos	(H)
DROOPING BROME	Bromus tectorum	(G)
DROOPING JUNIPER	Juniperus recurva	(C)
DROOPING STAR OF BETHLEHEM	Ornithogallum nutans	(BB)
DROPWORT	Filipendula vulgaris	(H)
DRUMSTICK PRIMROSE	Primula denticulata	(H)
DRUNKARD'S DREAM	Hatiora salicornioides	(CS)
DRUNKEN SAILOR	Centranthus ruber	(H)
DRY WHISKY	Lophophora williamasii	(CS)
DRYAD'S SADDLE	Polyporus squamosus	(FU)
DUCK POTATO	Sagittaria latifolia	(WP)
DUCKSFOOT	Podophyllum pertatum	(H)
DUCKWEED	Lemna	(WP)
DUDGEON	Buxus sempervirens	(S/T)
DUKE CHERRY	Prunus x gondounii	(T)
DUKE OF ARGYLE'S TEA TREE	Lycium chinense	(S)
DUKE OF BEDFORD'S WILLOW	Salix 'Russeliana'	(S)
DULSE	Rhodymania palmata	(SW)
DUMB CANE	Dieffenbachia	(HP)
DUMPLING CACTUS	Coryphantha runyonii	(CS)
DUMPLING CACTUS	Lophophora williamsii	(CS)
DUN DAISY	Leucanthemum vulgare	(H)
DUNE FELWORT	Gentianella uliginosa	(H)
DUNE FESCUE	Vulpia fasciculata	(G)
DUNE HELLEBORINE	Epipactis dunensis	(O)
DUNKELD LARCH	Larix x eurolepis	(C)
DURIAN	Durio zibathinus	(F)
DURMAST OAK	Quercus petraea	(T)

Common	Botanical	Type
DURRA	Sorghum vulgare durra	(G)
DURUM WHEAT	Triticum durum	(G)
DUSKY CORAL PEA	Kennedia rubicunda	(CL)
DUSKY CRANESBILL	Geranium phaeum	(H)
DUSTY MILLER	Artemisia stelleriana	(H)
DUSTY MILLER	Cerastium tomentosum	(H)
DUSTY MILLER	Primula auricula	(R)
DUSTY MILLER GRAPE	Vitis vinifera 'Incana'	(CL)
DUTCH AGRIMONY	Eupatorium cannabinum	(H)
DUTCH CLOVER	Trifolium repens	(H)
DUTCH ELM	Ulmus x hollandica	(T)
DUTCH IRIS	Iris xiphium (hybrids)	(BB)
DUTCH LAVENDER	Lavandula ang. 'Vera'	(S)
DUTCH RUSH	Equisetum hyemale	(G)
DUTCH WINGS	Gasteria	(HP)
DUTCH WOODBINE	Lonicera periclymenum 'Belgica'	(CL)
DUTCH YELLOW CROCUS	Crocus flavus	(BB)
DUTCHMAN'S BREECHES	Dicentra	(H)
DUTCHMAN'S PIPE	Aristolochia	(CL)
DWALE	Atropa belladonna	(A)
DWARF ALBERTA SPRUCE	Picea glauca albertiana 'Glauca'	(C)
DWARF ALDER	Fothergilla	(S)
DWARF AMERICAN CHERRY	Prunus pumila	(S)
DWARF BILBERRY	Vaccinium caespitosum	(S)
DWARF BIRCH	Betula nana	(S)
DWARF BUCKEYE	Aesculus parviflora	(S)
DWARF CHINA FLOWER	Adenandra fragrans	(S)
DWARF COMFREY	Symphytum grandiflorum	(H)
DWARF CORNEL	Chamaepericlymenum suecicum	(S)
DWARF DANDELION	Krigia	(H)
DWARF EEL-GRASS	Zostera noltii	(WP)
DWARF ELDER	Sambucus ebulus	(H)
DWARF FLAG	Iris pumila	(H)
DWARF GORSE	Ulex minor	(S)
DWARF GRASS-WRACK	Zostera noltii	(WP)
DWARF HAWTHORN	Crataegus monogyna 'Compacta'	(S)
DWARF HUCKLEBERRY	Gaylussacia dumosa	(S)
DWARF MALLOW	Malva neglecta	(H)
DWARF MORNING GLORY	Convolvulus tricolor	(A)
DWARF MOUNTAIN PINE	Pinus mugo	(C)
DWARF ORCHID	Orchis ustulata	(O)
DWARF PALMETTO	Sabal minor	(P)
DWARF POINCIANA	Caesalpinia pulcherrima	(TT)
DWARF POMEGRANATE	Punica granatum 'Nana'	(S)
DWARF RUSH	Juncus capitatus	(G)
DWARF RUSSIAN ALMOND	Prunus tenella	(S)
DWARF SEDGE	Carex humilis	(G)

Common	Botanical	Type
DWARF SIBERIAN PINE	Pinus pumila	(C)
DWARF SPURGE	Euphorbia exigua	(H)
DWARF SUMACH	Rhus copallina	(S)
DWARF THISTLE	Cirsium acaule	(H)
DWARF WHITE WOOD LILY	Trillium nivale	(H)
DWARF WILLOW	Salix herbacea	(S)
DYE FIG	Ficus tinctoria	(HP)
DYER'S BROOM	Genista tinctoria	(S)
DYER'S CHAMOMILE	Anthemis tinctoria	(H)
DYER'S GREENWEED	Genista tinctoria	(S)
DYER'S ROCKET	Reseda luteola	(H)
DYER'S SAFFRON	Carthamus tinctorius	(H)
DYER'S WOODRUFF	Asperula tinctoria	(H)
DYSENTERY BARK	Simaruba amara	(TT)
EAGLE'S CLAW MAPLE	Acer platanoides 'Laciniatum'	(T)
EAGLES CLAW	Echinocactus	(CS)
EAGLEWOOD	Aquilaria	(TT)
EARED WILLOW	Salix aurita	(S)
EARLY CREAM HONEYSUCKLE	Lonicera caprifolium	(CL)
EARLY DOG VIOLET	Viola reichenbachiana	(H)
EARLY DUTCH HONEYSUCKLE	Lonicera periclymenum 'Belgica'	(CL)
EARLY HAIR GRASS	Aira praecox	(G)
EARLY MARSH ORCHID	Dactylorhiza incarnata	(O)
EARLY PURPLE ORCHID	Orchis mascula	(O)
EARLY SPIDER ORCHID	Ophrys sphegodes	(O)
EARTH NUT	Arachis hypogaea	(H)
EARTH NUT	Conopodium majus	(H)
EARTH SMOKE	Fumaria officinalis	(H)
EARTH STAR	Cryptanthus bivittatus	(HP)
EARTH STAR	Geastrum	(FU)
EAST AFRICAN JUNIPER	Juniperus procera	(C)
EAST HIMALAYAN SPRUCE	Picea spinulosa	(C)
EAST INDIAN ARROWROOT	Curcuma angustifolia	(TS)
EAST INDIAN EBONY	Diospyros ebenum	(TT)
EAST INDIAN WALNUT	Albizzia lebbeck	(TT)
EASTER CACTUS	Rhipsalidopsis gaertneri	(HP)
EASTER LILY	Lilium longiflorum	(BB)
EASTERN COTTONWOOD	Populus deltoides	(T)
EASTERN HEMLOCK	Tsuga canadensis	(C)
EASTERN HOP HORNBEAM	Ostrya virginiana	(T)
EASTERN LARCH	Larix laricina	(C)
EASTERN RED CEDAR	Juniperus virginiana	(C)
EASTERN ROCKET	Sisymbrium orientale	(H)
EASTERN WHITE PINE	Pinus strobus	(C)
EAU-DE-COLOGNE MINT	Mentha x piperita citrata	(HB)
EBONY	Diospyros ebenum	(T)
EBONYWOOD	Bauhinia variegata	(S)

Common	Botanical	Type
ECUADOR LAUREL	Cordia alliadora	(TS)
EDDO	Colocasia esculenta	(F)
EDELWEISS	Leontopodium alpinum	(R)
EDGING BOX	Buxus semperrirens 'Suffruticosa'	(S)
EDGING LOBELIA	Lobelia erinus	(A)
EEL GRASS	Vallisneria spiralis	(G/WP)
EEL GRASS	Zostera	(G/WP)
EGGPLANT	Solanum melongena	(V)
EGGS AND BACON	Linaria vulgaris	(H)
EGLANTINE	Rosa rubiginosa	(S)
EGYPTIAN COTTON	Gossypium bardadense	(S)
EGYPTIAN LOTUS	Nymphaea lotus	(WP)
EGYPTIAN ONION	Allium cepa aggregatum	(V)
EGYPTIAN PAPER PLANT	Cyperus papyrus	(G)
EGYPTIAN PAPER RUSH	Cyperus papyrus	(G)
EGYPTIAN PRIVET	Lawsonia inermis	(S)
EGYPTIAN STAR CLUSTER	Pentas lanceolata	(HP)
EGYPTIAN THORN	Acacia senegal	(T)
EIGHTY-DAY-HEALING BUSH	Lobostemon fruticosus	(S)
ELDER	Sambucus	(HS)
ELECAMPANE	Inula helenium	(H)
ELEPHANT APPLE	Dillenia indica	(TT)
ELEPHANT BUSH	Portulacaria afra	(S)
ELEPHANT EAR WATTLE	Acacia dunnii	(T)
ELEPHANT GRASS	Typha elephanta	(G)
ELEPHANT HEDGE BEAN TREE	Schotia latifolia	(TT)
ELEPHANT LILY	Crinum powellii	(BB)
ELEPHANT TREE	Phytolacca dioica	(H)
ELEPHANT'S APPLE	Feronia limonia	(S)
ELEPHANT'S EAR	Begonia	(HP)
ELEPHANT'S EAR	Bergenia	(H/A)
ELEPHANT'S EAR BEGONIA	Begonia scharffii	(HP)
ELEPHANT'S EARS	Caladium	(HP)
ELEPHANT'S FOOT	Beaucarnea recurvata	(T)
ELEPHANT'S FOOT	Dioscorea elephantipes	(F)
ELEPHANT'S FOOT	Testudinaria elephantipes	(F)
ELK'S HORNS	Rhombophyllum nelii	(HP)
ELM	Ulmus	(T)
ELONGATED SEDGE	Carex elongata	(G)
EMBELIA	Embelia ribes	(H)
EMERALD RIPPLE	Peperomia caperata	(HP)
EMMERSON'S THORN	Crataegus submollis	(T)
EMPRESS OF BRAZIL	Worsleya procera	(TS)
EMPRESS TREE	Paulownia	(T)
EMU BUSH	Eremophila	(TS)
ENCHANTER'S NIGHTSHADE	Circaea lutetiana	(H)
ENCINA	Quercus agrifolia	(T)

Common	Botanical	Type
ENDIVE	Cichorium endivia	(V)
ENGELMANN SPRUCE	Picea engelmannii	(C)
ENGLISH DAISY	Bellis	(H)
ENGLISH ELM	Ulmus procera	(T)
ENGLISH HAREBELL	Campanula rotundifolia	(H)
ENGLISH HOLLY	Ilex aquifolium	(ST)
ENGLISH IRIS	Iris latifolia	(BB)
ENGLISH OAK	Quercus robur	(T)
ENGLISH SCURVY GRASS	Cochlearia anglica	(H)
ENGLISH STONECROP	Sedum anglicum	(H)
ENGLISH WALNUT	Juglans regia	(T)
ENGLISH WILD HONEYSUCKLE	Lonicera periclymenum	(CL)
ENGLISH YEW	Taxus Baccata	(C)
EPAULETTE TREE	Pterostyrax hispida	(T)
ERECT CLEMATIS	Clematis recta	(H)
ERECT SWORD FERN	Nephrolepis cordifolia	(FN)
ERGOT	Claviceps purpurea	(PE)
ERYNGO	Eryngium	(H)
ESCABON	Cytisus proliferus	(S)
ESCALLONIA	Escallonia	(S)
ESPARTO GRASS	Stipa tenacissima	(G)
ESTRAGON	Artemisia dracunculus	(HB)
EUROPEAN ALDER	Alnus incana	(T)
EUROPEAN ASPEN	Populus tremula	(T)
EUROPEAN BIRD CHERRY	Prunus padus	(T)
EUROPEAN CRANBERRY BUSH	Viburnum opulus	(S)
EUROPEAN FIELD ELM	Ulmus carpinifolia	(T)
EUROPEAN GINGER	Asarum europaeum	(H)
EUROPEAN GLOBE FLOWER	Trollius europaeus	(H)
EUROPEAN GREEN ALDER	Alnus viridis	(T)
EUROPEAN HOP HORNBEAM	Ostrya carpinifolia	(T)
EUROPEAN LARCH	Larix decidua	(C)
EUROPEAN LINDEN	Tilia x europaea	(T)
EUROPEAN MICHAELMAS DAISY	Aster amellus	(H)
EUROPEAN MOUNTAIN ASH	Sorbus aucuparia	(T)
EUROPEAN SCRUB PINE	Pinus mugo pumilio	(C)
EUROPEAN SHRUBBY HORSETAIL	Ephedra distachya	(S)
EUROPEAN SILVER FIR	Abies alba	(C)
EUROPEAN WHITE BIRCH	Betula pendula	(T)
EUROPEAN WHITE ELM	Ulmus laevis	(T)
EVE'S PIN CACTUS	Opuntia subulata	(CS)
EVENING CAMPION	Lychnis	(H)
EVENING FLOWER	Hesperantha	(H)
EVENING FLOWER	Hesperus	(H)
EVENING PRIMROSE	Oenothera biennis	(H)
EVENING STAR	Cooperia	(BB)
EVER-READY ONION	Allium cepa perutile	(V)

Common	Botanical	Type
EVERGREEN BITTERSWEET	Euonymus fortunei	(CL)
EVERGREEN BLUEBERRY	Vaccinium myrsinites	(S)
EVERGREEN CURRANT	Ribes viburnumifolium	(S)
EVERGREEN LABURNUM	Piptanthus	(S)
EVERGREEN MAGNOLIA	Magnolia grandiflora	(ST)
EVERGREEN OAK	Quercus ilex	(T)
EVERLASTING DAISY	Helichrysum bellidiodes	(R)
EVERLASTING FLOWER	Acroclinium	(A)
EVERLASTING FLOWER	Helichrysum, Anaphalis, Limonium	(H)
EVERLASTING ONION	Allium perutile	(HB)
EVERLASTING PEA	Lathyrus latifolius	(H)
EVERLASTING SAND FLOWER	Ammobium	(H)
EWE DAISY	Potentilla erecta	(H)
EXMOUTH MAGNOLIA	Magnolia grandiflora 'Exmouth'	(ST)
EYEBRIGHT	Euphrasia memorosa	(H)
EYELASH BEGONIA	Begonia boweri	(HP)
EYELASH PEARL GRASS	Melica ciliata	(G)
FAIR MAIDS OF FEBRUARY	Galanthus nivalis	(BB)
FAIR MAIDS OF FRANCE	Saxifraga granulata	(R)
FAIR MAIDS OF KENT	Ranunculus aconitifolius	(H)
FAIRY AGAVE	Hechtia scariosa	(CS)
FAIRY CAKE FUNGUS	Hebeloma crustuliniforme	(FU)
FAIRY CLOCK	Taraxacum officinale	(H)
FAIRY CUPS	Primula varis	(H)
FAIRY DUSTER	Calliandra eriophylla	(S)
FAIRY FLAX	Linum catharticum	(H)
FAIRY FORGET-ME-NOT	Eritrichium	(R)
FAIRY FOXGLOVE	Erinus alpinus	(R)
FAIRY LANTERN	Calochortus albus	(BB)
FAIRY MOSS	Azolla	(MS)
FAIRY PRIMROSE	Primula malacoides	(HP)
FAIRY RING CHAMPIGNON	Marasmius oreades	(FU)
FAIRY RING MUSHROOM	Marasmius oreades	(FU)
FAIRY THIMBLES	Digitalis purpurea	(B)
FAIRY'S THIMBLE	Campanula cochlearifolia	(H)
FAIRYBELLS	Disporum	(H)
FAIRYBELLS	Disporum trachycarpum	(H)
FAKE SAFFRON	Carthamus tinctorius	(H)
FALSE ACACIA	Robinia	(ST)
FALSE AFRICAN VIOLET	Streptocarpus saxorum	(HP)
FALSE ALUM ROOT	Tellima	(H)
FALSE ARALIA	Dizygotheca	(HP)
FALSE ARBORVITAE	Thujopsis	(C)
FALSE BISHOP'S WEED	Ammi majus	(H)
FALSE BROME	Brachypodium sylvaticum	(G)
FALSE BUGBANE	Trautvetteria carolinensis	(H)
FALSE CASTOR OIL PLANT	Fatsia japonica	(S)

Know Your Common Plant Names

Common	Botanical	Type
FALSE CYPRESS	Chamaecyparis	(C)
FALSE DEATH CAP	Amanita citrina	(FU)
FALSE DRAGONHEAD	Physostegia	(H)
FALSE FOX SEDGE	Carex otrubae	(G)
FALSE GOATSBEARD	Astilbe	(H)
FALSE HEATH	Fabiana	(S)
FALSE HEATHER	Hudsonia ericoides	(S)
FALSE HELLEBORE	Veratrum	(H)
FALSE HOLLY	Osmanthus heterophyllus	(S)
FALSE INDIGO	Amorpha fruticosa	(H)
FALSE INDIGO	Baptisia	(H)
FALSE JASMINE	Gelsemium	(CL)
FALSE JERUSALEM CHERRY	Solanum capsicastrum	(HP)
FALSE LOMBARDY POPLAR	Populus 'robusta'	(T)
FALSE LONDON ROCKET	Sisymbrium loeselii	(H)
FALSE MALLOW	Malvastrum	(H)
FALSE MALLOW	Sidalcea	(H)
FALSE MEDLAR	Sorbus chamaemespilus	(S)
FALSE MITREWORT	Tiarella	(H)
FALSE MUSK ORCHID	Chamorchis alpina	(O)
FALSE OAT GRASS	Arrhenatherum elatius	(G)
FALSE PLANTAIN	Heliconia	(H)
FALSE SAFFRON	Carthamus	(A)
FALSE SEDGE	Kobresia simpliciuscula	(G)
FALSE SOLOMON'S SEAL	Smilacina	(H)
FALSE SPIKENARD	Smilacina racemosa	(H)
FALSE SPIRAEA	Sorbaria	(S)
FALSE SUNFLOWER	Heliopsis	(H)
FALSE TAMARISK	Myricaria	(S)
FALSE UNICORN ROOT	Chamaelirion luteum	(H)
FALSE WINTER'S BARK	Cinnamodendron corticosum	(TS)
FAMEFLOWER	Talinum	(H)
FANCY ANNY	Delonix regia	(TT)
FANWORT	Cabomba caroliniana	(WP)
FAREWELL TO SPRING	Godetia	(A)
FARGES FIR	Abies fargesii	(C)
FARKLEBERRY	Vaccineum arboreum	(S)
FAT DUCKWEED	Lemna gibba	(WP)
FAT HEN	Chenopodium album	(A)
FEARN TREE	Jacaranda acutifolia	(TT)
FEATHER CACTUS	Mammillaria plumosa	(CS)
FEATHER CLIMBER	Acridocarpus natalitius	(CL)
FEATHER FLOWER	Verticordia	(S)
FEATHER GRASS	Stipa pennata	(G)
FEATHER HYACINTH	Muscari comosum	(BB)
FEATHERFOIL	Hottonia palustris	(H)
FELT BUSH	Kalanchoe beharensis	(HP)

Common	Botanical	Type
FEN BEDSTRAW	Galium uliginosum	(II)
FEN ORCHID	Liparis loeselii	(O)
FEN PONDWEED	Potamogeton coloratus	(WP)
FEN SEDGE	Cladium mariscus	(G)
FEN VIOLET	Viola stagnina	(H)
FENNEL	Foeniculum vulgare	(HB)
FENNEL FLOWER	Nigella sativa	(A)
FENNEL PONDWEED	Potamogeton pectinatus	(WP)
FENNEL-FLOWER	Nigella	(A/H)
FENUGREEK	Trifolium ornithopodioides	(V)
FENUGREEK	Trigonella foenum-graecum	(H)
FERN GRASS	Desmazeria rigida	(G)
FERN PALM	Cycas circinalis	(P)
FERN-LEAF BEECH	Fagus sylvatica heterophylla	(T)
FERN-LEAVED CLEMATIS	Clematis cirrhosa balearica	(CL)
FERN-LEAVED ELDER	Sambucus nigra 'Laciniata'	(S)
FERN-LEAVED OAK	Quercus x rosacea 'Filicifolia'	((T)
FESCUE	Festuca	(G)
FETTER-BUSH	Lyonia lucida	(S)
FETTERBUSH	Leucothoe fontanesiana	(S)
FEVER BUSH	Garrya fremontii	(S)
FEVERBUSH	Lindera	(S)
FEVERFEW	Tanacetum coccineum	(F)
FEVERFEW	Tanacetum parthenium	(HB)
FEW-FLOWERED LEEK	Allium paradoxum	(BB)
FEW-FLOWERED SEDGE	Carex pauciflora	(G)
FIBROUS-ROOTED BEGONIA	Begonia semperflorens	(A)
FIDDLE DOCK	Rumex pulcher	(H)
FIDDLE LEAF FIG	Ficus lyrata	(HP)
FIDDLER'S TRUMPETS	Sarracenia leucophylla	(HP)
FIDDLEWOOD	Cithahexylum	(T)
FIELD BRIAR	Rosa agrestis	(S)
FIELD BROME	Bromus arvensis	(G)
FIELD COW-WHEAT	Melampyrum arvense	(H)
FIELD DAISY	Leucanthemum vulgare	(H)
FIELD DODDER	Cuscuta campestris	(CL)
FIELD ERYNGO	Eryngium campestre	(H)
FIELD FELWORT	Gentianella campestris	(H)
FIELD FLEAWORT	Senecio integrifolius	(H)
FIELD FORGET-ME-NOT	Myosotis arvensis	(H)
FIELD GARLIC	Allium oleraceum	(BB)
FIELD GENTIAN	Gentianella campestris	(H)
FIELD HORSETAIL	Equisetum arvense	(H)
FIELD MADDER	Sherardia arvensis	(H)
FIELD MAPLE	Acer campestre	(ST)
FIELD MOUSE-EAR	Cerastium arvense	(H)
FIELD MUSHROOM	Agaricus campestris	(FU)

Common	Botanical	Type
FIELD MUSTARD	Sinapis arvensis	(H)
FIELD PANSY	Viola arvensis	(H)
FIELD PENNYCRESS	Thlaspi arvense	(H)
FIELD PEPPERWORT	Lepidium campestre	(H)
FIELD POPPY	Papaver rhoeas	(A)
FIELD PRIMROSE	Oenothera biennis	(H)
FIELD ROSE	Rosa arvensis	(S)
FIELD SCABIOUS	Knautia arvensis	(H)
FIELD SOUTHERNWOOD	Artemisia campestris	(H)
FIELD SPEEDWELL	Veronica agrestis	(H)
FIELD WOOD-RUSH	Luzula campestris	(G)
FIELD WORMWOOD	Artemisia campestris	(H)
FIELD WOUNDWORT	Stachys arvensi	(H)
FIG	Ficus carica	(F)
FIG MARIGOLD	Mesembryanthemum	(A)
FIG OF INDIA	Opuntia ficus-indica	(CS)
FIG-LEAVED GOOSEFOOT	Chenopodium ficifolium	(H)
FIGWORT	Scrophularia	(H)
FIJIAN KAURI PINE	Agathis vitiensis	(C)
FILBERT	Corylus maxima	(F)
FILLET FERN	Taenitis blechnoides	(FN)
FILMY FERN	Hymenophyllum	(FN)
FINE-LEAVED SANDWORT	Minuartia hybrida	(R)
FINE-LEAVED WATER DROPWORT	Oenanthe aquatica	(H)
FINGER ARALIA	Dizygotheca	(HP)
FINGER-GRASS	Digitaria	(G)
FINGER-LIME	Microcitrus	(S)
FINGERED SEDGE	Carex digitata	(G)
FINGERNAIL PLANT	Neoregelia spectabilis	(HP)
FINOCCHIO	Foeniculum vulgare dulce	(HB)
FIR	Abies	(C)
FIRE CROWN	Rebutia senilis	(CS)
FIRE CROWN CACTUS	Rebutia senilis	(CS)
FIRE DRAGON PLANT	Acalypha wilkesiana	(HP)
FIRE LILY	Lilium bulbiferum	(BB)
FIRE ON THE MOUNTAIN	Euphorbia heterophylla	(H)
FIRE PLANT	Euphorbia pulcherrima	(A)
FIRE TREE	Nuytsia floribunda	(TT)
FIRE-BUSH	Kochia scoparia trichophylla	(A)
FIRECRACKER	Russelia juncea	(TS)
FIRECRACKER CACTUS	Cleistocactus smaragdiflorus	(CS)
FIRECRACKER FLOWER	Crossandra	(HP)
FIRECRACKER PLANT	Crossandra	(HP)
FIRECRACKER VINE	Manattia inflata	(HP)
FIRETHORN	Pyracantha	(S)
FIREWEED	Epilobium angustifolium	(A.H)
FIREWEED	Erechtites hieracifolia	(H)

Common	Botanical	Type
FIREWHEEL TREE	Stenocarpus sinuatus	(HP)
FIRST-AID PLANT	Aloe vera	(CS)
FISH GRASS	Cabomba caroliniana	(G)
FISH-BONE COTONEASTER	Contoneaster horizontalis	(S)
FISH-BONE THISTLE	Chamaepeuce diacantha	(H)
FISH-POISON TREE	Piscidia erythrina	(TS)
FISHBONE CACTUS	Epiphyllum anguliger	(CS)
FISHHOOK CACTI	Ferocactus	(CS)
FISHPOLE BAMBOO	Phyllostachys aurea	(G)
FISHTAIL PALMS	Caryota spp	(P)
FIVE FINGER	Potentilla	(H.S)
FIVE FINGERS	Potentilla reptans	(H)
FIVE FINGERS	Pseudopanax arboreus	(S)
FIVE FINGERS	Syngonium auritum	(HP)
FIVE SPOT	Nemophile maculata	(A)
FIVE-FACED BISHOP	Adoxa moschatellina	(H)
FIVE-LEAF GRASS	Potentilla reptans	(H)
FIVE-SPOT BABY	Nemophila maculata	(A)
FLAC LILY	Iris versicular	(H)
FLAG IRIS	Iris pseudacorus	(W.P)
FLAGEOLET BEAN	Phaseolus vulgaris	(V)
FLAKY FIR	Abies squamata	(C)
FLAMBOYANT	As hedging, 2 Prunus cerasifera "Pissardii" to 1 Prunus cerasifera	(S)
FLAMBOYANT	Delonix regia	(TT)
FLAMBOYANT TREE	Delonix regia	(T.T)
FLAME BOTTLE TREE	Brachychiton acerfolium	(TT)
FLAME CREEPER	Tropaealum speciosum	(CL)
FLAME FLOWER	Pyrostegia venusta	(CL)
FLAME FLOWER	Tropaeolum speciosum	(CL)
FLAME NASTURTIUM	Tropaeolum speciosum	(CL)
FLAME NETTLE	Coleus	(HP)
FLAME OF THE FOREST	Delonix regia	(T.T.)
FLAME OF THE FOREST	Spathoden campanulata	(TT)
FLAME OF THE WOOD	Ixora coccinea	(HP)
FLAME TREE	Brachychiton acerfolium	(TT)
FLAME TREE	Delonix regia	(T.T.)
FLAME TREE	Sterculia acerfolia	(TT)
FLAME VINE	Pyrostegia venusta	(TCL)
FLAME VIOLET	Episcia cupreata	(HP)
FLAME-LILY	Pyrolirion	(HP)
FLAMES	Homoglossum merianella	(BB)
FLAMING KATY	Kalanchoe	(HP)
FLAMING SWORD	Vriesea hieroglyphica splendens	(HP)
FLAMINGO FLOWER	Anthurium	(HP)
FLANNEL BUSH	Fremontodendron	(S)
FLANNEL FLOWER	Actinotus helianthi	(A)

Know Your Common Plant Names

Common	Botanical	Type
FLANNEL PLANT	Verbascum thapsus	(H)
FLAT PEA	Platylobium	(F)
FLAT SEDGE	Blysmus compressus	(G)
FLAT-STALKED PONDWEED	Potamogeton friesii	(WP)
FLAX	Linum usitatissimum	(H)
FLAX LILY	Dianella	(H)
FLAX-LEAVED ST. JOHN'S WORT	Hypericum linarifolium	(H)
FLAX-LILY	Dianella	(BB)
FLAX-LILY	Phormium	(S)
FLAXWEED	Linaria vulgaris	(H)
FLEA SEDGE	Carex pulicaris	(G)
FLEABANE	Pulicaria dysenterica; Erigeron	(H)
FLEECE VINE	Fallopia baldschuanicum	(CL)
FLEUR-DE-LYS	Iris florentina	(H)
FLEXIBLE NAIAD	Najas flexilis	(WP)
FLIXWEED	Descurainia sophia	(H)
FLOATING BUR-REED	Sparganium angustifolium	(WP)
FLOATING FERN	Salvinia auriculata	(WP)
FLOATING MARSH-WORT	Apium inundatum	(WP)
FLOATING PONDWEED	Potamogeton natans	(WP)
FLOATING SWEET GRASS	Glyceria fluitans	(G)
FLOATING WATER PLANTAIN	Luronium natans	(WP)
FLOODED GUM	Eucalyptus grandis	(T)
FLORAL FIRECRACKER	Brevoortia	(HP)
FLORAL FIRECRACKER	Dichelostemma ida-maia	(H)
FLORENCE FENNEL	Foeniculum vulgare dulce	(V)
FLORIDA CORKWOOD	Leitneria floridana	(T)
FLORIST'S CHRYSANTHEMUM	Dendranthema	(A)
FLORIST'S CYCLAMEN	Cyclamen persicum	(HP)
FLORIST'S FERN	Dryopteris dilatata	(FN)
FLORIST'S GENISTA	Genista canariensis	(S)
FLORIST'S GLOXINIA	Sinningia speciosa	(HP)
FLORIST'S VERBENA	Verbena x hybrida	(H)
FLOSS FLOWER	Ageratum	(A)
FLOSS SILK TREE	Chorisia speciosa	(T)
FLOWER FERN	Aneimia	(FN)
FLOWER OF AN HOUR	Hibiscus trionum	(A)
FLOWER OF JOVE	Lychnis flos-jovis	(H)
FLOWER OF THE GODS	Dianthus	(H/R)
FLOWER OF THE INCAS	Ipheion	(BB)
FLOWER OF THE WESTERN WIND	Zephyranthes candida	(BB)
FLOWER-OF-THE-WEST-WIND	Zephyranthes	(BB)
FLOWERING ASH	Fraxinus ornus	(T)
FLOWERING BANANA	Musa ornata	(H)
FLOWERING CHERRY	Prunus	(T)
FLOWERING CURRANT	Ribes sanguineum	(S)
FLOWERING DOGWOOD	Cornus florida	(S)

Common	Botanical	Type
FLOWERING FERN	Osmunda	(FN)
FLOWERING FERNS	Aneimia	(FN)
FLOWERING INCH PLANT	Tradescantia blossfeldiana	(HP)
FLOWERING MAPLE	Abutilon	(S)
FLOWERING NUTMEG	Leycesteria formosa	(S)
FLOWERING PLUM	Prunus cerasifera	(T)
FLOWERING RASPBERRY	Rubus odoratus	(S)
FLOWERING RUSH	Butomus umbellatus	(G)
FLOWERING SPURGE	Euphorbia corollata	(H)
FLOWERING TOBACCO	Nicotiana sylvestris	(H)
FLUELLEN	Kickxia	(H)
FLY AGARIC	Amanita muscaria	(FU)
FLY HONEYSUCKLE	Lonicera xylosteum	(S)
FLY ORCHID	Ophrys insectifera	(O)
FOAM FLOWER	Tiarella	(H)
FOAM-OF-MAY	Spiraea x arguta	(S)
FODDER VETCH	Vicia villosa	(H)
FOETID YEW	Torreya taxifolia	(C)
FOLGNER'S WHITEBEAM	Sorbus folgneri	(T)
FOLHADO	Clethra arborea	(T)
FOOD OF THE GODS	Ferula foetida	(H)
FOOL'S MUSHROOM	Amanita verna	(FU)
FOOL'S PARSLEY	Aethusa cynapium	(H)
FOOL'S WATER-CRESS	Apium nodiflorum	(WP)
FOREST FEVER TREE	Anthockistazam besiaca	(TT)
FOREST LILY	Veltheimia viridiflora	(BB)
FOREST RED GUM	Eucalyptus tereticornis	(T)
FOREST WILD MEDLAR	Vangueria esculenta	(S)
FORGET-ME-NOT	Myosotis	(H)
FORKED CATCHFLY	Silene dichotoma	(H)
FORKED SPLEENWORT	Asplenium septentrionale	(FN)
FORKING LARKSPUR	Consolida regalis	(A)
FORMOSAN AZALEA	Rhododendron oldhamii	(S)
FORMOSAN CHERRY	Prunus campanulata	(T)
FORREST FIR	Abies delavayi forrestii	(C)
FORREST'S SILVER FIR	Abies delavayi forrestii	(C)
FOUNTAIN BUDDLEIA	Buddleia alternifolia	(S)
FOUNTAIN BUSH	Russelia equisetiformis	(TS)
FOUNTAIN FLOWER	Ceropegia sandersonii	(S)
FOUNTAIN GRASS	Pennisetum setaceum	(G)
FOUNTAIN PLANT	Russelia juncea	(TS)
FOUNTAIN TREE	Spathodea camanulata	(TT)
FOUR O'CLOCK PLANT	Mirabilis jalapa	(H)
FOUR WING SALTBUSH	Atriplex canescens	(S)
FOUR-LEAVED ALLSEED	Polycarpon tetraphyllum	(H)
FOUR-O'-CLOCK	Mirabilis jalapa	(S)
FOUR-WING SALT BUSH	Atriplex canescens	(S)

Know Your Common Plant Names

Common	Botanical	Type
FOUR-WINGED MALLEE	Eucalyptus tetraptera	(T)
FOX GRAPE	Vitis labrusca	(CL)
FOX SEDGE	Carex vulpina	(G)
FOX'S GRAPE	Fritillaria uva-vulpis	(BB)
FOX-GLOVE	Digitalis	(H)
FOX-GLOVE TREE	Paulownia	(T)
FOX-TAIL ORCHID	Aerides	(O)
FOXBANE	Aconitum lycotonum vulparia	(H)
FOXTAIL BARLEY	Hordeum jubatum	(G)
FOXTAIL BRISTLE-GRASS	Setaria italica	(G)
FOXTAIL GRASS	Alopecurus	(G)
FOXTAIL GRASSES	Setaria	(G)
FOXTAIL LILY	Eremurus	(B)
FOXTAIL MILLET	Setaria italica	(G)
FOXTAIL PINE	Pinus balfouriana	(C)
FOXY SPOT	Collybia maculata	(FU)
FRAGRANT BUCKLER FERN	Dryopteris fragrans	(FN)
FRAGRANT EVENING PRIMROSE	Oenothera stricta	(H)
FRAGRANT OLIVE	Osmanthus fragrans	(S)
FRAGRANT ORCHID	Gymnadenia conopsea	(O)
FRAGRANT PLAINTAIN LILY	Hosta plantaginea	(H)
FRAGRANT SUMACH	Rhus aromatica	(S)
FRANGIPANI	Plumeria rubra	(TT)
FRANKINCENSE	Boswellia thurifera	(T)
FRANKINCENSE PINE	Pinus Toeda	(C)
FRAXINELLA	Dictamnus alpus	(H)
FRECKLE FACE	Hypoestes	(HP)
FREMONTIA	Fremontodendron	(S)
FRENCH ASPARAGUS	Ornithogalum pyrenaicum	(BB)
FRENCH BEAN	Phaseolus vulgaris	(V)
FRENCH CRANE'S BILL	Geranium endressii	(H)
FRENCH HALES	Sorbus devoniensis	(T)
FRENCH HAWK'S BEARD	Crepis nicaeensis	(H)
FRENCH HEATHER	Erica hyemalis	(HP)
FRENCH HONEYSUCKLE	Hedysarum coronarium	(S)
FRENCH LAVENDER	Lavandula stoechas	(S)
FRENCH LILAC	Galega officinalis	(H)'
FRENCH MARIGOLD	Tagetes patula	(A)
FRENCH MULBERRY	Callicarpa	(S)
FRENCH PHYSIC NUT	Jatropha curcas	(TS)
FRENCH ROSE	Rosa gallica	(S)
FRENCH SORREL	Rumex scutatus	(HB)
FRENCH TAMARISK	Tamarix gallica	(S)
FRENCH TARRAGON	Artemisia dracunculus	(HB)
FRENCH WILLOW	Salix triandra	(S/T)
FRIAR'S CAP	Aconitum napellus	(H)
FRIARS COWL	Arum maculatum	(H)

Common	Botanical	Type
FRIENDSHIP TREE	Crassula ovata	(CS)
FRINGE CUPS	Tellima grandiflora	(H)
FRINGE FLOWER	Schinzanthus	(H/P)
FRINGE LILY	Thysanotus multiflorus	(H)
FRINGE MYRTLE	Calytrix tetragona	(S)
FRINGE TREE	Chionanthus virginicus	(S)
FRINGECUPS	Tellima grandiflora	(H)
FRINGED HIBISCUS	Hibiscus schizopetalus	(TS)
FRINGED LAVENDER	Lavandula dentata	(S)
FRINGED ORCHIS	Habenaria	(O)
FRINGED SANDWORT	Arenaria ciliata	(R)
FRITILLARY	Fritillaria	(BB)
FROG ORCHID	Coeloglossum viride	(O)
FROG-BIT	Hydrocharis morsus ranae	(W.P.)
FROST FLOWER	Aster	(H)
FROSTED ORACHE	Atriplex lociniata	(H)
FROSTED THORN	Crataegus prunifolia	(T)
FROSTWEED	Helianthemum canadense	(S)
FROSTWORT	Helianthemum canadense	(S)
FRUITING MYRTLE	Eugenia	(S)
FUCHSIA BEGONIA	Begonia fuchsoides	(HP)
FUCHSIA GUM	Eucalyptus forrestiana	(T)
FUCHSIA-FLOWERED GOOSEBERRY	Ribes speciosum	(S)
FUJI CHERRY	Prunus incisa	(S.T)
FULHAM OAK	Quercus x hispanica 'Fulhamensis'	(T)
FULLER'S TEASEL	Dipsacus fullonum sativus	(H)
FULLMOON MAPLE	Acer japonicum	(S.T)
FUMITORY	Fumaria officinalis	(H/A)
FUNKIA	Hosta	(H)
FURRY WILLOW	Salix cordata	(S)
FURZE	Ulex	(S)
FUSTIC	Chlorophora tinctoria	(TT)
GABOON	Aucomea klainiana	(TT)
GALANGAL	Alpinia officinarum	(TS)
GALAPEE TREE	Sciadophyllum brownii	(TT)
GALBANUM	Ferula gabaniflua	(HB)
GALE	Myrica gale	(S)
GALINGALE	Cyperus longus	(G)
GALLANT SOLDIER	Galinsoga	(H)
GAMBOGE	Garcinia cambogia	(F)
GANDERGOOSE	Orchis moro	(O)
GANJA	Cannabis sativa	(H)
GARBANZO	Cicer arietinum	(F)
GARDEN ARABIS	Arabis caucasica	(R)
GARDEN CHERVIL	Anthriscus cerefolium	(HB)
GARDEN CRESS	Lepidium sativum	(V)
GARDEN LUPIN	Lupinus polyphyllus	(H)

Common	Botanical	Type
GARDEN MINT	Mentha spicata	(H)
GARDEN PANSY	Viola x wittrockiana	(H)
GARDEN SORREL	Rumex acetosa	(HB)
GARDEN STRAWBERRY	Fragaria x ananassa	(F)
GARDEN THYME	Thymus vulgaris	(S)
GARDENER'S GARTERS	Phalaris arundinacea 'Picta'	(G)
GARGET	Phytolacea	(H)
GARLAND CRAB	Malus coronaria	(T)
GARLAND FLOWER	Daphne cneorum	(S)
GARLAND FLOWER	Hedychium coronarium	(TH)
GARLAND WREATH	Spiraea x arguta	(S)
GARLIC	Allium sativum	(HB)
GARLIC MUSTARD	Alliaria sativum	(H)
GARLIC PEAR	Crataera gynandra	(T)
GARLIC PENNYCRESS	Thlaspi alliaceum	(H)
GAS PLANT	Dictamus	(H)
GAS TAR FUNGUS	Tricholoma sulphureum	(FU)
GAYFEATHER	Liatris	(H)
GBANJA COLA	Cola nitida	(TF)
GEAN	Prunus avium	(T)
GEIGER TREE	Cordia sebestana	(TT)
GENIP	Melicocca bijuja	(S)
GENIP TREE	Melicocca bijuga	(S)
GENIPAP	Genipa americana	(S)
GENIPAP FRUIT	Genipa americana	(F)
GENOA BROOM	Genista januensis	(S)
GENTIAN	Gentiana	(RH)
GENTIAN SAGE	Salvia patens	(A)
GENTLEMAN'S POCKET HANDKERCHEIF TREE	Davidia involucrata	(T)
GERALDTON WAX	Chamaelaucium uncinatum	(TS)
GERANIUM	Pelargonium	(A)
GERANIUM TREE	Cordia sebestana	(TT)
GERMAN ASPHODEL	Tofieldia calyculata	(H)
GERMAN CHAMOMILE	Matricaria recutita	(H)
GERMAN GARLIC	Allium senescens	(BB)
GERMAN GREENWEED	Genista germanica	(S)
GERMAN IRIS	Iris germanica	(H)
GERMAN IVY	Senecio mikanioides	(HP)
GERMAN PRIMROSE	Primula obconica	(H/P)
GERMAN VIOLET	Exacum affine	(HP)
GERMANDER	Teucrium	(HS)
GERMANDER SPEEDWELL	Veronica chamaedrys	(H)
GHERKIN	Cucumis sativus	(V)
GHOST FLOWER	Monotropa uniflora	(H)
GHOST GUM	Eucalyptus papuana	(T)
GHOST PLANT	Graptopetalum paraguayense	(H)
GHOST TREE	Davidia involucrata	(T)

Common	Botanical	Type
GHOSTFLOWER	Monotropa uniflora	(S)
GIANT BAMBOO	Dendrocalamus	(G)
GIANT BELLFLOWER	Campanula latifolia	(H)
GIANT BELLFLOWER	Ostrowskia magnifica	(BB)
GIANT BLUEBELL	Hyacinthoides hispanica	(BB)
GIANT BUTTERBUR	Petasites japonicus	(H)
GIANT CANE	Arundinaria gigantea	(G)
GIANT DEAD NETTLE	Lamium orvala	(H)
GIANT FENNEL	Ferula communis	(HB)
GIANT FESCUE	Festuca gigantea	(G)
GIANT FIR	Abies grandis	(C)
GIANT GRANADILLA	Passiflora quadrangularis	(CL)
GIANT GUM	Eucalyptus regnans	(T)
GIANT HIMALAYAN LILY	Cardiocrinum giganteum	(BB)
GIANT HOGWEED	Heracleum mantegazzianum	(H)
GIANT HONEYSUCKLE	Lonicera hildebrandtiana	(CL)
GIANT HYSSOP	Agastache urticifolia	(H)
GIANT INULA	Inula magnifica	(H)
GIANT KELP	Macrocystis	(SW)
GIANT KNOTWEED	Fallopia sachalinensis	(H)
GIANT MILKWEED	Calotropis procera	(TH)
GIANT PINEAPPLE FLOWER	Eucomis pallidiflora	(BB)
GIANT PRICKLY RHUBARB	Gunnera	(H)
GIANT PROTEA	Protea cynaroides	(TS)
GIANT REED	Arundo donax	(G)
GIANT SCABIOUS	Cephalaria	(H)
GIANT SEA HOLLY	Eryngium giganteum	(H)
GIANT SNOWDROP	Galanthus elwesii	(BB)
GIANT SOLOMON'S SEAL	Polygonatum commutatum	(H)
GIANT SPANIARD	Aciphylla scott-thomsonii	(H)
GIANT SPIDER PLANT	Cleome spinosa	(BB)
GIANT STAPELIA	Stapelia gigantea	(HP)
GIANT SUMMER HYACINTH	Galtonia candicans	(BB)
GIANT TOAD FLOWER	Stapelia gigantea	(HP)
GIANT VELVET ROSE	Aeonium canariense	(HP)
GIANT WOOD FERN	Dryopteris goldiana	(FN)
GIANT WOOLLY PROTEA	Protea barbigera	(TS)
GIANT YELLOW COWSLIP	Primula florindae	(H)
GIBB'S FIRETHORN	Pyracantha atalantoides	(S)
GILL-OVER-THE-GROUND	Glechoma hederacca	(H)
GILLY FLOWER	Dianthus caryophyllus	(H)
GILLYFLOWER	Cheiranthus cheiri	(H)
GINGER	Zingiber officinale	(HB)
GINGER LILY	Hedychium	(BB)
GINGER MINT	Mentha x gentilis	(HB)
GINGERBREAD PLUM	Parinari macrophylla	(TT)
GINGERBREAD TREE	Parinarium macrophyllum	(T)

Common	Botanical	Type
GINGILLY	Sesame indicum	(F)
GINSENG	Panax ginseng	(HB)
GIPPSLAND FOUNTAIN PALM	Livistona australis	(P)
GIPPSLAND WARATAH	Telopea oreades	(S/T)
GIPSYWEED	Lycopus virginicus	(H)
GIPSYWORT	Lycopus europaeus	(H)
GIRASOLE	Helianthus tuberosus	(V)
GLABROUS RUPTUREWORT	Herniaria glabra	(R)
GLACIER PINK	Dianthus glacialis	(H)
GLACIER WORMWOOD	Artemisia glacidis	(H)
GLADDON	Iris foetidissima	(H)
GLADWYN	Iris foetidissima	(H)
GLASSWORT	Salicornia	(H)
GLASTONBURY THORN	Crataegus monogyna 'Biflora'	(T)
GLOBE AMARANTH	Gomphrena globosa	(A)
GLOBE ARTICHOKE	Cynara scoymus	(VH)
GLOBE DAISY	Globuria	(R)
GLOBE FLOWER	Globularia	(H)
GLOBE FLOWER	Trollius	(H)
GLOBE LILY	Calochortus albus	(BB)
GLOBE MALLOW	Sphaeralcea	(A)
GLOBE THISTLE	Echinops	(H)
GLOBE TULIP	Calochortus	(BB)
GLORY BUSH	Tibouchina urvilleana	(HP)
GLORY FLOWER	Eccremocarpus	(CL)
GLORY LILY	Gloriosa	(BB)
GLORY OF TEXAS	Thelocactus bicolor	(CS)
GLORY OF THE SUN	Leucocoryne ixioides	(BB)
GLORY PEA	Clianthus formosus	(S)
GLORY TREE	Clerodendrum trichotomum	(S)
GLORY-OF-THE SNOW	Chionodoxa	(BB)
GLORY-OF-THE-MARSH	Primula helodoxa	(H)
GLORY-OF-THE-SUN	Leucocoryna ixioides	(BB)
GLOSSY PRIVET	Ligustrum lucidum	(ST)
GLOXINIA	Sinningia speciosa	(HP)
GOAT HONEYSUCKLE	Lonicera caprifolium	(CL)
GOAT WILLOW	Salix capra	(ST)
GOAT'S BEARD	Aruncus, Tragopogon	(H)
GOAT'S HORN CACTUS	Astrophytum capricorne	(CS)
GOAT'S RUE	Galega officinalis	(H)
GOAT'S THORN	Astragalus	(S)
GOAT-ROOT	Ononis natrix	(S)
GOATS FOOT	Oxalis caprina	(H)
GOBO	Arctium lappa anagyroides	(H)
GODETIA	Godetia grandiflora	(A)
GOLD CUP	Ranunculus acris	(H)
GOLD DUST	Alyssum saxatile	(R)

Common	Botanical	Type
GOLD FERN	Pityrogramma	(FN)
GOLD FLAME	Spirnea bumalda 'Gold Flame'	(S)
GOLD HEDGEHOG HOLLY	Ilex aquifolium 'Ferox Aurea'	(S)
GOLD LACE CACTUS	Mammillaria elongata	(CS)
GOLD THREAD	Coptis	(H)
GOLD THREAD	Coptis trifolia	(H)
GOLD TREE	Tabebuia	(TS)
GOLD-OF-PLEASURE	Camelina sativa	(H)
GOLDEN ACACIA	Robinia pseudo acacia 'Frisia'	(ST)
GOLDEN ALYSSUM	Alyssum saxatile	(R)
GOLDEN AMERICAN ELDER	Sambucus canadensis 'Aurea'	(S)
GOLDEN ANGEL'S TRUMPET	Brugmansia aurea	(TH)
GOLDEN APPLE	Spondias lutea	(T)
GOLDEN ASTER	Chrysopsis	(H)
GOLDEN ATLAS CEDAR	Cedrus atlantica 'Aurea'	(C)
GOLDEN BALL	Echinocactus grusonii	(CS)
GOLDEN BALL CACTUS	Notocactus leninghausii	(CS)
GOLDEN BALM	Melissa officinalis aurea	(HB)
GOLDEN BAMBOO	Phyllostachys aurea	(G)
GOLDEN BANDED LILY	Lilium auratum	(BB)
GOLDEN BARREL CACTUS	Echinocactus grunsonii	(C)
GOLDEN BAY	Laurus nobilis aureus	(HB)
GOLDEN BEECH	Fagus sylvatica 'Zlatia'	(T)
GOLDEN BELL	Forsythia	(S)
GOLDEN CALLA	Zantedeschia elliottiana	(H)
GOLDEN CASCADES	Coryanthera flava	(S)
GOLDEN CASCADES	Corynanthera flava	(S)
GOLDEN CHAIN	Laburnum	(T)
GOLDEN CHALICE	Solandra nitida	(TCL)
GOLDEN CHESTNUT	Chrysolepis chrysophylla	(T)
GOLDEN CLEMATIS	Clematis tangutica	(CL)
GOLDEN CLUB	Orontium	(H)
GOLDEN COLUMN	Trichocereus spachianus	(CS)
GOLDEN CURLS	Salix babylonica pikinensis "Tortuosa Aurea"	(T)
GOLDEN CURLS	Salix xerythroflexuosa	(ST)
GOLDEN CURRANT	Ribes odoratum	(S)
GOLDEN DEODAR CEDAR	Cedrus deodora 'Aurea'	(C)
GOLDEN DOCK	Rumex maritimus	(H)
GOLDEN DOGWOOD	Cornus alba 'Aurea'	(S)
GOLDEN EARDROPS	Dicentra chrysantha	(H)
GOLDEN ELDER	Sambucus nigra 'Aurea'	(S)
GOLDEN FAIRY LANTERN	Calochortus amabilis	(BB)
GOLDEN FEATHER	Tanacetum parthenium 'Aureum'	(H)
GOLDEN FEATHER-GRASS	Stipa pulcherrima	(G)
GOLDEN FEVER FEW	Tanacetum parthenium 'Aureum'	(H)
GOLDEN FLAG	Iris aurea	(H)
GOLDEN FLAX	Linum flavum	(H)

Common	Botanical	Type
GOLDEN FLEECE	Thymophylla tenuiloba	(H)
GOLDEN FOXTAIL	Alopecurus pratensis 'Aureo-variegatus'	(G)
GOLDEN GARLIC	Allium moly	(BB)
GOLDEN GROUNDSEL	Senecio aureus	(H)
GOLDEN HAZEL	Corylus avellana 'Aurea'	(S)
GOLDEN HEATHER	Cassinia fulvida	(S)
GOLDEN HOP	Humulus lupulus 'Aureus'	(CL)
GOLDEN HUNTERS ROBE	Epipremnum aureum	(HP)
GOLDEN IRISH YEW	Taxus baccata 'Aureovariegata'	(C)
GOLDEN LARCH	Pseudolarix amabills	(C)
GOLDEN LILY	Lycoris aurea	(BB)
GOLDEN LOCUST	Robinia pseud. 'Frisia'	(T)
GOLDEN MARGUERITE	Anthemis tinctoria	(H)
GOLDEN MARJORY	Origanum vulgare 'Aureum'	(HB)
GOLDEN MOSS	Sedum acre	(H)
GOLDEN OAK	Quercus robur 'Concordia'	(T)
GOLDEN OAK OF CYPRUS	Quercus alnifolia	(T)
GOLDEN OATS	Stipa gigantea	(G)
GOLDEN PFITZER JUNIPER	Juniperus x media 'Pfitzerana Aurea'	(C)
GOLDEN POPLAR	Populus 'Serotina Aurea'	(T)
GOLDEN PRIVET	Ligustrum ovalifolium 'Aureum'	(S)
GOLDEN PURSLANE	Portulaca oleracea sativa	(H)
GOLDEN RAIN	Koelreuteria	(T)
GOLDEN RAIN	Laburnum	(T)
GOLDEN ROD	Solidago virgaurea	(H)
GOLDEN SAMPHIRE	Inula crithmoides	(H)
GOLDEN SAXIFRAGE	Chrysosplenium oppositifolium	(R)
GOLDEN SEAL	Hydrastis canadensis	(H)
GOLDEN SEDUM	Sedum adolphi	(HP)
GOLDEN SHOWER	Pyrostegia venusta	(CL)
GOLDEN SHOWER TREE	Cassia fistula	(TT)
GOLDEN SPANIARD	Aciphylla aurea	(H)
GOLDEN SPIDER LILY	Lycoris africana	(BB)
GOLDEN SPIDER-LILY	Lycoris aurea	(BB)
GOLDEN SPRAY	Viminaria juncea	(H)
GOLDEN STAR	Chrysogonum virginianum	(R)
GOLDEN SYCAMORE	Acer pseudoilatanus 'Worlei'	(T)
GOLDEN THISTLE	Scolymus hispanicus	(H)
GOLDEN TOM THUMB	Parodia aureispina	(CS)
GOLDEN TOP	Lamarckia	(S)
GOLDEN TREE FERN	Dicksonia fibrosa	(FN)
GOLDEN TRUMPET	Allamanda cathartica	(HP)
GOLDEN TRUMPET-TREE	Tabebuia chrysantha	(TT)
GOLDEN TUFT	Alyssum saxatile	(R)
GOLDEN VARIEGATED DOGWOOD	Cornus alba 'Spaethii'	(S)
GOLDEN VINE	Stigmaphyllon	(G)
GOLDEN WATTLE	Acacia pycnantha; Longifolia	(ST)

Common	Botanical	Type
GOLDEN WEEPING ASH	Fraxinus excelsior 'Aurea Pendula'	(T)
GOLDEN WEEPING WILLOW	Salix x sepulcralis chrysocoma	(T)
GOLDEN WILLOW	Salix alba 'vitellina'	(ST)
GOLDEN WONDER	Cassia didymobotrya	(S)
GOLDEN YEW	Taxus baccata 'Aurea'	(C)
GOLDEN-BARKED ASH	Fraxinus excelsior 'Jaspidea'	(T)
GOLDEN-CHALICE VINE	Solandra maxima	(CL)
GOLDEN-CUP OAK	Quercus chrysolepis	(T)
GOLDEN-FEATHER PALM	Chrysalidocarpus	(P)
GOLDEN-FLOWERED DAPHNE	Daphne aurantiaca	(S)
GOLDEN-GROOVE BAMBOO	Phyllostachys aureosulcata	(G)
GOLDEN-LEAVED BERBERIS	Berberis thunbergii 'Aurea'	(S)
GOLDEN-LEAVED CATALPA	Catalpa bignonioides 'Aurea'	(T)
GOLDEN-LEAVED JAPANESE MAPLE	Acer shirasawanum 'Aureum'	(S)
GOLDEN-LEAVED LABURNUM	Laburnum anagyroides 'Aureum'	(T)
GOLDEN-RAYED LILY	Lilium auratum	(BB)
GOLDEN-SCALED MALE FERN	Dryopteris borreri	(FN)
GOLDFISH PLANT	Columnea gloriosa	(HP)
GOLDILOCKS	Helichrysum stoechas	(S)
GOLDILOCKS	Ranunculus auricumus	(H)
GOLDILOCKS ASTER	Aster linosyris	(H)
GOLDS	Calendula officinalis	(A)
GOMBO	Abelmoschus esculentus	(V)
GOMUTI	Arenga pinnata	(P)
GOOD KING HENRY	Chenopodium bonus-henricus	(A)
GOOD LUCK PLANT	Cordyline fruticosa	(TH)
GOOD LUCK PLANT	Cordyline terminalis	(S)
GOOD LUCK PLANT	Kalanchoe daigremontianum	(HP)
GOOD LUCK PLANT	Sansevieria	(HP)
GOOD-LUCK PLANT	Cordyline fruticosa	(TH)
GOOSEBERRY	Ribes uva-crispi	(F)
GOOSEBERRY GERANIUM	Pelargonium grossularioides	(A)
GOOSEFOOT	Chenopodium	(HA)
GOOSEFOOT PLANT	Syngonium podophyllum	(HP)
GOOSEGOG	Ribes uva-crispa	(F)
GOOSEGRASS	Galium aparine	(HA)
GOOSEWORT	Achillea ptarmica	(H)
GORGON'S HEAD	Euphorbia gorgonis	(CS)
GORSE	Ulex	(S)
GOURD	Cucurbita, Lagenaria, Cucumis	(V)
GOUTWEED	Aegopodium podagraria	(H)
GOWEN CYPRESS	Cupressus goveniana	(C)
GRANADILLA	Passiflora edulis	(F)
GRANADILLA	Passiflora quandrangularis	(F)
GRAND BELLFLOWER	Adenophora	(H)
GRAND FIR	Abies grandis	(C)
GRANITE BOTTLEBRUSH	Melaleuca elliptica	(S)

Common	Botanical	Type
GRANJENO	Celtis iguanaea	(TT)
GRANNY POP OUT OF BED	Calystegia sepium	(HCL)
GRANNY'S BONNET	Aquilegia	(H)
GRAPE	Vitis	(CL.F)
GRAPE FERN	Botrychium	(FN)
GRAPE HYACINTH	Muscari	(BB)
GRAPE IVY	Cissus rhombifolia	(HP)
GRAPEFRUIT	Citrus x paradisi	(F)
GRAPPLE PLANT	Harpagophytum procumbens	(H)
GRASS OF PARNASSUS	Parnassia palustris	(H)
GRASS PEA	Lathyrus sativus	(H)
GRASS PINK	Dianthus plumarius	(A)
GRASS TREE	Xanthorrhoea	(S)
GRASS TREES	Xanthorrhoea spp	(S)(T)
GRASS VETCHLING	Lathyrus nissolia	(H)
GRASS WIDOW	Sisyrinchium douglasii	(H)
GRASS-POLY	Lythrum hyssopifolia	(H)
GRASS-TREES	Xanthorrhoea	(S/T)
GRASS-WRACK PONDWEED	Potamogeton compressus	(WP)
GRASSY PONDWEED	Potamogeton obtusifolius	(WP)
GRAVEL WEED	Eupatorium purpureum	(H)
GRAVELROOT	Eupatorium purpureum	(HB)
GREASEWOOD	Sarcobatus vermiculatus	(H)
GREAT BINDWEED	Calystegia silvatica	(CL)
GREAT BROME	Bromus diandrus	(G)
GREAT BUR-PARSLEY	Caucalis latifolia	(H)
GREAT BURDOCK	Arctium lappa	(B)
GREAT BURNET	Sanguisorba officinalis	(HB)
GREAT CHICKWEED	Stallaria neglecta	(H)
GREAT DUCKWEED	Spirodela polyrhiza	(WP)
GREAT EARTHNUT	Bunium bulbocastanum	(H)
GREAT FEN SEDGE	Cladium mariscus	(G)
GREAT GOLDEN KNAPWEED	Centaurea macrocephala	(H)
GREAT HORSETAIL	Equisetum telmateia	(H)
GREAT KNAPWEED	Centaurea scabiosa	(H)
GREAT LAUREL	Rhododendron maximum	(S)
GREAT LEOPARD'S BANE	Doronicum pardalianches	(H)
GREAT LETTUCE	Lactuca virosa	(H)
GREAT LOBELIA	Lobelia siphililea	(H)
GREAT MARSH THISTLE	Carduus personata	(H)
GREAT MILLET	Sorghum halepense	(G)
GREAT PIGNUT	Bunium bulbocastanum	(H)
GREAT PLAINS COTTONWOOD	Populus sargentii	(T)
GREAT PLANTAIN	Plantago major	(H)
GREAT POND SEDGE	Carex kiparia	(G)
GREAT PURPLE FLAG	Iris pallida	(H)
GREAT SALLOW	Salix caprea	(ST)

Know Your Common Plant Names

Common	Botanical	Type
GREAT SPEARWORT	Ranunculus lingua	(H)
GREAT SUNDEW	Drosera anglica	(H)
GREAT WATER DOCK	Rumex hydrolapathan	(WP)
GREAT WATER PLANTAIN	Alisma plantago-aquatica	(WP)
GREAT WHITE CHERRY	Prunus 'tai-haku'	(T)
GREAT WILLOWHERB	Epilobium hirsutum	(H)
GREAT WOOD-RUSH	Luzula sylvatica	(G)
GREAT YELLOWCRESS	Rorippa amphibia	(H)
GREATER BITTER CRESS	Cardamine flexuosa	(H)
GREATER BROOMRAPE	Orobanche rapum-genistre	(PE/H)
GREATER BURNET SAXIFRAGE	Pimpinella major	(HB)
GREATER BUTTERFLY ORCHID	Platanthera chloranthe	(O)
GREATER BUTTERWORT	Pinguicula grandiflora	(R)
GREATER CELANDINE	Chelidonium majus	(H)
GREATER CHICKWEED	Stellaria neglecta	(H)
GREATER DODDER	Cuscuta europaea	(CL)
GREATER DUCKWEED	Spirodela polyrhiza	(WP)
GREATER EYEBRIGHT	Euphorbia arctica	(H)
GREATER HAWK'S BEARD	Crepis biennis	(H)
GREATER HAYRATTLE	Rhinanthus serotinus	(H)
GREATER KNAPWEED	Centaurea scabiosa	(H)
GREATER MALAYAN CHESTNUT	Castonopsis megacarpa	(TT)
GREATER NAIAD	Najas marina	(WP)
GREATER PERIWINKLE	Vinca major	(S)
GREATER POND SEDGE	Carex riparia	(G)
GREATER SAND SPURREY	Spergularia media	(H)
GREATER SPEARWORT	Ranunculus lingua	(H)
GREATER STITCHWORT	Stellaria holostea	(H)
GREATER TUSSOCK SEDGE	Carex paniculata	(G)
GREATER WATER-THYME	Elodea callitrichoides	(WP)
GREATER YAM	Dioscorea alata	(F)
GRECIAN FIR	Abies cephalonica	(C)
GRECIAN JUNIPER	Juniperus excelsa	(C)
GRECIAN STRAWBERRY TREE	Arbutus andrachne	(T)
GREEK FIR	Abies cephalonica	(C)
GREEK HAY-SEED	Trigonella foenum-graecum	(H)
GREEK JUNIPER	Juniperus excelsa	(C)
GREEK MALLOW	Sidalcea	(H)
GREEK VALERIAN	Polemonium coeruleum	(H)
GREEK WINDFLOWER	Anemone blanda	(BB)
GREEN ALDER	Alnus viridis	(T)
GREEN ALKANET	Pentaglottis sempervirens	(H)
GREEN AMARANTH	Amaranthus hybridus	(H)
GREEN ARROW ARUM	Peltandra undulata	(H)
GREEN ASH	Fraxinus pennsylvanica lanceolata	(T)
GREEN BIRDFLOWER	Crotalaria cunninghamii	(S)
GREEN BRIAR	Smilax	(CL)

Know Your Common Plant Names

Common	Botanical	Type
GREEN BRIER	Smilax rotundifolia	(CL)
GREEN CARPET	Herniaria ghabra	(H)
GREEN CLIFF BRAKE	Pellaea viridis	(FN)
GREEN CLIFFBRAKE	Pellaea viridis	(FN)
GREEN DRAGON	Arisaema dracontium	(H)
GREEN EBONY	Tabebuia flavescens	(TT)
GREEN FALSE HELLEBORE	Varatrum viride	(H)
GREEN FIGWORT	Scrophularia umbrosa	(H)
GREEN GINGER	Artemisia absinthium	(H)
GREEN GRAM	Phaseolus aureus	(V)
GREEN HAIR-WEED	Chaetomorpha linum	(SW)
GREEN HEART	Ocotea	(TT)
GREEN HELLEBORE	Helleborus viridis	(H)
GREEN HELLEBORE	Veratrum viride	(H)
GREEN HOUND'S TONGUE	Cynoglossum germanicum	(H)
GREEN IXIA	Ixia viridiflora	(BB)
GREEN LAVER	Ulva lactuca	(SW)
GREEN MAN ORCHID	Aceras anthropothora	(O)
GREEN MOUNTAIN SALLOW	Salix andersoniana	(S)
GREEN PEPPER	Capsicum annuum	(F)
GREEN PEPPER	Capsicum annuum	(F)
GREEN ROSE	Rosa chinensis 'Viridiflora'	(S)
GREEN SAUCE	Rumex acetosa	(HB)
GREEN SPLEENWORT	Asplenium viride	(FN)
GREEN WATTLE	Acacia decurrens	(T)
GREEN-FLOWERED HELLEBORINE	Epipactis phyllanthes	(O)
GREEN-FLOWERED PITAYA	Echinocerous viridiflorous	(CS)
GREEN-FLOWERED TORCH CACTUS	Echinocerous viridiflorous	(CS)
GREEN-RIBBED SAGE	Carex binervis	(G)
GREEN-WINGED ORCHID	Orchis morio	(O)
GREENBIRD FLOWER	Crotalaria cunninghamii	(S)
GREENGAGE	Prunus domestica italica	(F)
"GREENGLOW"	Prunus cerasifera	(S.T)
GREENHEART	Nectandra rodiaei	(TT)
GREENHEART	Ocotea radiaei	(TT)
GREENLEAF MANZANITA	Arctostaphylos patula	(S)
GREENWEED	Genista tinctoria	(S)
GREY ALDER	Alnus incana	(T)
GREY BRICH	Betula populifolia	(T)
GREY CARABEEN	Sloanea woolii	(MS)
GREY CINQUEFOIL	Potentilla cinerea	(H)
GREY DOGWOOD	Cornus racemosa	(S)
GREY FESCUE	Festuca glauca	(G)
GREY GOOSEFOOT	Chenopodium opulifolium	(H)
GREY GUM	Eucalyptus tereticornis	(T)
GREY HAIR-GRASS	Corynephorus canescens	(G)
GREY HEATH	Erica cinerea	(S)

Common	Botanical	Type
GREY IRON DARK	Eucalyptus paniculata	(T)
GREY PEPPERMINT	Eucalyptus radiata	(T)
GREY POPLAR	Populus canescens	(T)
GREY SAGE BRUSH	Atriplex canescens	(S)
GREY SAGE BUSH	Atriplex canescens	(S)
GREY SALLOW	Salix cinerea	(ST)
GREY SEDGE	Carex divulsa	(G)
GREY WILLOW	Salix cinerea	(ST)
GREY-BUDDED SNAKE-BARK MAPLE	Acer rufinerve	(T)
GREYBEARD	Tillandsia usneoides	(HP)
GREYHEAD CONEFLOWER	Ratibida pinnata	(S)
GREYLEAF CHERRY	Prunus canescens	(S)
GRIM THE COLLIER	Hieracium aurantiacum	(H)
GROMWELL	Lithospermum officinale	(H)
GROUND APPLE	Chamaemelum nobile	(H)
GROUND BOX	Polygala chamaebuxus	(S)
GROUND CHERRY	Prunus fruticosa	(S)
GROUND CISTUS	Rhodothamnus chamaecistus	(S)
GROUND ELDER	Aegopodium podagraria	(H)
GROUND FURZE	Ononis arvensis	(S)
GROUND IVY	Glechoma hederacea	(H)
GROUND JASMINE	Passerina stelleri	(S)
GROUND LAUREL	Epigaea repens	(S)
GROUND LILY	Trillium erectum	(H)
GROUND NUT	Apios tuberosa	(H)
GROUND OAK	Teucrium chamaedrys	(H)
GROUND PINE	Lycopodium	(H)
GROUND RASPBERRY	Hydrastis canadensis	(H)
GROUND RATTAN	Rhapis	(P)
GROUND RATTAN CANE	Rhapis excelsa	(P)
GROUND SENNA	Cassia chamaecrista	(S)
GROUND SQUIRREL TEA	Jeffersonia diphylla	(H)
GROUND THISTLE	Cirsium acaule	(H)
GROUND-PINE	Ajuga chamaepitys	(H)
GROUNDNUT	Arachis hypogaea	(F)
GROUNDSEL	Senecia vulgaris	(A)
GROUNDSEL TREE	Baccharis	(S)
GROVE FERN	Alsophila	(FN)
GUARANA	Paullinia cupana	(TF)
GUATEMALAN RHUBARB	Jatropha podagrica	(TS)
GUAVA	Psidium guajava	(F)
GUELDER ROSE	Viburnum opulus	(S)
GUERNSEY LILY	Nerine Sarniensis	(BB)
GUINDO	Nothofagus antarctica	(T)
GUINEA FLOWER	Hibbertia scandens	(H)
GUINEA GOLD VINE	Hibbertia scandens	(CL)
GUINEA PEACH	Sarcocephalus esculentus	(TS)

Know Your Common Plant Names

Common	Botanical	Type
GUINEA PEPPER	Xylopia aethiopica	(TS)
GUINEA PLUM	Parinari excelsa	(TT)
GUINEA RUSH	Cyperus articulatus	(G)
GUINEA-WING BEGONIA	Begonia albo-picta	(HP)
GULLY ASH	Eucalyptus smithii	(T)
GULMOHUR	Delonix regia	(TT)
GUM ACACIA	Acacia nilotica	(TT)
GUM ACACIA	Acacia senegal	(TT)
GUM AMMONIAC	Dorema ammoniacum	(S)
GUM ARABIC	Acacia arabica	(TT)
GUM ARABIC	Acacia nilotica	(T.T)
GUM ARABIC	Acacia senegal	(T.T)
GUM ARABIC	Acacia seyal	(T.T)
GUM CISTUS	Cistus ladanifer	(S)
GUM MYRTLE	Angophora	(S)
GUM PLANT	Grindelia robusta	(S)
GUM TRAGACANTH	Astragalus gummifer	(TT)
GUM TREE	Eucalyptus	(T)
GUM-TOP STRINGY BARK	Eucalyptus delegatensis	(T)
GUMBO	Abelmoschus esculentus	(V)
GUMBO-LIMBO	Bursera simaroba	(S/T)
GUMPLANT	Grindelia	(S)
GUNGURRU	Eucalyptus caesia	(T)
GUTA KOLA	Hydrocotyle asiatica	(TS)
GUTTA PERCHA	Palaquium gutta	(TT)
GUTTA-PERCHA TREE	Eucommia ulmoides	(T)
HACKBERRY	Celtis occidentalis	(T)
HAG BRIER	Smilax hispida	(S)
HAG'S TAPER	Verbascum thapsus	(H)
HAI-TUNG CRAB	Malus spectabilis	(T)
HAIR GRASS	Aira; Deschampsia	(G)
HAIR SEDGE	Carex capillaris	(G)
HAIR-LIKE PONDWEED	Potamogeton trichoides	(WP)
HAIRY ALPEN ROSE	Rhododendron hirsutum	(S)
HAIRY BITTER CRESS	Cardaria hirsuta	(H)
HAIRY BITTER CRESS	Cardomine hirsuta	(R)
HAIRY BROME	Bromus ramosus	(G)
HAIRY CHERVIL	Chaerophyllum hirsutum	(H)
HAIRY GREENWOOD	Genista pilosa	(S)
HAIRY HUCKLEBERRY	Vaccinium hirsutum	(S)
HAIRY LIP FERN	Cheilanthes lamosa	(FN)
HAIRY ROCK-CRESS	Arabis hirsuta	(R)
HAIRY ROCKET	Erucastrum gallicum	(H)
HAIRY SEABLITE	Bassia hirsuta	(H)
HAIRY SEDGE	Carex hirta	(G)
HAIRY SPURGE	Euphorbia villosa	(H)
HAIRY ST. JOHN'S WORT	Hypericum hirsutum	(H)

Common	Botanical	Type
HAIRY STONECROP	Sedum villosum	(H)
HAIRY TARE	Vicia hirsuta	(H)
HAIRY THYME	Thymus praecox	(H)
HAIRY VETCHLING	Lathyrus hirsutus	(H)
HAIRY VIOLET	Viola hirta	(H)
HAIRY WATTLE	Acacia pubescens	(T)
HAIRY WILLOW HERB	Epilobium parviflorum	(H)
HAIRY WOOD-RUSH	Luzula pilosa	(G)
HALBERD-LEAVED WILLOW	Salix hastata	(S)
HALL'S APPLE	Malus xhalliana	(T)
HAMBURG PARSLEY	Carum petroselinum tuberosum	(HB)
HAMMOCK FERN	Blechnum occidentale	(FN)
HAMPSHIRE PURSLANE	Ludwigia palustris	(H)
HAND PLANT	Cheirostemon platanoides	(S)
HANDFLOWER TREE	Chiranthodendron pentadactylon	(TT)
HANDKERCHIEF TREE	Davidia involucrata	(T)
HANGING BASKET LOBELIA	Lobelia erinus pendula	(A)
HARD BEECH	Nothofagus truncata	(T)
HARD FERN	Blechnum spicant	(FN)
HARD FESCUE	Festuca longifolia	(G)
HARD GRASS	Parapholis strigosa	(G)
HARD RUSH	Juncus inflexus	(G)
HARD RUSH	Juncus inflexus	(G)
HARD SHIELD FERN	Polystichum aculeatum	(FN)
HARD WHEAT	Triticum durum	(G)
HARDHACK	Spiraea douglasii	(S)
HARDHACK	Spiraea tomentosa	(S)
HARDHEADS	Centaurea nigra	(H)
HARDY AGE	Eupatorium rugosum	(H)
HARDY GLOXINIA	Incarvillea	(H)
HARDY ORANGE	Poncirus trifoliata	(S)
HARDY PLUMBAGO	Ceratostigma	(H)
HARE'S EAR	Bupleurum rotundifolium	(H)
HARE'S FOOT CLOVER	Trifolium arvense	(H)
HARE'S FOOT FERN	Davallia fejeensis	(FN)
HARE'S FOOT FERN	Polypodium aureum	(FN)
HARE'S TAIL	Lagurus ovatus	(G)
HARE'S-EAR CABBAGE	Conringia orientalis	(H)
HARE'S-TAIL GRASS	Lagurus ovatus	(G)
HAREBELL	Campanula rotundifolia	(H)
HAREBELL BELLFLOWER	Campanula rotundifolia	(H)
HAREBELL POPPY	Meconopsis quintuplinervia	(H)
HARES TAIL GRASS	Lagurus ovatus	(G)
HARESFOOT SEDGE	Carex lachenalii	(G)
HARESTAIL COTTON-GRASS	Eriophorum vaginatum	(G)
HARESTAIL GRASS	Lagurus ovatus	(G)
HARICOT BEAN	Phaseolus vulgaris	(V)

Know Your Common Plant Names

Common	Botanical	Type
HARLEQUIN FLOWER	Sparaxis tricolor	(BB)
HARRY LAUDER'S WALKING STICK	Corylus avellana 'Contorta'	(S)
HART'S TONGUE FERN	Phyllitis scolopendrium	(FN)
HARTWORT	Tordylium maximum	(H)
HASHISH	Cannabis sativa	(H)
HASTATE ORACHE	Atriplex hastata	(H)
HAUSA POTATO	Coleus rotundifolius	(TS)
HAUTBOIS STRAWBERRY	Fragaria moschata	(F)
HAWK'S BEARD	Crepis	(H)
HAWKBIT	Leontodon	(H)
HAWKWEED	Hieracium	(H)
HAWKWEED OX-TONGUE	Picris hieracioides	(H)
HAWKWEED SAXIFRAGE	Saxifraga hieracifolia	(R)
HAWTHORN	Crataegus monogyna	(S.T)
HAWTHORN-LEAVED CRAB APPLE	Malus florentina	(T)
HAWTHORN-LEAVED MAPLE	Acer crataegifolium	(T)
HAY-RATTLE	Rhinanthus minor	(H)
HAY-SCENTED BUCKLER FERN	Dryopteris aemula	(FN)
HAYRATTLE	Rhinanthus minor	(A)
HAZEL NUT	Corylus	(S.T)
HAZELWORT	Asarum europaeum	(H)
HEADACHE TREE	Umbelluria californica	(S.T)
HEAL-ALL	Prunella vulgaris	(H)
HEART FLOWER	Anthurium	(HP)
HEART OF FLAME	Bromelia balansae	(HP)
HEART OF JESUS	Caladium	(HP)
HEART PEA	Cardiospermum halicacabum	(CL)
HEART SEED	Cardiospermum halicacabum	(CL)
HEART-LEAVED SILVER GUM	Eucalyptus cordata	(T)
HEART-LEAVED VALERIAN	Valeriana pyrenaica	(H)
HEART-LEAVED WILLOW	Salix cordata	(S)
HEARTLEAF MANZANITA	Arctostaphylos andersonii	(S)
HEARTLEAF PHILODENDRON	Philodendron scandens	(HP)
HEARTNUT	Juglans ailantifolia	(T)
HEARTSEASE	Viola tricolor	(H)
HEATH	Erica, Calluna	(S)
HEATH BEDSTRAW	Galium saxatile	(H)
HEATH CUDWEED	Omalotheca sylvatica	(H)
HEATH GRASS	Danthonia decumbens	(G)
HEATH LOBELIA	Lobelia urens	(H)
HEATH MILKWORT	Polygala serpyllifolia	(H)
HEATH PEARLWORT	Sagina subulata	(R)
HEATH RUSH	Juncus squarrosus	(G)
HEATH SEDGE	Carex ericetorum	(G)
HEATH SPEEDWELL	Veronica officinalis	(H)
HEATH SPOTTED ORCHID	Dactylorhiza maculata	(O)
HEATH WOOD-RUSH	Luzula multiflora	(G)

Common	Botanical	Type
HEATHER	Calluna, Erica	(S)
HEAVENLY BAMBOO	Nandina	(S)
HEDGE BAMBOO	Bambusa multiplex	(G)
HEDGE BEDSTRAW	Galium album	(H)
HEDGE BINDWEED	Calystegia sepium	(CL)
HEDGE HYSSOP	Gratiola officinalis	(HB)
HEDGE MAPLE	Acer campestre	(S.T)
HEDGE MUSTARD	Sisymbrium officinale	(H)
HEDGE PARSLEY	Torilis japonica	(H)
HEDGE STONEWORT	Sison amomum	(H)
HEDGE WATTLE	Acacia armata	(T)
HEDGE WOUNDWORT	Stachys sylvatica	(H)
HEDGE-NETTLE	Stachys	(H)
HEDGEBURS	Galium aparine	(H)
HEDGEHOG	Hericium erinaceum	(FU)
HEDGEHOG BROOM	Erinacea	(S)
HEDGEHOG CACTUS	Echinocactus ferocactus	(S)
HEDGEHOG CACTUS	Echinocactus pectinatus	(S)
HEDGEHOG CACTUS	Echinocereus	(CS)
HEDGEHOG GARLIC	Alliaria sativa	(H)
HEDGEHOG GOURD	Cucumis dipsaceus	(F)
HEDGEHOG GRASS	Echinochloa	(G)
HEDGEHOG HOLLY	Ilex aquifolium 'Ferox'	(S.T)
HEDGEHOG ROSE	Rosa rugosa	(R)
HEDGEHOG-CORY CACTUS	Coryphanthus echinus	(CS)
HEDGEROW CRANE'S BILL	Geranium pyrenaicum	(H)
HELIOTROPE	Heliotropium	(A)
HELLEBORE	Helleborus	(H)
HELLEBORINE	Cephalanthera/Epipactis	(O)
HELMET FLOWER	Coryanthes	(H)
HELMET FLOWER	Scutellaria	(H)
HELMET FLOWER	Sinningia cardinalis	(HP)
HELONIAS	Chamaelirion luteum	(H)
HEMLOCK	Conium maculatum	(H)
HEMLOCK	Tsuga	(C)
HEMLOCK WATER DROPWORT	Oenanthe crocata	(H)
HEMP	Cannabis sativa	(A)
HEMP AGRIMONY	Eupatorium cannabinum	(H)
HEMP BROOMRAPE	Orobanche ramosa	(PE/H)
HEMP NETTLE	Galeopsis	(H)
HEN AND CHICKEN FERN	Asplenium bulbiferum	(FN)
HEN AND CHICKENS HOUSELEEK	Jovibarba sobolifera	(R)
HEN AND CHICKENS MARIGOLD	Calendula officinalis prolifera	(H)
HEN PEN	Bryopsis plumosa	(SW)
HENBANE	Hyoscyamus niger	(H)
HENBIT	Lamium amplexicaule	(H)
HENBIT DEADNETTLE	Lamium amplexicaule	(H)

Know Your Common Plant Names

Common	Botanical	Type
HENEQUEN	Agave fourcroydes	(CS)
HENNA	Lawsonia inermis	(S)
HENS AND CHICKEN	Coruphanthus vivpara bisbeerna	(CS)
HEPTAPLEURUM	Schefflera arboricola	(HP)
HERALD OF HEAVEN	Eritrichium nanum	(R)
HERALD'S TRUMPET	Beaumontia	(S)
HERALDIC THISTLE	Onopordon arabicum	(H)
HERB BENNET	Geum urbanum	(H)
HERB CHRISTOPHER	Actaea spicata	(H)
HERB OF GRACE	Ruta graveolens	(HB)
HERB OF THE CROSS	Verbenna officinalis	(H)
HERB PARIS	Paris quadrifolia	(H)
HERB PATIENCE	Rumex patientia	(H)
HERB PETER	Primula veris	(H)
HERB ROBERT	Geranium robertianum	(H)
HERB TRINITY	Viola tricolor	(H)
HERB-MERCURY	Mercurialis	(H)
HERCULES' CLUB	Aralia spinosa	(S)
HERON'S BILL	Erodium	(H)
HEROPITO	Pseudowintera axillaris	(S)
HERRING-BONE COTONEASTER	Cotoneaster horizontalis	(S)
HERRINGBONE PLANT	Maranta tricolor	(HP)
HIBA	Thujopsis dolobrata	(C)
HICK'S YEW	Taxus media 'Hicksii'	(C)
HICKORY	Carya	(T)
HICKORY PINE	Pinus pungens	(C)
HIGAN CHERRY	Prunus subhirtella 'Autumnalis'	(T)
HIGH-BUSH BLUEBERRY	Vaccinium corymbosum	(F)
HIGHCLERE HOLLY	Ilex x altaclarensis	(S)
HIGHLAND CUDWEED	Omalotheca norvegica	(H)
HIGHLAND PINE	Pinus sylvestris rubra	(C)
HILL CHERRY	Prunus serrulata spontanea	(T)
HIMALAYA BERRY	Rubus procerus	(S)
HIMALAYAN ALDER	Alnus nitida	(T)
HIMALAYAN BALSAM	Impatiens glandulifera	(A)
HIMALAYAN BAMBOO	Arundinaria anceps	(G)
HIMALAYAN BIRCH	Betula utilis	(T)
HIMALAYAN BIRD CHERRY	Prunus cornuta	(S)
HIMALAYAN BLUE POPPY	Meconopsis betonifolia	(H)
HIMALAYAN CEDAR	Cedrus deodora	(C)
HIMALAYAN CHERRY	Prunus rufa	(T)
HIMALAYAN COMFREY	Onosma pyramidale	(H)
HIMALAYAN COTONEASTER	Cotoneaster simonsii	(S)
HIMALAYAN COWSLIP	Primula florindae	(H)
HIMALAYAN CYPRESS	Cupressus torulosa	(C)
HIMALAYAN FIR	Abies spectabilis	(C)
HIMALAYAN HEMLOCK	Tsuga dumosa	(C)

Know Your Common Plant Names

Common	Botanical	Type
HIMALAYAN HOLLY	Ilex dipyrena	(S)
HIMALAYAN HONEYSUCKLE	Leycesteria formosa	(S)
HIMALAYAN IVY	Hedera nepalensis	(CL)
HIMALAYAN JASMINE	Jasminum humile	(S)
HIMALAYAN KNOTGRASS	Persicaria polystachyum	(H)
HIMALAYAN LARCH	Larix griffithiana	(C)
HIMALAYAN LAUREL	Aucuba	(S)
HIMALAYAN LILAC	Syringa emodi	(S)
HIMALAYAN MUSK ROSE	Rosa brunonii	(S)
HIMALAYAN PARSLEY	Selinum tenuifolium	(HB)
HIMALAYAN PINE	Pinus wallichianum	(C)
HIMALAYAN SPRUCE	Picea smithiana	(C)
HIMALAYAN WHITEBEAM	Sorbus cuspidata	(T)
HINOKI CYPRESS	Chamaecyparis obtusa	(C)
HOARHOUND	Marrubium	(H)
HOARY ALISON	Berteroa incana	(R)
HOARY CINQUEFOIL	Potentilla argentea	(H)
HOARY CRESS	Cardaria draba	(H)
HOARY MANZANITA	Arctostaphylos canescens	(S)
HOARY MUGWORT	Artemisia stellerana	(H)
HOARY MULLEIN	Verbascum pulverulentum	(H)
HOARY MUSTARD	Hlrschfeldia incana	(H)
HOARY PLANTAIN	Plantago media	(H)
HOARY RAGWORT	Senecio erucifolius	(H)
HOARY STOCK	Mathiola incana	(H)
HOARY WHITLOW GRASS	Draba incana	(H)
HOARY WILLOW	Salix eleagnos	(S)
HOARY WILLOWHERB	Epilobium parviflorum	(H)
HOARYLEAF CEANOTHUS	Ceanothus crassifolius	(S)
HOBBLE BUSH	Viburnum lantanoides	(S)
HOG NUT	Carya glabra	(T)
HOG PLUM	Spondias mombin	(H)
HOG PLUM	Ximenia americana	(TT)
HOG'S FENNEL	Peucedanum officinale	(H)
HOGBEAN	Hyoscyamus niger	(B)
HOGWEED	Heracleum sphondylium	(H)
HOLFORD'S PINE	Pinus x holfordiana	(C)
HOLLY	Ilex	(ST)
HOLLY FERN	Phanerophlebia falcatum	(FN)
HOLLY FERN	Polystichum lonchitis	(FN)
HOLLY FLAME PEA	Chorizema illicifolium	(S)
HOLLY OAK	Quercus ilex	(T)
HOLLY-LEAF SWEETSPIRE	Itea illicifolia	(S)
HOLLY-LEAVED BARBERRY	Mahonia aquifolium	(S)
HOLLY-LEAVED CHERRY	Prunus illicifolia	(T)
HOLLYHOCK	Alcea rosea	(H)
HOLLYHOCK BEGONIA	Begonia gracilis	(HP)

Know Your Common Plant Names

Common	Botanical	Type
HOLLYWOOD JUNIPER	Juniperus chinensis 'Kaizuka'	(C)
HOLM OAK	Quercus ilex	(T)
HOLY FLAX	Santolina rosmarinifolia	(S)
HOLY GHOST	Angelica archangelica	(HB)
HOLY GHOST FLOWER	Peristeria elata	(H)
HOLY GRASS	Hierochloe odorata	(G)
HOLY HEAD	Eriodictyon glutinosum	(H)
HOLY ROPE	Eupatorium cannabinum	(H)
HOLY THISTLE	Cnicus benedictus	(H)
HOLY THISTLE	Silybum marianum	(H)
HONDAPARA	Dillenia indica	(S)
HONDO SPRUCE	Picea jezoensis hondoensis	(C)
HONESTY	Lunaria annua	(B)
HONEY BUSH	Melianthus major	(S)
HONEY FUNGUS	Armillariella mellea	(FU)
HONEY LOCUST	Gleditsia triacanthos	(T)
HONEY PLANT	Hoya carnosa	(HP)
HONEY-BELL	Mahernia verticilliata	(S)
HONEY-BERRY	Melicocca bijuga	(S)
HONEYSUCKLE	Lonicera	(S.CL)
HONEYWORT	Cerinthe major	(H)
HONEYWORT	Trinia glauca	(H)
HOODED LILY	Johnsonia lupulina	(HP)
HOOP PINE	Araucaria cunninghamii	(C)
HOOP-PETTICOAT	Narcissus bulbocodium	(BB)
HOP	Humulus lupulus	(CL)
HOP HORNBEAM	Ostrya carpinfolia	(T)
HOP TREE	Ptelea trifoliata	(ST)
HOP TREFOIL	Trifolium campestre	(H)
HOREHOUND	Ballota nigra	(H)
HOREHOUND	Marrubium	(H)
HORN OF PLENTY	Craterellus cornucopioides	(FU)
HORN OF PLENTY	Fedia cornucopiae	(H)
HORNBEAM MAPLE	Acer carpinifolia	(T)
HORNBEAN	Carpinus	(ST)
HORNED HOLLY	Ilex cornuta	(S/T)
HORNED MAPLE	Acer diabolicum	(T)
HORNED PANSY	Viola cornuta	(H)
HORNED PONDWEED	Zannichellia palustris	(WP)
HORNED POPPY	Glaucium flavum	(H)
HORNED RAMPION	Phyteuma scheuchzeri	(H)
HORNED TULIP	Tulipa acuminata	(BB)
HORNWORT	Ceratophyllum demersum	(WP)
HORNY CUCUMBER	Cucumis metuliferus	(H)
HORSE BEAN	Vicia faba	(V)
HORSE BRIAR	Smilax rotundifolia	(CL)
HORSE BRIER	Smilax rotundifolia	(S)

Know Your Common Plant Names

Common	Botanical	Type
HORSE CHESTNUT	Aesculus hippocastanum	(ST)
HORSE DAISY	Leucanthemum vulgare	(H)
HORSE GENTIAN	Triosteum	(H)
HORSE MINT	Mentha longifolia	(HB)
HORSE MINT	Monarda punctata	(H)
HORSE MUSHROOM	Agaricus arvensis	(FU)
HORSE RADISH	Armoracia rusticana	(HB)
HORSE RADISH TREE	Moringa	(TT)
HORSE SUGAR	Symplocos tinctoria	(T)
HORSE TAIL	Equisetum	(H)
HORSE WEED	Conyza canadensis	(H)
HORSE'S TAIL	Sedum morganianum	(HP)
HORSE-BALM	Collinsonia	(H)
HORSE-FLY WEED	Baptisia tinctoria	(H)
HORSE-WEED	Collinsonia	(H)
HORSEBANE	Oenanthe crocata	(H)
HORSEBRUSH	Tetradymia	(H)
HORSEHAIR FUNGUS	Marasmius androsaccus	(FU)
HORSENETTLE	Solanum carolinense	(H)
HORSERADISH TREE	Moringa oleifera	(TT)
HORSESHOE VETCH	Hippocrepis comosa	(H)
HORSETAIL TREE	Casuarina equisetifolia	(T)
HORSEWEED	Collinsonia canadensis	(H)
HOT WATER PLANT	Achimenes	(HP)
HOTDOG PLANT	Kleinia articulata	(HP)
HOTTENTOT BREAD	Dioscorea elephantipes	(F)
HOTTENTOT BREAD	Testudinaria elephantipes	(F)
HOTTENTOT CHERRY	Maurovenia capensis	(A)
HOTTENTOT FIG	Carpobrotus edulis	(H)
HOTTENTOT'S HEAD	Stangeria criopus	(H)
HOUND'S TONGUE	Cynoglossum officinale	(H)
HOUSE HOLLY FERN	Phanerophlebia falcata	(FN)
HOUSE LEEK	Sempervivum	(R)
HOUSE LIME	Sparmannia	(HP)
HUALLE	Nothofagus obliqua	(T)
HUALO	Nothofagus glauca	(T)
HUCKLEBERRY	Gaylussacia	(F)
HUCKLEBERRY	Vaccineum myrtillus	(F)
HUCKLEBERRY OAK	Quercus vacciniifolia	(T)
HUEVIL	Vestia foetida	(H)
HULVER BUSH	Ilex aquifolium	(S/T)
HUMBLEPLANT	Mimosa pudica	(HP)
HUMMING BIRD'S TRUMPET	Zauschneria californica	(R)
HUMPED FIG	Ficus tinctoria	(HP)
HUNANGEMOHO GRASS	Chionochloa conspicua	(G)
HUNGARIAN BROME	Bromus inermis	(G)
HUNGARIAN DAISY	Leucanthemella serotina	(H)

Common	Botanical	Type
HUNGARIAN LILAC	Syringa josikaea	(S)
HUNGARIAN OAK	Quercus frainetto	(T)
HUNGARIAN THORN	Crataegus nigra	(T)
HUNTINGDON ELM	Ulmus xvegeta	(T)
HUNTSMAN'S CUP	Sarracenia purpurea	(H)
HUNTSMAN'S HORN	Sarracenia	(HP)
HUON PINE	Lagarostrobus franklinii	(C)
HUPEH CHERRY	Prunus serrulata huphensis	(T)
HUPEH CRAB	Malus huphensis	(T)
HYACINTH	Hyacinthus orientalis	(BB)
HYACINTH BEAN	Lablab purpureus	(H)
HYBRID BLACK POPLAR	Populus x canadensis	(T)
HYBRID CATALPA	Catalpa x erubescens	(T)
HYBRID COCKSPUR THORN	Crataegus x lavallei	(T)
HYBRID STRAWBERRY TREE	Arbutus x andrachnoides	(T)
HYBRID WINGNUT	Pterocarya x rehderana	(T)
HYSSOP	Hyssopus officinalis	(HB)
IBERIAN CRANE'S BILL	Geranium ibericum	(H)
ICE PLANT	Mesembryanthemum crystallinum	(A)
ICE PLANT	Sedum spectabile	(H)
ICELAND MOSS	Cetraria islandica	(MS)
ICHANG LEMON	Citrus ichangense	(S)
IDIGBO	Terminalia ivorensis	(TS)
IGIRI TREE	Idesia polycarpa	(T)
IGNATIUS BEAN	Strychnos ignatii	(TS)
ILLAWARRA FLAME TREE	Brachychiton acerifolius	(T)
ILLAWARRA PALM	Archontiphoenix cunninghamiana	(P)
ILLYARRI	Eucalyptus erythro	(T)
IMMORTELLE	Xeranthemum	(H)
IMMORTELLES	Helichrysum; Xeranthemum; Erythina	(A)
INCENSE CEDAR	Calocedrus decurrens	(C)
INCENSE JUNIPER	Juniperus thurifera	(C)
INCENSE PLANT	Calomeria amaranthoides	(H)
INCENSE PLANT	Humea elegans	(A)
INCENSE ROSE	Rosa primula	(S)
INCH PLANT	Callisia	(H)
INDIA HAWTHORN	Raphiolepis	(S)
INDIA LOTUS	Nymphaea	(WP)
INDIA-RUBBER PLANT	Ficus elastica	(HP)
INDIAN ALMOND	Terminalia catappa	(T)
INDIAN AZALEA	Rhododendron simsii	(HP)
INDIAN BALSAM	Impatiens glandulifera	(A)
INDIAN BEAN TREE	Catalpa bignonioides	(T)
INDIAN CEDAR	Cedrus deodora	(C)
INDIAN CHERRY	Rhamnus caroliana	(S)
INDIAN CHOCOLATE	Geum urbanum	(H)
INDIAN CORN	Zea mays	(V)

Know Your Common Plant Names

Common	Botanical	Type
INDIAN COTTON	Gossypium indicum	(H)
INDIAN CRESS	Tropacolum	(H)
INDIAN CRESS	Tropaeolum majus	(H)
INDIAN CROCUS	Pleione	(O)
INDIAN CUP-PLANT	Silphium perfoliatum	(H)
INDIAN CURRANT	Symphoricarpos orbiculatus	(S)
INDIAN ELEPHANT FLOWER	Crinum x powellii	(BB)
INDIAN ELM	Ulmus rubra	(T)
INDIAN FIG	Opuntia	(CS)
INDIAN FIG CACTUS	Opuntia ficus-indica	(CS)
INDIAN GINGER	Alpinia calcarata	(H)
INDIAN GOOSEBERRY	Phyllanthus acidus	(TS)
INDIAN GRASS	Arundo	(G)
INDIAN GRASS	Sorghatrum avenaceum	(G)
INDIAN GUM	Acacia arabica	(TT)
INDIAN HAWTHORN	Raphiolepis umbellata	(S)
INDIAN HEMP	Cannabis sativa	(A)
INDIAN HIPPO	Gillenia trifoliata	(H)
INDIAN HORSE CHESTNUT	Aesculus indica	(T)
INDIAN JALAP	Ipomoea turpethum	(TS)
INDIAN LABURNUM	Cassia fistula	(TT)
INDIAN LAUREL	Persea indica	(TS)
INDIAN LAUREL	Terminalia alata	(TS)
INDIAN LILAC	Melia azedarach	(T)
INDIAN LIQUORICE	Abrus precatorius	(TS)
INDIAN MULBERRY	Morinda	(S)
INDIAN MUSTARD	Brassica juncea	(V)
INDIAN NIGHT JASMINE	Nyctanthes arbortristis	(CL)
INDIAN OLIVE	Olea ferruninea	(T)
INDIAN PAINT	Hydrastis canadensis	(H)
INDIAN PAINT	Sanguinaria canadensis	(H)
INDIAN PAINT-BRUSH	Castilleja	(S)
INDIAN PENNYWORT	Hydrocotyle asiatica	(H)
INDIAN PHYSIC	Gillenia	(H)
INDIAN PINK	Dianthus chinensis	(A)
INDIAN PINK	Spigelia marilandica	(BB)
INDIAN PIPE	Monotropa uniflora	(H)
INDIAN PLUM	Oemleria cerasiformis	(S)
INDIAN POKE	Veratrum viride	(H)
INDIAN POSY	Gnaphalium polycephalum	(H)
INDIAN SARSAPARILLA	Hemidesmus indica	(TS)
INDIAN SENNA	Cassia angustifolia	(TS)
INDIAN SHAMROCK	Trillium erectum	(H)
INDIAN SHELL FLOWER	Alpina	(H)
INDIAN SHOT	Canna indica	(BB)
INDIAN SILK-COTTON TREE	Bombax malaboricum	(TT)
INDIAN SNUFF	Olmadioperebea sclerophylla	(H)

Common	Botanical	Type
INDIAN SPRUCE	Picea smithiana	(C)
INDIAN STRAWBERRY	Duchesnea indica	(F)
INDIAN TOBACCO	Lobelia inflata	(H)
INDIAN TURMERIC	Hydrastis canadensis	(TS)
INDIAN TURNIP	Arisaema triphyllum	(H)
INDIAN VALERIAN	Valeriana walichii	(H)
INDIGO	Indigofera tinctoria	(S)
INDIGO-WEED	Baptisia tinctoria	(H)
INDOOR LINDEN	Sparmannia	(HP)
INDOOR OAK	Nicodemia diversifolia	(HP)
INK CAP	Coprinus comatus	(FU)
INKBERRY	Ilex glabra	(S)
INNOCENCE	Collinsia bicolor	(A)
INNOCENCE	Hedyotis caerulea	(H)
INSIDE-OUT FLOWER	Vancouveria	(H)
INTOXICATING MINT	Lagochilus inebrians	(H)
IPECACUANHA	Cephaelis ipecacuanha	(TT)
IPECACUANHA	Uragoga ipecacuanha	(TS)
IRISH GORSE	Ulex europaeus 'Strictus'	(S)
IRISH HEATH	Daboecia cantabrica	(S)
IRISH HEATH	Erica erigena	(S)
IRISH IVY	Hedera helix 'Hibernica'	(CL)
IRISH JUNIPER	Juniperus communis 'Hibernica'	(C)
IRISH MOSS	Chondrus crispus	(MS)
IRISH SAXIFRAGE	Saxifraga rosacea	(R)
IRISH SPURGE	Euphorbia hyberna	(H)
IRISH YEW	Taxus baccata 'Fastigiata'	(C)
IROKO	Chlorophora excelsa	(TT)
IRON CROSS BEGONIA	Begonia masoniana	(HP)
IRON SHRUB	Sauvagesia erecta	(S)
IRON TREE	Metrosideros	(T)
IRON WEED	Verononia	(H)
IRON-WOOD	Argania	(TS)
IRONBARK	Eucalyptus	(T)
IRONHEAD	Centaurea scabiosa	(H)
IRONTREE	Parrotia persica	(T)
IRONWOOD	Mesurea ferrea	(TT)
IRONWOOD	Ostryavirginiana	(T)
IRONWOOD	Parrotia persica	(T)
IRONWORT	Sideritis	(S)
ISLAND POPPY	Papaver nudicaule	(A)
ISPAGHUL PLAINTAIN	Plantago ovata	(H)
ITALIAN ALDER	Alnus cordata	(T)
ITALIAN ARUM	Arum italicum	(H)
ITALIAN BELLFLOWER	Campanula isophylla	(HP)
ITALIAN CATCHFLY	Silene italica	(H)
ITALIAN CYPRESS	Cupressus sempervirens	(C)

Know Your Common Plant Names

Common	Botanical	Type
ITALIAN HONEYSUCKLE	Lonicera caprifolium	(CL)
ITALIAN IVY	Hedera helix poetica	(CL)
ITALIAN JASMINE	Jasminum humile	(S)
ITALIAN MAPLE	Acer opalus	(T)
ITALIAN MILLET	Setaria italica	(G)
ITALIAN POPLAR	Populus nigra 'Italica'	(T)
ITALIAN RYEGRASS	Lolium multiflorum	(G)
ITALIAN STARWORT	Aster amellus	(H)
ITALIAN STONE PINE	Pinus pinea	(C)
IVORY-NUT PALM	Phytelephas macrocarpa	(P)
IVY	Hedera	(CL)
IVY ARUM	Scindapsusn	(HP)
IVY BROOMRAPE	Orobanche hederae	(PE/H)
IVY DUCKWEED	Lemna trisulca	(WP)
IVY GOURD	Coccinia cordifolia	(H)
IVY LEAF PEPEROMIA	Peperomia griseoargentea	(HP)
IVY LEAVED GERANIUM	Pelargonium peltatum	(A)
IVY PEPEROMIA	Peperomia griseoargentea	(HP)
IVY TREE	x Fatschedera lizei	(S)
IVY-LEAVED BELLFLOWER	Wahlenbergia hederacea	(H)
IVY-LEAVED CROWFOOT	Ranunculus hederaceus	(H)
IVY-LEAVED DUCKWEED	Lemna trisulca	(WP)
IVY-LEAVED GERANIUM	Pelargonium peltatum	(A)
IVY-LEAVED HAREBELL	Wahlenbergia hederacea	(H)
IVY-LEAVED SPEEDWELL	Veronica hederifolia	(H)
IVY-LEAVED TOADFLAX	Cymbalaria muralis	(H)
JABORAND	Pilocarpus jaborandi	(T)
JABORANDI	Pilocarpus jaborandi	(TS)
JACAREUBA	Calophyllum brasiliense	(TT)
JACK BEAN	Canaralia ensiformis	(TS)
JACK FRUIT	Artocarpus scortechinii	(F)
JACK JUMP UP AND KISS ME	Viola tricolor	(H)
JACK PINE	Pinus banksiana	(C)
JACK-BY-THE-HEDGE	Alliaria petiolata	(H)
JACK-GO-TO-BED-AT-NOON	Tragopogon pratensis	(H)
JACK-IN-THE-PULPIT	Arisaema triphyllum	(H)
JACOB'S COAT	Acalypha wilkesiana	(HP)
JACOB'S LADDER	Polemonium coeruleum	(H)
JACOB'S ROD	Asphodeline	(H)
JACOB'S STAFF	Fouquiera splendens	(H)
JACOB'S STAFF	Verbascum thapsus	(H)
JACOBEA	Senecio jacobaea	(H)
JACOBEAN LILY	Sprekelia	(HP)
JACOBITE ROSE	Rosa x alba 'Maxima'	(S)
JACOBS LADDER	Pedilanthus	(H)
JADE TREE	Crassula ovata	(CS)
JAGGERY PALM	Caryota urens	(P)

Common	Botanical	Type
JALAP	Ipomoea purga	(TS)
JALAP	Mirabilis jalapa	(H)
JALAP BINDWEED	Convolvulus jalapa	(TS)
JAM TARTS	Gaillardia	(H)
JAMAICA DOGWOOD	Piscidia erythrina	(TS)
JAMAICA HONEYSUCKLE	Passiflora laurifolia	(CL)
JAMAICA PEPPER	Pimenta officinalis	(S)(T)
JAMAICA PLUM	Spondias lutea	(T)
JAMAICA QUASSIA	Picraena excelsa	(TT)
JAMAICA SARSAPARILLA	Smilax ornata	(TS)
JAMAICA SORREL	Hibiscus sabdariffa	(TS)
JAMAICA VERVAIN	Verbena jamaicensis	(TH)
JAMAICAN DOGWOOD	Piscidia erythrina	(TS)
JAMBOLAN	Eugenia jambolana	(TT)
JAMBUL	Eugenia jambolana	(TS)
JAMESTOWN WEED	Datura stramonium	(H)
JAP WEED	sargassum muticum	(SW)
JAPAN PEPPER	Zanthoxylum piperitum	(S/T)
JAPAN VARNISH TREE	Rhus vernicifera	(T)
JAPANESE ALPINE CHERRY	Prunus nipponica	(T)
JAPANESE ANEMONE	Anemone x hybrida	(H)
JAPANESE ANGELICA TREE	Aralia elata	(ST)
JAPANESE APRICOT	Prunus mume	(ST)
JAPANESE ARBOR-VITAE	Thuja standishii	(C)
JAPANESE ARROWHEAD	Sagittaria sagittifolia leucopetala	(WP)
JAPANESE ASPEN	Populus sieboldii	(T)
JAPANESE BALLOON FLOWER	Platycodon	(H)
JAPANESE BANANA	Musa basjoo	(F)
JAPANESE BARBERRY	Berberis thunbergii	(S)
JAPANESE BEECH	Fagus japonica	(T)
JAPANESE BELLFLOWER	Platycodon	(H)
JAPANESE BIG-LEAVED MAGNOLIA	Magnolia hypoleuca	(ST)
JAPANESE BITTER ORANGE	Poncirus	(S)
JAPANESE BLACK PINE	Pinus thunbergii	(C)
JAPANESE BROME	Bromus japonicus	(G)
JAPANESE BUNCHING ONION	Allium fistulosum	(V)
JAPANESE CEDAR	Cryptomeria japonica	(C)
JAPANESE CHERRY BIRCH	Betula grossa	(T)
JAPANESE CHESTNUT	Castanea crenata	(T)
JAPANESE CHESTNUT OAK	Quercus acutissima	(T)
JAPANESE CHINQUAPIN	Castanopsis cuspidata	(T)
JAPANESE CLIMBING FERN	Lygodium japonicum	(FN)
JAPANESE CORK TREE	Phellodendron japonicum	(T)
JAPANESE CRAB	Malus floribunda	(T)
JAPANESE CREEPER	Parthenocissus tricuspidata	(CL)
JAPANESE DOGWOOD	Cornus kousa	(S)
JAPANESE DOUGLAS FIR	Pseudotsuga japonica	(C)

Common	Botanical	Type
JAPANESE ELM	Ulmus davidiana japonica	(T)
JAPANESE EUONYMUS	Euonymus japonicus	(S)
JAPANESE EVERGREEN OAK	Quercus acuta	(T)
JAPANESE FIGLEAF PALM	Fatsia	(S)
JAPANESE FIR	Abies firma	(C)
JAPANESE FLAG IRIS	Iris kaempferi	(H)
JAPANESE FOAM FLOWER	Tanakaea radicans	(S)
JAPANESE GENTIAN	Gentiana scabrae	(H)
JAPANESE HAZEL	Corylus sieboldiana	(T)
JAPANESE HEMLOCK	Tsuga sieboldii	(C)
JAPANESE HOLLY	Ilex crenata	(S)
JAPANESE HOLLY FERN	Phanerophlebia falcata	(FN)
JAPANESE HONEYSUCKLE	Lonicera japonica	(CL)
JAPANESE HOP	Humulus japonicus	(CL)
JAPANESE HOP HORNBEAM	Ostrya japonica	(T)
JAPANESE HORNBEAM	Carpinus japonica	(T)
JAPANESE HORSE-CHESTNUT	Aesculus turbinata	(T)
JAPANESE HORSERADISH	Eutrema wasabi	(V)
JAPANESE HYDRANGEA VINE	Schizophragma hydrangeoides	(CL)
JAPANESE IRIS	Iris kaempferi	(H)
JAPANESE ISINGLASS	Gelidium amansii	(SW)
JAPANESE IVY	Hedera rhombea	(CL)
JAPANESE KNOTWEED	Fallopia japonica	(H)
JAPANESE LADY'S SLIPPER	Cypripedium japonicum	(O)
JAPANESE LARCH	Larix kaempferi	(C)
JAPANESE LAUREL	Aucuba	(S)
JAPANESE LINDEN	Tilia japonica	(T)
JAPANESE LOQUAT	Eriobotrya japonica	(S)
JAPANESE LOVE GRASS	Eragrostis amabilis	(G)
JAPANESE MAPLE	Acer japonicum/palmatum	(S)
JAPANESE MILLET	Echinochlea crus-galli	(G)
JAPANESE MINT	Mentha arvensis piperascens	(HB)
JAPANESE MUTMEG	Torraya nucifera	(C)
JAPANESE PAGODA TREE	Sophora japonica	(T)
JAPANESE PAINTED FERN	Athyrium nipponicum 'Pictum'	(FN)
JAPANESE PERSIMMON	Diospyros kaki	(T)
JAPANESE PLUM	Prunus salicina	(S)
JAPANESE PLUM YEW	Cephalotaxus harringtonia drupacea	(C)
JAPANESE POLYGONUM	Fallopia japonica	(H)
JAPANESE PRIVET	Ligustrum japonicum	(S)
JAPANESE PUSSY WILLOW	Salix gracilistyla	(S)
JAPANESE QUINCE	Chaenomeles	(S)
JAPANESE RAISIN TREE	Hovenia dulcis	(T)
JAPANESE RED CEDAR	Cryptomeria japonica	(C)
JAPANESE RED PINE	Pinus densiflora	(C)
JAPANESE ROSE	Rosa rugosa	(S)
JAPANESE ROWAN	Sorbus commixta	(T)

Common	Botanical	Type
JAPANESE SAGO PALM	Cycas revoluta	(P)
JAPANESE SHIELD FERN	Dryopteris erythosora	(FN)
JAPANESE SNOW-FLOWER	Deutzia gracilis	(S)
JAPANESE SNOWBALL	Viburnum plicatum	(S)
JAPANESE SNOWBELL	Styrax japonica	(S/T)
JAPANESE SPRUCE	Picea polita	(C)
JAPANESE SPURGE	Pachysandra terminalis	(S)
JAPANESE STEWARTIA	Stewartia pseudocamellia	(T)
JAPANESE STONE PINE	Pinus pumila	(C)
JAPANESE SWEETSPIRE	Itea japonica	(S)
JAPANESE THUJA	Thuja standishii	(C)
JAPANESE TOAD-LILY	Tricyrtis	(H)
JAPANESE TORREYA	Torreya nucifera	(C)
JAPANESE UMBRELLA PINE	Sciadopitys verticilliata	(C)
JAPANESE VIBURNUM	Viburnum japonicum	(S)
JAPANESE WALNUT	Juglans ailantifolia	(T)
JAPANESE WHITE BIRCH	Betula platyphylla japonica	(T)
JAPANESE WHITE PINE	Pinus parviflora	(C)
JAPANESE WINDFLOWER	Anemone hybrida	(H)
JAPANESE WING NUT	Pterocarya rhoifolia	(T)
JAPANESE WISTERIA	Wisteria floribunda	(CL)
JAPANESE WITCH HAZEL	Hamamelis japonica	(S)
JAPANESE YELLOW WOOD	Cladrastis platycarpa	(T)
JAPANESE YEW	Taxus cuspidata	(C)
JAPANESE ZELKOVA	Zelkova serrata	(T)
JAPONICA	Chaenomeles	(S)
JARRAH	Eucalyptus marginata	(T)
JASMINE	Jasminum	(CL)
JASMINE BOX	Phillyrea	(S)
JASMINE NIGHTSHADE	Solanum jasminoides	(CL)
JAVA MOSS	Microsorium pteropus	(FN)
JAVA PLUM	Eugenia jambolana	(TS)
JAVA RADISH	Raphanus caudatus	(V)
JEFFREY'S PINE	Pinus jeffreyi	(C)
JEFFREYS HYBRID HEMLOCK	Tsuga x jeffreyi	(C)
JELECOTE PINE	Pinus patula	(C)
JELLY PALM	Butia capitata	(P)
JELLY PALM	Butia capitata	(P)
JELLY PLANT	Gelidium spp	(SW)
JEQUITIBA	Cariniana	(TT)
JERSEY COW BOLETE	Suillus bovinus	(FU)
JERSEY CUDWEED	Gnaphalium luteoalbum	(H)
JERSEY ELM	Ulmus minor sarniensis	(T)
JERSEY FERN	Anogramma leptophylla	(FN)
JERSEY KALE	Brassica oleracea longata	(V)
JERSEY ORCHID	Orchis laxiflora	(O)
JERSEY THRIFT	Armeria alliacea	(R)

Common	Botanical	Type
JERUSALEM ARTICHOKE	Helianthus tuberosus	(V)
JERUSALEM CHERRY	Solanum pseudocapsicum	(HP)
JERUSALEM COWSLIP	Pulmonaria	(H)
JERUSALEM CROSS	Lychnis chalcedonica	(H)
JERUSALEM OAK	Chenopodium botrys	(H)
JERUSALEM PINE	Pinus halepensis	(C)
JERUSALEM SAGE	Phlomis fruticosa	(S)
JERUSALEM THORN	Paliurus spina-christi	(S)
JERUSALEM THORN	Parkinsonia aculeata	(TT)
JESSAMINE	Jasminum	(CL)
JESUIT'S BARK	Cinchona	(TT)
JESUIT'S TEA	Chenopodium anthelminticum	(H)
JESUITS NUT	Trapa natans	(WP)
JEW'S APPLE	Solanum melongena	(H)
JEW'S MALLOW	Corchorus olitorius	(S)
JEW'S MALLOW	Kerria japonica	(S)
JEW'S MYRTLE	Ruscus aculeatus	(S)
JEW-BUSH	Pedilanthus tithymaloides	(S)
JEWEL OF THE VELDT	Ursinia	(H)
JEWEL ORCHID	Anoechtochilus	(0)
JEWEL WEED	Impatiens	(H)
JEWELWEED	Impatiens aurea	(H)
JEWS MALLOW	Kerria japonica	(S)
JICAMA	Pachyrhizus tuberosus	(H)
JIM BRUSH	Ceanothus sorediatus	(S)
JIMSON WEED	Datura stramonium	(H)
JINBUL	Eucalyptus microtheca	(T)
JOB'S TEARS	Coix lacryma-jobi	(H)
JOE-PYE WEED	Eupatorium maculatum	(H)
JOE-PYE WEED	Eupatorium prupureum	(H)
JOHNSON GRASS	Sorghum almum	(G)
JOHNSON GRASS	Sorghum halepense	(G)
JOINT PINE	Ephedra distachya	(H)
JOINTED RUSH	Juncus articulatus	(G)
JOJOBA	Simmondsia chinensis	(S)
JONQUIL	Narcissus jonquilla	(BB)
JOSEPH'S COAT	Amaranthus tricolor	(A)
JOSEPHINE'S LILY	Brunsvigia josephinae	(BB)
JOSHUA TREE	Yucca brevifolia	(S)
JOY WEED	Alternanthera	(H)
JOY-WEED	Alternanthera	(H)
JUDAS TREE	Cercis siliquastrum	(S/T)
JUJUBE	Ziziphus zizyphus	(F)
JUMPING BEAN	Sebastiana pringlei	(TS)
JUMPING BEAN PLANT	Sebastiana pringlei	(TS)
JUMPING JACK	Impatiens glandulifera	(HP)
JUNE BERRY	Amelanchier	(S)

Common	Botanical	Type
JUNE BERRY	Amelanchier arborea	(S)
JUNGLE FLAME	Ixora coccinea	(HP)
JUNGLE WEED	Combretum sundaicum	(H)
JUNIPER	Juniperus	(C)
JUNIPER MYRTLE	Verticordia	(S)
JUNIPER RUSH	Genista raetam	(S)
JUNIPER-MYRTLE	Verticordia	(S)
JUPITER'S BEARD	Anthyliis barba-jovis	(H)
JUPITER'S BEARD	Centranthus ruber	(H)
JUPITER'S EYE	Sempervivum tectorum	(H)
JUPITER'S NUTS	Juglans	(T)
JUPITER'S STAFF	Verbascum thapsus	(H)
JUPITERS DISTAFF	Salvia glutinosa	(H)
JUTE	Corchorus capsularis	(TS)
JUTE	Corchorus olitorius	(TS)
KAFFIA PLUM	Acokanthera	(TT)
KAFFIR LILY	Clivia	(HP)
KAFFIR LILY	Schizostylis	(H)
KAFFIR PLUM	Harpephyllum caffrum	(S)
KAFFIR-THORN	Lycium afrum	(TS)
KAHIKATEA	Dacrycarpus dacrydioides	(C)
KAHLI GINGER	Hedychium gardnerianum	(BB)
KAKI	Diospyros kaki	(T)
KALE	Brassica oleracea sabellica	(V)
KAMAHI	Weinmannia racemosa	(S)
KAMALA	Mallotus philippinensis	(T)
KAMILA TREE	Mallotus	(T)
KANGAROO APPLE	Solanum aviculare	(S)
KANGAROO APPLE	Solanum laciniatum	(CL)
KANGAROO PAW	Anigozanthus	(HP)
KANGAROO THORN	Acacia armata	(ST)
KANGAROO VINE	Cissus antartica	(HP)
KANNIEDOOD ALOE	Aloe variegata	(HP)
KANOOKA	Tristania laurina	(S)
KANSAS GAYFEATHER	Liatris	(H)
KANSAS NIGGERHEAD	Echinacea angustifloria	(H)
KAPOK	Ceiba pentandra	(TT)
KAPOK BUSH	Cochlospermum fraseri	(TS)
KAPOK TREE	Ceiba pentandra	(TT)
KAPUR	Dryobalanops	(TT)
KARAKA	Corynocarpus laevigata	(T)
KARAPINCHA	Murraya koenigii	(S)
KARO	Pittosporum crassifolium	(S)
KARRI	Eucalyptus diversicolor	(T)
KARST GENTIAN	Gentiana tergestina	(H)
KASHMIR CYPRESS	Cupressus cashmeriana	(C)
KASHMIR MAIDENHAIR FERN	Adiantum venustum	(FN)

Know Your Common Plant Names

Common	Botanical	Type
KASHMIR ROWAN	Sorbus cashmeriana	(T)
KATSURA TREE	Cercidiphyllum	(T)
KAURI PINE	Agathis	(C)
KAURI PINE	Agathis australis	(C)
KAVA KAVA	Piper methysticum	(F)
KAWAKA	Libocedrus plumosa	(C)
KAZANLIK ROSE	Rosa damascena "Trigintipetala"	(S)
KEAKI	Zelkova serrata	(T)
KEELED GARLIC	Allium carinatum	(BB)
KEI APPLE	Doryalis caffra	(TS)
KELP	Laminaria sp.	(SW)
KENAF	Hibiscus cannabinus	(TS)
KENARI	Canarium commune	(TT)
KENILWORTH IVY	Cymbalaria muralis	(H)
KENTIA PALM	Howea forsteriana	(P)
KENTUCKY BLUE GRASS	Poa pratensis	(G)
KENTUCKY COFFEE TREE	Gymnocladus dioica	(T)
KENTUCKY HEMP	Urtica canadensis	(H)
KERMES OAK	Quercus coccifera	(T)
KERNERA	Kernera saxatilis	(H)
KERRY LILY	Simethis planifolia	(BB)
KERVING	Dipterocarpus sp.	(TT)
KEYFLOWER	Primula veris	(H)
KHASYA PINE	Pinus khasya	(C)
KHAT TREE	Catha edulis	(TT)
KHINGAN FIR	Abies nephrolepis	(C)
KIDNEY BEAN	Phaseolus vulgaris	(V)
KIDNEY BEGONIA	Begonia 'Erythrophylla'	(HP)
KIDNEY SAXIFRAGE	Saxifraga hirsuta	(R)
KIDNEY VETCH	Anthyllis velneraria	(H)
KIDNEYWORT	Cotyledon umbilicus	(H)
KIDNEYWORT	Umbilicus ruprestris	(H)
KIFTSGATE ROSE	Rosa filipes 'Kiftsgate'	(CL)
KILLARNEY FERN	Trichomanes speciosum	(FN)
KILLARNEY STRAWBERRY TREE	Arbutus unedo	(ST)
KILMARNOCK WILLOW	Salix caprea 'Pendula' (female)	(T)
KING BORIS FIR	Abies borisii-regis	(C)
KING OF BROMELIADS	Vriesea hieroglyphica splendens	(HP)
KING OF THE ALPS	Eritrichium nanum	(R)
KING PALM	Archontophoenix	(P)
KING PROTEA	Protea cynaroides	(TS)
KING WILLIAM PINE	Athrotaxis selaginoides	(C)
KING'S CLOVER	Melilotus officinalis	(H)
KING'S CROWN	Jacobinia carnea	(HP)
KING'S CURE	Chimaphila umbellata	(H)
KING'S SPEAR	Asphodeline lutea	(H)
KING'S SPEAR	Asphodelus	(H)

Know Your Common Plant Names

Common	Botanical	Type
KING-NUT	Carya laciniosa	(T)
KINGCUP	Caltha palustris	(WP)
KINGFISHER DAISY	Felicia bergeriona	(H)
KINNIKINICK	Arctostaphylos uva-ursi	(S)
KINOS	Pterocarpus marsupium	(TT)
KISS HER IN THE BUTTERY	Viola tricolor	(H)
KISS-ME-QUICK	Brunfelsia latifolia	(S)
KIWANO	Cucumis metuliferus	(H)
KIWI FRUIT	Actinidia deliciosa	(F.CL)
KLINKI PINE	Araucaria hunsteinii	(C)
KNAPWEED	Centaurea nigra	(H)
KNAWEL	Scleranthus	(A)
KNEEHOLY	Ruscus aculeatus	(S)
KNICKER TREE	Gymnocladus dioica	(T)
KNIFE-LEAF WATTLE	Acacia cultriformis	(T)
KNIGHT'S STAR	Hippeastrum	(BB)
KNITBONE	Symphytum officinale	(H)
KNOBROOT	Collinsonia canadensis	(H)
KNOBCONE PINE	Pinus attenuata	(C)
KNOBWEED	Collinsonia canadensis	(H)
KNOT-GRASS	Illecebrum verticilliatum	(H)
KNOTGRASS	Polygonum aviculare	(H)
KNOTTED FIGWORT	Scrophularia nodosa	(H)
KNOTTED HEDGE PARSLEY	Torilis nodosa	(H)
KNOTTED PEARLWORT	Sagina nodosa	(H)
KNOTTED WRACK	Ascophyllum nodosum	(SW)
KNOTWEED	Polygonum	(H)
KOHL RABI	Brassica oleracea gongylodes	(V)
KOHUHU	Pittosporum tenuifolium	(S)
KOKOONTREE	Kokoona zeylanica	(TT)
KOLA	Cola acuminata	(TS)
KOLA	Cola nitida	(TS)
KOLA NUT	Cola acuminata	(T)
KOLA NUTS	Kola vera	(T)
KOREAN CHRYSANTHEMUM	Chrysanthemum rubellum	(H)
KOREAN FIR	Abies koreana	(C)
KOREAN FORSYTHIA	Forsythia ovata	(S)
KOREAN GRASS	Zoysia tenuifolia	(G)
KOREAN HILL CHERRY	Prunus serrulata 'Pubescens'	(T)
KOREAN LAWN GRASS	Zoyzia japonica	(G)
KOREAN LILAC	Syringa meyeri 'Palibin'	(S)
KOREAN MINT	Agastache rugosa	(HB)
KOREAN PINE	Pinus koraiensis	(C)
KOUSSO	Hagenia abyssinica	(TT)
KOWHAI	Sophora tetraptera	(S)
KOYAMA SPRUCE	Picea koyamai	(C)
KRIS PLANT	Alocasia sanderiana	(H)

Common	Botanical	Type
KUDZU	Pueraria lobata	(CL)
KUDZU VINE	Pueraria thunbergiana	(CL)
KUMOI	Pyrus pyrifolia	(F)
KUMQUAT	Fortunella	(F)
KUSAMAKI	Podocarpus macrophyllus	(C)
KUTHMITHI	Withania somnifera	(H)
LABLAB	Lablab purpureus	(H)
LABRADOR TEA	Ledum groenlandicum	(S)
LABURNUM	Laburnum	(T)
LACE ALOE	Aloe aristata	(CS)
LACE BARK	Hoheria lyallii	(S)
LACE CACTUS	Mammillaria elongata	(CS)
LACE FERN	Cheilanthes gracillima	(FN)
LACE FLOWER	Episcia dianthiflora	(H)
LACE FLOWER VINE	Episcia dianthiflora	(H)
LACE ORCHID	Odontoglossum crispum	(O)
LACE TRUMPETS	Sarracenia leucophylla	(HP)
LACE-BARK PINE	Pinus bungeana	(C)
LACE-CAP HYDRANGEA	Hydrangea macrophylla	(S)
LACE-CUP VIBURNUM	Viburnum plicatum tomentosum	(S)
LACE-LEAF	Aponogeton fenestralis	(WP)
LACEBARK PINE	Pinus bungeana	(C)
LACQUER TREE	Rhus vernicifera	(S)
LAD'S LOVE	Artemisia abrotanum	(HB)
LADIES HANDKERCHIEF	Davidia involucrata	(T)
LADIES LOCKET	Dicentra spectabilis	(H)
LADIES' TRESSES	Spiranthes	(
LADY FERN	Athyrium filix-foemina	(FN)
LADY FINGER CACTUS	Echinocereus pentalophus	(CS)
LADY OF THE WOODS	Betula pendula	(T)
LADY ORCHID	Orchis purpurea	(O)
LADY PALM	Rhapis	(P)
LADY TULIP	Tulipa clusiana	(BB)
LADY'S BEDSTRAW	Galium vernum	(AH)
LADY'S EARDROPS	Fuchsia	(S)
LADY'S FINGERS	Abelmoschus esculentus	(V)
LADY'S FINGERS	Anthyllis vulneraria	(H)
LADY'S FOXGLOVE	Verbascum thapsus	(H)
LADY'S GLOVE	Digitalis purpurea	(H)
LADY'S LOCKET	Dicentra spectabilis	(H)
LADY'S MAID	Artemisia chamaemelifolia	(H)
LADY'S MANTLE	Alchemilla vulgaris etc.	(H)
LADY'S POCKET HANDKERCHIEF TREE	Davidia involucrata	(T)
LADY'S PURSE	Capsella bursa-pastoris	(A)
LADY'S SEAL	Polygonatum multiflorum	(H)
LADY'S SLIPPER	Cypridium calceolus	(O)
LADY'S SMOCK	Cardamine pratensis	(R)

Know Your Common Plant Names

Common	Botanical	Type
LADY'S THISTLE	Silybum marianum	(H)
LADY-OF-THE-NIGHT	Brunfelsia americana	(S)
LADY-OF-THE-NIGHT-ORCHID	Brassavola	(O)
LADYBIRD POPPY	Papaver commutatum	(A)
LAGOS EBONY	Diospyros mespiliformis	(TT)
LAMB KILL	Kalmia angustifolia	(S)
LAMB MINT	Mentha spicata	(HB)
LAMB'S EAR	Stachys byzantina	(H)
LAMB'S LETTUCE	Valerianella locusta	(V)
LAMB'S LUGS	Stachys byzantina	(H)
LAMB'S QUARTERS	Chenopodium	(H)
LAMB'S QUARTERS	Trillium erectum	(H)
LAMB'S SKIN	Arnica	(H)
LAMB'S TAIL	Sedum morganianum	(HP)
LAMB'S TAIL CACTUS	Echinocereus schmollii	(CS)
LAMB'S TAIL GRASS	Alopecurus	(G)
LAMB'S TONGUE	Stachys byzantina	(H)
LAMBS SUCCORY	Arnoseris minima	(H)
LAMBSWOOL	Lachnostachys eriobotrya	(H)
LAMPSHADE POPPY	Meconopsis integrifolia	(H)
LANCEWOOD	Oxandra lanceolata	(TT)
LANCEWOOD	Pseudopanax crassifolius	(S)
LAND CRESS	Barbarea verna	(V)
LANGSAT	Lansium domesticum	(TF)
LANLADY'S WIG	Ahnfeltia plicata	(SW)
LANTERN TREE	Crinodendron hookerianum	(S)
LAPLAND WILLOW	Salix lapponum	(S)
LARCH	Larix	(C)
LARD FRUIT	Hodgsonia heteroclita	(TS)
LARGE BITTER CRESS	Cardamine amara	(H)
LARGE BLUE ALKANET	Anchusa azurea	(H)
LARGE CUCKOO-PINT	Arum italicum	(H)
LARGE FLOWERED HEMP-NETTLE	Galeopsis speciosa	(H)
LARGE PINK	Dianthus superbus	(H)
LARGE SELF-HEAL	Prunella grandiflora	(H)
LARGE SPEEDWELL	Veronica austriaca	(H)
LARGE THYME	Thymus pulegioides	(H)
LARGE VETCH	Vicia gigantea	(H)
LARGE WINTERGREEN	Pyrola rotundifolia	(H)
LARGE YELLOW FOXGLOVE	Digitalis grandiflora	(H)
LARGE YELLOW OX-EYE	Telekia speciosa	(H)
LARGE YELLOW REST-HARROW	Ononis natrix	(H)
LARGE-CONED DOUGLAS FIR	Pseudotsuga macrocarpa	(C)
LARGE-FLOWERED BUTTERWORT	Pinguicula grandiflora	(R)
LARGE-LEAVED EVENING PRIMROSE	Oenothera glazioviana	(H)
LARGE-LEAVED LIME	Tilia platyphyllos	(T)
LARGER BINDWEED	Calystegia sepium	(H)

Common	Botanical	Type
LARKSPUR	Consolida	(A)
LARKSPUR	Consolida ambigua	(A)
LASER	Laser trilobum	(H)
LATE DUTCH HONEYSUCKLE	Lonicera periclymenum 'Serotina'	(CL)
LATE SPIDER ORCHID	Ophrys holoserica	(O)
LATTICE LEAF	Aponogeton fernestralis	(WP)
LAUREL	Prunus laurocerasus	(S)
LAUREL MAGNOLIA	Magnolia grandiflora	(ST)
LAUREL OAK	Quercus laurifolia	(T)
LAUREL WILLOW	Salix pentandra	(S)
LAURUSTINUS	Viburnum tinus	(S)
LAVENDER	Lavandula	(S)
LAVENDER COTTON	Santolina chamaecyparisus	(S)
LAVENDER TREE	Heteropyxis natalensis	(TS)
LAVER	Porphyra umbilicalis	(SW)
LAWN CHAMOMILE	Chamaemelum nobilis 'Treneague'	(H)
LAWSON CYPRESS	Chamaecyparis lawsoniana	(C)
LAWYER'S TONGUE	Gasteria	(HP)
LAWYER'S WIG	Coprinus comatus	(FU)
LEAD PLANT	Amorpha canescens	(S)
LEADWORT	Plumbago	(HP)
LEAF BEET	Beta vulgaris cicla	(V)
LEAFY HAWKWEED	Hieracium umbellatum	(H)
LEAFY SPURGE	Euphorbia esula	(H)
LEAST BULRUSH	Typha minima	(WP)
LEAST GAGEA	Gagea minima	(H)
LEAST LETTUCE	Lactuca saligna	(H)
LEAST WHITEBEAM	Sorbus minima	(T)
LEAST WILLOW	Salix herbacea	(S)
LEATHER FERN	Acrostichum aureum	(FN)
LEATHER LEAF	Chamaedaphne calyculata	(S)
LEATHER-COAT TREE	Coccoloba pubescens	(H)
LEATHERWOOD	Cyrilla racemiflora	(S)
LEATHERWOOD	Dirca palustris	(S)
LEATHERWOOD	Eucryphia lucida	(S)
LEATHERWOOD FERN	Dryopteris marginalis	(FN)
LEATHERY MOONWORT	Botrychium multifidum	(FN)
LEBANON OAK	Quercus libani	(T)
LECHUGUILLA	Agave lophantha poselgeri	(CS)
LEEK	Allium porrum	(V)
LEMON	Citrus limon	(F)
LEMON BALM	Melissa officinalis	(HB)
LEMON BERGAMOT	Monarda citriodora	(H)
LEMON BOTTLEBRUSH	Callistemon citrinus	(S)
LEMON GRASS	Cymbopogon citratus	(G)
LEMON MINT	Mentha citrata	(HB)
LEMON PLANT	Aloysia triphylla	(S)

Know Your Common Plant Names

Common	Botanical	Type
LEMON THYME	Thymus citriodorus	(R)
LEMON VERBENA	Aloysia triphylla	(S)
LEMON VINE	Pereskia aculeata	(CL)
LEMON-SCENTED FERN	Oreopteris limbosperma	(FN)
LEMON-SCENTED GERANIUM	Pelargonium citriodorum	(A)
LEMON-SCENTED GERANIUM	Pelargonium crispum	(A)
LEMON-SCENTED GUM	Eucalyptus citriodora	(T)
LEMON-SCENTED IRON BARK	Eucalyptus staigeriana	(T)
LEMON-SCENTED VERBENA	Aloysia triphylla	(S)
LEMONADE BERRY	Rhus integrifolia	(S)
LEMONADE TREE	Adensonia digitata	(TT)
LENGA	Nothofagus pumilio	(T)
LENT LILY	Narcissus pseudonarcissus	(BB)
LENTEN ROSE	Helleborus orientalis	(H)
LENTIL	Lens culinaris	(V)
LENTIL	Lens esculenta	(V)
LEOPARD LILY	Lilium pardalinum	(BB)
LEOPARD'S BANE	Doronicum pardalianches	(H)
LEOPARD'S FLOWER	Belamcanda chinensis	(I)
LEOPARD'S LILY	Dieffenbachia	(HP)
LESSER BINDWEED	Convolvulus arvensis	(H)
LESSER BLADDERWORT	Utricularia minor	(H)
LESSER BUGLOSS	Lycopsis arvensis	(H)
LESSER BULRUSH	Typha angustifolia	(WP)
LESSER BURDOCK	Arctium minus	(H)
LESSER BURNET SAXIFRAGE	Pimpinella saxifraga	(HB)
LESSER BUTTERFLY ORCHID	Platanthera bifolia	(O)
LESSER CALAMINT	Calamintha nepeta	(H)
LESSER CAT'S TAIL	Phleum bertulonii	(G)
LESSER CELANDINE	Ranunculus ficaria	(H)
LESSER CENTAURY	Centaurum pulchellum	(H)
LESSER CHICKWEED	Stellaria pallida	(H)
LESSER DANDELION	Taraxacum erythrospermum	(H)
LESSER DANDELION	Taraxacum laevicatum	(H)
LESSER DUCKWEED	Lemna miniscula	(WP)
LESSER HAWKBIT	Leontondon taraxacoides	(H)
LESSER HERB ROBERT	Geranium purpureum	(H)
LESSER KNAPWEED	Centaurea nigra	(H)
LESSER MEADOW-RUE	Thalictrum minus	(H)
LESSER PERIWINKLE	Vinca minor	(S)
LESSER SKULL-CAP	Scutellaria minor	(H)
LESSER SPEARWORT	Ranunculus flammula	(H)
LESSER STITCHWORT	Stellaria graminea	(H)
LESSER TREFOIL	Trifolium dubium	(H)
LESSER TUSSOCK SEDGE	Carex diandra	(G)
LESSER TWAYBLADE	Listera cordata	(O)
LESSER WATER PARSNIP	Berula erecta	(H)

Know Your Common Plant Names

Common	Botanical	Type
LESSER WATER PLANTAIN	Baldellia ranunculoides	(WP)
LESSER YELLOW ROCKET	Barbarea stricta	(H)
LESSER YELLOW TREFOIL	Trifolium dubium	(H)
LETTUCE	Lactuca sativa	(AV)
LETTUCE TREE	Pisonia alba	(TS)
LEVANT COTTON	Gossypium herbaceum	(H)
LEVANT WORMSEED	Artemisia chamaemelifolia	(H)
LEVER-WOOD	Ostrya virginiana	(T)
LEYLAND CYPRESS	Cupressocyparis leylandii	(C)
LIBERIAN COFFEE	Coffea liberica	(F)
LIBERTY CAP	Psilocybe semilanceata	(FU)
LICHEE	Litchi chinensis	(F)
LIGHTWOOD	Ceratopetalum apetalum	(TT)
LIGIRI TREE	Idesia	(T)
LIGNUM VITAE	Guaiacum officinale	(TT)
LILAC	Syringa	(ST)
LILLY-PILLY	Eugenia smithii	(S)
LILY	Lilium	(BB)
LILY LEEK	Allium moly	(BB)
LILY OF CHINA	Rohdea japonica	(HP)
LILY OF THE FIELD	Sternbergia	(BB)
LILY OF THE VALLEY ORCHID	Odontoglossum pulchellum	(O)
LILY THORN	Catesbaea spinosa	(H)
LILY TREE	Magnolia denudata	(S)
LILY TURF	Liriope	(H)
LILY-OF-THE-FIELD	Sternbergia	(BB)
LILY-OF-THE-NILE	Agapanthus	(H)
LILY-OF-THE-VALLEY	Convallaria majalis	(H)
LILY-OF-THE-VALLEY ORCHID	Odontoglossum pulchellum	(O)
LILY-OF-THE-VALLEY SHRUB	Pieris	(S)
LILY-OF-THE-VALLEY TREE	Clethra arborea	(S)
LILY-THORN	Catesbaea spinosa	(H)
LIMA BEAN	Phaseolus limensis	(V)
LIMA BEAN	Phaseolus lunatus	(V)
LIMBER PINE	Pinus flexilis	(C)
LIME	Citrus aurantifolia	(F)
LIME	Tilia	(T)
LIME BERRY	Triphasia trifolia	(H)
LIME-LEAVED MAPLE	Acer distylum	(T)
LIMPWORT	Veronica beccabunga	(H)
LINDEN	Tilia	(T)
LINDEN VIBURNUM	Viburnum dilatatum	(S)
LING	Calluna vulgaris	(S)
LINSEED	Linum usitatissimum	(A)
LION'S EAR	Leonotis leonurus	(S)
LION'S FOOT	Alchemilla vulgaris	(H)
LION'S FOOT	Leontopodium alpinum	(R)

Know Your Common Plant Names

Common	Botanical	Type
LION'S FOOT	Prenanthes alba	(H)
LION'S TAIL	Leonurus	(S)
LION'S TEETH	Taraxacum officinale	(H)
LIP FERN	Cheilanthes	(FN)
LIPSTICK VINE	Aeschynanthus	(HP)
LIQUORICE	Glycyrrhiza glabra	(HB)
LIQUORICE FERN	Polypodium glycyrrhiza	(FN)
LITCHI	Litchi chinensis	(F)
LITTLE CANDLES	Mammillaria prolifera	(CS)
LITTLE LADY PALM	Rhapis excelsa	(P)
LITTLE MARY	Bellium minutum	(H)
LITTLE NAIL FUNGUS	Mycena ribula	(FU)
LITTLE TREE WILLOW	Salix arbuscula	(S)
LIVE FOR EVER	Sedum telephium	(HR)
LIVE OAK	Quercus virginiana	(T)
LIVELONG	Sedum telephium	(H)
LIVERWORT	Hepatica	(R)
LIVING ROCK	Pleiospilos bolusii	(CS)
LIVING STONES	Lithops	(R)
LIVINGSTONE DAISY	Dorotheanthus bellidiformis	(A)
LIZARD ORCHID	Himantoglossum hircinun	(O)
LIZARD PLANT	Tetrastigma voinieranum	(HP)
LIZARD'S TAIL	Saururus	(H)
LOBEL'S MAPLE	Acer x lobelii	(T)
LOBLOLLY BAY	Gordonia lasianthus	(S)
LOBLOLLY MAGNOLIA	Magnolia grandiflora	(ST)
LOBLOLLY PINE	Pinus taeda	(C)
LOBSTER CLAW	Heliconia	(TS)
LOBSTER CLAWS	Heliconia	(TS)
LOBSTER PLANT	Euphorbia pulcherrima	(HP)
LOBSTER'S CLAW	Clianthus puniceus	(S)
LOCOWEED	Astragalus	(H)
LOCOWEED	Oxytropis	(H)
LOCUST	Robinia pseudoacacia	(T)
LOCUST PODS	Ceratonia siliqua	(T)
LOCUST TREE	Hymenaea courbaril	(T)
LODDON LILY	Leucojum aestivum	(BB)
LODDON PONDWEED	Potamogeton nodosus	(WP)
LODGEPOLE PINE	Pinus contorta latifolia	(C)
LOGANBERRY	Rubus loganobaccus	(F)
LOGWOOD	Haematoxylum campeachianum	(T)
LOLLIPOP PLANT	Pachystachys lutea	(HP)
LOMBARDY POPLAR	Populus nigra 'Italica'	(T)
LOMBARDY POPLAR CHERRY	Prunus 'Amanogawa'	(T)
LONDON PLANE	Platanus x hispanica	(T)
LONDON PRIDE	Saxifraga urbium	(R)
LONDON ROCKET	Sisymbrium irio	(H)

Common	Botanical	Type
LONG DUCHU	Agathosma crenulata	(TS)
LONGROOT	Oudemansiella radicata	(FU)
LONG-HEADED POPPY	Papaver dubium	(A)
LONG-LEAVED HARE'S EAR	Bupleurum longifolium	(H)
LONG-LEAVED INDIAN PINE	Pinus roxhurgii	(C)
LONG-STALKED CRANE'S BILL	Geranium columbinum	(H)
LONGLEAF	Falcaria vulgaris	(H)
LONGLEAF PINE	Pinus palustris	(C)
LOOFAH	Luffa cylindrica	(V)
LOOFAH GOURD	Luffa cylindrica	(V)
LOOKING GLASS TREE	Heritiera macrophylla	(TT)
LOOSE SILKY BENT	Apera spica-venti	(G)
LOOSESTRIFE	Lysimachia	(H)
LOPEZ ROOT	Toddalia asiatica	(H)
LOQUAT	Eriobotrya japonica	(S)
LORD ANSON'S PEA	Lathyrus nervosus	(H)
LORDS AND LADIES	Arum maculatum	(H)
LORRAINE BEGONIA	Begonia x cheimantha	(HP)
LOTUS	Nelumbo nucifera	(WP)
LOTUS FRUIT	Zizyphus lotus	(F)
LOUSEWORT	Pedicularis sylvatica	(H)
LOVAGE	Levisticum officinale	(HB)
LOVE APPLE	Lycopersicon esulentum	(F)
LOVE FLOWER	Agapanthus	(H)
LOVE GRASS	Eragrostis	(G)
LOVE GRASS	Eragrostis elegans	(G)
LOVE-IN-A-MIST	Nigella damascena	(A)
LOVE-IN-A-PUFF	Cardiospermum halicacabum	(CL)
LOVE-IN-IDLENESS	Viola (pansy)	(H)
LOVE-LIES-BLEEDING	Amaranthus caudatus	(A)
LOVING IDOL	Viola tricolor	(H)
LOW-BUSH BLUEBERRY	Vaccinium angustifolium	(S)
LUCERNE	Medicago sativa	(H)
LUCHU PINE	Pinus luchuensis	(C)
LUCKY BEAN TREE	Erythrina lysistemon	(S/T)
LUCKY PLANT	Sansevieria	(HP)
LUCOMBE OAK	Quercus x hispanica 'Lucombeana'	(T)
LUDWIG'S OAK	Quercus x ludoviciana	(T)
LUNDY CABBAGE	Rhynchosinapis wrightii	(H)
LUNGWORT	Pulmonaria	(H)
LUPIN	Lupinus	(H)
LYCHEE	Litchi chinensis	(F)
LYME GRASS	Elymus arenarius	(G)
LYRE FLOWER	Dicentra spectabilis	(H)
MA HUANG	Ephedera vulgaris	(S)
MACARTNEY ROSE	Rosa bracteata	(S)
MACE	Myristica fragrans	(HB)

Common	Botanical	Type
MACE SEDGE	Carex grayi	(G)
MACEDONIAN OAK	Quercus trojana	(T)
MACEDONIAN PINE	Pinus peuce	(C)
MACKAYS HEATH	Erica mackaiana	(S)
MAD APPLE	Datura stramonium	(S)
MAD-DOG SCULLCAP	Scutellaria lateriflora	(H)
MAD-DOG WEED	Alisma plantago-aquatica	(WP)
MADAGASCAR DRAGON TREE	Dracaena marginata	(HP)
MADAGASCAR JASMINE	Stephanotis	(HP)
MADAGASCAR NUTMEG	Ravensara aromatica	(TS)
MADAGASCAR PALM	Chrysalidocarpus lutescens	(P)
MADAGASCAR PERIWINKLE	Catharanthus rosea	(HP)
MADAKE	Phyllostachys bambosoides	(C)
MADDER	Rubia peregrina	(H)
MADDER	Rubia tinctoria	(H)
MADEIRA BROOM	Genista virgata	(S)
MADEIRA HOLLY	Ilex perado	(T)
MADEIRA VINE	Boussingaultia	(CL)
MADEIRA VINE	Boussingaultia gracilis	(CL)
MADEIRA WHORTLEBERRY	Vaccineum padifolium	(S)
MADONNA LILY	Lilium candidum	(BB)
MADRONA	Arbutus menziesii	(T)
MADWEED	Scutellaria lateriflora	(H)
MADWORT	Alyssum; Asperugo procumbens	(R)
MAGDEBURG CRAB	Malus 'Magdeburgensis'	(T)
MAGIC FLOWER	Achimenes	(HP)
MAGIC LILY	Lycoris squamigera	(BB)
MAGIC MUSHROOMS	Psilocybe; Conocybe	(FU)
MAGNOLIA	Magnolia	(ST)
MAGNOLIA-LEAFED WILLOW	Salix magnifica	(ST)
MAGPIE	Coprinus picaceus	(FU)
MAHOE	Hibiscus elatus	(TS)
MAHOE	Melicytus ramiflorus	(S)
MAHOE	Thespesia populnea	(T)
MAHOGANY	Swietenia macrophylla	(TT)
MAID OF THE MIST	Gladiolus primulinus	(BB)
MAIDEN HAIR	Ectocarpus spp	(SW)
MAIDEN PINK	Dianthus deltoides	(R)
MAIDEN'S WREATH	Francoa ramosa	(R)
MAIDENHAIR FERN	Adiantum pedatum	(FN)
MAIDENHAIR SPLEENWORT	Asplenium trichomanes	(FN)
MAIDENHAIR TREE	Gingko biloba	(C)
MAITEN	Maytenus boaria	(S)
MAIZE	Zea mays	(V)
MALABAR NIGHTSHADE	Basella alba	(THB)
MALABAR NIGHTSHADE	Basella rubra	(THB)
MALABAR NUT	Adhatoda vasica	(TS)

Common	Botanical	Type
MALACCA CANE	Calamus scipionum	(G)
MALAY APPLE	Eugenia malaccensis	(TP)
MALAY GINGER	Costus speciosus	(H)
MALAYAN SWORD	Aglaonema simplex	(WP)
MALE FERN	Dryopteris filix-mas	(FN)
MALEE BOX	Eucalyptus bakeri	(T)
MALLEE	Eucalyptus spp.	(T)
MALLOW	Malva	(AH)
MALLOW-WORT	Malope trifolia	(A)
MALMONCILLO	Melicocca bijuga	(TT)
MALTESE CROSS	Lychnis chalcedonica	(H)
MAMMEE-APPLE	Mammea americana	(F)
MAMMOTH TREE	Sequoiadendron giganteum	(C)
MAN OF THE EARTH	Ipomoea pandurata	(CL)
MAN ORCHID	Aceras anthropophorum	(O)
MANACA ROOT	Brunfelsia hopeana	(TS)
MANAOS BEAUTY	Centratherum intermedium	(TS)
MANCHESTER POPLAR	Populus nigra 'Betulifolia'	(T)
MANCHINEEL	Hippomane mancinella	(S)
MANCHURIAN CHERRY	Prunus maackii	(T)
MANCHURIAN FIR	Abies holophylla	(C)
MANCHURIAN WILD RICE	Zizania caducifolia	(F)
MANDARIN	Citrus reticulata	(F)
MANDARIN LIME	Citrus x limonia	(F)
MANDIOCA	Manihot esculenta	(TT)
MANDRAKE	Mandragora officinarum	(H)
MANGE TOUT	Pisum sativum saccharata	(V)
MANGEL	Beta vulgaris	(V)
MANGEL WURZEL	Beta vulgaris	(V)
MANGLE'S KANGAROO PAW	Anigozanthus manglesii	(H)
MANGO	Mangifera indica	(F)
MANGOLD	Beta vulgaris	(V)
MANGOSTEEN	Garcinia mangostana	(TT)
MANGROVE	Rhizophora	(TT)
MANGROVE DATE PALM	Phoenix paludosa	(P)
MANILA COPAL	Agathis	(C)
MANILA GRASS	Zoysia matrella	(G)
MANILA HEMP	Musa textilis	(CF)
MANILA PALM	Veitchia merrillii	(P)
MANIOC	Manihot esculenta	(F)
MANNA	Tamarix gallica mannifera	(S)
MANNA ASH	Fraxinus ornus	(T)
MANNA GRASS	Glyceria	(G)
MANNA GUM	Eucalyptus viminalis	(T)
MANNA TREE	Alhagi maurorum	(TT)
MANUKA	Leptospermum scoparium	(S)
MANZANITA	Arctostaphylos manzanita	(S)

Common	Botanical	Type
MAORI HOLLY	Olearia illicifolia	(S)
MAPLE	Acer	(ST)
MAPLE-LEAF BEGONIA	Begonia dregei	(HP)
MARABA	Kaempferia galanga	(H)
MARAJA PALM	Bactris	(P)
MARE'S TAIL	Hippuris vulgaris	(H)
MARGUERITE	Argyranthemum frutescens	(A)
MARGUERITE	Leucanthemum vulgare	(H)
MARIGOLD	Calendula, Tagetes	(A)
MARIGOLD OF PERU	Helianthus annuus	(A)
MARIHUANA	Cannabis sativa	(HB)
MARIPOSA LILY	Calochortus	(BB)
MARITIME PINE	Pinus pinaster	(C)
MARJORY	Origanum	(HB)
MARKING NUT	Anacardium	(F)
MARKING-NUT TREE	Semecarpus anacardium	(TT)
MARLBERRY	Ardisia	(S)
MARMALADE BOX	Genipa americana	(TF)
MARMALADE BUSH	Streptosolen jamesonii	(HP)
MARMALADE PLUM	Manilkara zapota	(TT)
MAROC FIR	Abies marocana	(C)
MARRAM GRASS	Ammophila arenaria	(G)
MARROW	Cucurbita pepo ovifera	(V)
MARSH BEDSTRAW	Galium palustre	(H)
MARSH BIRD'S FOOT TREFOIL	Lotus pedunculatus	(H)
MARSH CINQUEFOIL	Potentilla palustris	(H)
MARSH CLOVER	Menyanthes trifoliata	(WP)
MARSH CUDWEED	Gnaphalium uliginosum	(H)
MARSH DOCK	Rumex palustris	(H)
MARSH FELWORT	Swertia perennis	(H)
MARSH FERN	Thelypteris palustris	(FN)
MARSH FLEAWORT	Senecio palustris	(H)
MARSH FLOWER	Limnanthes	(A)
MARSH FLOWER	Villarsia calthifolia	(H)
MARSH FORGET-ME-NOT	Myosotis secunda	(H)
MARSH FOXTAIL	Alopecurus geniculatus	(G)
MARSH GENTIAN	Gentiana pneumonanthe	(H)
MARSH HAWK'S-BEARD	Crepis paludosa	(H)
MARSH HELLEBORINE	Epipactis palustris	(O)
MARSH LOUSEWORT	Pedicularis palustris	(A)
MARSH MALLOW	Althaea officinalis	(H)
MARSH MARIGOLD	Caltha palustris	(WA)
MARSH MEADOW GRASS	Poa palustris	(G)
MARSH PEA	Lathyrus palustris	(H)
MARSH PENNYWORT	Hydrocotyle vulgaris	(H)
MARSH RAGWORT	Senecio aquaticus	(B)
MARSH ROSEMARY	Andromeda polifolia	(S)

Know Your Common Plant Names

Common	Botanical	Type
MARSH ROSEMARY	Ledum palustre	(S)
MARSH ROSEMARY	Limonium	(H)
MARSH SOW-THISTLE	Sonchus palustris	(H)
MARSH SPEEDWELL	Veronica scutellata	(H)
MARSH ST. JOHN'S WORT	Hypericum elodes	(WP)
MARSH STITCHWORT	Stellaria palustris	(H)
MARSH TEA	Ledum palustre	(S)
MARSH THISTLE	Cirsium palustre	(H)
MARSH TREFOIL	Menyanthes trifoliata	(WP)
MARSH VALERIAN	Valeriana dioica	(H)
MARSH WILLOWHERB	Epilobium palustra	(H)
MARSH WOUNDWORT	Stachys palustris	(H)
MARSH YELLOW CRESS	Rorippa islandica	(H)
MARTAGON LILY	Lilium martagon	(BB)
MARVEL OF PERU	Mirabilis jalapa	(H)
MARYLAND DITTANY	Cunila origanoides	(H)
MARYLAND PINK ROOT	Spigelia marilandica	(BB)
MASCARENE GRASS	Zoysia tenuifolia	(G)
MASK FLOWER	Alonsoa warscewiczii	(A)
MASTERWORT	Astrantia;	(H)
MASTERWORT	Peucedanum ostruthium	(H)
MASTIC	Pistacia lentiscus	(T)
MAT GRASS	Nardus stricta	(G)
MAT-GRASS FESCUE	Vulpia unilateralis	(G)
MATA KUCHING	Nephelium malaiense	(TT)
MATA NEGRA	Verbena tridens	(H)
MATAI	Podocarpus spicatus	(C)
MATAI	Prumnopitys taxifolia	(C)
MATCH-ME-IF-YOU-CAN	Acalypha wilkesiana	(HP)
MATE	Ilex paraguensis	(TT)
MATICO	Piper angustifolium	(S)
MATILIJA POPPY	Romneya coulteri	(H/S)
MATRIMONY VINE	Lycium balbarum	(S)
MATTED SEA-LAVENDER	Limonium bellidifolium	(H)
MAUL OAK	Quercus chrysolepis	(ST)
MAXWELL SPRUCE	Picea abies 'Maxwellii'	(C)
MAY	Crataegus laevigata	(ST)
MAY	Crataegus monogyna	(ST)
MAY APPLE	Passiflora incarnata	(CL)
MAY APPLE	Podophyllum pelatum	(H)
MAY LILY	Convallaria majalis	(H)
MAY LILY	Maianthemum bifolium	(H)
MAY POLE	Spathelia simplex	(S)
MAY ROSE	Rosa majalis	(S)
MAYFLOWER	Epigaea repens	(S)
MAYPOP	Passiflora incarnata	(CL)
MAYWEED	Anthemis	(AH)

Common	Botanical	Type
MAYWEED	Matricaria	(H)
MAZZARD	Prunus avium	(T)
MEADOW ANEMONE	Pulsatilla vulgaris	(R)
MEADOW BARLEY	Hordeum secalinum	(G)
MEADOW BEAUTY	Rhexia	(S)
MEADOW BLOOM	Ranunculus acris	(H)
MEADOW BROME	Bromus commutatus	(G)
MEADOW BUTTERCUP	Ranunculus acris	(A)
MEADOW CABBAGE	Symplocarpus foetidus	(H)
MEADOW CLARY	Salvia pratensis	(H)
MEADOW CRANESBILL	Geranium pratense	(H)
MEADOW FESCUE	Festuca pratensis	(G)
MEADOW FOAM	Limmanthes douglasii	(A)
MEADOW FOXTAIL	Alopecurus pratensis	(G)
MEADOW GAGEA	Gagea pratensis	(H)
MEADOW GERANIUM	Geranium pratense	(H)
MEADOW GRASS	Poa pratensis	(G)
MEADOW LILY	Lilium canadense	(BB)
MEADOW OAT GRASS	Arenula pratensis	(G)
MEADOW ORCHID	Dactylorhiza incarnata	(O)
MEADOW ROSE	Rosa blanda	(S)
MEADOW RUE	Thalictrum	(H)
MEADOW SAFFRON	Colchicum autumnale	(BB)
MEADOW SAXIFRAGE	Saxifraga granulata	(R)
MEADOW SWEET	Filipendula ulmaria	(H)
MEADOW THISTLE	Cirsium dissectum	(H)
MEADOW VETCHLING	Lathyrus pratensis	(CL)
MEADOW-BEAUTY	Rhexia	(H)
MEAL TREE	Viburnum lantana	(S)
MEDICINE PLANT	Aloe vera	(CS)
MEDICK	Medicago	(H)
MEDITERRANEAN LILY	Pancratium maritimum	(BB)
MEDLAR	Mespilus germanica	(T)
MEDUSA'S HEAD	Euphorbia caput-medusae	(H)
MEGASEA	Bergenia	(H)
MELANCHOLY GENTLEMAN	Astrantia major	(H)
MELANCHOLY THISTLE	Cirsium heterophyllum	(H)
MELIC GRASS	Melica	(G)
MELILOT	Melilotus officinalis	(H)
MELON	Cucumis melo	(F)
MELON CACTUS	Melocactus communis	(CS)
MELON PEAR	Solanum muricatum	(S)
MELONCILLO	Passiflora suberosa	(TS)
MELUKHIE	Corchorus olitorius	(S)
MEMORIAL ROSE	Rosa wichuraiana	(R)
MERCURY	Mercurialis	(H)
MERMAID'S HAIR	Chorda filum	(SW)

Common	Botanical	Type
MERRY BELLS	Uvularia grandiflora	(H)
MESCAL	Agave spp.	(CS)
MESCAL BEAN	Sophora secundiflora	(T)
MESCAL BUTTONS	Lophophora williamsii	(CS)
MESQUITE	Prosopis juliflora	(S)
MESSMATE	Eucalyptus obliqua	(T)
METALLIC LEAF BEGONIA	Begonia metallica	(HP)
MEXICAN ASTER	Cosmos bipinnatus	(A)
MEXICAN BLOOD FLOWER	Distictis buccinatoria	(CL)
MEXICAN BUCKEYE	Ungnadia speciosa	(T)
MEXICAN BUSH SAGE	Salvia leucantha	(S)
MEXICAN CHERRY	Prunus capuli	(TS)
MEXICAN CLOVER	Richordia scabra	(TS)
MEXICAN COTTON	Gossypium mexicanum	(H)
MEXICAN CREEPER	Antigonon leptopus	(TCL)
MEXICAN CYPRESS	Cupressus lusitanica	(C)
MEXICAN DAMIANA	Turnera aphrodisiaca	(S)
MEXICAN ELM	Ulmus mexicana	(T)
MEXICAN FAN PALM	Washingtonia robusta	(P)
MEXICAN FLAME VINE	Senecio confusus	(CL)
MEXICAN FLEABANE	Erigeron karkinskianus	(H)
MEXICAN FOXGLOVE	Tetranema mexicana	(H)
MEXICAN JUNIPER	Juniperus flaccida	(C)
MEXICAN LILY	Hippeastrum reginae	(BB)
MEXICAN NUT PINE	Pinus cembroides	(C)
MEXICAN ORANGE BLOSSOM	Choisya ternata	(S)
MEXICAN PETUNIA	Strobilanthes	(HP)
MEXICAN POPPY	Argemone mexicana	(H)
MEXICAN RED SAGE	Salvia fulgens	(S)
MEXICAN SHELL FLOWER	Tigridia	(BB)
MEXICAN STONE PINE	Pinus cembroides	(C)
MEXICAN SUNFLOWER	Tithonia rotundifolia	(H)
MEXICAN SWAMP CYPRESS	Taxodium mucronatum	(C)
MEXICAN TEA	Chenopodium ambrosioides	(H)
MEXICAN TULIP POPPY	Hunnemannia fumariifolia	(A)
MEXICAN WEEPING-PINE	Pinus patula	(C)
MEXICAN WHITE PINE	Pinus ayacahuite	(C)
MEXICAN YAM	Dioscorea mexicana	(F)
MEZEREON	Daphne mezereum	(S)
MICHAELMAS DAISY	Aster novi-belgii	(H)
MICKEY-MOUSE PLANT	Ochna serrulata	(S)
MIDLAND HAWTHORN	Crataegus laevigata	(T)
MIDSUMMER MEN	Rhodiola rosea	(H)
MIDSUMMER MEN	Sedum telephium	(H)
MIGNONETTE	Reseda odorata	(A)
MIGNONETTE PEPEROMIA	Peperomia fraseri	(HP)
MIGNONETTE TREE	Lawsonia inermis	(S)

Know Your Common Plant Names

Common	Botanical	Type
MILANJI CEDAR	Widdringtonia whytei	(C)
MILE-A-MINUTE VINE	Fallopia baldschuanicum	(CL)
MILFOIL	Achillea millefolium	(H)
MILK CAPS	Lactarius sp.	(FU)
MILK CUP	Lactarius	(FU)
MILK PURSLANE	Euphorbia maculata	(A)
MILK THISTLE	Silybum marianum	(H)
MILK THISTLE	Sonchus oleraceus	(H)
MILK TREE	Sapium hippomane	(T)
MILK VETCH	Astragalus, oxytropis	(S)
MILK-PARSLEY	Peucedanum palustre	(H)
MILK-VETCH	Astragalus glycyphyllos	(H)
MILKWEED	Asclepias	(H)
MILKWHITE ROCK-JASMINE	Androsace lactea	(R)
MILKWORT	Polygala	(SH)
MILLET	Eleusine sp.	(V)G.
MILLET	Panicum sp.	(V)G.
MILLET	Paspalum sp.	(V)G.
MILLET	Sorghum vulgare	(G)
MILLET GRASS	Milium	(G)
MIMICRY PLANT	Pleiospilos bolusii	(CS)
MIMOSA	Acacia	(ST)
MIND YOUR OWN BUSINESS	Soleirolia	(HP)
MINER'S LETTUCE	Claytonia perfoliata	(V)
MINIATURE DATE PALM	Phoenix roebelenii	(P)
MINIATURE GRAPE IVY	Cissus striata	(HP)
MINORCA HONEYSUCKLE	Lonicera implexa	(CL)
MINT	Mentha species	(HB)
MINT BUSH	Elsholtzia stauntonii	(S)
MINT BUSH	Prostranthera rotundifolia	(S)
MINT GERANIUM	Balsamita major	(HB)
MIRACULOUS BERRY	Synsepalum dulciferum	(TS)
MIRBECK'S OAK	Quercus canariensis	(T)
MIRO	Prumnopitys ferruginea	(C)
MIRROR PLANT	Coprosma repens	(S)
MISS WILLMOTT'S GHOST	Eryngium giganteum	(H)
MISSEY-MOOSEY	Sorbus americana	(T)
MISSION BELLS	Fritillaria biflora	(BB)
MISSISSIPPI HACKBERRY	Celtis laevigata	(T)
MIST FLOWER	Eupatorium coelestinum	(H)
MIST FLOWER	Eupatorium rugosum	(H)
MISTLETOE	Viscum album	(PE)
MISTLETOE CACTUS	Rhipsalis baceifera	(CS)
MISTLETOE FIG	Ficus deltoidea	(HP)
MITRE CRESS	Myagrum perfoliatum	(H)
MITRE FLOWER	Mitraria coccinea	(S)
MITREWORT	Mitella	(H)

Know Your Common Plant Names

Common	Botanical	Type
MOA GRASS	Gynerium sagittatum	(G)
MOBALA PLUM	Parinari curatellifolia	(II)
MOCCASIN FLOWER	Cypripedium	(O)
MOCK CYPRESS	Kochia scoparia trichophylla	(A)
MOCK ORANGE	Philadelphus	(S)
MOCK PLANE	Acer pseudoplatanus	(T)
MOCK STRAWBERRY	Duchesnea indica	(H)
MOCKERNUT	Carya tomentosa	(T)
MODERN PINK	Dianthus allwoodii	(H)
MODOC CYRPRESS	Cupressus bakeri	(C)
MOGADORE GUM	Acacia gummifera	(T)
MOLDAVIAN BALM	Dracocephalum moldavica	(H)
MOLE PLANT	Euphorbia lathyris	(H)
MOLLY BLOBS	Caltha palustris	(WP)
MOLUCCA BALM	Molucella laevis	(H)
MOLY	Allium moly	(BB)
MOMBIN	Spondias	(B)
MONARCH BIRCH	Betula maximowicziana	(T)
MONARCH OF THE EAST	Sauromatum guttatum	(H)
MONARCH OF THE EAST	Sauromatum venosum	(H)
MONARCH OF THE VELDT	Venidium	(A)
MONDO GRASS	Ophiopogon japonicus	(H)
MONEY FLOWER	Lunaria	(A/H)
MONEY TREE	Crassula ovata	(CS)
MONEYWORT	Lysimachia nummularia	(H)
MONGOLIAN LIME	Tilia monogolica	(T)
MONK'S HOOD	Aconitum napellus	(H)
MONK'S PEPPER TREE	Vitex agnus-castus	(S)
MONK'S RHUBARB	Rumex alpinus	(H)
MONKEY FLOWER	Mimulus	(RH)
MONKEY MUSK	Mimulus luteus	(H)
MONKEY NUT	Arachis hypogaea	(V)
MONKEY ORCHID	Orchis simia	(O)
MONKEY POT TREE	Lecythis usitata	(TF)
MONKEY PUZZLE	Araucaria araucana	(C)
MONKEY ROPE	Rhoicissus capensis	(CL)
MONKEY TAIL	Acalypha hispida	(HP)
MONKEY-BREAD TREE	Adansonia digitata	(F)
MONKEY-POD TREE	Samanea saman	(TT)
MONSTER PLANT	Rafflesia arnoldii	(TS)
MONTBRETIA	Crocosmia	(BB)
MONTEREY CYPRESS	Cupressus macrocarpa	(C)
MONTEREY PINE	Pinus radiata	(C)
MONTEZUMA PINE	Pinus montezumae	(C)
MONTHLY ROSE	Rosa chinensis	(S)
MONTPELIER BROOM	Cytisus monspessulanus	(S)
MONTPELIER MAPLE	Acer monspessulanum	(T)

Common	Botanical	Type
MONTPELIER ROCK ROSE	Cistus monspeliensis	(S)
MOOLAR	Eucalyptus microtheca	(T)
MOON CARROT	Seseli libanotis	(H)
MOON DAISY	Leucanthemella serotina	(H)
MOON DAISY	Leuconthemum vulgare	(H)
MOONFLOWER	Calonyction aculeatum	(CL)
MOONFLOWER	Ipomoea alba	(H)
MOON TREFOIL	Medicago arborea	(S)
MOONFLOWER	Ipomoea alba	(CL)
MOONLIGHT HOLLY	Ilex aquifolium 'Flavescens'	(S)
MOONSEED	Menispermum canadense	(CL)
MOONSTONES	Pachyphytum oviferum	(CS)
MOONWORT	Botrychium	(FN)
MOONWORT	Lunaria	(B)
MOONWORT	Soldanella	(R)
MOONWORT FERN	Botrychium lunaria	(FN)
MOOR MAT GRASS	Nardus stricta	(G)
MOOR-KING	Pedicularis sceptrum-carolinum	(H)
MOOSE BARK	Acer pensylvanicum	(T)
MOOSE ELM	Ulmus rubra	(T)
MOOSEBERRY	Viburnum pauciflorum	(S)
MOOSEWOOD	Acer pensylvanicum	(T)
MOP-HEAD ACACIA	Robinia pseudoacacia 'Umbraculifera'	(T)
MOP-HEAD HYDRANGEA	Hydrangea 'hortensia'	(S)
MORETON BAY CHESTNUT	Castanospermum australe	(TT)
MORETON BAY FIG	Ficus macrophylla	(HP)
MORETON BAY PINE	Araucaria cunninghamii	(C)
MORINDA SPRUCE	Picea smithiana	(C)
MORMON TEA	Ephedra nevadensis	(H)
MORNING GLORY	Ipomoea	(A.CL)
MORNING GLORY BUSH	Ipomoea fistulosa	(TS)
MORNING GLORY TREE	Ipomoea arborescens	(TT)
MOROCCAN BROOM	Cytisus battandieri	(S)
MOROCCAN FIR	Abies macrocana	(C)
MOSAIC PLANT	Fittonia argyroneura	(HP)
MOSCHATEL	Adoxa moschatellina	(H)
MOSES IN THE CRADLE	Tradescantia spathacea	(HP)
MOSO-CHIKU	Phyllostachys pubescens	(C)
MOSQUITO GRASS	Bouteloua gracilis	(G)
MOSS CAMPION	Silene acaulis	(H)
MOSS PHLOX	Phlox subulata	(R)
MOSS ROSE	Rosa centifolia muscosa	(S)
MOSSY CYPHEL	Minuartia sedoides	(H)
MOSSY ROCKFOIL	Saxifraga hypnoides	(R)
MOSSY SANDWORT	Mochringia muscosa	(H)
MOSSY SAXIFRAGE	Saxifraga hyproides	(R)
MOSSY-CUP OAK	Quercus macrocarpa	(T)

Common	Botanical	Type
MOTH MULLEIN	Verbascum blattaria	(H)
MOTH ORCHID	Phalaenopsis	(O)
MOTHER OF PEARL PLANT	Graptopetalum paraguayense	(H)
MOTHER OF THOUSANDS	Saxifraga stolonifera	(HP)
MOTHER OF THOUSANDS	Tolmiea menziesii	(HP)
MOTHER-IN-LAW'S-TONGUE	Sansevieria trifasciata	(HP)
MOTHER-IN-LAWS SEAT	Echinocactus grusonii	(CS)
MOTHER-OF-PEARL PLANT	Graptopetalum paraguayense	(CS)
MOTHER-OF-THOUSANDS	Tolmiea menziesii	(HP)
MOTHERWORT	Leonurus cardiaca	(HB)
MOTILLO	Soleanea berteriana	(TT)
MOUNT ATLAS DAISY	Anacyclus depressus	(A)
MOUNT ETNA BROOM	Genista aetnensis	(S)
MOUNT MORRISON BERDERIS	Berberis morrisonensis	(S)
MOUNT MORRISON SPRUCE	Picea morrisonicola	(C)
MOUNT OMEI ROSE	Rosa sericea	(S)
MOUNT WELLINGTON PEPPERMINT	Eucalyptus coccifera	(T)
MOUNTAIN ALISON	Alyssum montanum	(R)
MOUNTAIN ANDROMEDA	Pieris floribunda	(S)
MOUNTAIN ASH	Eucalyptus regnans	(T)
MOUNTAIN ASH	Sorbus aucuparia	(T)
MOUNTAIN AVENS	Dryas octopetala	(R)
MOUNTAIN AZALEA	Loiseleuria procumbens	(C)
MOUNTAIN BEECH	Nothofagus cliffortioides	(T)
MOUNTAIN BLADDER FERN	Cystopteris montana	(FN)
MOUNTAIN BOX	Arctostaphylos uva-ursi	(S)
MOUNTAIN BUCKLER FERN	Thelypteris oreopteris	(FN)
MOUNTAIN CEDAR	Juniperus ashei	(C)
MOUNTAIN CHERRY	Prunus prostrata	(S)
MOUNTAIN CRANESBILL	Geranium pyrenaicum	(H)
MOUNTAIN CURRANT	Ribes alpinum	(S)
MOUNTAIN CYPRESS	Widdrintonia cupressoides	(C)
MOUNTAIN EBONY	Bauhinia	(T/CS)
MOUNTAIN EVERLASTING	Antennaria dioica	(R)
MOUNTAIN FLAX	Phormium colensoi	(S)
MOUNTAIN FLAX	Phormium cookianum	(S)
MOUNTAIN FLEECE	Polygonum amplexicaule	(H)
MOUNTAIN FOXGLOVE	Ourisia macrophylla	(H)
MOUNTAIN FRINGE	Adlumia fungosa	(CL)
MOUNTAIN GARLAND	Clarkia unquiculata	(A)
MOUNTAIN GERMANDER	Teucrium montanum	(H)
MOUNTAIN GRAPE	Mahonia aquifolium	(S)
MOUNTAIN GREEN	Spathelia simplex	(S)
MOUNTAIN GUAVA	Psidium montanum	(F)
MOUNTAIN HEATH	Phyllodoce caerulea	(H)
MOUNTAIN HEMLOCK	Tsuga mertensiana	(C)
MOUNTAIN HICKORY	Acacia penninervis	(T)

Know Your Common Plant Names

Common	Botanical	Type
MOUNTAIN HOLLY	Nemopanthus	(S)
MOUNTAIN HOLLY	Olearia illicifolia	(S)
MOUNTAIN HOLLYHOCK	Iliamna rivularis	(A)
MOUNTAIN KIEPERSOL	Cussonia paniculata	(S)
MOUNTAIN KNAPWEED	Centaurea montana	(H)
MOUNTAIN LAUREL	Kalmia latifolia	(S)
MOUNTAIN MAHOE	Hibiscus elatus	(TT)
MOUNTAIN MAHOGANY	Cercocarpus montanus	(S)
MOUNTAIN MALE FERN	Dryopteris oreades	(FN)
MOUNTAIN MAPLE	Acer spicatum	(T)
MOUNTAIN MELICK	Melica nutans	(G)
MOUNTAIN MINT	Micromeria thymifolia	(H)
MOUNTAIN MINT	Pycnanthemum	(H)
MOUNTAIN PANSY	Viola lutea	(H)
MOUNTAIN PAPAW	Carica cundinamarcensis	(F)
MOUNTAIN PEPPER	Drimys lanceolata	(S)
MOUNTAIN PHLOX	Linanthus grandiflorus	(H)
MOUNTAIN PINE	Dacrydium bidwillii	(C)
MOUNTAIN PINE	Pinus mugo	(C)
MOUNTAIN PINE	Pinus uncinata	(C)
MOUNTAIN PRIDE	Penstemon newberryi	(R)
MOUNTAIN ROCKET	Bellendena montana	(R)
MOUNTAIN ROSE BAY	Rhododendron catawbiense	(S)
MOUNTAIN SANDWORT	Minuartia rubella	(H)
MOUNTAIN SEDGE	Carex montana	(G)
MOUNTAIN SILVERBELL	Halesia monticola	(T)
MOUNTAIN SNOW	Euphorbia marginata	(H)
MOUNTAIN SNOWDROP TREE	Halesia monticola	(T)
MOUNTAIN SORREL	Oxyria digyna	(H)
MOUNTAIN SPEEDWELL	Veronica montana	(H)
MOUNTAIN SPIDERWORT	Lloydia serotina	(BB)
MOUNTAIN SPURGE	Pachysandra	(S)
MOUNTAIN ST. JOHN'S WORT	Hypericum montanum	(S)
MOUNTAIN TASSEL	Soldanella montana	(R)
MOUNTAIN TEA	Gaultheria	(S)
MOUNTAIN TOBACCO	Arnica montana	(H)
MOUNTAIN VALERIAN	Valeriana montana	(H)
MOUNTAIN VIOLET	Viola lutea	(H)
MOUNTAIN WHITE PINE	Pinus monticola	(C)
MOUNTAIN WILLOW	Salix arbuscula	(S)
MOURNFUL WIDOW	Scabiosa atropurpurea	(H)
MOURNING BRIDE	Scabiosa	(H)
MOURNING CYPRESS	Cupressus funebris	(C)
MOURNING IRIS	Iris susiana	(BB)
MOURNING WIDOW	Geranium phaeum	(H)
MOUSE TAIL	Myosurus minimus	(H)
MOUSE TAIL PLANT	Arisarum probiscideum	(H)

Common	Botanical	Type
MOUSE-EAR	Cerastium	(H)
MOUSE-EAR HAWKWEED	Hieraceum pilosella	(AH)
MOUSE-TAIL	Myosurus minimus	(H)
MOUSETAIL	Myosurus minimus	(H)
MOUTAN	Paeonia suffruticosa	(S)
MOUTHROOT	Coptis	(H)
MUDGEE WATTLE	Acacia spectabilis	(T)
MUDWORT	Limosella aquatica	(H)
MUGGA	Eucalyptus sideroxylon	(T)
MUGWORT	Artemisia vulgaris	(HA)
MUHUGU	Brachylaena huillensis	(TS)
MULBERRY	Morus	(T)
MULBERRY FIG	Ficus sycomorus	(HP)
MULE'S EAR DAISY	Wyethia helenioides	(S)
MULLEIN	Verbascum	(H)
MUNG BEAN	Phaseolus aureus	(V)
MURIEL BAMBOO	Thamnocalamus spathaceus	(G)
MURRAY RED GUM	Eucalyptus camaldulensis	(T)
MURRAY RIVER PINE	Callitris columellaris	(C)
MURRAY RIVER PINE	Callitris glauca	(C)
MURTILLO	Ugni molinae	(T)
MUSCADINE	Vitis rotundifolia	(F)
MUSHROOM	Agaricus bisporus	(FU)
MUSK	Mimulus moschatus	(HA)
MUSK HYACINTH	Muscari moschatum	(BB)
MUSK HYACINTH	Muscari muscarini	(BB)
MUSK MALLOW	Malva moschata	(H)
MUSK ORCHID	Herminium monorchis	(O)
MUSK ORCHIS	Herminium monorchis	(O)
MUSK ROSE	Rosa moschata	(S)
MUSK SEED	Abelmoschus moschatus	(V)
MUSK THISTLE	Carduus nutans	(H)
MUSK WILLOW	Salix aegyptiaca	(ST)
MUSKMELON	Cucumis melo	(F)
MUSKRAT WEED	Conium maculatum	(H)
MUSKWOOD	Olearia argophylla	(S)
MUSKY SAXIFRAGE	Saxifraga moschata	(R)
MUSQUASH ROOT	Conium maculatum	(H)
MUSSEL WRACK	Ascophyllum nodosum	(SW)
MUSTANG GRAPE	Vitis candicans	(F)
MUSTARD	Brassica nigra	(V)
MUSTARD	Sinapis alba	(V)
MYROBALAN PLUM	Prunus cerasifera	(ST)
MYRRH	Commifera abyssinica	(TT)
MYRRH	Commifera molmol	(TT)
MYRRH	Commifera myrrha	(TT)
MYRRH	Myrrhis odorata	(HB)

Know Your Common Plant Names

Common	Botanical	Type
MYRTLE	Myrtus	(S)
MYRTLE BEECH	Nothofagus cunninghamii	(T)
MYRTLE FLAG	Acorus calamus	(H)
MYRTLE GRASS	Acorus calamus	(H)
MYRTLE SEDGE	Acorus calamus	(H)
NAILWORT	Draba	(R)
NAILWORT	Paronychia	(R)
NAKED LADIES	Colchicum autumnale	(BB)
NAMAQUALAND DAISY	Dimorphotheca pluvialis	(H)
NAMAQUALAND DAISY	Dimorphotheca sinuata	(A)
NAMAQUALAND DAISY	Venidium fastuosum	(H)
NAN SHAN	Cotoneaster adpressus praecox	(S)
NANCY-PRETTY	Saxifraga umbrosa	(CR)
NANCY-PRETTY	Saxifraga urbium	(R)
NANKEEN LILY	Lilium testaceum	(BB)
NANKING CHERRY	Prunus tomentosa	(S)
NANNY-BERRY	Viburnum lentago	(S)
NANTEN	Nandina	(S)
NAPIER GRASS	Pennisetum purpureum	(G)
NAPOLEAN'S BUTTON	Napoleona heudottii	(TT)
NARANJILLA	Solanum quitoense	(TS)
NARANJILLO	Villaresia mucronata	(S)
NARIHIRA BAMBOO	Semiarundinaria fastuosa	(G)
NARROW-LEAVED ASH	Fraxinus angustifolia	(T)
NARROW-LEAVED BITTER CRESS	Cardamine impatiens	(H)
NARROW-LEAVED EEL-GRASS	Zostera angustifolia	(WP)
NARROW-LEAVED GRASS-WRACK	Zostera angustifolia	(WP)
NARROW-LEAVED INULA	Inula ensifolia	(H)
NARROW-LEAVED LUNGWORT	Pulmonaria longifolia	(H)
NARROW-LEAVED PEPPERMINT	Eucalyptus radiata	(T)
NARROW-LEAVED PEPPERWORT	Lepidium ruderale	(H)
NARROW-LEAVED PLANTAIN LILY	Hosta lancifolia	(CH)
NARROW-LIPPED ORCHID	Epipactis leptochila	(O)
NASEBERRY	Manilkara zapota	(F)
NASHI	Pyrus pyrifolia	(F)
NASTURTIUM	Tropaeolum majus	(A)
NATAL GRASS	Rhynchelytrum repens	(G)
NATAL GRASS	Tricholaena rosea	(G)
NATAL PLUM	Carissa grandiflora	(S)
NATIVE FRANGIPANI	Hymenosporum flavum	(TS)
NATIVE'S COMB	Pachycereus pecten-aboriginum	(CS)
NAVELWORT	Omphalodes; Umbilicus	(H)
NECKLACE POPLAR	Populus deltoides	(T)
NECTARINE	Prunus persica nectarina	(F)
NEEDLE BUSH	Azima tetracantha	(S)
NEEDLE FURZE	Genista anglica	(S)
NEEDLE JUNIPER	Juniperus rigida	(C)

Know Your Common Plant Names

Common	Botanical	Type
NEEDLE ROSE	Rosa acicularis	(S)
NEEDLE SPIKE-RUSH	Eleocharis acicularis	(G)
NEMESIA	Nemesia strumosa	(A)
NEMU TREE	Albizzia	(TT)
NEPAL BARBERRY	Berberis aristata	(S)
NEPAL LABURNUM	Piptanthus	(S)
NEPALESE WHITE THORN	Pyracantha crenulata	(S)
NERO'S CROWN	Tabernaemontana coronaria	(S)
NERVE ROOT	Cypripedium	(O)
NEST SPRUCE	Picea abies 'Nidiformis'	(C)
NET-LEAVED WILLOW	Salix reticulata	(S)
NETFERN	Gleichenia	(FN)
NETTED IRIS	Iris reticulata	(BB)
NETTED WILLOW	Salix reiculata	(S)
NETTLE	Urtica	(HA)
NETTLE TREES	Celtis species	(T)
NETTLE-LEAVED BELLFLOWER	Campanula trachelium	(H)
NEVER NEVER PLANT	Ctenanthe oppenheimiana	(HP)
NEW ENGLAND BOXWOOD	Cornus florida	(S/T)
NEW HOLLAND VIOLET	Viola hederacea	(H)
NEW JERSEY TEA PLANT	Ceanothus americanus	(S)
NEW ZEALAND BRACKEN	Hypolepis	(FN)
NEW ZEALAND BURR	Acaena microphylla	(R)
NEW ZEALAND CHRISTMAS TREE	Metrosideros tomentosa	(T)
NEW ZEALAND DAISY	Celmisia	(H)
NEW ZEALAND DAISY BUSH	Olearia	(S)
NEW ZEALAND EDELWEISS	Leucogenes	(H)
NEW ZEALAND FLAX	Linum monogynum	(H)
NEW ZEALAND FLAX	Phormium	(S)
NEW ZEALAND HOLLY	Olearia macrodonta	(S)
NEW ZEALAND HONEYSUCKLE	Knightia Excelsa	(T)
NEW ZEALAND LABURNUM	Sophora tetraptera	(S)
NEW ZEALAND LAUREL	Corynocarpus	(T)
NEW ZEALAND LILAC	Hebe hulkeana	(S)
NEW ZEALAND SATIN FLOWER	Libertia grandiflora	(H)
NEW ZEALAND SPINACH	Tetragonia expansa	(V)
NEW ZEALAND TEA TREE	Leptospermum	(S)
NEW ZEALAND TREE FERN	Dicksonia squarrosa	(FN)
NEW ZEALAND WHITE PINE	Dacrycarpus dacrydioides	(C)
NEW ZEALAND WILLOW HERB	Epilobium brunnescens	(H)
NGAIO	Myoporum laetum	(S)
NICKER-BEAN	Caesalpinia	(S)
NICOBAR BREADFRUIT	Pandanus leram	(TS)
NIGER SEED	Guizotia abyssinica	(TS)
NIGHT JASMINE	Cestrum nocturnum	(S/T)
NIGHT SHADE	Solanum, Atropa	(AH)
NIGHT-BLOOMING CEREUS	Hylocereus undatus	(CS)

Know Your Common Plant Names

Common	Botanical	Type
NIGHT-BLOOMING CEREUS	Selenicereus grandiflorus	(CS)
NIGHT-BLOOMING JESSAMINE	Cestrum nocturnum	(S)
NIGHT-FLOWERING CATCHFLY	Silene noctiflora	(H)
NIGHT-SCENTED STOCK	Matthiola bicornis	(A)
NIKKO FIR	Abies homolepis	(C)
NIKKO MAPLE	Acer maximowicziana	(T)
NINE BARK	Physocarpus opulifolius	(S)
NINE-JOINTS	Polygonum aviculare	(A)
NIPPLE CACTUS	Neobessya similis	(CS)
NIPPLEWORT	Lapsana communis	(H)
NIRE	Nothofagus antarctica	(T)
NIRRE	Nothofagus antartica	(T)
NISH BROOM	Genista nyssana	(S)
NIT GRASS	Gastridium ventricosum	(G)
NOAH'S ARK JUNIPER	Juniperus communis 'Compressa"	(C)
NOBLE FIR	Abies procera	(C)
NODDING AVENS	Geum rivale	(WP)
NODDING BUR-MARIGOLD	Bidens cernua	(WP)
NODDING THISTLE	Carduus nutans	(H)
NONE-SO-PRETTY	Saxifraga urbium	(R)
NONEA	Nonea pulla	(H)
NONSUCH	Medicago lupulina	(H)
NOOTKA CYPRESS	Chamaecyparis nootkatensis	(C)
NOPAL	Opuntia megacantha	(CS)
NORFOLK ISLAND HIBISCUS	Lagunaria patersonii	(S)
NORFOLK ISLAND PINE	Araucaria heterophylla	(C)
NORFOLK ISLAND TREE FERN	Alsophila	(FN)
NORTH AMERICAN SUNFLOWER	Actinomeris	(H)
NORTHERN BAYBERRY	Myrica pennsylvanica	(S)
NORTHERN DOWNY ROSE	Rosa sherardii	(S)
NORTHERN DRAGONHEAD	Dracocephalum ruyschiana	(H)
NORTHERN FOX GRAPE	Vitis labrusca	(F)
NORTHERN HAWK'S BEARD	Crepis mollis	(H)
NORTHERN JAPANESE HEMLOCK	Tsuga diversifolia	(C)
NORTHERN JAPANESE MAGNOLIA	Magnolia kobus	(S)
NORTHERN MARSH ORCHID	Dactylorhiza purpurella	(O)
NORTHERN PITCH PINE	Pinus rigida	(C)
NORTHERN ROCKCRESS	Cardaminopsis petraea	(H)
NORTHERN SHORE-WORT	Mertensia maritima	(H)
NORTHERN WHITE CEDAR	Thuya occidentalis	(C)
NORTHERN WOLFSBANE	Aconitum lycotonum lycotonum	(H)
NORWAY MAPLE	Acer platanoides	(T)
NORWAY SPRUCE	Picea abies	(C)
NOSEBLEED	Achillea millefolium	(H)
NOTTINGHAM CATCHFLY	Silene nutans	(H)
NUT GRASS	Cyperus rotundus	(G)
NUT ORCHID	Achimenes	(HP)

Common	Botanical	Type
NUT PINE	Pinus cembroides	(C)
NUTMEG	Myristica flagrans	(HB)
NUTMEG FLOWER	Nigella sativa	(A)
NUTMEG HICKORY	Carya myristiciformis	(T)
NUTMEG-SCENTED GERANIUM	Pelargonium x fragrans	(A)
NUTPINE	Pinus cembroides	(C)
NUTTALL'S DOGWOOD	Cornus nuttallii	(T)
NUTTALL'S WATER-THYME	Elodea nuttallii	(WP)
NUX REGIA	Juglans regia	(T)
NUX VOMICA	Strychnos nux-vomica	(TT)
OAK	Quercus	(T)
OAK FERN	Gymnocarpium dryopteris	(FN)
OAK LEAVED GERANIUM	Pelargonium quercifolium	(HP)
OAK-LEAFED HYDRANGEA	Hydrangea quercifolia	(S)
OAK-LEAVED GOOSEFOOT	Chenopodium glaucum	(H)
OAR WEED	Laminaria longicruris	(SW)
OAT GRASS	Arrhenatherum elatius	(G)
OAT GRASS	Helictotrichon sempervirens	(G)
OATS	Avena sativa	(V)
OBECHE	Triplochiton scleroxylon	(TT)
OBEDIENT PLANT	Physostegia	(H)
OCEAN SPRAY	Holodiscus discolor	(S)
OCONEE BELLS	Shortia galacifolia	(R)
OCOTILLO	Fouquieria splendens	(CS)
OCTOPUS PLANT	Aloe arborescens	(HP)
OFFICINAL SPURGE	Euphorbia resinifera	(H)
OGECHEE LIME	Nyssa candicans	(T)
OHIO BUCKEYE	Aesculus glabra	(T)
OIL PALM	Elaeis guineensis	(P)
OILCLOTH FLOWER	Anthurium andraenum	(HP)
OILSEED RAPE	Brassica napus oleifera	(F)
OKINAWA PINE	Pinus luchuensis	(C)
OKRA	Abelmoschus esculentus	(V)
OLD ENGLISH LAVENDER	Lavendula angustifolia	(S)
OLD LADY	Mammillaria hahniana	(CS)
OLD MAID	Catharanthus	(HP)
OLD MAN	Artemisia abrotanum	(H)
OLD MAN CACTUS	Cephalocereus senilis	(CS)
OLD MAN OF THE ANDES	Borzicactus celsianus	(CS)
OLD MAN OF THE ANDES	Oreocereus trollii	(CS)
OLD MAN OPUNTIA	Opuntia vestita	(CS)
OLD MAN'S BEARD	Chionanthus virginicus	(S)
OLD MAN'S BEARD	Clematis vitalba	(CL)
OLD MANS NIGHT CAP	Calystegia sepium	(CL)
OLD WARRIOR	Artemisia pontica	(HB)
OLD WOMAN	Artemisia stellerana	(H)
OLD-MAN CACTUS	Cephalocereus senilis	(CS)

Common	Botanical	Type
OLD-WITCH GRASS	Panicum capillare	(G)
OLEANDER	Nerium oleader	(S)
OLEASTER	Elaeagnus angustifolia	(ST)
OLIBANUS TREE	Boswellia	(TT)
OLIVE	Olea europaea	(ST)
OLIVE BARK TREE	Terminalia catappa	(TT)
OLIVER'S LIME	Tilia oliveri	(T)
OMBU	Phytolacca dioica	(H)
ONE-FLOWERED PYROLA	Moneses uniflora	(H)
ONE-LEAFED ASH	Fraxinus exc. 'Diversifolia'	(T)
ONION	Allium cepa	(V)
ONTARIO POPLAR	Populus candicans	(T)
OPITONG	Dipterocarpus sp.	(TT)
OPIUM POPPY	Papaver somniferum	(A)
OPPOSITE-LEAVED PONDWEED	Groenlandia densa	(WP)
ORACHE	Atriplex hortensis	(AH)
ORANGE	Citrus sinensis	(F)
ORANGE BALL TREE	Buddleia globosa	(S)
ORANGE BALSAM	Impatiens capensis	(A)
ORANGE CHEMPACA	Michelia champaca	(S/T)
ORANGE DAISY	Erigeron aurantiacus	(H)
ORANGE FOXTAIL	Alopecurus aequalis	(G)
ORANGE HAWKWEED	Hieracium aurantiacum	(H)
ORANGE HAWKWEED	Hieracium brunneocroceum	(H)
ORANGE JESSAMINE	Murraya exotica	(S)
ORANGE LILY	Lilium bulbiferum	(BB)
ORANGE MILKWEED	Asclepias tuberosa	(H)
ORANGE MULLEIN	Verbascum phlomoides	(H)
ORANGE ROOT	Hydrastis canadensis	(H)
ORANGE SUNFLOWER	Heliopsis	(H)
ORANGE TRUMPET HONEYSUCKLE	Lonicera ciliosa	(CL)
ORANGE TRUMPET VINE	Pyrostegia venusta	(TCL)
ORANGE-BARK MYRTLE	Luma apiculata	(T)
ORANGE-PEEL CLEMATIS	Clematis orientalis	(CL)
ORANGE-SCENTED GERANIUM	Pelargonium 'Prince of Orange'	(A)
ORCHARD APPLE	Malus domestica	(T)
ORCHARD GRASS	Dactylis glomerata	(G)
ORCHID CACTUS	Epiphyllum	(CS)
ORCHID CACTUS	Nopalxochia ackermannii	(CS)
ORCHID TREE	Bauhinia purpurea	(TT)
ORDEAL BEAN	Physostigma venenosum	(TS)
OREGANO	Origanum vulgare	(HB)
OREGON ALDER	Alnus rubra	(T)
OREGON ASH	Fraxinus latifolia	(T)
OREGON CRAB	Malus fusca	(T)
OREGON DOUGLAS FIR	Pseudotsuga menziesii	(C)
OREGON GRAPE	Mahonia aquifolium	(S)

Know Your Common Plant Names

Common	Botanical	Type
OREGON IRIS	Iris tenax	(H)
OREGON MAPLE	Acer macrophyllum	(T)
OREGON MYRTLE	Umbellularia californica	(S)
OREGON OAK	Quercus garryana	(T)
OREGON PLUM	Prunus subcordata	(S)
OREGON TEA	Ceanothus sanguineus	(S)
ORGAN-PIPE CACTUS	Lemaireocereus marginatus	(CS)
ORGAN-PIPE CACTUS	Lemairocereus thurbori	(CS)
ORIENTAL BEECH	Fagus orientalis	(T)
ORIENTAL CORKOAK	Quercus variabilis	(T)
ORIENTAL GINSENG	Panax ginseng	(TS)
ORIENTAL PLANE	Platanus orientalis	(T)
ORIENTAL POPPY	Papaver orientale	(H)
ORIENTAL SPRUCE	Picea orientalis	(C)
ORIENTAL THORN	Crataegus laciniata	(T)
ORLAYA	Orlaya grandiflora	(H)
ORNAMENTAL BRAMBLE	Rubus	(S)
ORNAMENTAL CABBAGE	Brassica oleracea acephala	(A)
ORNAMENTAL CORN	Zea japonica	(H)
ORNAMENTAL MAIZE	Zea japonica	(A)
ORNAMENTAL MONK'S HOOD	Astrophytum ornatum	(CS)
ORNAMENTAL PEPPER	Capsicum annuum	(F)
ORNAMENTAL QUINCE	Chaenomeles	(S)
ORNAMENTAL RHUBARB	Rheum	(H)
ORNAMENTAL YAM	Dioscorea discolor	(F)
ORPINE	Sedum telephium	(H)
ORRIS ROOT	Iris florentina	(H)
OSAGE ORANGE	Maclura pomifera	(ST)
OSHIMA CHERRY	Prunus speciosa	(T)
OSIER	Salix viminalis	(ST)
OSOBERRY	Oemleria cerasiformis	(S)
OSTRICH FERN	Matteucia struthiopteris	(FN)
OSWEGO TEA	Monarda didyma	(H)
OTAHEITE APPLE	Spondias dulcis	(T)
OTAHEITE CHESTNUT	Inocarpus edulis	(TT)
OTAHEITE GOOSEBERRY	Phyllanthus	(S)
OTAHEITE MYRTLE	Securinega durissima	(TS)
OTENIQUA YELLOW WOOD	Podocarpus falcatus	(C)
OUCH BUSH	Daviesia acicularis	(S)
OUCH BUSH	Daviesia pachyphylla	(S)
OUR LADY'S TEARS	Convallaria majalis	(H)
OUR LADY'S THISTLE	Silybum marianum	(H)
OUR LORD'S CANDLE	Yucca whipplei	(S)
OUTDOOR FREESIA	Freesia hybrida	(BB)
OVAL SEDGE	Carex ovalis	(G)
OVAL-LEAF PRIVET	Ligustrum ovalifolium	(S)
OVENS WATTLE	Acacia pravissima	(T)

Common	Botanical	Type
OVERCUP OAK	Quercus lyrata	(T)
OWE COLA	Cola verticilliata	(TF)
OX HOOF TREE	Bauhinia purpurea	(TT)
OX-EYE CHAMOMILE	Anthemis tinctoria	(H)
OX-EYE DAISY	Leucanthemum vulgare/	(H)
OX-TONGUE LILY	Haemanthus coccineus	(HP)
OXFORD RAGWORT	Senecio squalidus	(A)
OXLIP	Primula elatior	(H)
OYSTER FUNGUS	Pleurotus ostreatus	(FU)
OYSTER NUTS	Telfairia occidentalis	(TS)
OYSTER PLANT	Mertensia maritima	(H)
OYSTER PLANT	Tragopogon porrifolius	(V)
OZARK WITCH HAZEL	Hamamelis vernalis	(S)
PACIFIC DOGWOOD	Cornus nuttallii	(ST)
PACIFIC SILVER FIR	Abies amabilis	(C)
PACIFIC WHITE FIR	Abies concolor lowiana	(C)
PACIFIC WILLOW	Salix lasiandra	(S)
PACIFIC YEW	Taxus brevifolia	(C)
PADDY RIVER BOX	Eucalyptus macarthurii	(T)
PAEONY	Paeonia	(H/S)
PAGODA DOGWOOD	Cornus alternifolia	(S)
PAGODA FLOWER	Clerodendrum paniculatum	(TS)
PAGODA TREE	Plueria rubra	(TT)
PAGODA TREE	Sophora japonica	(T)
PAHAUTEA	Libocedrus bidwillii	(C)
PAIGLE	Primula elatior	(H)
PAIGLES	Primula elatior	(H)
PAINROOT	Lachnanthes tinctoria	(H)
PAINTED CUP	Castilleja	(H)
PAINTED DAISY	Chrysanthemum carinatum	(A)
PAINTED DAISY	Tanacetum coccineum	(H)
PAINTED DROP-TONGUE	Aglaonema crispum 'Silver Queen'	(HP)
PAINTED FEATHER	Vriesia carinata	(HP)
PAINTED LADY	Echeveria derenbergii	(CS)
PAINTED LEAF	Eurphorbia pulcherrima	(A)
PAINTED TONGUE	Salpiglossis	(A)
PAINTED TRILLIUM	Trillium undulatum	(H)
PAINTED WOOD-LILY	Trillium undulatum	(H)
PAINTER'S PALETTE	Anthurium andreanum	(HP)
PAK-CHOI	Brassica chinensis	(V)
PALE DOG-VIOLET	Viola lactea	(H)
PALE FLAX	Linum bienne	(B)
PALE PERSICARIA	Polygonum lapathifolium	(H)
PALE SEDGE	Carex curta	(G)
PALE SEDGE	Carex pallescens	(G)
PALE TOADFLAX	Linaria repens	(H)
PALE WILLOWHERB	Epilobium roseum	(H)

Common	Botanical	Type
PALESTINE OAK	Quercus calliprinos	(T)
PALM WILLOW	Salix caprea	(ST)
PALM-LEAF BEGONIA	Begonia luxurians	(HP)
PALM-LEAF FERN	Blechnum capense	(FN)
PALMA CHRISTI	Ricinus	(P)
PALMA CHRISTI	Ricinus communis	(A)
PALMETTO	Sabal palmetto	(T)
PALSYWORT	Primula veris	(H)
PAMPAS GRASS	Cortaderia	(G)
PAN-AMERICAN FRIENDSHIP PLANT	Pilea involucrata	(HP)
PANAMA CANDLE TREE	Parmentiera cercifera	(TT)
PANAMA HAT PLANT	Carludovica palmata	(TS)
PANAMA RUBBER	Castilloa elastica	(TT)
PANAMIGO	Pilea involucrata	(HP)
PANDA PLANT	Kalanchoe tomentosa	(HP)
PANSY	Viola tricolor	(H)
PANSY ORCHID	Miltonia	(O)
PANTHER CAP	Amanita pantherina	(FU)
PANTHER LILY	Lilium pardalinum	(BB)
PAPAYA	Carica papaya	(T)
PAPER BARK	Melaleuca	(T)
PAPER BIRCH	Betula papyrifera	(T)
PAPER BUSH	Edgeworthia	(S)
PAPER DAISY	Helipterum	(H)
PAPER FLOWER	Bougainvillea	(HP)
PAPER FLOWER	Psilostrophe cooperi	(A)
PAPER MULBERRY	Broussonetia papyrifera	(S)
PAPER PLANT	Cyperus papyrus	(G)
PAPER REED	Cyperus papyrus	(G)
PAPER-BARK TREE	Melaleuca quinquenervia	(T)
PAPER-HEATH	Sohenotoma gracilis	(S)
PAPERBARK CHERRY	Prunus serrula	(T)
PAPERBARK MAPLE	Acer griseum	(T)
PAPERWHITES	Narcissus tazetta papyraceus	(BB)
PAPOOSE ROOT	Caulophyllum thalictroides	(S)
PAPRIKA	Capsicum spp.	(F)
PAPYRUS	Cyperus papyrus	(G)
PARA PARA	Pisonia umbellifera	(HP)
PARA RUBBER	Hevea brasiliensis	(TT)
PARACHUTE PLANT	Ceropegia sandersonii	(S)
PARADISE NUT	Lecythis zabucajo	(TT)
PARADISE PALM	Howea forsteriana	(P)
PARAGUAY TEA	Ilex paraguensis	(ST)
PARANA TREE	Araucaria angustifolia	(C)
PARASOL DE ST.JULIEN	Populus tremuloides 'pendula'	(T)
PARASOL MUSHROOM	Lepiota procera	(FU)
PARASOL MUSHROOM	Macrolepiota procera	(FU)

Know Your Common Plant Names

Common	Botanical	Type
PARASOL PINE	Sciadopitys verticilliata	(C)
PARASOL PLANT	Schefflera arboricola	(HP)
PARCHMENT-BARK	Pittosporum	(S/T)
PAREIRA	Chondrodendron tomentosum	(TT)
PARIETARIA	Parietaria officinalis	(H)
PARIS DAISY	Argyranthemum frutescens	(H)
PARLOUR IVY	Senecio mikanioides	(HP)
PARLOUR MAPLE	Abutilon	(S/CL)
PARLOUR PALM	Chamaedorea elegans	(P)
PARMA VIOLET	Viola odorata sp.	(H)
PARROT FUNGUS	Hygrocybe psittacina	(FU)
PARROT LILY	Alstroemeria psittacina	(H)
PARROT'S BILL	Clianthus puniceus	(S)
PARROT'S PLANTAIN	Heliconia psittacorum	(TH)
PARROTS FEATHER	Myriophyllum aquaticum	(WP)
PARRYA	Parrya nudicaulis	(H)
PARSLEY	Petroselinum crispum	(HB)
PARSLEY FERN	Cryptogramma crispa	(FN)
PARSLEY- LEAVED BRAMBLE	Rubus lacinatus	(F)
PARSLEY- LEAVED BRAMBLE	Rubus 'Oregon Thornless'	(F)
PARSLEY PIERT	Aphanes armensis	(H)
PARSLEY VINE	Vitis vinifera 'alpiifolia'	(CL)
PARSLEY WATER DROPWORT	Oenanthe lachenalis	(WP)
PARSLEY-LEAVED ELDER	Sambucus nigra 'laciniata'	(S)
PARSNIP	Pastinaca sativa	(V)
PARSON AND CLERK	Arum maculatum	(H)
PARTRIDGE BERRY	Gaultheria procumbens	(S)
PARTRIDGE BERRY	Mitchella repens	(S)
PARTRIDGE CANE	Rhapis excelsa	(P)
PARTRIDGE PEA	Cassia fasciculata	(TS)
PARTRIDGE PEA	Chamaecrista fasciculata	(V)
PARTRIDGE-BREASTED ALOE	Aloe variegata	(HP)
PASQUE FLOWER	Pulsatilla vulgaris	(R)
PASSION FLOWER	Passiflora incarnata	(CL)
PASSION FRUIT	Passiflora edulis	(F)
PATAGONIAN CYPRESS	Fitzroya	(C)
PATANA PALM	Oenocarpus batava	(P)
PATCHOULI	Pogostemon patchouli	(TS)
PATIENCE	Rumex patientia	(H)
PAWPAW	Asimina triloba	(ST)
PAWPAW	Carica papaya	(TT)
PE-TSAI	Brassica pekinensis	(V)
PEA	Pisum sativum	(V)
PEA TREE	Caragana arborescens	(T)
PEACE LILY	Spathiphyllum wallisii	(HP)
PEACH	Prunus persica	(F)
PEACH PALM	Gulielma gassipaes	(TT)

Know Your Common Plant Names

Common	Botanical	Type
PEACH WOOD	Caesalpinia echinata	(TS)
PEACH-LEAVED BELLFLOWER	Campanula persicifolia	(H)
PEACHWOOD	Haematoxylon campeachianum	(TT)
PEACOCK FLOWER	Caesalpinia pulcherrima	(TT)
PEACOCK FLOWER	Delonix regia	(TT)
PEACOCK IRIS	Moraea	(BB)
PEACOCK PLANT	Calathea makoyana	(HP)
PEACOCK POPPY	Papaver pavoninum	(A)
PEACOCK TIGER FLOWER	Tigridia paronia	(BB)
PEANUT	Arachis hypogaea	(V)
PEANUT CACTUS	Chamaecereus sylvestri	(CS)
PEAR	Pyrus	(F)
PEAR THORN	Crataegus tomentosa	(T)
PEARL BARLEY	Hordeum distichon	(G)
PEARL BERRY	Margyricarpus pinnatus	(S)
PEARL BUSH	Exochorda	(S)
PEARL FRUIT	Margyricarpus pinnatus	(S)
PEARL GRASS	Briza maxima	(G)
PEARL MILLET	Pennisetum glaucum	(G)
PEARL PLANT	Haworthia margaritiflora	(CS)
PEARLWORT	Sagina	(R)
PEARLY EVERLASTING FLOWER	Anaphalis	(H)
PEBBLE PLANTS	Lithops	(R)
PECAN	Carya illinoensis	(T)
PEDLAR'S BASKET	Linaria vulgaris	(H)
PEDUNCULATE OAK	Quercus robur	(T)
PEE IN THE BED	Taraxacum officinale	(H)
PEEPUL TREE	Ficus religiosa	(T)
PEKING WILLOW	Salix babylonica pekinensis	(T)
PELARGONIUM	Pelargonium	(A)
PELICAN FLOWER	Aristolochia grandiflora	(CL)
PELLITORY	Anacyclus pyrethrum	(R)
PELLITORY OF SPAIN	Anacyclus pyrethrum	(H)
PELLITORY-OF-THE-WALL	Parietaria judaica	(R)
PEN WIPER	Kalanchoe marmorata	(HP)
PENCIL CACTUS	Wilcoxia poselgeri	(CS)
PENCIL CHOLLA	Opunta arbuscula	(CS)
PENCIL JUNIPER	Juniperus virginiana	(C)
PENCIL PINE	Athrotaxis	(C)
PENDANT SILVER LIME	Tilia petiolaris	(T)
PENDULOUS BEGONIA	Begonia x tuberhybrida	(BB)
PENDULOUS SEDGE	Carex pendula	(G)
PENNYCRESS	Thlaspi	(R)
PENNYROYAL	Mentha Pulegium	(HB)
PENNYWORT	Cymbalaria muralis	(H)
PENNYWORT	Umbilicus rupestris	(H)
PENWIPER PLANT	Notothlaspi rosulatum	(H)

Know Your Common Plant Names

Common	Botanical	Type
PEONY	Paeonia	(HS
PEPINO	Solanum muricatum	(V)
PEPPER	Capsicum	(F)
PEPPER	Piper nigrum	(F)
PEPPER AND SALT	Capsella bursa-pastoris	(A)
PEPPER AND SALT	Eriostemon gardneri	(H)
PEPPER ELDER	Peperomia	(HP)
PEPPER HIBISCUS	Malaviscus arboreus	(TS)
PEPPER NETTLE	Micromeria	(H)
PEPPER ROOT	Dentaria	(H)
PEPPER SAXIFRAGE	Silaum silaus	(H)
PEPPER TREE	Pseudowintera colorata	(S/T)
PEPPER TREE	Schinus molle	(T)
PEPPER VINE	Ampelopsis arborea	(CL)
PEPPER-GRASS	Lepidium	(H)
PEPPER-SAXIFRAGE	Silaum silaus	(H)
PEPPERGRASS	Lepidium sativum	(H)
PEPPERIDGE	Nyssa sylvatica	(T)
PEPPERMINT	Mentha piperita	(HB)
PEPPERMINT TREE	Agonis flexuosa	(T)
PEPPERMINT-SCENTED GERANIUM	Pelargonium tomentosum	(A)
PEPPERWORT	Lepidium sativum	(H)
PERE DAVID'S MAPLE	Acer davidii	(T)
PEREGRINA	Jatropha integerrima	(TS)
PERENNIAL CENTAURY	Centaurium scilloides	(H)
PERENNIAL CORNFLOWER	Centaurea montana	(H)
PERENNIAL FORGET-ME-NOT	Brunnera	(H)
PERENNIAL GLASSWORT	Arthrocnemum perenne	(H)
PERENNIAL HONESTY	Lunaria rediviva	(H)
PERENNIAL KNAWEL	Scleranthus perennis	(H)
PERENNIAL RYEGRASS	Lolium perenne	(G)
PERENNIAL SAGE	Salvia superba	(H)
PERENNIAL SWEET PEA	Lathyrus latifolius	(H)
PERENNIAL WALL ROCKET	Diplotaxis tenuifolia	(H)
PERFOLIATE HONEYSUCKLE	Lonicera caprifolium	(CL)
PERFOLIATE PENNYCRESS	Thlaspi perfoliatum	(H)
PERFOLIATE PONDWEED	Potamogeton perfoliatus	(WP)
PERFORATE ST. JOHN'S WORT	Hypericum perforatum	(A)
PERIGORD TRUFFLE	Tuber melanosporum	(FU)
PERIWINKLE	Vinca	(S)
PERNY'S HOLLY	Ilex pernyi	(T)
PERRY'S SILVER WEEPING HOLLY	Ilex aquifilium 'Argenteomarginata Pendula'	(ST)
PERSIAN ACACIA	Albizia julibrissin	(T)
PERSIAN BUTTERCUP	Ranunculus asiaticus	(BB)
PERSIAN EVERLASTING PEA	Lathyrus rotundifolium	(H)
PERSIAN IRONWOOD	Parrotia	(T)
PERSIAN IVY	Hedera colchica	(CL)

Common	Botanical	Type
PERSIAN LILAC	Syringa persica	(S)
PERSIAN LIQUORICE	Glycyrrhiza glandulifera	(H)
PERSIAN PELLITORY	Tanacetum coccineum	(H)
PERSIAN SHIELD	Strobilanthes dyerianus	(H)
PERSIAN SPEEDWELL	Veronica persica	(A)
PERSIAN STONE CRESS	Aethionema grandiflorum	(R)
PERSIAN SUN'S EYE	Tulipa occulus-solis	(BB)
PERSIAN VIOLET	Exacum affine	(A)
PERSIAN WALNUT	Juglans regia	(T)
PERSIAN YELLOW ROSE	Rosa foetida 'Persiana'	(S)
PERSIMMON	Diospyros kaki	(T)
PERSIMMON	Diospyros virginiana	(T)
PERUVIAN APPLE CACTUS	Cereus peruvianus	(CS)
PERUVIAN BARK	Cinchona succirubra	(TT)
PERUVIAN DAFFODIL	Hymenocallis narcissiflora	(BB)
PERUVIAN LILY	Alstroemeria	(H)
PERUVIAN MASTIC TREE	Schinus molle	(TT)
PESTLE PARSNIP	Lomatium nudicaule	(H)
PETAI	Parkia speciosa	(TT)
PETAL WEED	Petalonia fasciata	(SW)
PETER'S STAFF	Verbascus thapsus	(H)
PETTICOAT PALM	Copernicia macroglossa	(P)
PETTICOAT PALM	Washingtonia filifera	(P)
PETTY SPURGE	Euphorbia peplus	(H)
PETTY WHIN	Genista anglica	(S)
PEYOTE	Lophophora williamsii	(CS)
PFITZER JUNIPER	Juniperus x media 'Pfitzerana'	(C)
PHACELIA	Phacelia campanularia	(A)
PHAROAHS FIG	Ficus sycomorus	(HP)
PHEASANT BERRY	Leycesteria formosa	(S)
PHEASANT FOOT	Pelargonium glutinosum	(A)
PHEASANT GRASS	Stipa arundinacea	(G)
PHEASANT TAIL GRASS	Stipa arundinacea	(G)
PHEASANT'S EYE	Adonis annua	(A)
PHEASANT'S WINGS	Aloe variegata	(HP)
PHEASANT-EYE NARCISSUS	Narcissus 'Actaea' (false)	(BB)
PHEASANT-EYE NARCISSUS	Narcissus poeticus recurvus	(BB)
PHENOMENAL BERRY	Rubus loganobaccus	(F)
PHILLIPINE MAHOGANY	Parachorea sp.	(TT)
PHILLIPINE MEDUSA	Acalypha hispida	(HP)
PHILLIPINE VIOLET	Barleria cristata	(S)
PHU	Valeriana officinalis	(H)
PHYSIC NUT	Jatropha curcas	(T)
PIASSABA	Attalea funifira	(P)
PIASSABA	Leopoldinia piassaba	(P)
PICCABEEN PALM	Archontophoenix cunninghamiana	(P)
PICHI	Fabiana imbricata	(S)

Common	Botanical	Type
PICKEREL-WEED	Pontaderia cordata	(WP)
PICOTEE	Dianthus caryophyllus	(H)
PIEDMONT TRUFFLE	Tuber magnatum	(FU)
PIG LILY	Zantedeschia aethiopica	(H)
PIG NUT	Conopodium majus	(H)
PIG NUT HICKORY	Carya glabra	(T)
PIGEON BERRY	Duranta repens	(S)
PIGEON BERRY	Phytolacca americana	(H)
PIGEON PEA	Cajanas cajan	(V)
PIGGY-BACK PLANT	Tolmiea menziesii	(HP)
PIGMY SUNFLOWER	Actinea grandiflora	(H)
PIGNUT PALM	Hyophorbe	(P)
PIGROOT	Sisyrinchium	(H)
PIGWEED	Aegopodium podagaria	(H)
PIGWEED	Chenopodium album	(H)
PILEWORT	Erechtites hieracifolia	(A)
PILEWORT	Ranunculus ficaria	(H)
PILL SEDGE	Carex pilulifera	(G)
PILL-BEARING SPURGE	Euphorbia hirta	(H)
PILLAR APPLE	Malus tschonoskii	(T)
PILOT WEED	Silphium laciniatum	(H)
PIMENTO	Capiscum frutescens	(HB)
PIMENTO	Pimenta	(HB)
PIN CHERRY	Prunus pensylvanica	(T)
PIN OAK	Quercus palustris	(T)
PIN-WHEEL	Aeonium haworthii	(HP)
PINCUSHION FLOWER	Scabiosa	(HR)
PINDO PALM	Butia	(P)
PINE	Pinus	(C)
PINE FERN	Aneimia adiantifolia	(FN)
PINE-MAT MANZANITA	Arctostaphylos nevadensis	(S)
PINE-SCENTED GERANIUM	Pelargonium x fragrans	(A)
PINEAPPLE	Ananas comosus	(F)
PINEAPPLE BROOM	Cytisus battandieri	(S)
PINEAPPLE BUSH	Dasypogon bromeliaefolius	(S)
PINEAPPLE FLOWER	Eucomis	(BB)
PINEAPPLE GUAVA	Acca sellowiona	(S)
PINEAPPLE MINT	Mentha suaveolens	(HB)
PINEAPPLE SAGE	Salvia rutilans	(HB)
PINEAPPLE WEED	Chamomilla suaveolens	(HA)
PINGUIN	Bromelia pinguin	(H)
PINK	Dianthus	(HR)
PINK ACANTHUS	Jacobinia carnea	(H)
PINK ARUM	Zantedeschia rehmannii	(H)
PINK BALL TREE	Dombeya wallichii	(TS)
PINK BROOM	Notospartium carmicheliae	(S)
PINK CALLA	Zantedeschia rehmannii	(H)

Common	Botanical	Type
PINK CASSIA	Cassia javanica	(TT)
PINK DANDELION	Crepis incana	(H)
PINK DOGWOOD	Cornus florida rubra	(S)
PINK EVENING PRIMROSE	Oenothera rosea	(H)
PINK HORSE CHESTNUT	Aesculus carnea	(T)
PINK OXALIS	Oxalis articulata	(H)
PINK PEARL LILAC	Syringa swegiflexa	(S)
PINK POKERS	Limonium suworowi	(H)
PINK POUI	Tabebuia pentaphylla	(TT)
PINK PURSLANE	Montia sibirica	(A)
PINK QUILL	Tillandsia cyanea	(H)
PINK ROCK-JASMINE	Androsace carnea	(R)
PINK ROOT	Spigelia marylandica	(H)
PINK SAND VERBENA	Abronia umbellata	(H)
PINK SHOWER	Cassia grandis	(T)
PINK SIRIS	Albizia julibrissin	(ST)
PINK SNOWBALL	Dombeya x cayeuxii	(T)
PINK TECOMA	Tabebuia pentaphylla	(TT)
PINK TRUMPET VINE	Podranea ricasoliana	(TCL)
PINK TRUMPET-TREE	Tabebuia rosea	(TT)
PINK TULIP TREE	Magnolia campbellii	(T)
PINK VINE	Antigonon leptopus	(TCL)
PINK-ROOT	Spigelia marilandiea	(H)
PINTO BEAN	Phaseolus vulgaris	(V)
PINYON PINE	Pinus cembroides	(C)
PIPE TREE	Sambucus nigra	(T)
PIPE-VINE	Aristolochia macrophylla	(CL)
PIPEWORT	Eriocaulon aquaticum	(WP)
PIPPERIDGE	Berberis vulgaris	(S)
PIPSISSEWA	Chimaphila umbellata	(H)
PISS-THE-BED	Taraxacum	(H)
PISTACHIO	Pistacia vera	(T)
PISTOL BUSH	Duvernoia adhatodioides	(S)
PITAYA	Echinocereus enneacanthus	(CS)
PITCH PINE	Pinus palustris	(C)
PITCHER PLANT	Sarracenia purpurea	(HP)
PITH-TREE	Herminiera elaphroxylon	(TT)
PITURI	Duboisia myoporoides	(H)
PLAID CACTUS	Gymnocalycium mihanouichii	(O)
PLAINS CACTUS	Pediocactus simpsonii	(CS)
PLANE	Platanus	(T)
PLANTAIN	Plantago	(H)
PLANTAIN BANANA	Musa paradisiaca	(F)
PLANTAIN LEOPARD'S BANE	Filago lutescens	(H)
PLANTAIN LILY	Hosta	(H)
PLEURISY ROOT	Asclepias tuberosa	(H)
PLOUGH BREAKER	Erythrina zeyheri	(TS)

Common	Botanical	Type
PLOUGHMAN'S SPIKENARD	Inula conyza	(H)
PLOVER EGGS	Adromischus cooperi	(HP)
PLUM	Prunus domestica	(F)
PLUM AND CUSTARD	Tricholomopsis rutilans	(FU)
PLUM YEW	Cephalotaxus	(C)
PLUM-FRUITED YEW	Podocarpus andinus	(C)
PLUME BUSH	Calomeria amaranthoides	(S)
PLUME FLOWER	Celosia plumosa	(A)
PLUME GRASS	Erianthus ravennnae	(G)
PLUME NUTMEG	Atherosperma moschata	(S)
PLUME POPPY	Macleaya	(H)
PLUME-GRASS	Erianthus	(G)
PLUMED GOLDEN ROD	Chrysothamnus	(H)
PLUMED THISTLE	Cirsium	(H)
PLUMS AND CUSTARD	Tricholomopsis rutilans	(FU)
PLUMWOOD	Eucryphia moorai	(S)
PLYMOUTH CROWBERRY	Corema conradii	(S)
POACHED EGG FUNGUS	Oudemansiella mucida	(FU)
POACHED EGG PLANT	Limnanthes douglasii	(A)
POACHED EGGS	Myriocephalus stuartii	(H)
POCKET HANDKERCHIEF TREE	Davidia involucrata	(T)
POET'S LAUREL	Laurus nobilis	(HB)
POET'S NARCISSUS	Narcissus poeticus	(BB)
POINCIANA	Delonix regia	(TT)
POINSETTIA	Euphorbia pulcherrima	(A)
POISON ASH	Chionanthus virginicus	(S)
POISON FLAG	Iris versicolor	(H)
POISON HEMLOCK	Conium maculatum	(H)
POISON IVY	Rhus toxicodendron	(S)
POISON OAK	Rhus toxicodendron	(CL)
POISON PARSLEY	Conium maculatum	(H)
POISON PIE	Hebeloma crustuliniforma	(FU)
POISON POTATO	Solanum caralinense	(H)
POISON SUMACH	Rhus vernix	(S)
POISONOUS GUM-THISTLE	Euphorbia resinifera	(H)
POKE ROOT	Phytolacca americana	(H)
POKEBERRY	Phytolacca americana	(H)
POKER PLANT	Kniphofia	(H)
POKEWEED	Phytolacca americana	(H)
POLAR PLANT	Silphium laciniatum	(H)
POLECAT WEED	Symplocarpus foetidus	(H)
POLICEMAN'S HELMET	Impatiens glandulifera	(A)
POLKA-DOT PLANT	Hypoestes	(HP)
POLYANTHUS	Primula polyantha	(H)
POLYCNEMUM	Polycnemum majus	(H)
POLYPODY	Polypodium vulgare	(FN)
POMEGRANATE	Punica granatum	(F)

Know Your Common Plant Names

Common	Botanical	Type
POMELO	Citrus x paradisi	(F)
POMETTE BLEUE	Crataegus brachyacantha	(T)
POND CYPRESS	Taxodium ascendens	(C)
POND SEDGE	Carex riparia	(G)
POND WATER CROWFOOT	Ranunculus peltatus	(H)
POND WEED	Potamogeton	(WP)
POND-LILY BEGONIA	Begonia 'Erythrophylla'	(HP)
PONDEROSA PINE	Pinus ponderosa	(C)
PONTINE OAK	Quercus pontica	(T)
PONY-TAIL	Beaucarnea recurvata	(T)
POOR MAN'S BOX	Lonicera nitida	(S)
POOR MAN'S ORCHID	Schizanthus	(A)
POOR MAN'S WEATHER GLASS	Anagallis arvensis	(A)
POP CORN	Zea mays everta	(V)
POP WEED	Fucas vesicosus	(SW)
POPINAC	Acacia farnesiana	(T)
POPLAR	Populus	(T)
POPPY	Papaver	(AH)
POPPY ANEMONE	Anemone coronaria	(BB)
POPPY MALLOW	Callirhoe	(H)
PORK AND BEANS	Sedum x rubrotinctum	(H)
POROPORO	Solanum laciniatum	(H)
PORT MACQUARIE PINE	Callitris macleayana	(C)
PORT ORFORD CEDAR	Chamaecyparis lawsoniana	(C)
PORTIA OIL NUT	Thespesia populnea	(S)
PORTIA TREE	Thespesia populnea	(TT)
PORTUGAL HEATH	Erica lusitanica	(S)
PORTUGAL LAUREL	Prunus lusitanica	(S)
PORTUGUESE CABBAGE	Brassica oleracea costata	(V)
PORTUGUESE CROWBERRY	Corema album	(S)
PORTUGUESE OAK	Quercus faginea	(T)
POSSUMHAW HOLLY	Ilex decidua	(S)
POST OAK	Quercus stellata	(T)
POSY BUSH	Dais cotonifolia	(TS)
POT	Cannabis sativa	(H)
POT MARIGOLD	Calendula officinalis	(A)
POT MARJORAM	Origanum onites	(HB)
POTATO	Solanum tuberosum	(V)
POTATO BEAN	Apios americana	(H)
POTATO CREEPER	Solanum seaforthianum	(CL)
POTATO ONION	Allium cepa aggregatum	(V)
POTATO YAM	Dioscorea bulbifera	(F)
POTATO-BEAN	Apios americana	(H)
POTHOS VINE	Epipremnum aureum	(HP)
POTTERY TREE	Moquila utilis	(TT)
POWDER-PUFF BUSH	Calliandra haematocephala	(S)
POWDER-PUFF CACTUS	Mammillaria bocasana	(CS)

Know Your Common Plant Names

Common	Botanical	Type
POWDER-PUFF TREE	Calliandra inaequilatera	(TT)
POWDERPUFF	Mammillaria bocasana	(CS)
PRAIRIE BLAZING STAR	Liatris pycnostachya	(H)
PRAIRIE BUTTON	Liatris	(H)
PRAIRIE CLOVER	Petalostemon purpureum	(H)
PRAIRIE CONEFLOWER	Ratibida columnifera	(S)
PRAIRIE CRAB	Malus ioensis	(T)
PRAIRIE DOCK	Silphium terebinthinaceum	(H)
PRAIRIE EVENING PRIMROSE	Oenothera missouriensis	(H)
PRAIRIE FLAX	Linum lewisii	(H)
PRAIRIE LILY	Mentzelia	(H)
PRAIRIE LUPIN	Lupinus lepidus	(H)
PRAIRIE MALLOW	Sidalcea	(H)
PRAIRIE POTATO	Psoralea	(H)
PRAIRIE ROSE	Rosa setigera	(S)
PRAIRIE SENNA	Chamaecrista fasciculata	(S)
PRAIRIE WILLOW	Salix humilis	(S)
PRAIRIE-GENTIAN	Eustoma	(H)
PRAIRIE-LILY	Cooperia	(BB)
PRAIRIE-LILY	Cooperia mentzelia	(S)
PRAYER BEADS	Abrus precatorius	(H)
PRAYER PLANT	Maranta	(HP)
PRECATORY BEAN	Abrus precatorius	(H)
PRETTY BETSY	Centranthus ruber	(H)
PRICKLY ASH	Zanthoxylum americanum	(S)
PRICKLY BROOM	Ulex europaeus	(S)
PRICKLY CARDINAL	Erythrina zeyheri	(TS)
PRICKLY CASTOR OIL TREE	Kalopanax	(T)
PRICKLY CONESTICKS	Petrophila sessilis	(R)
PRICKLY CUCUMBER	Echinocystis lobata	(H)
PRICKLY DATE PALM	Acanthophoenix	(P)
PRICKLY HEATH	Gaultheria mucronata	(S)
PRICKLY JUNIPER	Juniperus oxycedrus	(C)
PRICKLY LETTUCE	Lactuca serriola	(H)
PRICKLY MOSES	Acacia verticilliata	(T)
PRICKLY PEAR	Opuntia microdasys	(CS)
PRICKLY PHLOX	Gilia californica	(H)
PRICKLY PINE	Pinus pungens	(C)
PRICKLY POPPY	Argemone mexicana	(H)
PRICKLY RHUBARB	Gunnera	(H)
PRICKLY SEDGE	Carex muricata	(G)
PRICKLY SOW THISTLE	Sonchus asper	(H)
PRICKLY THRIFT	Acantholimon	(R)
PRICKLY-POPPY	Argemone	(H)
PRIDE OF BARBADOS	Caesalpinia pulcherrima	(TT)
PRIDE OF BOLIVIA	Tipuana tipu	(TT)
PRIDE OF BURMA	Amhertsia nobilis	(TT)

Common	Botanical	Type
PRIDE OF CALIFORNIA	Lathyrus splendens	(H)
PRIDE OF CHINA	Melia azedarach	(T)
PRIDE OF INDIA	Koelreuteria	(T)
PRIDE OF INDIA	Lagerstroemia speciosa	(TT)
PRIDE OF INDIA	Melia azedarach	(T)
PRIDE OF MADEIRA	Echium fastuosum	(TS)
PRIEST'S CROWN	Taratacum officianale	(H)
PRIMROSE	Primula vulgaris	(H)
PRIMROSE JASMINE	Jasminum mesnyi	(CL)
PRIMROSE PEERLESS	Narcissus x medioluteus	(BB)
PRIMROSE TREE	Lagunaria patersonii	(T)
PRIMROSE WILLOW	Ludwigia	(S)
PRINCE ALBERT'S YEW	Saxegothea conspicua	(C)
PRINCE OF WALES FEATHERS	Celosia argentea pyramidalis	(A)
PRINCE OF WALES FEATHERS	Leptopteris superba	(FN)
PRINCE OF WALES FEATHERS	Tanacetum densum amani	(R)
PRINCE RUPPRECHT LARCH	Larix gmelini principis-rupprechtii	(C)
PRINCE'S FEATHER	Amaranthus hypochondriacus	(A)
PRINCE'S PINE	Chimaphila umbellata	(H)
PRINCESS FLOWER	Tibouchina urvilleana	(HP)
PRINCESS OF THE NIGHT	Selenicereus pteronthus	(CS)
PRINCESS TREE	Paulownia tomentosa	(T)
PRINCESS VINE	Cissus sicyoides	(CL)
PRIVET	Ligustrum	(S.T)
PROCUMBENT CINQUEFOIL	Potentilla anglica	(H)
PROLIFEROUS PINK	Petrorhagia prolifera	(H)
PROPHET FLOWER	Arnebia echiodes	(R)
PROSO	Panicum miliaceum	(G)
PROSTRATE GLASSWORT	Salicornia ramosissima	(H)
PROVENCE ROSE	Rosa centifolia	(S)
PROVINS ROSE	Rosa gallica	(S)
PRUNE	Prunus domestica	(F)
PSYLLIUM SEEDS	Plantago indica	(H)
PTYCHOTIS	Ptychotis saxifraga	(H)
PUCCOON	Lithospermum carolinense	(H)
PUCCOON	Sanguinaria	(H)
PUDDING GRASS	Mentha pulegium	(HB)
PUDDING PIPE TREE	Cassia fistula	(TT)
PUFFBALL	Leycoperdon species	(FU)
PUKAPUKA	Brachyglottis repanda	(S)
PULASAN	Nephelium lappaceum	(TT)
PULASAN	Nephelium mutabile	(TF)
PULQUE	Agave americana	(CS)
PULSE	Lathyrus	(H)
PUMMELO	Citrus maxima	(V)
PUMPKIN	Cucurbita pepo	(V)
PUMPKIN ASH	Fraxinus tomentosa	(T)

Know Your Common Plant Names

Common	Botanical	Type
PUMPKIN NUTS	Cucurbita pepo styriaca	(V)
PURGING CASSIA	Cassia fistula	(S)
PURGING NUT	Jatropha curcas	(TS)
PURPLE ANISE	Illicium floridanum	(S)
PURPLE APPLE-BERRY	Billardiera longiflora	(CL)
PURPLE ARCHANGEL	Lamium purpureum	(H)
PURPLE BEECH	Fagus sylvatica Purpurea	(S.T)
PURPLE BELL VINE	Rhodochiton atrosonguineum	(CL)
PURPLE BELL VINE	Rhodochiton volubile	(CL)
PURPLE BIRCH	Betula pendula 'Purpurea'	(T)
PURPLE BONESET	Eupatorium purpureum	(H)
PURPLE BROOM	Cytisus purpureus	(S)
PURPLE BUGLOSS	Echium plantagineum	(H)
PURPLE CHOKEBERRY	Aronia prunifolia	(S)
PURPLE CLIFF BRAKE	Pellaea atropurpurea	(FN)
PURPLE CONEFLOWER	Echinacea purpurea	(H)
PURPLE CRAB	Malus x purpurea	(T)
PURPLE DEAD-NETTLE	Lamium purpureum	(H)
PURPLE ENGLISH OAK	Quercus robur 'Purpurascens'	(T)
PURPLE FERN-LEAVED BEECH	Fagus sylvatica 'Rohanii'	(T)
"PURPLE FLASH"	Prunus cerasifera "Pissardii"	(S)
PURPLE GLORY TREE	Tibouchina urvilleana	(HP)
PURPLE GRANADILLA	Passiflora edulis	(CL)
PURPLE GROMWELL	Buglossoides purpurocaerulea	(H)
PURPLE HEART	Setcreasea purpurea	(HP)
PURPLE HEATHER	Erica cinerea	(S)
PURPLE LETTUCE	Prenanthes purpurea	(H)
PURPLE LOOSESTRIFE	Lythrum salicaria	(H)
PURPLE MILK-VETCH	Astragalus danicus	(H)
PURPLE MOOR-GRASS	Molina caerulea	(G)
PURPLE MULLEIN	Verbascum phoeniceum	(H)
PURPLE ORCHID TREE	Bauhinia variegata	(TT)
PURPLE OSIER	Salix purpurea	(S)
PURPLE OXYTROPIS	Oxytropis halleri	(H)
PURPLE PASSION VINE	Cynura sarmentosa	(HP)
PURPLE PITAYA	Echinocereus dubius	(CS)
PURPLE PRICKLY PEAR	Opuntia santa-rita	(CS)
PURPLE SAGE	Salvia officinalis 'Purpurascens'	(S)
PURPLE SAXIFRAGE	Saxifraga oppositifolia	(R)
PURPLE SMALL-REED	Calamagrostis canescens	(G)
PURPLE SMOKE TREE	Cotinus coggygria 'Rubrifolius'	(S)
PURPLE SPRUCE	Picea likiangensis purpurea	(C)
PURPLE SPURGE	Euphorbia peplis	(H)
PURPLE TOADFLAX	Linaria purpurea	(H)
PURPLE VELVET PLANT	Gynura sarmentosa	(HP)
PURPLE WEIGELA	Weigela florida 'Foliis purpureis'	(S)
PURPLE WILLOW HERB	Lythrum salicaria	(H)

Know Your Common Plant Names

Common	Botanical	Type
PURPLE WREATH	Petrea volubilis	(H)
PURPLE-LEAF BARBERRY	Berberis thunbergii 'Atropurpurea'	(S)
PURPLE-LEAF BIRCH	Betula pendula 'Purpurea'	(T)
PURPLE-LEAF BIRD CHERRY	Prunus padus 'Colorata'	(T)
PURPLE-LEAF FENNEL	Foeniculum vulgare purpureum	(HB)
PURPLE-LEAF FILBERT	Corylus maxima 'Purpurea'	(S)
PURPLE-LEAF SAND CHERRY	Prunus 'Cistena'	(S)
PURPLE-LEAVED ELDER	Sambucus nigra 'Guincho Purple'	(S)
PURPLE-LEAVED PLUM	Prunus cerasifera 'Plssardii'	(S.T)
PURPLE-LEAVED SYCAMORE	Acer pseudoplatanus 'Atropurpureum'	(T)
PURPLE-LEAVED VINE	Vitis vinifera 'Purpurea'	(CL)
PURPLE-LEAVED WEEPING BEECH	Fagus sylvatica 'Purpurea Pendula'	(T)
PURPLE-STEM CAT'S TAIL	Phleum phleoides	(G)
PURSLANE	Portulaca oleracea	(A)
PUSSY EARS	Cyanotis somaliensis	(H)
PUSSY EARS	Kalanchoe tomentosa	(HP)
PUSSY PAWS	Spraguea multiceps	(A)
PUSSY WILLOW	Salix caprea	(ST)
PUSSY'S TOES	Antennaria	(R)
PUTTYROOT	Aplectrum hyemale	(O)
PYGMY HAWKSBEARD	Crepis pygmaea	(H)
PYGMY ROWAN	Sorbus reducta	(S)
PYRAMIDAL BUGLE	Ajuga pyramidalis	(H)
PYRAMIDAL ORCHID	Anacamptis pyramidalis	(O)
PYRAMIDAL SAXIFRAGE	Saxifraga cotyledon	(R)
PYRENEAN MEADOW SAFFRON	Merendera	(H)
PYRENEAN OAK	Quercus pyrenaica	(T)
PYRENEAN PINE	Pinus nigra cebennensis	(C)
PYRENEAN VALERIAN	Valeriana pyrenaica	(H)
PYRENEAN WHITEBEAM	Sorbus mougeotii	(T)
PYRETHRUM	Tanacetum cinerarii folium	(H)
PYRETHRUM	Tanacetum coccineum	(H)T
QUAKER LADIES	Houstonia; Hedyotis	(H)
QUAKING ASPEN	Populus tremuloides	(T)
QUAKING GRASS	Briza media	(G)
QUALUP BELL	Pimelia physodes	(S)
QUAMASH	Camassia	(BB)
QUANDONG	Fusanus acuminatus	(TS)
QUASSIA	Picreana excelsa	(T)
QUEBRACHO	Aspidosperma quebracho-blanco	(TS)
QUEBRACHO	Schinopsis balansae	(TS)
QUEBRACHO	Schinopsis lorentzii	(TS)
QUEEN ANNE'S LACE	Anthriscus sylvestris	(H)
QUEEN ANNE'S LACE	Daucus carota	(V)
QUEEN ANNE'S THIMBLES	Gilia capitata	(H)
QUEEN LILY	Phaedranassa	(BB)
QUEEN OF THE MEADOW	Eupatorium purpureum	(H)

Know Your Common Plant Names

Common	Botanical	Type
QUEEN OF THE MEADOW	Filipendula ulmaria	(H)
QUEEN OF THE NIGHT	Ipomoea noctiflora	(A)
QUEEN OF THE NIGHT	Selenicereus grandiflorus	(CS)
QUEEN OF THE PRAIRIE	Filipendula rubra	(H)
QUEEN PALM	Arecastrum romanzoffianum	(P)
QUEEN VICTORIA WATERLILY	Victoria amazonica	(WP)
QUEEN'S DELIGHT	Stillingia sylvatica	(H)
QUEEN'S JEWELS	Antigonon leptopus	(TCL)
QUEEN'S SPIDERWORT	Dichorisandra reginae	(HP)
QUEEN'S TEARS	Bilbergia nutans	(HP)
QUEEN'S WREATH	Petrea volubilis	(H)
QUEEN-OF-THE-NIGHT	Hylocereus undatus	(CS)
QUEEN-OF-THE-NIGHT	Selenicereus grandiflorus	(CS)
QUEENCUP	Clintonia uniflora	(H)
QUEENS SPIDERWORT	Dichorisandra reginae	(HP)
QUEENSLAND ARROWROOT	Canna edulis	(TS)
QUEENSLAND BOTTLE TREE	Sterculia rupestris	(TT)
QUEENSLAND FIREWHEEL TREE	Stenocarpus sinuatus	(TT)
QUEENSLAND ITCH TREE	Davidsonia pruriens	(T)
QUEENSLAND KAURI	Agathis brownii	(C)
QUEENSLAND NUT	Macadamia ternifolia	(TT)
QUEENSLAND PYRAMIDAL TREE	Lagunaria patersonii	(TT)
QUEENSLAND UMBRELLA TREE	Schefflera actinophylla	(HP)
QUEENSLAND WATTLE	Acacia podalyriifolia	(T)
QUERCITRON OAK	Quercus velutina	(T)
QUICK	Crataegus monogyna	(S)
QUICKEN TREE	Sorbus aucuparia	(T)
QUICKTHORN	Crataegus monogyna	(S.T)
QUILLWORT	Isoetes	(H)
QUINCE	Cydonia oblonga	(T.T)
QUININE	Cinchona officinalis	(T)
QUININE BRUSH	Purshia tridentata	(S)
QUININE BUSH	Garrya elliptica	(S)
QUINOA	Chenopodium quinoa	(H)
RABBIT ROOT	Aralia nudicaulis	(S)
RABBIT TRACKS	Maranta leuconeura Kerchoviana	(HP)
RABBIT'S FOOT FERN	Davallia canariensis	(FN)
RABBIT'S FOOT FERN	Davallia fejeensis	(FN)
RABBITEYE BLUEBERRY	Vaccinium virgatum	(S)
RACOON BERRY	Podophyllum peltatum	(H)
RADISH	Raphanus sativus	(V)
RAFFIA	Raphia	(T.T)
RAG GOURD	Luffa	(H)
RAG PAPER	Verbascum thapsus	(H)
RAGGED CUP	Silphium perfoliatum	(H)
RAGGED ROBIN	Lychnis flos-cuculi	(H)
RAGWEED	Ambrosia	(H)

Common	Botanical	Type
RAGWEED	Ambrosia artemisiifolia	(A)
RAGWORT	Senecio jacobaea	(H)
RAILWAY POPLAR	Populus 'Regenerata'	(T)
RAIN DAISY	Dimorphotheca pluvialis	(H)
RAIN LILY	Zephyranthes	(BB)
RAIN-TREE	Samanea saman	(TT)
RAINBOW CACTUS	Echinocereus pectinatus	(CS)
RAINBOW DOGWOOD	Cornus florida 'Rainbow'	(S)
RAINBOW PLANT	Byblis liniflora	(S)
RAINBOW VINE	Pellionia pulchra	(HP)
RAKKYO	Allium chinense	(BB)
RAMANAS ROSE	Rosa rugosa	(S)
RAMBUTAN	Nephelium lappaceum	(TF)
RAMERO	Trichostema lanatum	(S)
RAMGOAT ROSE	Catharanthus roeus	(HP)
RAMIE	Boehmeria nivea	(S)
RAMIE FIBRE	Bochmeria nivea	(G)
RAMIN	Gonystylus bancanus	(TT)
RAMPING FUMITORY	Fumaria capreolata	(H)
RAMPION	Campanula rapunculus	(H)
RAMPION	Phyteuma	(H)
RAMPION BELLFLOWER	Campanula rapunculus	(H)
RAMSONS	Allium ursinum	(H)
RAMSONS WOOD GARLIC	Allium ursinum	(BB)
RAMSTHORN	Rhamnus cathartica	(S/T)
RANGIORA	Brachyglottis repanda	(S)
RANGOON CREEPER	Quisqualis indica	(CL)
RANNOCH RUSH	Scheuchzeria palustris	(H)
RANTRY	Sorbus aucuparia	(T)
RAOUL	Nothofagus procera	(T)
RAPE	Brassica napus	(V)
RASAMALA	Altingia excelsa	(S)
RASPBERRY	Rubus idaeus	(F)
RAT'S TAIL CACTUS	Aporocactus flagelliformis	(CS)
RAT'S TAIL RADISH	Raphanus caudatus	(V)
RAT'S-TAIL CACTUS	Aporocactus flagelliformis	(O)
RATA	Metrosideros robusta	(TS)
RATSTAIL FESCUE	Vulpoia myuros	(G)
RATTAN	Calamus	(G)
RATTAN VINE	Berchemia	(CL)
RATTLE-BOX	Crotalaria	(S)
RATTLES	Rhinanthus	(H)
RATTLESNAKE FERN	Botrychium virginianum	(FN)
RATTLESNAKE MASTER	Liatris squarrosa	(H)
RATTLESNAKE ORCHID	Pholidota	(O)
RATTLESNAKE PLANTAIN	Goodyera	(O)
RATTLESNAKE PLANTAIN	Goodyera oblongifolia	(O)

Common	Botanical	Type
RATTLESNAKE ROOT	Polygala senega	(H)
RAULI	Nothofagus procera	(T)
RAY'S KNOTGRASS	Polygonum oxyspermum	(H)
RAYLESS MAYWEED	Chamomilla suaveolens	(H)
RED ALDER	Alnus rubra	(T)
RED ALOE	Aloe ferox	(CS)
RED ASH	Fraxinus pennsylvanica	(T)
RED BANEBERRY	Actaea erythocarpa	(H)
RED BARTSIA	Odontites verna	(H)
RED BAY	Persea borbonia	(T)
RED BEARBERRY	Arctostaphylos uva-ursi	(S)
RED BEECH	Nothofagus fusca	(T)
RED BEEFWOOD	Casuarina equisetifolia	(T)
RED BIDI-BIDI	Acaena novae-zealandiae	(R)
RED BILBERRY	Vaccinium parvifolium	(S)
RED BILBERRY	Vaccinium vitis-idaea	(S)
RED BIRCH	Betula nigra	(T)
RED BLOODWOOD	Eucalyptus gumnifera	(T)
RED BONNETS	Burtonia hendersonii	(S)
RED BROOMRAPE	Orobanche alba	(PE/H)
RED BUCKEYE	Aesculus pavia	(S)
RED BUNNY EARS	Opuntia rufida	(CS)
RED CAMPION	Silene dioica	(H)
RED CANELLA	Cinnamodendron corticosum	(TS)
RED CAPE TULIP	Haemanthus	(HP)
RED CATCHFLY	Lychnis viscaria	(H)
RED CEDAR	Juniperus virginiana	(C)
RED CENTAURY	Centaurium erythraea	(H)
RED CHOKEBERRY	Aronia arbutifolia	(S)
RED CINCHONA	Cinchona succirula	(TT)
RED CLOVER	Trifolium pratense	(H)
RED CROWN	Rebutia minuscula	(CS)
RED CROWN CACTUS	Rebutia minuscula	(CS)
RED CYPRESS PINE	Callitris endlicheri	(C)
RED DEAD-NETTLE	Lamium purpureum	(H)
RED ELDER	Viburnum opulus	(S)
RED ELM	Ulmus rubra	(T)
RED FESCUE	Festuca rubra	(G)
RED FIR	Abies magnifica	(C)
RED FLAG BUSH	Mussaenda erythrophylla	(TS)
RED FLAX	Linum grandiflorum	(H)
RED GINGER	Alpinia purpurata	(TH)
RED GOOSEFOOT	Chenopodium rubrum	(H)
RED GUM	Ceratopetalum gummiferum	(TT)
RED GUM	Liquidambar styraciflua	(T)
RED HAW	Crataegus mollis	(T)
RED HELLEBORINE	Cephalanthera rubra	(O)

Know Your Common Plant Names

Common	Botanical	Type
RED HEMP NETTLE	Galeopsis angustifolia	(A)
RED HICKORY	Carya ovalis	(T)
RED HORSECHESTNUT	Aesculus carnea 'Brioti'	(T)
RED HOT CAT'S TAIL	Acalypha hispida	(HP)
RED HUCKLEBERRY	Vaccinium parvifolium	(S)
RED INK PLANT	Phytolacca americana	(H)
RED IRIS	Iris fulva	(H)
RED IRONBARK	Eucalyptus sideroxylon	(T)
RED IVY	Hemigraphis alternata	(HP)
RED JASMINE	Plumera rubra	(TT)
RED KALE	Rhodymenia palmata	(SW)
RED KANGAROO PAW	Anigozanthus rufus	(H)
RED KNEES	Polygonum hydropiper	(H)
RED LEGS	Persicaria bistorta	(H)
RED MAHOGANY	Eucalyptus resinifera	(T)
RED MAIDS	Calandrinia menziesii	(A)
RED MANGROVE	Rhizophora mangle	(TT)
RED MAPLE	Acer rubrum	(T)
RED MAY	Crataegus laevigata 'Paul's Scarlet'	(T)
RED MOMBIN	Spondias purpurea	(TT)
RED MORNING GLORY	Ipomoea coccinea	(CL)
RED MULBERRY	Morus rubra	(T)
RED OAK	Quercus rubra	(T)
RED ORACHE	Atriplex hortensis rubra	(HB)
RED ORCHID CACTUS	Nopalxochia ackermannii	(CS)
RED OSIER DOGWOOD	Cornus stolonifera	(S)
RED PASSION FLOWER	Passiflora racemosa	(CL)
RED PEPPER	Capsicum annuum	(F)
RED PINE	Dacrydium cupressinum	(C)
RED PINE	Pinus resinosa	(C)
RED PINEAPPLE	Ananas bracteatus	(HP)
RED POKERS	Hakea bucculenta	(S)
RED PUCOON	Sanguinaria canadensis	(H)
RED RATTLE	Pedicularis palustris	(A)
RED RIBBONS	Clarkia concinna	(A)
RED RIVER GUM	Eucalyptus camaldulensis	(T)
RED ROOT	Ceanothus americanus	(S)
RED ROOT	Potentilla erecta	(H)
RED ROSE	Rosa gallica	(S)
RED ROSE OF LANCASTER	Rosa gallica 'Officinalis'	(S)
RED SANDALWOOD	Santalum rubrum	(TT)
RED SANDALWOOD TREE	Adenanthera pavonina	(TT)
RED SAUNDERS	Pterocarpus santalinus	(TT)
RED SHANK	Polygonum persicaria	(A)
RED SIGNAL HEATH	Erica mammosa	(S)
RED SILVER FIR	Abies amabilis	(C)
RED SIRIS	Albizzia toona	(T)

Know Your Common Plant Names

Common	Botanical	Type
RED SNAKE-BARK MAPLE	Acer capillipes	(T)
RED SPIDER LILY	Lycoris radiata	(BB)
RED SPIKE	Cephalophyllum alstonii	(CS)
RED SPOTTED GUM	Eucalyptus mannifera	(T)
RED SPRUCE	Picea rubens	(C)
RED SPURREY	Spergularia rubra	(H)
RED SQUILL	Urginea maritima	(BB)
RED STAR-THISTLE	Centaurea calcitrapa	(H)
RED TREFOIL	Trifolium rubens	(H)
RED VALERIAN	Centranthus ruber	(H)
RED WILLOW	Salix laevigata	(S)
RED-BARKED DOGWOOD	Cornus alba	(S)
RED-BERRIED ELDER	Sambucus racemosa	(S)
RED-BUD MAPLE	Acer trautvetteri	(T)
RED-FLOWERED MALLEE	Eucalyptus erythronema	(T)
RED-FLOWERED YUCCA	Hesperaloe parviflora	(H)
RED-FLOWERING GUM	Eucalyptus ficifolia	(T)
RED-HOT CAT TAIL	Acalypha hispida	(HP)
RED-HOT CAT'S TAIL	Acalypha hispida	(HP)
RED-HOT POKER	Kniphofia	(H)
RED-TIPPED CUDWEED	Filago lutescens	(H)
RED-TWIGGED LIME	Tilia platyphyllos 'Rubra'	(T)
RED-VEINED DOCK	Rumex sanguineus viridis	(H)
REDBIRD FLOWER	Pedilanthus tithymaloides	(CS)
REDBUD	Cercis canadensis	(S.T)
REDBUD MAPLE	Acer trautvetteri	(T)
REDDISH PONDWEED	Potamogeton alpinus	(WP)
REDLEAF PHILODENDRON	Philodendron erubescens	(HP)
REDLEGS	Polygonum persicaria	(H)
REDOUL	Coriaria myrtifolia	(S)
REDROOT	Ceanothus	(S)
REDROOT	Lachnanthes tinctoria	(H)
REDSHANK	Polygonum persicaria	(H)
REDWOOD	Sequoia sempervivens	(C)
REDWOOD IVY	Vancouveria planipetala	(H)
REDWOOD LILY	Lilium rubescens	(BB)
REDWOOD ROSE	Rosa gymnocarpa	(S)
REED	Phragmites communis	(G)
REED CANARY-GRASS	Phalaris arundinacea	(G)
REED MACE	Typha latifolia	(G)
REED MANNA-GRASS	Catabrosa	(G)
REED PALM	Chamaedorea seifrizii	(P)
REED RHAPIS	Rhapis humilis	(P)
REED SWEET GRASS	Glyceria maxima	(G)
REFLEXED STONECROP	Sedum reflexum	(H)
REGAL PELARGONIUM	Pelargonium x domesticum	(A)
REINDEER MOSS	Cladonia rangiferina	(MS)

Common	Botanical	Type
RENGARENGA	Arthropodium cirrhatum	(H)
RESCUE BROME	Bromus willdenowii	(G)
RESIN BUSH	Euryops tenuissimus	(H)
REST HARROW	Ononis repens	(H)
RESURRECTION LILY	Lycoris squamigera	(BB)
RESURRECTION PLANT	Anastatica hierochuntica	(H)
RESURRECTION PLANT	Selaginella lepidophylla	(H)
REWA REWA	Knightia excelsa	(T)
REX BEGONIA	Begonia rex	(HP)
REX-BEGONIA VINE	Cissus discolor	(HP)
RHATANY	Krameria triandra	(H)
RHEUMATISM ROOT	Jeffersonia diphylla	(H)
RHEUMATISM WEED	Chimaphila umbellata	(H)
RHUBARB	Rheum rhaponticum	(V)
RHUBARB	Rheum x cultorum	(V)
RIBBED MELILOT	Melilotus officinalis	(H)
RIBBON CACTUS	Pedilanthus tithymaloides	(CS)
RIBBON FERN	Pteris cretica	(FN)
RIBBON FERN	Taenitis blechnoides	(FN)
RIBBON GRASS	Oplismenus hirtellus	(HP)
RIBBON GRASS	Phalaris arundinacea	(G)
RIBBON GUM	Eucalyptus viminalis	(T)
RIBBON PLANT	Chlorophytum	(HP)
RIBBON PLANT	Dracaena sanderiana	(S)
RIBBONWOOD	Plagianthus	(T)
RIBBONWOOD	Hoheria lyallii	(S)
RIBWORT	Plantago lanceolata	(H)
RIBWORT PLANTAIN	Plantago lanceolata	(H)
RICE	Oryza sativa	(G)
RICE BEAN	Phaseolus calcaratus	(V)
RICE FLOWER	Pimelea	(S)
RICE GRASS	Spartina x townsendii	(G)
RICE-FLOWER	Pimelia	(S)
RICE-PAPER TREE	Tetrapananax papyrifera	(T.T)
RICHARDIA	Zantedeschia	(WP)
RICHLEAF	Collinsonia canadensis	(H)
RICHWEED	Collinsonia canadensis	(H)
RIENGA LILY	Arthropodium cirrhatum	(H)
RIGID BUCKLER FERN	Dryopteris submontana	(FN)
RIGID HORNWORT	Ceratophyllum demursum	(WP)
RIMU	Dacrydium cupressinum	(C)
RIMU PINE	Dacrydium cupressinum	(C)
RING O' BELLS	Hyacinthoides non-scripta	(BB)
RINGAL	Arundinaria anceps	(G)
RINGWORM POWDER	Andira araroba	(TT)
RINGWORM SENNA	Cassia alata	(TS)
RIVER BEAUTY	Chamerion latifolium	(H)

Know Your Common Plant Names

Common	Botanical	Type
RIVER BELLS	Phygelius capensis	(S)
RIVER BIRCH	Betula nigra	(T)
RIVER CROWFOOT	Ranunculus fluitans	(WP)
RIVER OAK	Casuarina cunninghamiana	(T)
RIVER WATER DROPWORT	Oenanthe fluviatilis	(H)
RIVER WATER-CROWFOOT	Ranunculus fluitans	(WP)
RIVERBANK GRAPE	Vitis riparia	(FCCL
ROAST-BEEF PLANT	Iris foetidissima	(H)
ROBB'S BONNET	Euphorbia robbiae	(H)
ROBLE BEECH	Nothofagus obliqua	(T)
ROBLE BLANCO	Nothofagus pumilio	(T)
ROBLE DE MAULE	Nothofagus glauca	(T)
ROBLE PELLIN	Nothofagus obliqua	(T)
ROBUST HEDGEHOG	Echinocereus fendleri robustus	(CS)
ROBUST PINCUSHION	Coryphantha muehlenfortii	(CS)
ROCAMBOLE	Allium scordoprasum	(BB)
ROCK BEAUTY	Petrocallis pyrenaica	(R)
ROCK BELLS	Aquilegia canadensis	(R)
ROCK BIRCH	Betula nana	(S)
ROCK BRAMBLE	Rubus saxatilis	(S)
ROCK BUCKTHORN	Rhamnus saxitilis	(R)
ROCK CAMPION	Silene rupestris	(R)
ROCK CHERRY	Prunus prostrata	(S)
ROCK CINQUEFOIL	Potentilla ruprestris	(R)
ROCK CRANESBILL	Geranium macrorrhizum	(H)
ROCK CRESS	Arabis	(B)
ROCK ELM	Ulmus thomasii	(T)
ROCK FRINGE	Epilobium obcordatum	(H)
ROCK JASMINE	Androsace	(R)
ROCK JESSAMINE	Androsace	(R)
ROCK LILY	Arthropodium cirrhatum	(H)
ROCK MAPLE	Acer glabrum	(T)
ROCK NETTLE	Eucnide	(TS)
ROCK PURSLANE	Calandrinia	(R)
ROCK ROSE	Cistus	(S)
ROCK ROSE	Helianthemum	(R)
ROCK SALLOW	Salix petraea	(S)
ROCK SAMPHIRE	Crithmum maritimum	(R)
ROCK SEA LAVENDER	Limonium binervosum	(H)
ROCK SEDGE	Carex rupestris	9G)
ROCK SOAPWORT	Saponaria ocymoides	(R)
ROCK SPEEDWELL	Veronica fruticans	(H)
ROCK SPLEENWORT	Asplenium forisiense	(FN)
ROCK SPURREY	Spergularia rupicola	(H)
ROCK STONECROP	Sedum forsteranum	(H)
ROCK WHITLOW GRASS	Draba norvegica	(R)
ROCK WINDFLOWER	Anemone rupicola	(R)

Common	Botanical	Type
ROCK FRINGE	Epilobium obcordatum	(H)
ROCKERY SPEEDWELL	Veronica prostrata	(R)
ROCKET	Eruca sativa	(H)
ROCKET	Hesperis matronalis	(H)
ROCKET LARKSPUR	Consolida ambigua	(A)
ROCKFOIL	Saxifraga	(R)
ROCKSIDA	Sida petrophila	(H)
ROCKWOOD LILY	Ranunculus lyalli	(H)
ROCKY MOUNTAIN CHERRY	Prunus besseyi	(S)
ROCKY MOUNTAIN COLUMBINE	Aquilegia caerulea	(H)
ROCKY MOUNTAIN FIR	Abies lasiocarpa	(C)
ROCKY MOUNTAIN JUNIPER	Juniperus scopulorum	(C)
ROCKY MOUNTAIN RASPBERRY	Rubus deliciosus	(S)
ROEBUCK BERRY	Rubus saxatilis	(S)
ROGATION FLOWER	Polygala	(H/S)
ROMAN CHAMOMILE	Chamaemelum nobile	(H)
ROMAN CORIANDER	Nigella sativa	(A)
ROMAN HYACINTH	Bellevalia romana	(BB)
ROMAN HYACINTH	Hyacinthus orientalis albulus	(BB)
ROMAN LAUREL	Laurus nobilis	(S/T)
ROMAN WORMWOOD	Artemisia pontica	(H)
ROOF IRIS	Iris tectorum	(R)
ROOIELS	Cunonia capensis	(T)
ROSA MUNDI	Rosa gallica 'Versicolor'	(S)
ROSARY PEA	Abrus precatorius	(H)
ROSARY VINE	Ceropegia woodii	(HP)
ROSE	Rosa	(T)
ROSE ACACIA	Robinia hispida	(S.T)
ROSE APPLE	Eugenia	(S)
ROSE APPLE	Eugenia aquea	(TF)
ROSE BAY	Rhododendron	(S)
ROSE BAY	Rhododendron maximum	(S)
ROSE BOX	Cotoneaster microphyllus	(S)
ROSE BUD CHERRY	Prunus subhirtella 'Ascendens'	(T)
ROSE CAMPION	Lychnis coronaria	(H)
ROSE GUM	Eucalyptus grandis	(T)
ROSE IMPERIAL	Cochlospermum vitifolium	(TT)
ROSE MALLOW	Lavatera trimestris	(A)
ROSE OF CHINA	Hibiscus rosa-sinensis	(HP)
ROSE OF JERICHO	Anastatica hierochuntica	(H)
ROSE OF JERICHO	Selaginella lepidophylla	(H)
ROSE OF SHARON	Hibiscus syriacus	(S)
ROSE OF SHARON	Hypericum calycinum	(S)
ROSE OF VENEZUELA	Brownea grandiceps	(TT)
ROSE PINCUSHION	Mammillaria zeilmanniana	(CS)
ROSE PINK	Sabbatia angularis	(TS)
ROSE VERVAIN	Verbena x hybrida	(H)

Know Your Common Plant Names

Common	Botanical	Type
ROSE-MALLOW	Hibiscus moscheutos	(HP)
ROSE-PLAID CACTUS	Gymnocalycium quehlianum	(CS)
ROSE-SCENTED GERANIUM	Pelargonium capitatum	(A)
ROSE-SCENTED GERANIUM	Pelargonium graveolens	(A)
ROSEBAY	Nerium oleander	(S)
ROSEBAY	Rhododendron maximum	(S)
ROSEBAY WILLOW-HERB	Epilobium angustifolium	(A)
ROSELLE	Hibiscus sabdarifa	(TS)
ROSEMARY	Rosmarinus	(HB)
ROSEROOT	Rhodiola rosea	(R)
ROSEWOOD	Dalbergia	(TT)
ROSIN PLANT	Silphium	(H)
ROSIN-WEED	Silphium pacinatum	(H)
ROSINWEED	Silphium	(H)
ROSY GARLIC	Allium roseum	(BB)
ROTTNEST ISLAND PINE	Callitris oblonga preissii	(C)
ROUEN LILAC	Syringa chinensis	(S)
ROUEN PANSY	Viola hispida	(H)
ROUGE BERRY	Rivina	(R)
ROUGE PLANT	Rivina humilis	(HP)
ROUGH BINDWEED	Smilax aspera	(S)
ROUGH CHERVIL	Chaerophyllum temulentum	(H)
ROUGH CLOVER	Trifolium scabrum	(H)
ROUGH COCKLEBUR	Xanthium strumarium	(H)
ROUGH HAWK'S BEARD	Crepis biennis	(B)
ROUGH HAWKBIT	Leontodon hispidus	(H)
ROUGH MARSH MALLOW	Althaea hirsuta	(H)
ROUGH MEADOW-GRASS	Poa trivialis	(G)
ROUGH-BARKED MAPLE	Acer triflorum	(T)
ROUGH-BARKED MEXICAN PINE	Pinus montezumae	(C)
ROUGH-LEAVED HYDRANGEA	Hydrangea aspera	(S)
ROUND BUCHU	Agathosma betulina	(TS)
ROUND CARDAMON	Amomum compaetum	(H)
ROUND KUMQUAT	Fortunella japonica	(F)
ROUND-EARED WILLOW	Salix avrita	(S)
ROUND-HEADED LEEK	Allium sphaerocephalon	(BB)
ROUND-HEADED ORCHID	Traunsteinera globosa	(O)
ROUND-LEAVED FLUELLEN	Kickxia spuria	(H)
ROUND-LEAVED SPEEDWELL	Veronica filiformis	(H)
ROUND-LEAVED WINTERGREEN	Pyrola rotundifolia	(H)
ROVEN VIOLET	Viola rothomagensis	(H)
ROWAN	Sorbus	(T)
ROXBURGH FIG	Ficus auriculata	(HP)
ROYAL AGAVE	Agave victoriae-reginae	(CS)
ROYAL BAY	Laurus nobilis	(S)
ROYAL FERN	Osmunda regalis	(FN)
ROYAL HAKEA	Hakea victoriae	(S)

Know Your Common Plant Names

Common	Botanical	Type
ROYAL JASMINE	Jasminum grandiflorum	(CL)
ROYAL LIME	Tilia europaea 'Pallida'	(T)
ROYAL PAINT BRUSH	Haemanthus magnificus	(HP)
ROYAL PAINTBRUSH	Scadoxus puniceus	(BB)
ROYAL PALM	Roystonea regia	(P)
ROYAL PALMS	Roystonea	(P)
ROYAL POINCIANA	Delonix regia	(TT)
ROYAL STAFF	Asphodelus albus	(H)
ROYAL VELVET PLANT	Gynura sarmentosa	(HP)
ROYAL WATER LILY	Victoria amazonica	(WP)
RUBBER PINE	Landolphia kirkii	(C)
RUBBER PLANT	Ficus elastica	(HP)
RUBBER RABBIT BUSH	Chrysothamnus nauseosus	(S)
RUBBER TREE	Hevea brasiliensis	(T)
RUBBER VINE	Cryptostegia	(HP)
RUBY GRASS	Rhynchelytrum repens	(G)
RUBY GRASS	Tricholaena rosea	(G)
RUBY SALTBUSH	Enchylaena tomentosa	(TS)
RUE	Ruta	(HB)
RUE-LEAVED SAXIFRAGE	Saxifraga tridactylotes	(H)
RUFFLED FAN PALM	Licula grandis	(P)
RUGBY FOOTBALL PLANT	Peperomia argyreia	(HP)
RUM CHERRY	Prunus serotina	(T)
RUMSLIND TREE	Sparmannia africana	(HP)
RUNNER BEAN	Phaseolus coccineus	(V)
RUNNING MYRTLE	Vinca minor	(H)
RUNNING POSTMAN	Kennedya prostrata	(HP)
RUPTUREWORT	Herniaria	(H)
RUSH	Juncus	(G)
RUSH FERN	Schizaea	(FN)
RUSH LILY	Sisyrinchium	(RH)
RUSSELL LUPINS	Lupinus polyphyllus 'Russell Hybrids'	(H)
RUSSET SEDGE	Carex saxatilis	(G)
RUSSIAN ACONITE	Aconitum orientale	(H)
RUSSIAN ALMOND	Prunus tenella	(S)
RUSSIAN COMFREY	Symphytum x uplandicum	(H)
RUSSIAN KNOTGRASS	Polygonum erectum	(H)
RUSSIAN LETTUCE	Lactuca tatarica	(H)
RUSSIAN LIQUORICE	Glycyrrhiza glandulifera	(H)
RUSSIAN MOUNTAIN ASH	sorbus aucuparia 'Rossica Major'	(T)
RUSSIAN OLIVE	Elaeagnus angustifolia	(ST)
RUSSIAN ROCK BIRCH	Betula ermanii	(T)
RUSSIAN SAGE	Perovskia	(S)
RUSSIAN TARRAGON	Artemisia dracunculus 'Inodora'	(H)
RUSSIAN THISTLE	Salsola	(H)
RUSSIAN VINE	Fallopia baldschuanicum	(CL)
RUSTY FIG	Ficus rubiginosa	(HP)

Common	Botanical	Type
RUSTY FOXGLOVE	Digitalis ferruginea	(H)
RUSTY-BACK FERN	Ceterach aureum	(FN)
RUTABAGA	Brassica napobrassica	(V)
RYE	Secale cereale	(V)
RYE BROME	Bromus secalinus	(G)
RYE GRASS	Lolium perenne	(G)
SABADILLA	Veratrum sabadilla	(H)
SABAL	Serenoa repens	(P)
SACRAMENTO ROSE	Rosa stellata mirifica	(S)
SACRED BAMBOO	Nandina	(S)
SACRED BEAN	Nelumbo	(H)
SACRED FIR	Abies religiosa	(C)
SACRED INDIAN LOTUS	Nelumbo nucifera	(WP)
SACRED LOTUS	Nelumbo	(WP)
SAFFLOWER	Carthamus tinctorius	(A)
SAFFRON	Crocus sativus	(BB)
SAFFRON SPIKE	Aphelandra squarrosa	(HP)
SAFFRON THISTLE	Carthamus tinctorius	(H)
SAGE	Salvia officinalis	(HB)
SAGE BRUSH	Artemisia tridentata	(H)
SAGE OF BETHLEHEM	Mentha spicata	(HB)
SAGE ROSE	Turnera ulmifolia	(TS)
SAGE WILLOW	Salix candida	(S)
SAGE-LEAVED ROCK ROSE	Cistus salviifolius	(S)
SAGE-LEAVED WILLOW	Salix salviaefolia	(S)
SAGO PALM	Caryota urens	(P)
SAGO PALM	Cycas revoluta	(P)(F)
SAGO PALM	Metroxylon sagu	(P)(F)
SAGUARO	Carnegiea gigantea	(CS)
SAINFOIN	Onobrychis viciifolia	(H)
SAINT MARY'S WOOD	Calophyllum	(S)
SAKHALIN SPRUCE	Picea glehnii	(C)
SAL	Shorea robusta	(TT)
SALAC	Salacea edulis	(P)
SALAD BURNET	Sanguisorba minor	(HB)
SALAD CHERVIL	Anthriscus	(HB)
SALAD ROCKET	Eruca sativa	(HB)
SALAL	Gaultheria shallon	(S)
SALLOW	Salix caprea	(ST)
SALLOW THORN	Hippothae rhamnoides	(S)
SALMON BERRY	Rubus spectabilis	(S)
SALMON GUM	Eucalyptus salmonophloia	(T)
SALPICHROA	Salpichroa origanifolia	(H)
SALSIFY	Tragopogon porrifolius	(V)
SALT BUSH	Atriplex	(S)
SALT CEDAR	Tamatix gallica	(S)
SALT TREE	Halimodendron	(ST)

Know Your Common Plant Names

Common	Botanical	Type
SALTMARSH GRASS	Puccinellia	(G)
SALTWORT	Batis maritima	(S)
SALTWORT	Salsola kaki	(H)
SAMBAL	Ferula suaveolens	(HB)
SAMPHIRE	Crithmum maritimum	(H)
SAND CAT'S TAIL	Phleum arenarium	(G)
SAND CATCHFLY	Silene conica	(H)
SAND CHERRY	Prunus besseyi	(S)
SAND CHERRY	Prunus pumila	(S)
SAND COUCH	Elymus farctus	(G)
SAND CROCUS	Romulea columnae	(BB)
SAND DOLLAR	Astrophytum asterias	(CS)
SAND LEEK	Allium scorodoprasum	(BB)
SAND LILY	Leucocrinum	(BB)
SAND MYRTLE	Leiophyllum buxifolium	(S)
SAND PINE	Pinus clausa	(C)
SAND PINK	Tunica	(H)
SAND SEDGE	Carex arenaria	(G)
SAND SPURREY	Spergularia rubra	(H)
SAND TOADFLAX	Linaria arenaria	(H)
SAND VERBENA	Abronia latifolia	(H)
SAND WILLOW	Salix arenaria	(S)
SAND-SPURREY	Spergularia rubra	(H)
SANDAL TREE	Sandoricum indicum	(TT)
SANDALWOOD	Santalum album	(TT)
SANDBAR WILLOW	Salix interior	(S)
SANDBOX TREE	Hura crepitans	(TT)
SANDFLY BUSH	Zieria smithii	(S)
SANDWORT	Arenaria	(R)
SANDWORT	Moehringia	(R)
SANICLE	Sanicula europaea	(H)
SANQI GINSENG	Panax pseudoginseng	(S)
SANTA BARBARA CEANOTHUS	Ceanothus dentatus	(S)
SANTA CRUZ CYPRESS	Cupressus abramsiana	(C)
SANTA LUCIA FIR	Abies bracteata	(C)
SAPELE	Entandophragma	(TT)
SAPELE	Entandrophragma cylindricum	(TT)
SAPODILLA	Manilkara zapota	(H)
SAPODILLA PLUM	Achras zapota	(TT)
SAPODILLA PLUM	Manilkara zapota	(TT)
SAPOTE	Pouteria sapota	(TS)
SAPPAN	Caesalpinia sappon	(TS)
SAPPHINE BERRY	Symplocos paniculata	(T)
SAPPHIRE FLOWER	Browalia speciosa	(HP)
SAPRAE WOOD	Widdringtonia cupressoides	(C)
SAPREE WOOD	Widdringtonia cupressoides	(C)
SARGENT'S CHERRY	Prunus sargentii	(T)

Common	Botanical	Type
SARSAPARILLA	Aralia nudicaulis	(S)
SARSAPARILLA	Smilax officinalis	(CL)
SASSY BARK	Erythrophloeum guineense	(TT)
SATAN'S APPLE	Mandragora officinarum	(HB)
SATIN FLOWER	Clarkia amoena	(A)
SATIN FLOWER	Lunaria	(A)
SATIN FLOWER	Sisyrinchium	(H)
SATIN HIBISCUS	Hibiscus huegelii	(S)
SATIN LEAF	Chrysophyllum oliviforme	(H)
SATIN PELLIONIA	Pellionia pulchra	(HP)
SATIN POPPY	Meconopsis napaulensis	(H)
SATIN WOOD	Chloroxylon swietenia	(TT)
SATIN-FLOWER	Lunaria	(H)
SATIN-FLOWER	Sisyrinchium	(H)
SATIN-LEAF	Heuchera hispida	(H)
SATINWOOD	Fagara Flava	(T)
SATINWOOD	Liquidambar styraciflua	(T)
SATINWOOD TREE	Murraya	(T)
SATINY WILLOW	Salix pellita	(S)
SATSUMA	Citrus reticulata unshiu	(F)
SAUCER PLANT	Aeonium undulatum	(HP)
SAUSAGE TREE	Kigelia africana	(TT)
SAVANNAH FLOWER	Echites andrewsii	(A)
SAVIN	Juniperus sabina	(C)
SAVOURY	Satureia	(HB)
SAVOY	Brassica oleracea bullata	(V)
SAW BRIER	Smilax glauca	(S)
SAW GRASS	Eleocharis effusum	(G)
SAW-PALMETTO	Serenoa repens	(P)
SAW-WORT	Serratula tinctoria	(H)
SAWARA CYPRESS	Chamaecyparis pisifera	(C)
SAWTOOTH OAK	Quercus acutissima	(T)
SAXIFRAGE	Saxifraga	(R)
SCABIOUS	Scabiosa	(H/R)
SCABWORT	Inula helenium	(H)
SCALLION	Allium fistulosum	(BB)
SCALY-LEAVED NEPAL JUNIPER	Juniperus squamata	(C)
SCAMMONY	Convolvulus scammonia	(H)
SCARBOROUGH LILY	Cyrtanthus purpureus	(BB)
SCARLET ANEMONE	Anemone fulgens	(BB)
SCARLET BALL CACTUS	Notocactus haselbergii	(CS)
SCARLET BANANA	Musa coccinea	(F)
SCARLET BIDI-BIDI	Acaena microphylla	(R)
SCARLET FLAX	Linum grandiflorum 'Rubrum'	(H)
SCARLET GINGER LILY	Hedychium coccineum	(BB)
SCARLET HAW	Crataegus pedicellata	(T)
SCARLET LARKSPUR	Delphinium cardinale	(H)

Know Your Common Plant Names

Common	Botanical	Type
SCARLET LOBELIA	Lobelia cardinalis	(H)
SCARLET MAPLE	Acer rubrum	(T)
SCARLET MARTAGON LILY	Lilium chalcedonicum	(BB)
SCARLET MONKEY FLOWER	Mimulus cardinalis	(H)
SCARLET OAK	Quercus coccinea cvs	(T)
SCARLET PAINTBRUSH	Castilleja miniata	(S)
SCARLET PIMPERNEL	Anagallis arvensis	(H)
SCARLET PLUME	Euphorbia fulgens	(TH)
SCARLET ROOT BLOSSOM	Agalmyla	(HP)
SCARLET RUNNER	Phaseolus coccineus	(V)
SCARLET SAGE	Salvia splendens	(A)
SCARLET TRUMPET HONEYSUCKLE	Lonicera brownii 'Fuchsoides'	(CL)
SCARLET TRUMPETILLA	Bouvardia ternifolia	(S)
SCARLET TWINFLOWER	Bravoa	(H)
SCARLET WILLOW	Salix alba 'Chermesina'	(ST)
SCARLET WINDFLOWER	Anemone fulgens	(BB)
SCENTED CUPS	Rothmannia capensis	(H)
SCENTED MAYWEED	Matricaria recutita	(H)
SCENTED PAPER-BARK	Melaleuca squarrosa	(S)
SCENTED VERNAL GRASS	Anthoxanthum odoratum	(G)
SCENTLESS CHAMOMILE	Matricaria perforata	(AH)
SCENTLESS MAYWEED	Matricaria perforata	(A)
SCHOLAR'S TREE	Sophora japonica	(T)
SCOPOLIA	Scopola carniolica	(S)
SCORPION GRASS	Myosotis	(B)
SCORPION SENNA	Coronilla emerus	(S)
SCORPION VETCH	Coronilla coronata	(H)
SCORZONERA	Scorzonera	(V)
SCOTCH BRIAR	Rosa pimpinellifolia	(S)
SCOTCH CREEPER	Tropaeolum speciosum	(CL)
SCOTCH CROCUS	Crocus biflorus	(BB)
SCOTCH ELM	Ulmus glabra	(T)
SCOTCH HEATHER	Calluna vulgaris	(S)
SCOTCH KALE	Brassica oleracea sabellica	(V)
SCOTCH LABURNUM	Laburnum alpinum	(T)
SCOTCH LOVAGE	Ligusticum scoticum	(H)
SCOTCH MARIGOLD	Calendula	(A)
SCOTCH ROSE	Rosa pimpinellifolia	(S)
SCOTCH THISTLE	Onopordon acanthium	(H)
SCOTS PINE	Pinus sylvestris	(C)
SCOTS PLANE	Acer pseudoplatanus	(T)
SCOTTISH ASPHODEL	Tofieldia pusilla	(H)
SCOTTISH BLUEBELL	Campanula rotundifolia	(H)
SCOTTISH THISTLE	Onopordon acanthium	(B)
SCREW PINE	Pandanus	(C)
SCRUB OAK	Quercus dumosa	(T)
SCRUB OAK	Quercus illicifolia	(T)

Common	Botanical	Type
SCRUB PINE	Pinus virginiana	(C)
SCURFY PEA	Psoralea	(V)
SCURVY GRASS	Cochlearia officinalis	(H)
SCYTHIAN LAMB	Cibotium	(FN)
SEA ALYSSUM	Lobularia maritima	(R)
SEA ARROW-GRASS	Triglochia palustris	(G)
SEA ARROW-GRASS	Triglochin maritima	(A/H)
SEA ASTER	Aster tripolium	(H)
SEA BEET	Beta vulgaris maritima	(V)
SEA BINDWEED	Calystegia soldanella	(H)
SEA BUCKTHORN	Hippothae rhamnoides	(S)
SEA CAMPION	Silene maritima	(R)
SEA CENTAURY	Centaurum littorale	(H)
SEA CLOVER	Trifolium squamosum	(H)
SEA COUCH	Elymus pycnanthus	(G)
SEA DAFFODIL	Pancratium maritimum	(BB)
SEA FENNEL	Crithmum maritimum	(H)
SEA GRAPE	Coccoloba uvifera	(TT)
SEA HEATH	Frankenia laevis	(R)
SEA HOLLY	Eryngium maritimum	(H)
SEA KALE	Crambe maritima	(H/V)
SEA KNOTGRASS	Polygonum maritimum	(H)
SEA LAVENDER	Limonium	(H)
SEA LETTUCE	Ulva lactuca	(SW)
SEA LILY	Pancratium maritimum	(BB)
SEA MAYWEED	Matricaria maritima	(H)
SEA MILKWORT	Glaux maritima	(R)
SEA NOODLE	Nemalion helminthoidesn	(SW)
SEA ONION	Urginea maritima	(BB)
SEA PEA	Lathyrus japonicus	(H)
SEA PEA	Lathyrus maritimus	(H)
SEA PEARLWORT	Sagina maritima	(R)
SEA PINK	Armeria maritima	(R)
SEA PLANTAIN	Plantago maritima	(H)
SEA POPPY	Glaucium	(H)
SEA PURSLANE	Atriplex portulacoides	(S)
SEA PURSLANE	Halimione portulacoides	(HS)
SEA PURSLANE	Honkenya peploides	(HS)
SEA RADISH	Raphanus raphanistrum maritimus	(H)
SEA ROCKET	Cakile maritima	(H)
SEA RUSH	Juncus maritimus	(G)
SEA SANDWORT	Honkenya peploides	(H)
SEA SORREL	Desmarestia spp	(SW)
SEA SPLEENWORT	Asplenium marinum	(FN)
SEA SPURGE	Euphorbia paralias	(H)
SEA SPURREY	Spergularia marina	(H)
SEA SQUILL	Urginea maritima	(BB)

Common	Botanical	Type
SEA STOCK	Mathiola sinuata	(H)
SEA STORK'S BILL	Erodium maritimum	(R)
SEA TWITCH	Agropyron pungens	(G)
SEA URCHIN	Hakea laurina	(S)
SEA URCHIN CACTUS	Echinopsis multiplex	(CS)
SEA WORMWOOD	Artemisia chamaemelifolia	(H)
SEA WORMWOOD	Artemisia maritima	(H)
SEABLITE	Suaeda maritima	(A)
SEAKALE	Crambe maritima	(H)
SEALING WAX PALM	Cyrtostachys lakka	(P)
SEALING-WAX PALM	Cyrtostachys renda	(P)
SEASIDE ALDER	Alnus maritima	(T)
SEASIDE CENTAURY	Centaurium littorale	(A)
SEASIDE GRAPE	Coccoloba uvifera	(CL)
SEDGE	Carex	(G)
SEERSUCKER PLANT	Geogenanthus undatus	(HP)
SELF-HEAL	Prunella vulgaris	(H)
SENEGA	Polygala senega	(H)
SENEGAL GUM	Acacia senegal	(TT)
SENITA CEREUS	Lophocereus schottii	(CS)
SENNA	Cassia acutifolia	(S)
SENSITIVE FERN	Onoclea sensibilis	(FN)
SENSITIVE PEA	Chamaecrista fasciculata	(S)
SENSITIVE PLANT	Mimosa pudica	(HP)
SENTOL	Sandoricum koetjapa	(TT)
SENTRY PALM	Howeia forsteriana	(P)
SERBIAN SPRUCE	Picea omorika	(C)
SERPENT GOURD	Trichosanthes	(S)
SERPENT MELON	Cucumis flexuosum	(V)
SERPENTS TONGUE	Erythronium americanum	(BB)
SERRATED WINTERGREEN	Pyrola secunda	(H)
SERRATED WRACK	Fucus serratus	(SW)
SERVICE BERRY	Amelanchier	(ST)
SERVICE TREE	Sorbus domestica	(T)
SERVICE TREE OF FONTAINEBLEAU	Sorbus latifolia	(T)
SESAME	Sesamum indicum	(S)
SESAMOIDES	Sesamoides canescens	(H)
SESSILE OAK	Quercus petraea	(T)
SETTERWORT	Helleborus foetidus	(H)
SETWALL	Valeriana	(H)
SEVEN BARKS	Hydrangea arborescens	(S)
SEVEN SISTERS ROSE	Rosa multiflora 'grevillei'	(S)
SEVEN SON FLOWER OF ZHEJIANG	Heptacodium jasminoides	(S)
SEVILLE ORANGE	Citrus autantium	(F)
SHABBY SEABLITE	Suaeda vera	(H)
SHADBLOW	Amelanchier	(ST)
SHADBUSH	Amelanchier	(ST)

Know Your Common Plant Names

Common	Botanical	Type
SHADDOCK	Citrus maxima	(F)
SHAGBARK HICKORY	Carya ovata	(T)
SHAGGY HAWKWEED	Hieracium villosum	(H)
SHAGGY INK CAP	Coprinus comatus	(FU)
SHAGGY PARASOL	Lepiota rhacodes	(FU)
SHAGGY SOLDIER	Galinsoga ciliata	(A)
SHAGGY-BARKED MANZANITA	Arctostaphylos tomentosa	(S)
SHALLOT	Allium cepa ascalonicum	(V)
SHAMROCK	Medicago lupulina	(H)
SHAMROCK	Oxalis Acetosella	(H)
SHAMROCK PEA	Parochetus	(H)
SHARP CEDAR	Juniperus oxycedrus	(C)
SHARP DOCK	Rumex conglomeratus	(H)
SHARP RUSH	Juncus acutus	(G)
SHARP-LEAVED FLUELLEN	Kickxia eletine	(H)
SHASTA DAISY	Leucanthemum x superbum	(H)
SHAVE GRASS	Equisetum arvense	(H)
SHE OAK	Casuarina stricta	(T)
SHE PINE	Podocarpus elatus	(C)
SHEA BUTTER TREE	Butyrospermum paradoxum	(TT)
SHEA BUTTER TREE	Butyrospermum parkii	(TT)
SHEEP LAUREL	Kalmia angustifolia	(S)
SHEEP'S BIT SCABIOUS	Jasione montana	(R)
SHEEP'S FESCUE	Festuca ovina	(G)
SHEEP'S SORREL	Rumex acetosella	(H)
SHEEPBERRY	Viburnum lentago	(S)
SHELL FLOWER	Alpinia zerumbet	(H)
SHELL FLOWER	Molucella	(H)
SHELL GINGER	Alpinia zerumbet	(TH)
SHELL-FLOWER	Molucella laevis	(H)
SHELLBARK HICKORY	Carya laciniosa	(T)
SHENSI FIR	Abies chensiensis	(C)
SHEPHERD'S BAROMETER	Anagalis arvensis	(A)
SHEPHERD'S BEARD	Andropogon	(H)
SHEPHERD'S CLUB	Verbascum thapsus	(H)
SHEPHERD'S CRESS	Teesdalia nudicaulis	(A)
SHEPHERD'S CROOK	Lysimachia clethroides	(H)
SHEPHERD'S KNOT	Potentilla tormentilla	(H)
SHEPHERD'S NEEDLE	Scandix pecten-veneris	(H)
SHEPHERD'S PURSE	Capsella bursa-pastoris	(A)
SHEPHERDS CRESS	Teesdalia nudicaulis	(H)
SHIELD FERN	Polystichum	(FN)
SHIELD WORT	Peltaria	(H)
SHIN OAK	Quercus gambelii	(T)
SHINGLE OAK	Quercus imbricaria	(T)
SHINGLE PLANT	Monstera acuminata	(HP)
SHINGLE PLANT	Monstera deliciosa	(HP)

Common	Botanical	Type
SHINING CRANESBILL	Geranium lucidum	(H)
SHINING PONDWEED	Potamogeton lucens	(WP)
SHINING PRIVET	Ligustrum lucidum	(ST)
SHINING SCABIOUS	Scabiosa lucida	(H)
SHINING SUMACH	Rhus copallina	(S)
SHINING WILLOW	Salix lucida	(S)
SHINLEAF	Pyrola	(S)
SHIPMAST ACACIA	Robinia pseudoacacia 'Appalachia'	(T)
SHIRLEY POPPY	Papaver rhoeas strains	(A)
SHITTIM WOOD	Acacia nilotica	(TT)
SHOCK-HEADED PETER	Clematopsis stanleyi	(H)
SHOO-FLY PLANT	Nicandra physaloides	(A)
SHOOTING STAR	Dodecatheon	(R)
SHORE DOCK	Rumex rupestris	(H)
SHORE GRASS	Stenotaphrum secundatum	(G)
SHORE JUNIPER	Juniperus conferta	(C)
SHORE PINE	Pinus contorta	(C)
SHORE-WEED	Littorella uniflora	(H)
SHORT-LEAF PINE	Pinus echinata	(C)
SHORT-LEAVED ALOE	Aloe brevifolia	(HP)
SHORT-LEAVED GENTIAN	Gentiana brachyphylla	(H)
SHOWER OF GOLD	Cassia fistula	(TT)
SHRIMP PLANT	Justicia brandegeana	(HP)
SHRUB VIOLET	Hybanthus floribundus	(S)
SHRUBBY ASTER	Aster albescens	(S)
SHRUBBY BUCKWHEAT	Atraphaxis	(S)
SHRUBBY CINQUEFOIL	Potentilla fruiticosa	(S)
SHRUBBY GERMANDER	Teucrium fruiticans	(S)
SHRUBBY HARE'S EAR	Bupleurum fruticosum	(S)
SHRUBBY HOREHOUND	Ballota frutescens	(S)
SHRUBBY MALLOW	Lavatera olba	(S)
SHRUBBY MILKWORT	Polygala chamaebuxus	(S)
SHRUBBY MUSK	Mimulus aurantiacus	(S)
SHRUBBY PAVIA	Aesculus parviflora	(S)
SHRUBBY PLUMBAGO	Ceratostigma	(S)
SHRUBBY RAGWORT	Brachyglottis	(S)
SHRUBBY SEA-BLITE	Suaeda vera	(S)
SHRUBBY TREFOIL	Ptelea trifoliata	(S/T)
SHRUBBY VERONICA	Hebe	(S)
SHUI-HSA	Metasequoia glyptostroboides	(C)
SHUMARD'S OAK	Quercus shumardii	(T)
SIBERIAN APRICOT	Prunus sibirica	(S)
SIBERIAN BUGLOSS	Brunnera macrophylla	(H)
SIBERIAN CRAB	Malus baccata cvs	(T)
SIBERIAN CRAB	Malus x robusta cvs	(T)
SIBERIAN FLAG	Iris sibirica	(H)
SIBERIAN GINSENG	Eleutherococcus senticosus	(S)

Common	Botanical	Type
SIBERIAN LARCH	Larix russica	(C)
SIBERIAN LARCH	Larix sibirica	(C)
SIBERIAN PEA TREE	Caragana arborescens	(ST)
SIBERIAN SPRUCE	Picea obovata	(C)
SIBERIAN SQUILL	Scillia sibirica	(BB)
SIBERIAN WALLFLOWER	Cheiranthus allionii	(H)
SICKLE HARE'S EAR	Bupleurum falcatum	(H)
SICKLE SENNA	Cassia tora	(TS)
SIDE-SADDLE FLOWER	Sarracenia	(HP)
SIERRA FIR	Abies concolor lowiana	(C)
SIERRA LAUREL	Leucothoe	(S)
SIERRA REDWOOD	Sequoiadendron giganteum	(C)
SIGNET MARIGOLD	Tagetes tenuifolia	(A)
SIKKIM LARCH	Larix griffithiana	(C)
SIKKIM SPRUCE	Picea spinulosa	(C)
SILK COTTON TREE	Ceiba pentandra	(TT)
SILK FRUIT	Sericocarpus conyzoides	(TT)
SILK GRASS	Yucca filamentosa	(S)
SILK OAK	Grevillea robusta	(HP)
SILK TASSEL BUSH	Garrya	(S)
SILK TREE	Albizia	(S)
SILK VINE	Periploca graeca	(CL)
SILK-WORM THORN	Cudrania tricuspidata	(T)
SILKWEED	Asclepias syriaca	(H)
SILKWORM MULBERRY	Morus alba	(T)
SILKY DOGWOOD	Cornus amomum	(S)
SILKY WISTERIA	Wisteria venusta	(CL)
SILVER BALL CACTUS	Notocactus scopa	(CS)
SILVER BEARD GRASS	Bothriochloa saccharoides	(G)
SILVER BEECH	Nothofagus menziesii	(T)
SILVER BELL	Helesia carolina	(ST)
SILVER BERRY	Elaeagnus commutata	(S)
SILVER BIRCH	Betula pendula	(T)
SILVER BUSH	Mundulea sericea	(S)
SILVER CHAIN	Dendrochilum glumaceum	(O)
SILVER CLUSTER CACTUS	Mammillaria prolifera	(CS)
SILVER CROWN	Cotyledon undulata	(H)
SILVER DOLLAR CACTUS	Astrophytum asterias	(CS)
SILVER DOLLAR GUM	Eucalyptus polyanthemos	(T)
SILVER FERN	Pityrogramma calomelanos	(FN)
SILVER FIR	Abies alba	(C)
SILVER FIR	Abies alba	(C)
SILVER GRASS	Miscanthus floridulus	(G)
SILVER HAIR GRASS	Aira caryophylla	(G)
SILVER HEDGEHOG HOLLY	Ilex aquifolium 'Ferox Argentea'	(ST)
SILVER HOLLY	Berberis hypokerina	(S)
SILVER KING FERN	Cyathea dealbata	(FN)

Common	Botanical	Type
SILVER LACE VINE	Fallopia baldschuanicum	(CL)
SILVER LEAF FUNGUS	Chondrostereum purpureum	(FU)
SILVER LIME	Tilia tomentosa	(T)
SILVER MALEE SCRUB	Eucalyptus polybractea	(T)
SILVER MAPLE	Acer saccharinum	(T)
SILVER MORNING GLORY	Argyreia nervosa	(H)
SILVER NET LEAF	Fittonia argyroneura	(HP)
SILVER PEAR	Pyrus salicifolius	(T)
SILVER PRIVET	Ligustrum ovalifolium 'Argenteum'	(S)
SILVER RAGWORT	Senecio bicolor cineraria	(H/S)
SILVER ROD	Asphodelus cerasiferus	(H)
SILVER SAGE	Artemisia cana	(H)
SILVER SAGE	Salvia argentea	(H)
SILVER SQUILL	Ledebouria socialis	(HP)
SILVER THISTLE	Onopordon arabicum	(B)
SILVER TOP	Eucalyptus nitens	(T)
SILVER TORCH	Cleistocactus strausii	(CS)
SILVER TREE	Leucadendron	(T)
SILVER VARIEGATED DOGWOOD	Cornus alba 'Elegantissima'	(S)
SILVER VINE	Actinidia polygama	(CL)
SILVER VINE	Epipremnum pictum 'Argyraeus'	(CL)
SILVER WATTLE	Acacia dealbata	(ST)
SILVER WILLOW	Salix alba 'Sericea'	(T)
SILVER WIRE NETTING PLANT	Calocephalus brownii	(H)
SILVERLEAF PEPEROMIA	Peperomia griseorgentea	(HP)
SILVERWEED	Potentilla anserina	(H)
SILVERY CINQUEFOIL	Potentilla anserina	(H)
SILVERY VETCH	Vicia argentea	(H)
SIMARUBA	Simaruba amara	(H)
SIMPLER'S JOY	Verbena hastata	(H)
SINGLE-LEAFED ASH	Fraxinus exc. 'Diversifolia'	(T)
SINICUICHI	Heimia salicifolia	(S)
SISAL	Agave sisalina	(CS)
SISAL HEMP	Agave fourcroydes	(CS)
SISKIYOU SPRUCE	Picea brewerana	(C)
SITKA ALDER	Alnus sinuata	(T)
SITKA SPRUCE	Picea sitchensis	(C)
SIX-ROWED BARLEY	Hordeum vulgare	(G)
SKELETON WEED	Chondrilla juncea	(TS)
SKEWERWOOD	Euonymus europaeus	(S)
SKIRRET	Sium sisarum	(H)
SKULLCAP	Scutellaria	(H)
SKUNK BUSH	Rhus trilobata	(S)
SKUNK CABBAGE	Lysichiton americanum	(WP)
SKUNK CABBAGE	Symplocarpus foetidus	(H)
SKUNK WEED	Symplocarpus foetidus	(H)
SKY VINE	Thunbergia grandiflora	(TCL)

Know Your Common Plant Names

Common	Botanical	Type
SKYFLOWER	Duranta repens	(S)
SLASH PINE	Pinus elliottii	(C)
SLEEPING HIBISCUS	Malvaviscus arboreu	(TS)
SLEEPY MALLOW	Malaviscus arboreus	(TS)
SLENDER BEDSTRAW	Galium pumilum	(H)
SLENDER BROME	Bromus lepidus	(G)
SLENDER BROOMRAPE	Orobanche gracilis	(PE/H)
SLENDER CENTAURY	Centaurium pulchellum	(A)
SLENDER HARE'S EAR	Bupleurum tenuissimum	(H)
SLENDER LADY PALM	Rhapis humilis	(P)
SLENDER RUSH	Juncus tenuis	(G)
SLENDER SANDWORT	Arenaria leptoclados	(R)
SLENDER SMOKE BUSH	Conospermum huegelii	(TS)
SLENDER SPIKE-RUSH	Eleocharis uniglumis	(G)
SLENDER TARE	Vicia laxiflora	(H)
SLENDER THISTLE	Carduus tenuiflorus	(H)
SLENDER TREFOIL	Trifolium micranthum	(H)
SLENDER-LEAVED PONDWEED	Potamogeton filiformis	(WP)
SLENDER-SPIKED SEDGE	Carex acuta	(G)
SLIPPER FLOWER	Caleolaria	(AS)
SLIPPER FLOWER	Pedilanthus tithymaloides	(CS)
SLIPPER ORCHID	Paphiopedilum	(O)
SLIPPER-WORT	Calceolaria	(H)
SLIPPERY ELM	Ulmus rubra	(T)
SLIPPERY JACK	Suillus luteus	(FU)
SLOE	Prunus spinosa	(ST)
SMALL BALSAM	Impatiens parviflora	(A)
SMALL BARREL CACTUS	Ferocactus viridescens	(CS)
SMALL BUR-PARSLEY	Caucalis platycarpos	(H)
SMALL BUR-REED	Sparganium minimum	(H)
SMALL CANE	Arundinaria tecta	(G)
SMALL CATCHFLY	Silene gallica	(H)
SMALL CUDWEED	Logfia minima	(A)
SMALL FURZE	Ulex minor	(S)
SMALL GRAPE HYACINTH	Muscari botryoides	(BB)
SMALL HARE'S EAR	Bupleurum baldense	(H)
SMALL MALLOW	Malva pusilla	(H)
SMALL NETTLE	Urtica urens	(H)
SMALL PONDWEED	Potamogeton pusillus	(WP)
SMALL SCABIOUS	Scabiosa columbaria	(H)
SMALL TEASEL	Dipsacus pilosus	(H)
SMALL TOADFLAX	Chaenorhinum minus	(H)
SMALL YELLOW FOXGLOVE	Digitalis lutea	(H)
SMALL-FRUITED GREY GUM	Eucalyptus propinqua	(T)
SMALL-LEAVED GUM	Eucalyptus parvifolia	(T)
SMALL-LEAVED LIME	Tilia cordata	(T)
SMALL-REED	Calamagrostis	(G)

Common	Botanical	Type
SMARTWEED	Polygonum hydropiper	(A)
SMITH'S CRESS	Lepidium heterophyllum	(H)
SMOKE BUSH	Cotinus coggygria	(S)
SMOKE TREE	Cotinus coggygria	(S)
SMOOTH ALDER	Alnus serrulata	(T)
SMOOTH ARIZONA CYPRESS	Cupressus glabra	(C)
SMOOTH BROME	Bromus racemosus	(G)
SMOOTH CAT'S EAR	Hypochoeris glabra	(H)
SMOOTH CORD GRASS	Spartina alternifolia	(G)
SMOOTH FINGER-GRASS	Digitaria ischaemum	(G)
SMOOTH HAWK'S BEARD	Crepis capillaris	(A)
SMOOTH HONEYWORT	Cerinthe glabra	(H)
SMOOTH JAPANESE MAPLE	Acer japonicum	(C)
SMOOTH MEADOW-GRASS	Poa pratensis	(G)
SMOOTH ROSE	Rosa blanda	(S)
SMOOTH SEDGE	Carex laevigata	(G)
SMOOTH SENNA	Cassia laevigata	(T)
SMOOTH SOW-THISTLE	Sonchus oleraceus	(H)
SMOOTH SUMACH	Rhus glabra	(S)
SMOOTH TARE	Vicia tetrasperma	(H)
SMOOTH TASMANIAN CEDAR	Athrotaxis cupressoides	(C)
SMOOTH WITHE ROD	Viburnum nudum	(S)
SMOOTH-LEAVED ELM	Ulmus carpinifolia	(T)
SNAIL FLOWER	Phaseolus caracalla	(H)
SNAIL-SEED	Cocculus carolinus	(H)
SNAILFLOWER	Vigna caracalla	(CL)
SNAILSEED	Cocculus carolinus	(H)
SNAKE BUSH	Duvernoia adhatodoides	(S)
SNAKE GOURD	Trichosanthes anguina	(H)
SNAKE GOURD	Trichosanthes cucumerina anguina	(F)
SNAKE PLANT	Sansevieria	(HP)
SNAKE VINE	Hibbertia scandens	(CL)
SNAKE'S BEARD	Ophiopogon	(H)
SNAKE'S HEAD FRITILLARY	Fritillaria meleagris	(BB)
SNAKE'S HEAD IRIS	Hermadoctylus turberosus	(H)
SNAKE'S MOUTH ORCHID	Pogonia	(O)
SNAKE'S TONGUE	Ophioglossum	(H)
SNAKEBARK MAPLE	Acer capillipes	(T)
SNAKEBARK MAPLE	Acer crataegifolium	(T)
SNAKEBARK MAPLE	Acer davidii cvs	(T)
SNAKEBARK MAPLE	Acer forrestii	(T)
SNAKEBARK MAPLE	Acer hersii	(T)
SNAKEBARK MAPLE	Acer laxiflorum	(T)
SNAKEBARK MAPLE	Acer pensylvanicum	(T)
SNAKEBARK MAPLE	Acer rufinerve	(T)
SNAKEGOURD	Trichosanthes anguine	(H)
SNAKEROOT	Aristolochia serpentaria	(CL)

Common	Botanical	Type
SNAKEROOT	Cimicifuga	(H)
SNAKEROOT	Polygala senega	(H)
SNAKES HEAD	Hermodactylus tuberosus	(H)
SNAKEWEED	Persicaria bistorta	(H)
SNAPDRAGON	Antirrhinum majus	(A)
SNAPWEED	Impatiens	(A/H)
SNEEZEWEED	Helenium autumnale	(H)
SNEEZEWORT	Achillea ptarmica	(H)
SNOW BRAKE	Pteris ensiformis	(FN)
SNOW BUSH	Breynia disticha	(S)
SNOW CAMELLIA	Camellia japonica rusticana	(S)
SNOW CREEPER	Porana paniculata	(CL)
SNOW FLOWER	Spathiphyllum floribundum	(TH)
SNOW GLORY	Chionodoxa	(BB)
SNOW GUM	Eucalyptus niphophila	(T)
SNOW HEATH	Erica herbacea	(S)
SNOW ON THE MOUNTAIN	Euphorbia marginata	(H)
SNOW PEAR	Pyrus nivalis	(T)
SNOW POPPY	Eomecon chionanthe	(H)
SNOW TRILLIUM	Trillium nivale	(H)
SNOW-BERRY	Gaultheria hispida	(S)
SNOW-BUSH	Ceanothus cordulatus	(S)
SNOW-IN-SUMMER	Cerastium tomentosum	(H)
SNOW-IN-SUMMER	Helichrysum thyrsoideum	(H)
SNOW-ON-THE-MOUNTAIN	Arabis albida	(R)
SNOWBALL CACTUS	Mammillaria bocasana	(CS)
SNOWBALL TREE	Viburnum opulus 'Sterile'	(S)
SNOWBELL	Soldanella	(R)
SNOWBELL TREE	Styrax	(T)
SNOWBERRY	Chiococca	(S)
SNOWBERRY	Symphoricarpos albus	(S)
SNOWDROP	Galanthus	(BB)
SNOWDROP ANEMONE	Anemone sylvestris	(BB)
SNOWDROP CACTUS	Rhipsalis houlletiana	(CS)
SNOWDROP TREE	Halesia	(ST)
SNOWDROP WINDFLOWER	Anemone sylvestris	(BB)
SNOWFLAKE	Leucojum	(BB)
SNOWFLOWER	Chionanthus virginicus	(S)
'SNOWMOUND'	Spiraea nipponica tosaensis	(S)
SNOWY MESPILUS	Amelanchier lamarckii	(ST)
SNOWY MINT-BUSH	Prostranthera nivea	(S)
SNOWY WOODRUSH	luzula nivea	(G)
SNOWY WOOLLYHEAD	Craspedia incana	(H)
SNUFFBOX TREE	Oncoba spinosa	(TT)
SOAP BARK	Quillaja saponaria	(TT)
SOAP BERRY	Sapindus drummondii	(T)
SOAP BUSH	Noltea africana	(S)

Common	Botanical	Type
SOAP TREE	Quillaja saponaria	(TT)
SOAP-BARK TREE	Quillaja saponaria	(T)
SOAPTREE YUCCA	Yucca elata	(S)
SOAPWORT	Saponaria officinalis	(RH)
SOCIETY GARLIC	Tulbaghia violacea	(HP)
SOFT BROME	Bromus hordeaceus	(G)
SOFT BROME	Bromus mollis	(G)
SOFT CLOVER	Trifolium striatum	(H)
SOFT CRANESBILL	Geranium molle	(H)
SOFT GRASS	Holcus mollis	(G)
SOFT HORNWORT	Ceratophyllum submersum	(WP)
SOFT RUSH	Juncus effusus	(G)
SOFT SHIELD FERN	Polystichum setiferum	(FN)
SOFT-LEAVED ROSE	Rosa villosa	(S)
SOLDIER ORCHID	Orchis militaris	(O)
SOLDIERS AND SAILORS	Pulmonaria officinalis	(H)
SOLEDAD PINE	Pinus torreyana	(C)
SOLID-TUBERED CORYDALIS	Corydalis solida	(H)
SOLOMON ISLAND'S IVY	Epipremnum aureum	(HP)
SOLOMON'S SEAL	Polygonatum x hybridum	(H)
SOMA	Sarcostemma acidum	(H)
SONG OF INDIA	Pleomele reflexa 'Variegata'	(HP)
SONG OF INDIA	Pleomeles reflexa	(HP)
SORGHUM	Sorghum vulgare	(G)
SORGHUM GRASS	Holeus sorghum	(G)
SORREL	Rumex acetosa	(HB)
SORREL TREE	Oxydendrum	(ST)
SOTOL	Dasylirion leiophyllum	(CS)
SOUR CHERRY	Prunus cerasus	(T)
SOUR GUM	Nyssa	(T)
SOUR SOP	Annona muricata	(TT)
SOUR WOOD	Oxydendrum arboreum	(ST)
SOUR-TOP	Vaccinium canadense	(S)
SOURSOP	Annona muricata	(TT)
SOUTH AFRICAN HAREBELL	Roella	(S)
SOUTH AFRICAN LEADWORT	Plumbaga auriculata	(TS)
SOUTH AFRICAN SAGE WOOD	Buddleja salviifolia	(S)
SOUTH AFRICAN THISTLE	Berkheya	(S)
SOUTH AMERICAN CROWBERRY	Empetrum rubrum	(S)
SOUTH AMERICAN ROYAL PALM	Roystonea oleracea	(P)
SOUTH SEA IRONWOOD	Casuarina equisetifolia	(TT)
SOUTHERN ARROW-WOOD	Viburnum dentatum	(S)
SOUTHERN BEECH	Nothofagus	(T)
SOUTHERN BLACK HAW	Viburnum rufidulum	(S)
SOUTHERN BUCKTHORN	Bumelia hycioides	(S)
SOUTHERN CATALPA	Catalpa bignonioides	(T)
SOUTHERN CRAB	Malus angustifolia	(T)

Know Your Common Plant Names

Common	Botanical	Type
SOUTHERN JAPANESE HEMLOCK	Tsuga sieboldii	(C)
SOUTHERN MAGNOLIA	Magnolia grandiflora	(ST)
SOUTHERN MARSH ORCHID	Dactylorhiza praetermissa	(O)
SOUTHERN NETTLE TREE	Celtis australis	(T)
SOUTHERN PINE	Pinus palustris	(C)
SOUTHERN PITCH PINE	Pinus palustris	(C)
SOUTHERN SASSAFRAS	Atherosperma moschatum	(T)
SOUTHERNWOOD	Artemisia abrotanum	(HB)
SOW'S EAR	Stachys byzantina	(H)
SOWBANE	Chenopodium hybridum	(H)
SOWBREAD	Cyclamen	(BB)
SOWTHISTLE	Sonchus species	(AH)
SOYA BEAN	Glycine max	(V)
SPANIARD	Aciphylla colensoi	(H)
SPANISH BAYONET	Yucca aloifolia	(HP)
SPANISH BLUEBELL	Endymion hispanicus	(BB)
SPANISH BROOM	Spartium junceum	(S)
SPANISH BUCKEYE	Ungnadia speciosa	(T)
SPANISH CATCHFLY	Silene otites	(H)
SPANISH CEDAR	Toona odorata	(T)
SPANISH CHESTNUT	Castanea sativa	(T)
SPANISH CORDIA	Cordia sebestana	(TT)
SPANISH DAGGER	Yucca aloifolia	(HP)
SPANISH FIR	Abies pinsapo	(C)
SPANISH GORSE	Genista hispanica	(S)
SPANISH HEATH	Erica australis	(S)
SPANISH IRIS	Iris xiphium	(BB)
SPANISH JASMINE	Jasminum grandiflorum	(CL)
SPANISH JUNIPER	Juniperus thurifera	(C)
SPANISH MOSS	Tillandsia usneoides	(HP)
SPANISH OAK	Quercus falcata	(T)
SPANISH OYSTER PLANT	Scolymus hispanicus	(H)
SPANISH POPPY	Papaver rupifragum	(H)
SPANISH SAVIN JUNIPER	Juniperus sabina tamariscifolia	(C)
SPANISH SHAWL	Schizocentron elegans	(HP)
SPARROW GRASS	Asparagus officinalis	(V)
SPARROW-WORT	Passerina	(H)
SPATTER-DOCK	Nuphar advena	(WP)
SPEAR FLOWER	Ardisia	(S)
SPEAR GRASS	Stipa	(G)
SPEAR LILY	Doryanthes	(H)
SPEAR THISTLE	Cirsium vulgare	(H)
SPEAR-LEAVED WILLOWHERB	Epilobium lanceolatum	(H)
SPEARFLOWER	Ardisia	(S)
SPEARGRASS	Aciphylla squarrosa	(H)
SPEARMINT	Mentha spicata	(HB)
SPECKLED ALDER	Alnus rugosa	(T)

Common	Botanical	Type
SPEEDWELL	Veronica	(H)
SPHAGNUM MOSS	Sphagnum cymbifolium	(MS)
SPICE BUSH	Lindera bnenzoin	(S)
SPICE GUAVA	Psidium montanum	(F)
SPIDER CACTUS	Gymnocalycium denudatum	(CS)
SPIDER FERN	Pteris multifida	(FN)
SPIDER FLOWER	Cleome	(A)
SPIDER LILY	Crinum	(BB)
SPIDER LILY	Hymenocallis	(BB)
SPIDER PLANT	Chlorophytum comosum	(HP)
SPIDER TASSEL PONDWEED	Ruppia cirrhosa	(WP)
SPIDER-FLOWER	Cleome	(HP)
SPIDERWORT	Tradescantia	(H)
SPIGNEL	Meum athamanticum	(H)
SPIGNET	Aralia racemosa	(S)
SPIKE HEATH	Bruckenthalia spiculifolia	(S)
SPIKE MOSS	Selaginella	(MS)
SPIKE RUSH	Eleocharis	(G)
SPIKED LOOSESTRIFE	Lythrum salicaria	(H)
SPIKED RAMPION	Phyteuma spicatum	(H)
SPIKED SEDGE	Carex spicata	(G)
SPIKED SPEEDWELL	Veronica spicata	(H)
SPIKED WATER MILFOIL	Myriophyllum spicatum	(WP)
SPIKED WOOD-RUSH	Luzula spicata	(G)
SPIKENARD	Aralia nudicaulis	(H)
SPIKENARD	Aralia racemosa	(H)
SPIKENARD	Nardostachys jatamansi	(TS)
SPINACH	Spinacia oleracea	(V)
SPINACH BEET	Beta vulgaris cicla	(V)
SPINACH DOCK	Rumex patientia	(H)
SPINDLE HEATH	Cosmelia rubra	(S)
SPINDLE PALM	Hyophorbe verschaffeltii	(P)
SPINDLE SHANK	Collybia fusipes	(FU)
SPINDLE TREE	Euonymus europeaus	(BB)
SPINELESS YUCCA	Yucca elephantipes	(S)
SPINIEST THISTLE	Cirsium spinosissimum	(H)
SPINNING GUM	Eucalyptus perriniana	(T)
SPINY COCKLEBUR	Xanthium spinosum	(H)
SPINY RESTHARROW	Ononis spinosa	(S)
SPIRAL GINGER	Costus afer	(TH)
SPIRAL RUSH	Juncus effusus 'Spiralis'	(WP)
SPIRAL-FLAG	Costus	(H)
SPIRE LILY	Galtonia candicans	(BB)
SPLEENWORT	Asplenium	(FN)
SPOON PLANT	Dasylirion leiophyllum	(CS)
SPOON TREE	Cunonia capensis	(T)
SPOONLEAF YUCCA	Yucca filamentosa	(S)

Common	Botanical	Type
SPOONWOOD	Kalmia latifolia	(S)
SPOTTED ARUM	Zantedeschia albomaculata	(H)
SPOTTED CALLA	Zantedeschia albomaculata	(H)
SPOTTED CAT'S EAR	Hypochoeris maculata	(H)
SPOTTED COWBANE	Conium maculatum	(H)
SPOTTED DEAD-NETTLE	Lamium maculatum	(H)
SPOTTED DOG	Pulmonaria officinalis	(H)
SPOTTED EMU BUSH	Eremophila maculata	(S)
SPOTTED GENTIAN	Gentiana punctata	(H)
SPOTTED GUM	Eucalyptus maculata	(T)
SPOTTED LAUREL	Aucuba japonica 'Variegata'	(S)
SPOTTED MEDICK	Medicago arabica	(H)
SPOTTED MOUNTAIN GUM	Eucalyptus goniocalyx	(T)
SPOTTED PERSICARIA	Polygonum nodosum	(H)
SPOTTED ROCKROSE	Tuberaria guttata	(R)
SPOTTED WINTERGREEN	Chimaphila maculata	(H)
SPRAY BUSH	Holodiscus discolor	(S)
SPREAD-LEAVED PINE	Pinus patula	(C)
SPREADING BELLFLOWER	Campanula patula	(H)
SPREADING-LEAVED PINE	Pinus patula	(C)
SPRING ADONIS	Adonis vernalis	(H)
SPRING BEAUTY	Claytonia	(H)
SPRING BEAUTY	Montia perfoliata	(H)
SPRING BELL	Sisyrinchium douglasii	(H)
SPRING CHERRY	Prunus subhirtella	(T)
SPRING CINQUEFOIL	Potentilla tabernaemontani	(H)
SPRING GENTIAN	Gentiana verna	(R)
SPRING GREENS	Brassica oleracea	(V)
SPRING HEATH	Erica herbacea	(S)
SPRING MEADOW SAFFRON	Bulbocodium	(H)
SPRING SANDWORT	Minuartia verna	(H)
SPRING SEDGE	Carex caryophyllea	(G)
SPRING SNOWFLAKE	Leucojum vernum	(BB)
SPRING SPEEDWELL	Veronica verna	(H)
SPRING SQUILL	Scilla verna	(BB)
SPRING STAR-FLOWER	Triteleia	(BB)
SPRING STARFLOWER	Ipheion	(BB)
SPRING VETCH	Lathyrus vernuus	(H)
SPRING VETCH	Vicia lathyroides	(H)
SPRING VETCHLING	Lathyrus vernuus	(H)
SPRIPED SQUILL	Puschkinia scilloides	(BB)
SPROUTING BROCCOLI	Brassica oleracea italica	(V)
SPRUCE	Picea	(C)
SPUR LEAF	Tetracentron sinense	(ST)
SPURGE	Euphorbia	(S)
SPURGE LAUREL	Daphne laureleola	(S)
SPURGE OLIVE	Cneorum tricoccum	(S)

Know Your Common Plant Names

Common	Botanical	Type
SPURRED VIOLET	Viola calcarata	(H)
SQUARE-STALKED WILLOW HERB	Epilobium tetragonum	(H)
SQUARE-STEMMED BAMBOO	Arundinaria quadrangularis	(G)
SQUARE-STEMMED ST. JOHN'S WORT	Hypericum tetrapterum	(H)
SQUASH	Cucurbita pepo	(V)
SQUAW CARPET	Ceanothus prostratus	(S)
SQUAW ROOT	Caulophyllum thalictroides	(S)
SQUAW VINE	Mitchella repens	(S)
SQUAW-BERRY	Mitchella repens	(S)
SQUILL	Scilla	(BB)
SQUINANCY WORT	Asperula cynanchica	(H)
SQUIRREL CORN	Dicentra canadensis	(H)
SQUIRREL'S FOOT FERN	Davallia bullata	(FN)
SQUIRREL-CORN	Dicentra canadensis	(H)
SQUIRREL-TAIL GRASS	Hordeum	(G)
SQUIRRELTAIL FESCUE	Vulpia bromoides	(G)
SQUIRTING CUCUMBER	Echallium elaterium	(HB)
ST. ANDREWS CROSS	Ascyrum hypericoides	(H)
ST. AUGUSTINE GRASS	Stenotaphrum secundatum	(G)
ST. BARNABY'S THISTLE	Centaurea solstitialis	(H)
ST. BENEDICT'S THISTLE	Cnicus benedictus	(A)
ST. BERNARD'S LILY	Anthericum liliago	(H)
ST BRIGID ANEMONE	Angemone coronaria	(BB)
ST. BRUNO'S LILY	Paradisea liliastrum	(H)
ST. CATHERINE'S LACE	Eriogonum giganteum	(S)
ST. DABOEC'S HEATH	Daboecia cantabrica	(S)
ST GEORGE'S MUSHROOM	Calocybe gambosa	(FU)
ST. GEORGES MUSHROOM	Tricholoma gambosum	(FU)
ST.JAME'S TEA	Ledum groenlandicum	(S)
ST. JAME'S WORT	Senecio jacobaca	(H)
ST. JOHN'S BREAD	Ceratonia siliqua	(T)
ST. JOHN'S HERB	Artemisia vulgaris	(H)
ST. JOHN'S HERB	Eupatorium cannabinum	(H)
ST. JOHN'S WORT	Hypericum	(S)
ST. JOHNS PLANT	Artemisia vulgaris	(H)
ST. LUCIE CHERRY	Prunus mahaleb	(T)
ST. MARK'S ROSE	Rose 'Rose d'amour'	(S)
ST. MARTIN'S FLOWER	Alstroemeria	(H)
ST. MARY'S THISTLE	Silybum marianum	(H)
ST. MARY'S WOOD	Calophyllum	(T)
ST. PATRICK'S CABBAGE	Saxifraga 'urbium'	(R)
ST. PETER'S WORT	Ascyrum	(S)
ST. PETER'S WORT	Hypericum	(S)
ST. PETER'S WORT	Hypericum ascyron	(H)
ST. PETER'S WORT	Primula veris	(H)
STAFF TREE	Celastrus scandens	(CL)
STAG BUSH	Viburnum prunifolium	(S)

Common	Botanical	Type
STAG'S HORN FERN	Platycerium bifurcatum	(FN)
STAG'S HORN SUMACH	Rhus hirta	(ST)
STAGGER BUSH	Lyonia mariana	(S)
STAGGERWEED	Dicentra canadensis	(H)
STAGGERWORT	Senecio jacobaea	(H)
STAGHORN CHOLLA	Opuntia versiculor	(CS)
STANDING CYPRESS	Ipomopsis rubra	(H)
STAR ACACIA	Acacia verticilliata	(T)
STAR ANISE	Illicium anisatum	(S)
STAR ANISE	Illicium verum	(S)
STAR APPLE	Chrysophyllum	(S)
STAR APPLE	Chrysophyllum cainito	(TS)
STAR CACTUS	Astrophytum ornatum	(CS)
STAR DAISY	Lindheimera texana	(A)
STAR FLOWER	Trientalis europaea	(H)
STAR FRUIT	Damasonium alisma	(S)
STAR GLORY	Iponioea coccinea	(CL)
STAR GRASS	Hypoxis	(BB)
STAR IPOMOEA	Ipomoea coccinea	(CL)
STAR JASMINE	Trachelospermum jasminoides	(CL)
STAR LILY	Arthropodium candidum	(H)
STAR OF BETHLEHEM	Campanula isophylla	(HP)
STAR OF BETHLEHEM	Ornithogalum umbellatum	(BB)
STAR OF BETHLEHEM ORCHID	Angraecum sesquipedale	(O)
STAR OF THE VELDT	Dimorphotheca	(AH)
STAR SEDGE	Carex echinata	(G)
STAR THISTLE	Centaurea calcitrapa	(H)
STAR WATTLE	Acacia verticilliata	(T)
STAR WINDFLOWER	Anemone stellata	(H)
STAR-APPLE	Chrysophyllum cainito	(TS)
STAR-FLOWER	Trientalis	(H)
STAR-FLOWERED FALSE SOLOMONS SEAL	Smilacina stellata	(H)
STAR-FLOWERED LILY OF THE VALLEY	Smilacina stellata	(H)
STAR-GRASS	Aletris	(H)
STARRY MAGNOLIA	Magnolia stellata	(S)
STARRY SAXIFRAGE	Saxifraga stellaris	(H)
STARRY SAXIFRAGE	Saxifraga stellata	(R)
STARWORT	Aletris farinosa	(H)
STARWORT	Aster	(H)
STARWORT MOUSE-EAR	Cerastium cerastoides	(H)
STATICE	Limonium sinuatum	(H)
STAVESACRE	Delphinium staphisagria	(H)
STEEPLE BELLFLOWER	Campanula pyramidalis	(H)
STEEPLEBUSH	Spiraea tomentosa	(S)
STICK-TIGHT	Bidens	(H)
STICKLEWORT	Agrimonia eupatoria	(H)
STICKY CATCHFLY	Lychnis viscaria	(H)

Common	Botanical	Type
STICKY GROUNDSEL	Senecio viscosus	(H)
STICKY MOONSTONES	Pachyphytum glutinicaule	(CS)
STICKY MOUSE-EAR	Cerastium glomeratum	(H)
STICKY SAGE	Salvia glutinosa	(H)
STICKY SANDWORT	Minuartia viscosa	(H)
STICKY-WILLIE	Galium aparine	(H)
STIFF BROME	Bromus rigidus	(G)
STIFF SEDGE	Carex bigelowii	(G)
STIFF-LEAVED JUNIPER	Juniperus rigida	(C)
STINGING NETTLE	Urtica dioica	(H)
STINK ASTER	Dittrichia graveolens	(H)
STINKHORN	Phallus impudicus	(FU)
STINKING ASH	Ptelea trifoliata	(S)
STINKING BENJAMIN	Trillium erectum	(H)
STINKING CEDAR	Torreya taxifolia	(C)
STINKING CHAMOMILE	Anthemis cotula	(AH)
STINKING COCKLEBUR	Xanthium echinatum	(H)
STINKING GOOSE-FOOT	Chenopodium vulvaria	(H)
STINKING HAWK'S BEARD	Crepis foetida	(H)
STINKING HELLEBORE	Helleborus foetidus	(H)
STINKING IRIS	Iris foetidissima	(H)
STINKING MAYWEED	Anthemis cotula	(AH)
STINKING TUTSAN	Hypericum hircinum	(S)
STINKWEED	Pluchea	(H)
STINKWOOD	Celtis kraussiana	(TT)
STINKWOOD	Gustavia augusta	(TT)
STITCHWORT	Stellaria	(H)
STOCK	Mathiola	(HA)
STOKE'S ASTER	Stokesia laevis	(H)
STOMPIE	Brunia nodiflora	(S)
STONE BRAMBLE	Rubus saxatilis	(H)
STONE HAIR	Entermorpha	(SW)
STONE MINT	Cunila origanoides	(H)
STONE PARSLEY	Sison amomum	(H)
STONE PINE	Pinus pinea	(C)
STONE ROOT	Collinsonia	(H)
STONE ROOT	Collinsonia canadensis	(H)
STONECRESS	Aethionema	(R)
STONECROP	Sedum	(RH)
STORAX	Liquidambar orientalis	(T)
STORAX	Styrax officinalis	(ST)
STORK'S BILL	Pelargonium erodium	(HP)
STRAINER VINE	Luffa acutangula	(TS)
STRAP CACTUS	Epiphyllum	(CS)
STRAP FLOWER	Anthurium crystallinum	(HP)
STRAPWORT	Corrigiola litoralis	(R)
STRAW DAISY	Helichrysum	(A/H)

Know Your Common Plant Names

Common	Botanical	Type
STRAW FLOWER	Helichrysum	(H/A)
STRAW FLOWER	Helichrysum bracteatum	(A)
STRAWBERRY	Fragaria	(F)
STRAWBERRY BUSH	Euonymus americanus	(S)
STRAWBERRY CACTUS	Echinocereus enneacanthus	(CS)
STRAWBERRY CACTUS	Hamatocactus setispinus	(CS)
STRAWBERRY CLOVER	Trifolium fragiferum	(H)
STRAWBERRY GUAVA	Psidium cattleianum	(F)
STRAWBERRY SPINACH	Chenopodium capitaton	(V)
STRAWBERRY TOMATO	Physalis peruviana	(H)
STRAWBERRY TREE	Arbutus	(ST)
STRAWBERRY-BLITE	Chenopodium capitatum	(H)
STRAWBERRY-RASPBERRY	Rubus illecebrosus	(S)
STRAWFLOWER	Helychrysum bracteatum	(A)
STREPTOPUS	Streptopus amlexifolius	(S)
STRIATED CATCHFLY	Silene conica	(H)
STRING OF BEADS	Senecio rowleyanus	(HP)
STRING OF SOVEREIGNS	Lysimachia nummularia	(H)
STRINGY BARK TREE	Eucalyptus globulus	(T)
STRIPED HEMLOCK	Molospermum peloponnesiacum	(H)
STRIPED INCH PLANT	Callisia	(HP)
STRYCHNINE	Strychnos nux vomica	(TT)
STUD FLOWER	Helonias bullata	(H)
STURT'S DESERT PEA	Clianthus formosus	(S)
SUBALPINE FIR	Abies lasiocarpa	(C)
SUBTERRANEAN CLOVER	Trifolium subterraneum	(H)
SUCCORY	Cicorium intybus	(H)
SUCKLING CLOVER	Trifolium dubium	(H)
SUGAR BEET	Beta vulgaris	(V)
SUGAR BUSH	Protea repens	(S)
SUGAR CANE	Saccharum officinarum	(G)
SUGAR GUM	Eucalyptus cladocalyx	(T)
SUGAR KELP	Laminaria saccharina	(SW)
SUGAR MAPLE	Acer saccharum	(T)
SUGAR PALM	Arenga pinnata	(P)
SUGAR PEA	Pisum sativum saccharatum	(V)
SUGAR PINE	Pinus lambertiana	(C)
SUGAR-APPLE	Annona squamosa	(V)
SUGARA	Scytosiphon lomentaria	(SW)
SUGARBERRY	Celtis laevigata	(T)
SUGARED-ALMOND PLUM	Pachyphytum oviferum	(CS)
SULPHUR CINQUEFOIL	Potentilla recta	(H)
SULPHUR CLOVER	Trifolium ochroleucum	(H)
SULPHUR ROSE	Rosa hemisphaerica	(S)
SULPHUR TUFT	Hypholoma fasciculare	(FU)
SULPHUR-WEED	Peucedanum officinale	(H)
SULPHURWORT	Peucedanum officinale	(H)

Common	Botanical	Type
SUMACH	Rhus	(ST)
SUMBUL	Ferula sumbul	(HB)
SUMMER ADONIS	Adonis aestivalis	(H)
SUMMER CYPRESS	Kochia scoparia	(A)
SUMMER CYPRESS	Kochia scoparia trichophylla	(A)
SUMMER GRAPE	Vitis aestivalis	(F)
SUMMER HOLLY	Comarostaphylis diversifolia	(S)
SUMMER HYACINTH	Galtonia candicans	(BB)
SUMMER LADY'S TRESSES	Spiranthes aestivalis	(O)
SUMMER LILAC	Buddleia davidii	(S)
SUMMER PHEASANT'S EYE	Adonis aestivalis	(H)
SUMMER SAVOURY	Satureia hortensis	(HB)
SUMMER SNOWFLAKE	Leucojum aestivum	(BB)
SUMMER STARWORT	Erinus alpinus	(H)
SUMMER TORCH	Billbergia nutans	(HP)
SUMMERSWEET	Clethra alnifolia	(S)
SUMMIT CEDAR	Athrotaxis laxifolia	(C)
SUN CACTUS	Heliocereus speciosus	(CS)
SUN DROPS	Oenothera perennis	(H)
SUN DROPS	Oenothera tetragona	(H)
SUN FLOWER	Helianthus	(H)
SUN FRUIT	Heliocarpus americanus	(TT)
SUN PLANT	Portulacca grandiflora	(A)
SUN SPURGE	Euphorbia helioscopia	(A)
SUNBERRY	Rubus 'Sunberry'	(F)
SUNDEW	Drosera	(H)
SUNDROPS	Oenothera fruticosa	(H)
SUNN HEMP	Crotalaria juncea	(S)
SUNRAY	Helipterum	(H)
SUNRISE HORSE CHESTNUT	Aesculus neglecta 'Erythroblastos'	(T)
SUNROSE	Helianthemum	(S)
SUNSET LILY	Lilium pardalinum giganteum	(BB)
SUNSHINE WATTLE	Acacia botrycephala	(T)
SUPPLE JACK	Ranunculus aconitifolius	(S)
SUPPLE JACK	Rhipogonum scandens	(S)
SUPPLE-JACK	Paullinia	(TS)
SURINAM CHERRY	Eugenia uniflora	(TT)
SWAINSON PEA	Swainsona	(S)
SWALLOW-WORT	Vincetoxicum hirundinaria	(H)
SWAMP BANKSIA	Banksia littoralis	(S)
SWAMP BAY	Magnolia virginiana	(S)
SWAMP BLUEBERRY	Vaccinium corymbosum	(F)
SWAMP COTTONWOOD	Populus heterophylla	(T)
SWAMP CYPRESS	Taxodium	(C)
SWAMP DOGWOOD	Ptelea trifoliata	(S/T)
SWAMP GRASS	Scolochloa festucacea	(G)
SWAMP GUM	Eucalyptus ovata	(T)

Know Your Common Plant Names

Common	Botanical	Type
SWAMP HELLEBONE	Veratrum viride	(H)
SWAMP HICKORY	Carya cordiformis	(T)
SWAMP HONEYSUCKLE	Rhododendron viscosum	(S)
SWAMP LAUREL	Kalmia glauca	(S)
SWAMP LILY	Crinum americanum	(BB)
SWAMP LILY	Lilium superbum	(BB)
SWAMP LILY	Saururus cernuus	(WP)
SWAMP MAHOGANY	Eucalyptus robusta	(T)
SWAMP MILKWEED	Asclepias incarnata	(H)
SWAMP PINK	Arethusa bulbosa	(H)
SWAMP PINK	Calopogon	(H)
SWAMP PINK	Helonias bullata	(H)
SWAMP PRIVET	Foresteria acuminata	(S)
SWAMP ROSE-MALLOW	Hibiscus moscheutos	(S)
SWAMP SWEETBELLS	Leucothoe racemosa	(S)
SWAMP WATTLE	Acacia elongata	(T)
SWAMP WHITE OAK	Quercus bicolor	(T)
SWAMP WILLOW HERB	Lythrum verticillatum	(H)
SWAN RIVER DAISY	Brachycome beridifolia	(A)
SWEATROOT	Polemonium reptans	(H)
SWEDE	Brassica napobrassica	(V)
SWEDISH BIRCH	Betula pendula 'Dalecarlica'	(T)
SWEDISH IVY	Plectranthus australis	(HP)
SWEDISH JUNIPER	Juniperus communis 'Suecica'	(C)
SWEDISH WHITEBEAM	Sorbus intermedia	(T)
SWEET ALICE	Pimpinella anisum	(H)
SWEET ALISON	Lobularia maritima	(R)
SWEET ALMOND	Prunus dulcis	(T)
SWEET ALYSSUM	Lobularia maritima	(R)
SWEET BASIL	Ocimum basilicum	(HB)
SWEET BAY	Laurus nobilis	(HB/S)
SWEET BAY	Magnolia virginiana	(S)
SWEET BERGAMOT	Monarda didyma	(H)
SWEET BIRCH	Betula lenta	(T)
SWEET BOX	Sarcococca	(S)
SWEET BRACKEN	Myrrhis odorata	(HB)
SWEET BRIAR	Rosa rubiginosa	(S)
SWEET BROOM	Scoparia dulcis	(S)
SWEET BUCKEYE	Aesculus flava	(T)
SWEET BUGLE	Lycopus virginicus	(H)
SWEET CALABASH	Passiflora maliformis	(CL)
SWEET CANE	Acorus calamus	(H)
SWEET CHAMOMILE	Chamaemelum nobile	(H)
SWEET CHERVIL	Myrrhis odorata	(HB)
SWEET CHESTNUT	Castanea sativa	(T)
SWEET CICELY	Myrrhis odorata	(HB)
SWEET CLOVER	Melilotus officinalis	(H)

Know Your Common Plant Names

Common	Botanical	Type
SWEET COLTSFOOT	Potaoitoo fragranc	(H)
SWEET CORN	Zea mays	(V)
SWEET CRAB APPLE	Malus coronaria	(T)
SWEET ELM	Ulmus fulva	(T)
SWEET FERN	Comptonia peregrina	(S)
SWEET FLAG	Acorus calamus	(WP)
SWEET GALE	Myrica gale	(S)
SWEET GALINGALE	Cyperus longus	(G)
SWEET GARLIC	Tulbaghia fragrans	(HP)
SWEET GOLDENROD	Solidago odora	(H)
SWEET GRASS	Glyceria	(G)
SWEET GUM	Liquidambar	(T)
SWEET LEMON	Citrus lumia	(F)
SWEET MARJORAM	Origanum majorana	(HB)
SWEET NANCY	Achillea ageratum	(H)
SWEET OLIVE	Osmanthus	(S)
SWEET ORANGE	Citrus sinensis	(F)
SWEET PEA	Lathyrus odoratus	(A)
SWEET PEPPER	Capsicum annuum	(F)
SWEET PEPPER BUSH	Clethra alnifolia	(S)
SWEET POTATO	Ipomoea batatas	(V)
SWEET ROCKET	Hesperis matrionalis	(H)
SWEET SCABIOUS	Erigeron annuus	(A)
SWEET SCABIOUS	Scabiosa atropurpurea	(H)
SWEET SEDGE	Acorus calamus	(H)
SWEET SPURGE	Euphorbia dulcis	(H)
SWEET SULTAN	Centaurea moschata	(H)
SWEET SUMACH	Rhus aromatica	(S)
SWEET THORN	Acacia karroo	(T)
SWEET VERBENA TREE	Backhousia citriodora	(T)
SWEET VERNAL GRASS	Anthoxanthum odoratum	(G)
SWEET VIBURNAM	Viburnham prunifolium	(S)
SWEET VIBURNUM	Viburnum odoratissimum	(S)
SWEET VIOLET	Viola odorata	(H)
SWEET WATER LILY	Nymphaea odorata	(WP)
SWEET WILLIAM	Dianthus barbatus	(B)
SWEET WILLIAM CATCHFLY	Silene armeria	(H)
SWEET WOODRUFF	Asperula odorata	(H)
SWEET-WILLIAM CATCHFLY	Silene armeria	(H)
SWEETHEARTS	Galium aparine	(A)
SWEETLEAF	Symplocos tinctoria	(T)
SWEETSOP	Annona squamosa	(TT)
SWINE CRESS	Coronopus didymus	(H)
SWINE CRESS	Coronopus squamatus	(H)
SWINE'S SUCCORY	Arnoseris minima	(H)
SWINES SNOUT	Taraxacum officinale	(H)
SWISS CHARD	Beta vulgaris cicla	(V)

Know Your Common Plant Names

Common	Botanical	Type
SWISS CHEESE PLANT	Monstera deliciosa	(HP)
SWISS SALLOW	Salix helvetica	(S)
SWISS STONE PINE	Pinus cembra	(C)
SWITCH CANE	Arundinaria tecta	(G)
SWITCH GRASS	Panicum virgatum	(G)
SWORD BEAN	Entada scandens	(H)
SWORD BRAKE	Pteris ensiformis	(FN)
SWORD FERN	Nephrolepis	(FN)
SWORD FERN	Polystichum munitum	(FN)
SWORD LILY	Gladiolus	(BB)
SYCAMORE	Acer pseudoplatanus	(T)
SYCAMORE FIG	Ficus sycamorus	(TT)
SYDNEY BLUE GUM	Eucalyptus saligna	(T)
SYDNEY GOLDEN WATTLE	Acacia longifolia	(T)
SYRIAN BINDWEED	Convolvulus scammonia	(H)
SYRIAN JUNIPER	Juniperus drupacea	(C)
SYRIAN RUE	Peganum harmala	(H)
SYRINGA	Philadelphus	(S)
SZECHWAN FIR	Abies sutchuenensis	(C)
TABASCO	Capsicum frutescens	(F)
TABLE DOGWOOD	Cornus controversa	(ST)
TABLE FERN	Pteris	(FN)
TABLE MOUNTAIN PINE	Pinus pungens	(C)
TABWEED	Grindelia camporum	(H)
TACAMAHAC	Populus balsamifera	(T)
TAG ALDER	Alnus serrulata	(T)
TAGASASTE	Cytisus palmensis	(S)
TAGETES	Tagetes signata	(A)
TAHITI ARROWROOT	Tacca oceanica	(TS)
TAIWAN SPRUCE	Picea morrisonicola	(C)
TALIPOT	Corypha umbraculifera	(P)
TALIPOT PALM	Corypha umbraculifera	(P)
TALL CONE-BUSH	Isopogon anemonifolius	(S)
TALL FESCUE	Festuca arundinacea	(G)
TALL ROCKCRESS	Cardaminopsis arenosa	(H)
TALL ROCKET	Sisymbrium altissimum	(H)
TALL TUTSAN	Hypericum x inodorum	(S)
TALLOW SHRUB	Myrica cerifera	(S)
TALLOW TREE	Sapium salicifolium	(T)
TALLOW WOOD	Eucalyptus microcorys	(T)
TALLOW WOOD	Ximenia americana	(TT)
TAMARACK	Larix laricina	(C)
TAMARIND	Tamarindus indica	(T)
TAMARISK	Tamarix	(S)
TANBARK OAK	Lithocarpus densiflorus	(T)
TANEKAHA	Phyllocladus trichomanoides	(C)
TANGERINE	Citrus reticulata deliciosus	(F)

Common	Botanical	Type
TANGIER PEA	Lathyrus tingitanus	(V)
TANGIER SCARLET PEA	Lathyrus tingitanus	(H)
TANGLEFOOT BEECH	Nothogagus gunnii	(T)
TANIER	Xanthosoma	(H)
TANNER'S CASSIA	Cassia auriculata	(TS)
TANNER'S SUMACH	Rhus coriaria	(S)
TANSY	Tanacetum vulgare	(HB)
TANSY-LEAVED THORN	Crataegus tanacetifolia	(T)
TAPE GRASS	Vallisneria spiralis	(CWP)
TAPEGRASS	Zostera	(G)
TAPIOCA	Manihot esculenta	(F)
TAR BRUSH	Flourensia cernua	(S)
TAR WEED	Madia	(H)
TARAJO HOLLY	Ilex latifolia	(T)
TARATA	Pittosporum eugenioides	(S)
TARE	Vicia sativa	(V)
TARO	Colocasia esculenta	(V)
TARRAGON	Artemisia dracunculus	(HB)
TARTARIAN DOGWOOD	Cornus alba	(S)
TARWEED	Madia	(H)
TASAJILLO	Opuntia leptocaulis	(CS)
TASMANIAN BLUE GUM	Eucalyptus globulus	(T)
TASMANIAN BROWN GUM	Eucalyptus johnstonii	(T)
TASMANIAN CEDAR	Athrotaxis	(C)
TASMANIAN CYPRESS PINE	Callitris oblonga	(C)
TASMANIAN DAISY BUSH	Olearia phlogopappa	(S)
TASMANIAN LAUREL	Anopterus glandulosa	(S)
TASMANIAN SNOW GUM	Eucalyptus coccifera	(T)
TASMANIAN WARATAH	Telopea truncata	(T)
TASMANIAN WAXBERRY	Gaultheria hispida	(S)
TASSEL BUSH	Garrya	(S)
TASSEL CHERRY	Prunus litigiosa	(T)
TASSEL FLOWER	Emilia javanica	(H)
TASSEL FLOWER	Emilia sagittata	(H)
TASSEL HYACINTH	Muscari comosum	(BB)
TATARIAN HONEYSUCKLE	Lonicera tatarica	(S)
TATARIAN MAPLE	Acer tataricum	(T)
TATARY BUCKWHEAT	Fagopyrum tataricum	(H)
TAWNY GRISETTE	Amanita fulva	(FU)
TAWNY SEDGE	Carex hostiana	(G)
TEA	Camellia sinensis	(VT)
TEA ROSE	Rosa odorata	(S)
TEA TREE	Leptospermum scoparium	(S)
TEA VIBURNUM	Viburnum setigerum	(S)
TEA-BERRY	Gaultheria procumbens	(S)
TEA-LEAF WILLOW	Salix phylicifolia	(S)
TEAK	Tectona grandis	(TT)

Common	Botanical	Type
TEASEL	Dipsacus fullonum	(B)
TEASEL GOURD	Cucumis dipsaceus	(F)
TECATE CYPRESS	Cupressus forbesii	(C)
TECATE CYPRESS	Cupressus guadalupensis	(C)
TECOMA	Bignonia, campsis	(CL)
TEDDY BEAR CHOLLA	Opuntia bigclorii	(CS)
TEDDY BEAR PLANT	Cyanotis kewensis	(HP)
TEESDALE VIOLET	Viola rupestris	(H)
TEINTURIER GRAPE	Vitis vinifera 'Purpurea'	(CL)
TELEGRAPH PLANT	Desmodium gyrans	(A)
TELEGRAPH PLANT	Desmodium motorium	(S)
TEMPLE BELLS	Naegelia zebrina	(HP)
TEMPLE BELLS	Smithiantha zebrina	(HP)
TEMPLE JUNIPER	Juniperus rigida	(C)
TEMPLE TREE	Plumeria rubra	(TT)
TEN WEEK STOCK	Matthiola incana annua	(A)
TENBY DAFFODIL	Narcissus pseudonarcissus obvallaris	(BB)
TENERIFE BROOM	Spartocytisus nubigenus	(S)
TEREBINTH	Pistacia terebinthus	(T)
TEXAN WALNUT	Juglans rupestris	(T)
TEXAS BLUEBONNET	Lupinus subcarnosus	(H)
TEXAS MOUNTAIN LAUREL	Sophora secundiflora	(S)
TEXAS PRIDE	Thelocactus bicolor	(CS)
TEXAS RAINBOW CACTUS	Echinocereus dasyacanthus	(CS)
TEXAS RANGER	Locophillum	(H)
TEXAS WALNUT	Juglans microcarpa	(T)
THALE CRESS	Arabidopsis thaliana	(A)
THANKSGIVING CACTUS	Schlumbergera truncata	(CS)
THATCH PALM	Thrinax	(P)
THE DECEIVER	Laccaria laccata	(FU)
THICK-LEAVED SALLLOW	Salix crassifolia	(S)
THICK-LEAVED STONECROP	Sedum dasyphyllum	(H)
THIMBLE-BERRY	Rubus porviflorus	(S)
THIMBLEWEED	Anemone virginiana	(H)
THIN-SPIKED WOOD SEDGE	Carex strigosa	(G)
THISTLE	Carduus	(H)
THISTLE	Cirsium	(H)
THISTLE	Cnicus	(H)
THISTLE	Onopordon	(H)
THISTLE GLOBE	Echinopsis	(CS)
THORN	Grataegus	(T)
THORN APPLE	Datura stramonium	(A)
THOROUGH-WORT	Eupatorium	(H)
THOROUGHWORT	Eupatorium perfoliatum	(H)
THOROW-WAX	Bupleurum rotundifolium	(H)
THOUSAND WEED	Achillea millefolium	(H)
THREAD AGAVE	Agave filifera	(CS)

Common	Botanical	Type
THREAD PALM	Washingtonia robusta	(P)
THREE-MEN-IN-A-BOAT	Tradescantia spathacea	(HP)
THREE-VEINED SANDWORT	Moehringia trinervia	(H)
THREEPENNY-BIT ROSE	Rosa elegantula 'Persetosa'	(S)
THRIFT	Armeria	(R)
THROATWORT	Trachelium coeruleum	(H)
THROATWORT	Uvularia	(H)
THUNDER-PLANT	Sempervivum	(R/H)
THURLOW WEEPING WILLOW	Salix x elegantissima	(T)
THYME	Thymus	(HB)
THYME BROOMRAPE	Orobanche alba	(PE/H)
THYME-LEAVED SANDWORT	Arenaria serpyllifolia	(R)
THYME-LEAVED SPEEDWELL	Veronica serpyllifolia	(H)
TIBETAN CHERRY	Prunus serrula	(T)
TIBETAN HAZEL	Corylus tibetica	(T)
TICK CLOVER	Desmodium	(S)
TICK TREFOIL	Desmodium	(S)
TICKSEED	Coreopsis	(H)
TIDY TIPS	Layia elegans	(HP)
TIDY TIPS	Layia platyglossa	(H)
TIGER ALOE	Aloe variegata	(HP)
TIGER FLOWER	Tigridia	(BB)
TIGER GRASS	Miscanthus sinensis 'Zebrinus'	(G)
TIGER JAW	Faucaria tigrina	(C)
TIGER LILY	Lilium lancifolium	(BB)
TIGER NUT	Cyperus esculentus	(G)
TIGER ORCHID	Odontoglossum grande	(O)
TIGER TAIL SPRUCE	Picea polita	(C)
TIGER'S CHAPS	Faucaria	(CS)
TIGER-TAIL SPRUCE	Picea polita	(C)
TIMOTHY GRASS	Phleum pratense	(G)
TINGIRINGI GUM	Eucalyptus glaucescens	(T)
TINNEVELLY SENNA	Cassia angustifolia	(TS)
TIPA TREE	Tipuana tipu	(TT)
TITOKI	Alectryon excelsum	(S)
TOAD LILY	Tricyrtis	(H)
TOAD PLANT	Stapelia variegata	(HP)
TOAD RUSH	Juncus bufonius	(G)
TOADFLAX	Linaria	(H)
TOADSHADE	Trillium sessile	(H)
TOATOA	Phyllocladus glaucus	(C)
TOBACCO	Nicotiana tabacum	(A)
TOBACCO PLANT	Nicotiana alata	(A)
TOBIRA	Pittosporum tobira	(S)
TODDY PALM	Caryota urens	(P)
TOE-TOE	Cortaderia richardii	(G)
TOLLON	Heteromeles arbutifolia	(S)

Common	Botanical	Type
TOLOACHI	Datura meteloides	(H)
TOLU BALSAM	Myroxylon pereirae	(TT)
TOLU TREE	Myroxylon balsamum	(P)
TOMATILLO	Physalis ixocarpa	(TS)
TOMATILLO	Physalis philadelphica	(H)
TOMATO	Lycopersicon esculentum	(F)
TONKA BEAN	Coumarouna odorata	(V)
TONKA BEAN	Dipteryx odorata	(V)
TONKA BEAN	Dipteryx oppositifolia	(V)
TOON	Toona sinensis	(T)
TOOTHACHE TREE	Zanthoxylum americanum	(S)
TOOTHBRUSH TREE	Salvadora persica	(TT)
TOOTHED ORCHID	Orchis tridentata	(O)
TOOTHED WRACK	Fucus serratus	(SW)
TOOTHPICK CACTUS	Stetsonia coryne	(CS)
TOOTHWORT	Dentaria	(H)
TOOTHWORT	Lathraea squamaria	(H)
TOPAL HOLLY	Ilex x attenuata	(S)
TOR GRASS	Brachypodium sylvaticum	(G)
TORCH FLOWER	Kniphofia	(H)
TORCH LILY	Kniphofia	(H)
TORCH PLANT	Aloe arborescens	(HP)
TORINGO CRAB	Malus sieboldii	(T)
TORMENTIL	Potentilla erecta	(H)
TORTOISE PLANT	Dioscorea elephantipes	(F)
TORTOISE PLANT	Testudinaria elephantipes	(F)
TOSSA JUTE	Corchorus olitorius	(TH)
TOTARA	Podocarpus totara	(C)
TOUCH-ME-NOT	Impatiens noli-tangere	(A)
TOUCH-ME-NOT	Mimosa pudica	(HP)
TOWAI	Weinmannia racemosa	(S)
TOWER CRESS	Arabis turrita	(H)
TOWER MUSTARD	Arabis glabra	(H)
TOWN HALL CLOCK	Adoxa moschatellina	(H)
TOYON	Heteromeles arbutifolia	(T)
TOZZIA	Tozzia alpina	(H)
TRAILING ARBUTUS	Epigaea repens	(S)
TRAILING AZALEA	Loiseleuria procumbens	(S)
TRAILING FIG	Ficus radicans	(HP)
TRAILING LOBELIA	Lobelia erinus pendula	(A)
TRAILING MYRTLE	Vinca	(S)
TRAILING ROSE	Rosa arvensis	(S)
TRAILING SALLOW	Salix aurita	(S)
TRAILING VELVET PLANT	Ruellia makoyana	(HP)
TRAILING WATERMELON BEGONIA	Pellionia dareavana	(HP)
TRANSCAUCASIAN BIRCH	Betula medwediewii	(T)
TRANSVAAL DAISY	Gerbera	(A)

Common	Botanical	Type
TRANSVAAL DAISY	Gerbera jamesonii	(H)
TRANSVAAL HARD PEAR	Olinia emarginata	(TT)
TRANSVAAL TEAK	Pterocarpus angolensis	(TT)
TRAVELLER'S JOY	Clematis vitalba	(CL)
TRAVELLER'S TREE	Ravenala madagascariensis	(TT)
TRAVELLERS PALM	Ravenala madagascariensis	(TT)
TREACLE MUSTARD	Erysimum cheiranthoides	(A)
TREASURE FLOWER	Gazania	(A)
TREE ASTER	Olearia	(S)
TREE CABBAGE	Brassica oleracea longata	(V)
TREE COTTON	Gossypium arboreum	(H)
TREE DAISY	Olearia	(S)
TREE DANDELION	Dendroseris macrophylla	(H)
TREE DATURA	Methysticodendron amnesianum	(S)
TREE FERN	Cyathea	(FN)
TREE FERN	Dicksonia	(FN)
TREE FLAX	Linum arboreum	(S)
TREE GROUNDSEL	Baccharis halimfolia	(S)
TREE HEATH	Erica arborea	(S)
TREE HIBISCUS	Hibiscus elatus	(TT)
TREE HOLLYHOCK	Hibiscus syriacus	(S)
TREE LUPIN	Lupinus arboreus	(S)
TREE MALLOW	Lavatera arborea	(S)
TREE MALLOW	Lavatera olbia	(S)
TREE OF HEAVEN	Ailanthus	(T)
TREE OF LIFE	Guaicum officinale	(TT)
TREE OF SADNESS	Nyctanthes arbor-tristis	(T)
TREE ONION	Allium cepa proliferum	(HB)
TREE PEONY	Paeonia delavayi	(S)
TREE PEONY	Paeonia lutea 'ludlowii'	(S)
TREE PEONY	Paeonia suffruticosa cvs	(S)
TREE POPPY	Dendromecon rigidum	(S)
TREE POPPY	Romneya cvs	(S)
TREE PURSLANE	Atriplex halimus	(S)
TREE TOMATO	Cyphomandra betacea	(TT)
TREE WISTERIA	Bolusanthus speciosus	(T)
TREE-OF-KINGS	Cordyline fruticosa	(TH)
TREE-TOMATO	Cyphomandra betacea	(TT)
TREFOIL	Lotus	(H)
TREFOIL	Trifolium	(H)
TREMBLING ASPEN	Populus temula	(T)
TREMBLING BRAKE	Pteris tremula	(H)
TREMBLING FERN	Pteris tremula	(FN)
TRIANGULAR-STALKED GARLIC	Allium triquetrum	(BB)
TRICOLOR PANSY	Viola tricolor	(H)
TRIDENT MAPLE	Acer buergeranum	(T)
TRIFOLIATE BITTERCRESS	Cardamine trifolia	(H)

Common	Botanical	Type
TRIGGER PLANT	Stylidium graminifolium	(H)
TRIGLAV GENTIAN	Gentiana terglouensis	(H)
TRINIDAD PALM	Sabal mauritiiformis	(P)
TRINITY FLOWER	Tradescantia	(H)
TRINITY FLOWER	Trillium	(H)
TRIQUETROS LEEK	Allium triquetrum	(BB)
TRITELIA	Brodiaea	(BB)
TRITOMA	Kniphofia	(H)
TROPIC LAUREL	Ficus benjamina	(HP)
TROUT LILY	Erythronium revolutum	(BB)
TRUE DAISY	Bellis	(H)
TRUE LAUREL	Laurus nobilis	(S/T)
TRUFFLE	Tuber aestivum	(FU)
TRUMPET CREEPER	Campsis	(CL)
TRUMPET FLOWER	Beaumontia	(H)
TRUMPET FLOWER	Datura	(H)
TRUMPET FLOWER	Incarvillea	(H)
TRUMPET GENTIAN	Gentiana acaulis	(R)
TRUMPET GENTIAN	Gentiana kochiana	(H)
TRUMPET HONEYSUCKLE	Lonicera sempervirens	(CL)
TRUMPET LILY	Zantedeschia aethiopica	(H)
TRUMPET OF DEATH	Craterellus cornucopioides	(FU)
TRUMPET TREE	Cecropia peltata	(TT)
TRUMPET VINE	Campsis	(CL)
TUBEROSE	Polianthes tuberosa	(H)
TUBEROUS BEGONIA	Begonia x tuberhybrida	(BB)
TUBEROUS CARAWAY	Bunium bulbocastanum	(H)
TUBEROUS COMFREY	Symphytum tuberosum	(H)
TUBEROUS PEA	Lathyrus tuberosus	(H)
TUFTED FESCUE	Festuca amethystina	(G)
TUFTED HAIR-GRASS	Deschampsia caespitosa	(G)
TUFTED HAREBELL	Wahlenbergia	(H)
TUFTED LOOSESTRIFE	Lysimachia thyrsiflora	(H)
TUFTED SAXIFRAGE	Saxifraga cespitosa	(H)
TUFTED SEDGE	Carex elata	(G)
TUFTED VETCH	Vicia cracca	(H)
TULIP	Tulipa	(BB)
TULIP POPPY	Papaver glaucum	(H)
TULIP TREE	Liriodendron	(T)
TULIP TREE	Magnolia (erroneus)	(ST)
TULIPAN	Spathodea campanulata	(TT)
TUMBLEWEED	Amaranthus graecizans	(H)
TUMBLING TED	Saponaria ocymoides	(R)
TUMMY WOOD	Careya	(TT)
TUNG OIL	Aleurites fordii	(TT)
TUNGTREE	Aleurites	(TT)
TUNIC FLOWER	Petrorhagia saxifraga	(H)

Know Your Common Plant Names

Common	Botanical	Type
TUNIS GRASS	Holcus virgatus	(G)
TUPELO	*Nyssa* Myssa sylvatica	(T)
TURBAN BUTTERCUP	Ranunculus asiaticus	(BB)
TURK'S CAP	Malaviscus arboreus	(TS)
TURK'S CAP LILY	Lilium martagon	(BB)
TURK'S HEAD	Hamatocactus hamatacanthus	(CS)
TURKEY BEARD	Xerophyllum	(H)
TURKEY CORN	Corydalis formosa	(H)
TURKEY CORN	Dicentra canadensis	(H)
TURKEY OAK	Quercus cerris	(T)
TURKEY PEA	Dicentra canadensis	(H)
TURKEY RHUBARB	Rheum palmatum	(H)
TURKEY'S BEARD	Xerophyllum	(H)
TURKISH FIR	Abies bornmuelleriana	(C)
TURKISH HAZEL	Corylus colurna	(T)
TURKISH TOBACCO	Nicotiana rustica	(H)
TURMERIC	Curcuma	(F)
TURMERIC	Curcuma longa	(V)
TURNER'S OAK	Quercus x turneri	(T)
TURNIP	Brassica rapa	(V)
TURNIP CABBAGE	Brassica napus napobrassica	(V)
TURNIP CABBAGE	Brassica oleracea gongylodes	(V)
TURNSOLE	Heliotropium	(A)
TURPENTINE	Siliphium terebinthaceum	(T)
TURPENTINE PINE	Callitris oblonga verrucosa	(C)
TURPENTINE PINE	Callitris verrucosa	(C)
TURPENTINE TREE	Coprifera mopane	(TT)
TURPENTINE TREE	Pistacia terabinthus	(T)
TURPENTINE TREE	Syncarpia glomulifera	(TT)
TURPETH	Ipomoea turpethum	(TS)
TURTLE VINE	Bauhinia cumanensis	(S)
TURTLEHEAD	Chelone	(H)
TUTSAN	Hypericum androsaemum	(S)
TWAYBLADE	Liparia	(H)
TWAYBLADE	Listera	(O)
TWIGGY MULLEIN	Verbascum virgatum	(H)
TWIN BERRY	Lonicera involucrata	(S)
TWIN-BERRY	Lonicera involucrata	(S)
TWIN-FLOWER	Bravoa geminiflora	(H)
TWIN-FLOWER	Linnaea borealis	(S)
TWIN-LEAF	Jeffersonia diphylla	(H)
TWIST-ARUM	Helicodiceros muscivorus	(H)
TWISTED STALK	Streptopus	(H)
TWISTED-LEAVED PINE	Pinus teocote	(C)
TWITCH	Elymus repens	(G)
TWO-LEAVED ALLSEED	Polycarpon diphyllum	(H)
TWO-STYLED HAWTHORN	Crataegus laevigata	(S/T)

Know Your Common Plant Names

Common	Botanical	Type
UDO	Aralia cordata	(S)
UGLI FRUIT	Citrus paradisi x Citrus reticulata	(F)
ULMO	Eucryphia cordifolia	(S)
UMBELLATE WINTERGREEN	Chimaphila umbellata	(H)
UMBRELLA GRASS	Cyperus alternifolius	(G)
UMBRELLA LEAF	Diphylleia cymosa	(H)
UMBRELLA PALM	Cyperus alternifolius	(G)
UMBRELLA PINE	Pinus pinea	(C)
UMBRELLA PINE	Sciadopitys	(C)
UMBRELLA PLANT	Darmera peltatum	(H)
UMBRELLA PLANT	Petasites hybridus	(H)
UMBRELLA TREE	Magnolia tripetalia	(T)
UMBRELLA TREE	Musanga cecropioides	(TT)
UMBRELLA TREE	Schefflera	(HP)
UNBRANCHED BUR-REED	Sparganium emersum	(WP)
UNI	Ugni molinae	(T)
UNICORN PLANT	Martynia annua	(A)
UNICORN PLANT	Proboscidea	(H)
UNICORN ROOT	Aletris farinosa	(S)
UPAS TREE	Antiaris toxicaria	(TT)
UPLAND COTTON	Gossypium hirsutum	(H)
UPLAND SUMACH	Rhus glabra	(S)
UPRIGHT BROME	Bromus erectus	(G)
UPRIGHT CHICKWEED	Moenchia erecta	(H)
UPRIGHT CINQUEFOIL	Potentilla recta	(H)
UPRIGHT CLOVER	Trifolium strictum	(H)
UPRIGHT SPURGE	Euphorbia stricta	(H)
URN FLOWER	Urceolina	(H)
URN PLANT	Aechmea fasciata	(HP)
URN-FRUITED GUM	Eucalyptus urnigera	(T)
UTAH ASH	Fraxinus anomala	(T)
VALERIAN	Valeriana	(H)
VALLEY LUPIN	Lupinus vallicola	(A)
VALLEY OAK	Quercus lobata	(T)
VALONIA OAK	Quercus macrolepis	(T)
VANILLA	Vanilla planifolia	(O)
VANILLA GRASS	Hierochloe odorata	(G)
VANILLA LEAF	Achlys triphylla	(H)
VANILLA LEAF	Liatris odoratissimum	(H)
VARIEGATED LAUREL	Aucuba japonica 'Variegata'	(S)
VARIEGATED LEMON BALM	Melissa officinalis Variegata	(HB)
VARIEGATED MAJOR PERIWINKLE	Vinca major 'Variegata'	(S)
VARIOUS-LEAVED PONDWEED	Potamogeton gramineus	(WP)
VARNISH TREE	Aleurites molluccana	(TT)
VARNISH TREE	Rhus verniciflua	(S)
VARNISH WATTLE	Acacia verniciflua	(T)
VARNISH-LEAVED GUM	Eucalyptus vernicosa	(T)

Common	Botanical	Type
VARNISH-LEAVED GUM	Fraxinus xanthoxyloides	(T)
VASE PLANT	Aechmea fasciata	(HP)
VEGETABLE MARROW	Cucurbita pepo ovifera	(V)
VEGETABLE OYSTER	Tragopogon porrifolius	(V)
VEGETABLE SHEEP	Raoulia eximia	(R)
VEGETABLE SPONGE	Luffa	(H)
VEITCH'S SILVER FIR	Abies veitchii	(C)
VELVET ASH	Fraxinus velutina	(T)
VELVET BENT	Agrostis canina	(G)
VELVET DOCK	Verbascus thapsus	(H)
VELVET GRASS	Holcus lanatus	(G)
VELVET GROUNDSEL	Senecio petasites	(H)
VELVET HORN	Codium tormentosum	(SW)
VELVET LEAF	Kalanchoe beharensis	(HP)
VELVET LEAF	Vaccinium canadense	(S)
VELVET SHANK	Flammulina velutipes	(FU)
VELVET TRUMPET FLOWER	Salpiglossis sinuata	(A)
VELVET-BEAN	Stizolobium	(CL)
VENETIAN SUMACH	Cotinus coggygria	(S)
VENUS FLY TRAP	Dionaea muscipula	(HP)
VENUS' HAIR	Adiantum capillus-veneris	(FN)
VENUS LOOKING GLASS	Legousia hybrida	(H)
VENUS'S COMB	Scandix pecten-veneris	(H)
VENUS'S LOOKING GLASS	Legousia speculum-veneris	(H)
VENUS'S NAVELWORT	Omphalodes linifolia	(H)
VERNAL GENTIAN	Gentiana verna	(R)
VERNAL SANDWORT	Minuartia verna	(R)
VERONICA (SHRUB)	Hebe	(S)
VERVAIN	Verbena officinalis	(H)
VETCH	Vicia	(H)
VICTORIA BOX	Pittosporum undulatum	(S)
VICTORIA WATER LILY	Victoria amazonica	(WP)
VICTORIAN BOX	Pittosporum undulatum	(V)
VINE	Vitis	(CL)
VINE LILAC	Hardenbergia violacea	(CL)
VINE MAPLE	Acer circinatum	(T)
VINE-LEAFED MAPLE	Acer cissifolium	(T)
VIOLET	Viola	(H)
VIOLET BIRD'S NEST ORCHID	Limodorum abortiva	(O)
VIOLET CRESS	Ionopsidium acaule	(A)
VIOLET HELLEBORINE	Epipactis purpurata	(O)
VIOLET WILLOW	Salix daphnoides	(ST)
'VIOLETS'	Salix daphnoides	(S)
VIPER'S BUGLOSS	Echium vulgare	(H)
VIPERS GRASS	Scorzonera	(V)
VIRGIN'S BOWER	Clematis virginiana	(CL)
VIRGIN'S PALM	Dioon edule	(TS)

Common	Botanical	Type
VIRGINIA CREEPER	Parthenocissus quinquefolia	(CL)
VIRGINIA DOGWOOD	Cornus florida	(S)
VIRGINIA SNAKEROOT	Aristolochia serpentaria	(H)
VIRGINIA STOCK	Malcolmia maritima	(A)
VIRGINIA SWEETSPIRE	Itea virginica	(S)
VIRGINIA THYME	Pycnanthemum virginianum	(H)
VIRGINIAN BIRD CHERRY	Prunus virginiana	(T)
VIRGINIAN COWSLIP	Mertensia pulmonarioides	(H)
VIRGINIAN MOONWORT	Botrychium virginianum	(FN)
VIRGINIAN POKE	Phytolacca americana	(H)
VIRGINIAN POKE WEED	Phytolacca americana	(H)
VIRGINIAN SKULLCAP	Scutellaria lateriflora	(H)
VIRGINIAN STONECROP	Penthorum sedoides	(H)
VIRGINIAN WILLOW	Itea virginica	(S)
VISCARIA	Viscaria oculenta	(H)
VOODOO LILY	Sauromatum venosum	(BB)
VOSS'S LABURNUM	Laburnum x watereri 'Vossii'	(T)
WADADURA	Lecythis grandiflora	(TS)
WAFER ASH	Ptelea trifoliata	(ST)
WAHOO	Euonymus atropurpureus	(S)
WAKE ROBIN	Trillium	(H)
WALKING FERN	Camptosorus rhizophyllus	(FN)
WALKING LEAF	Camptosorus	(H)
WALKING STICK EBONY	Diospyros monbuttensis	(TT)
WALKING-STICK CABBAGE	Brassica oleracea longata	(V)
WALKING-STICK PALM	Linospadix monostachyus	(P)
WALL BARLEY	Hordeum murinum	(G)
WALL BEDSTRAW	Galium parisiense	(H)
WALL CRESS	Arabis	(R)
WALL DAISY	Erigeron karvinskianus	(H)
WALL FERN	Polypodium	(FN)
WALL GERMANDER	Teucrium chamaedrys	(H)
WALL HAREBELL	Campanula portenschlagiana	(R)
WALL LETTUCE	Mycelis muralis	(H)
WALL MUSTARD	Diplotaxis tenuifolia	(H)
WALL PELLITORY	Parietaria diffusa	(R)
WALL PEPPER	Sedum acre	(A)
WALL ROCKET	Diplotaxis tenuifolia	(H)
WALL SPEEDWELL	Veronica arvensis	(H)
WALL-PENNYWORT	Umbilicus rupestris	(H)
WALL-RUE	Asplenium ruta-muraria	(FN)
WALLABA	Eperua falcata	(TT)
WALLFLOWER	Cheiranthus cheiri	(B)
WALLFLOWER CABBAGE	Rhynchosinapis cheiranthos	(H)
WALNUT	Juglans	(T)
WAMPEE	Clausena lansium	(T)
WAND FLOWER	Dierama	(H)

Know Your Common Plant Names

Common	Botanical	Type
WAND PLANT	Galax aphylla	(II)
WANDERING JENNY	Lysimachia nummularia	(H)
WANDERING JEW	Tradescantia fluminensis	(HP)
WANDERING JEW	Tradescantia zebrina	(HP)
WANDFLOWER	Sparaxis	(BB)
WARMINSTER BROOM	Cytisus x praecox	(S)
WARRATAH	Telopea	(ST)
WART PLANT	Haworthia tessellata	(HP)
WARTY CABBAGE	Bunias orientalis	(H)
WASHINGTON PALM	Washingtonia	(P)
WASHINGTON PLANT	Cabomba caroliniana	(WP)
WASHINGTON THORN	Crataegus phaenopyrum	(T)
WATER ALOE	Stratiotes aloides	(WP)
WATER ARCHER	Sagittaria sagittifolia	(WP)
WATER ARUM	Calla palustris	(WP)
WATER ASH	Acer negundo	(T)
WATER ASH	Fraxinus caroliniana	(T)
WATER AVENS	Geum rivale	(WP)
WATER BALSAM	Hydrocera angustifolia	(WP)
WATER BALSAM	Tytonia	(WP)
WATER BENT	Polypogon viridis	(G)
WATER BETONY	Scrophularia auriculata	(H)
WATER BIRCH	Betula occidentalis	(T)
WATER BLINKS	Montia fontana	(WP)
WATER BLOBS	Caltha palustris	(WP)
WATER BLOSSOM PEA	Podalyria calyptrata	(TS)
WATER BUGLE	Lycopus virginicus	(H)
WATER BUTTERCUP	Ranunculus aquatilis	(WP)
WATER CHESTNUT	Trapa natans	(WP)
WATER CHICKWEED	Myosotis aquaticum	(WP)
WATER CONVOLVULUS	Ipomoea aquatica	(WP)
WATER COWSLIP	Caltha palustris	(WP)
WATER CRESS	Nasturtium officinale	(CV)
WATER CROWFOOT	Ranunculus aquatilis	(WP)
WATER DOCK	Rumex hydrolapathum	(WP)
WATER DRAGON	Saururus cernuus	(WP)
WATER DROPWORT	Oenanthe fistulosa	(WP)
WATER ELDER	Viburnum opulus	(S)
WATER ELM	Planera aquatica	(T)
WATER FENNEL	Oenanthe aquatica	(H)
WATER FERN	Ceratopteris thalictroides	(WP)
WATER FIGWORT	Scrophularia aurieulata	(H)
WATER FIR	Metasequoia	(C)
WATER FLAG	Iris pseudocorus	(WP)
WATER FLOWER	Geum urbanum	(H)
WATER FORGET-ME-NOT	Myosotis scopioides	(WP)
WATER GERMANDER	Teucrium scordium	(H)

Know Your Common Plant Names

Common	Botanical	Type
WATER GOOSEFOOT	Chenopodium album	(H)
WATER HAWTHORN	Aponogeton distachyum	(WP)
WATER HEMLOCK	Cicuta virosa	(WP)
WATER HICKORY	Carya aquatica	(T)
WATER HOLLY	Mahonia nervosa	(S)
WATER HORSETAIL	Equisetum fluviatile	(H)
WATER HYACINTH	Eichhornia crassipes	(WP)
WATER IVY	Senecio mikanioides	(HP)
WATER LEAF	Hydrophyllum	(WP)
WATER LETTUCE	Pistia	(WP)
WATER LETTUCE	Pistia stratiotes	(WP)
WATER LILY	Nuphar	(WP)
WATER LILY	Nymphaea	(WP)
WATER LOBELIA	Lobelia dortmannia	(H)
WATER LOCUST	Gleditsia aquatica	(T)
WATER LOVAGE	Oenanthe crocata	(H)
WATER LOVAGE	Oenanthe fistulosa	(H)
WATER MELON	Citrullus lanatus	(F)
WATER MELON	Passiflora laurifolia	(CL)
WATER MINT	Mentha aquatica	(WP)
WATER MOSS	Fontinalis	(WP)
WATER OAK	Quercus nigra	(T)
WATER OATS	Zizania aquatica	(G)
WATER PARSNIP	Sium latifolium	(H)
WATER PEPPER	Polygonum hydropiper	(WP)
WATER PIMPERNEL	Samolus	(WP)
WATER PIMPERNEL	Veronica beccabunga	(H)
WATER PLANTAIN	Alisma plantago-aquatica	(WP)
WATER POPPY	Hydrocleys nymphoides	(WP)
WATER PURSLANE	Lythrum portula	(H)
WATER SALLOW	Salix aquatica	(S)
WATER SEDGE	Carex aquatilis	(G)
WATER SHAMROCK	Menyanthes trifoliata	(H)
WATER SHIELD	Brasenia	(WP)
WATER SOLDIER	Stratiotes aloides	(WP)
WATER SPEEDWELL	Veronica anagallis	(WP)
WATER SPEEDWELL	Veronica anagallis-aquatica	(WP)
WATER SPRITE	Certatopteris thalictroides	(WP)
WATER STAR GRASS	Heteranthera graminea	(G)
WATER STARWORT	Callitriche stagnalis	(WP)
WATER THYME	Anacharis	(WP)
WATER TRUMPET	Cryptocoryne	(WP)
WATER TUPELO	Nyssa aquatica	(T)
WATER VIOLET	Hottonia palustris	(WP)
WATER WELL TREE	Warszewiczia coccinea	(TS)
WATER WILLOW	Decodon	(H)
WATER WILLOW	Justicia americana	(WP)

Know Your Common Plant Names

Common	Botanical	Type
WATER WISTERIA	Hygrophila difformis	(WP)
WATER-FORGET-ME-NOT	Myosotis scorpioides	(WP)
WATER-LILY TULIP	Tulipa kaufmanniana	(BB)
WATER-MELON PEPEROMIA	Peperomia argyreia	(HP)
WATER-MILFOIL	Myriophyllum	(WP)
WATER-PENNYWORT	Hydrocotyle	(HP)
WATER-SHIELD	Brasenia schreberi	(WP)
WATERLILY PROTEA	Protea aurea	(TS)
WATERWORT	Elatine hexandra	(WP)
WATTLE	Acacia species	(ST)
WATTLE-LEAVED PEPPERMINT	Eucalyptus acacae formis	(T)
WAUKEGAN JUNIPER	Juniperus horizontalis "Douglasii"	(C)
WAVY BITTERCRESS	Cardamine flexuosa	(A)
WAVY HAIR-GRASS	Deschampsia flexuosa	(G)
WAVY ST. JOHN'S WORT	Hypericum undulatum	(S)
WAVY-LEAVED PLANTAIN LILY	Hosta undulata	(H)
WAX FLOWER	Hoya carnosa	(HP)
WAX FLOWER	Stephanotis floribunda	(HP)
WAX GOURD	Benincasa hispida	(F)
WAX GOURD	Benincasa hispida	(F)
WAX MALLOW	Malvaviscus arboreus	(TS)
WAX MYRTLE	Myrica cerifera	(S)
WAX PALM	Ceroxylon	(P)
WAX PLANT	Euphorbia antisyphilitica	(CS)
WAX PLANT	Hoya carnosa	(HP)
WAX PRIVET	Peperomia glabella	(HP)
WAX TREE	Rhus succedanka	(T)
WAX VINE	Senecio macroglossus	(HP)
WAX-LEAF PRIVET	Ligustrum lucidum	(S)
WAXWEED	Cuphea	(HP)
WAXWORK	Celastrus scandens	(CL)
WAYBREAD	Plantago major	(H)
WAYFARING TREE	Viburnum lantana	(S)
WEASEL'S SNOUT	Antirrhinum	(A)
WEASEL'S SNOUT	Lamium	(H)
WEATHER PLANT	Abrus precatorius	(CL)
WEAVER'S BROOM	Spartium junceun	(S)
WEAZEL SNOUT	Lamium galeobdolon	(H)
WEDDEL PALM	Microcoelum weddellianum	(P)
WEDDING-CAKE TREE	Cornus controversa	(ST)
WEDGE-PEA	Gompholobium	(S)
WEEPING ALDER	Alnus incana 'Pendula'	(T)
WEEPING ASH	Fraxinus excelsior 'Pendula'	(T)
WEEPING ASPEN	Populus tremula 'Pendula'	(T)
WEEPING ATLAS CEDAR	Cedrus atlantica 'Pendula'	(C)
WEEPING BEECH	Fagus sylvatica 'Pendula'	(T)
WEEPING BIRCH	Betula pendula 'Tristis'	(T)

Know Your Common Plant Names

Common	Botanical	Type
WEEPING BIRCH	Betula pendula 'Youngii'	(T)
WEEPING CHERRY	Prunus 'Hilling's Weeping'	(T)
WEEPING CHERRY	Prunus 'Ivensii'	(T)
WEEPING CHERRY	Prunus 'Kiku Shidare Sakura'	(T)
WEEPING CHERRY	Prunus 'Kiku-Shidare Sakura'	(T)
WEEPING CHERRY	Prunus 'Shidare Yoshino'	(T)
WEEPING CHERRY	Prunus sub.'Pendula'	(T)
WEEPING COTONEASTER	Cotoneaster 'Hybridus Pendulus'	(T)
WEEPING CRAB	Malus 'Echtermeyer'	(T)
WEEPING CRAB	Malus 'Red Jade'	(T)
WEEPING ELM	Ulmus glabra 'Camperdownii'	(T)
WEEPING EUROPEAN LARCH	Larix decidua 'Pendula'	(C)
WEEPING FIG	Ficus benjamina	(HP)
WEEPING FORSYTHIA	Forsythia suspensa	(S)
WEEPING HOLLY	Ilex aquifolium 'Pendula'	(T)
WEEPING JAPANESE LARCH	Larix kaempferi 'Pendula'	(C)
WEEPING LABURNUM	Laburnum anagyroides 'Pendulum'	(T)
WEEPING LARCH	Larix x pendula	(C)
WEEPING MOUNTAIN ASH	Sorbus aucuparia 'Pendula'	(T)
WEEPING MULBERRY	Morus alba 'Pendula'	(T)
WEEPING MYALL	Acacia pendula	(T)
WEEPING OAK	Quercus robur 'Pendula'	(T)
WEEPING PEAR	Pyrus salicifolia 'Pendula'	(T)
WEEPING PURPLE BEECH	Fagus sylvatica 'Purpurea Pendula'	(T)
WEEPING PURPLE OSIER	Salix purpurea 'pendula'	(T)
WEEPING SALLY	Eucalyptus mitchelliana	(T)
WEEPING SALLY	Salix caprea 'Pendula' (female)	(S)
WEEPING SCOTCH LABURNUM	Laburnum alpinum 'Pendulum'	(T)
WEEPING SILVER HOLLY	Ilex aquifolium 'Argenteomarginata Pendula'	(T)
WEEPING SILVER LIME	Tllia petiolaris	(T)
WEEPING SPRING CHERRY	Prunus sub. 'pendula'	(T)
WEEPING SPRUCE	Picea brewerana	(C)
WEEPING SWAMP CYPRESS	Taxodium distichum 'Pendens'	(C)
WEEPING THORN	Crataegus monogyna 'Pendula'	(T)
WEEPING WIDOW	Lacrymaria velutina	(FU)
WEEPING WILLOW	Salix babylonica	(T)
WEEPING WILLOW	Salix babylonica pekinensis 'Pendula'	(T)
WEEPING WILLOW	Salix caprea 'Pendula'	(T)
WEEPING WILLOW	Salix purpurea 'Pendula'	(T)
WEEPING WILLOW	Salix x sepulcralis chrysocoma	(T)
WEEPING WYCH ELM	Ulmus glabra 'Horizontalis'	(T)
WEEPING YOSHINO CHERRY	Prunus yedoensis 'Shidare Yoshino'	(T)
WEEVIL PLANT	Cureuligo	(H)
WEIGELA	Weigela	(S)
WELD	Reseda luteola	(H)
WELLINGTONIA	Sequoiadendron	(C)
WELSH ONION	Allium fistulosum	(HB)

Know Your Common Plant Names

Common	Botanical	Type
WELCH POPPY	Meconopsis cambrica	(H)
WELTED THISTLE	Carduus acanthoides	(H)
WEST AFRICAN BARWOOD	Pterocarpus angolensis	(TT)
WEST AFRICAN EBONY	Diospyros mespiliformis	(TT)
WEST AUSTRALIAN MAHOGANY	Eucalyptus marginata	(T)
WEST FELTON YEW	Taxus bacc. 'dovastoniana'	(C)
WEST HIMALAYAN FIR	Abies pindrow	(C)
WEST HIMALAYAN SPRUCE	Picea smithiana	(C)
WEST INDIAN ARROWROOT	Maranta arundinacea	(TS)
WEST INDIAN BIRCH	Bursera simaruba	(S/T)
WEST INDIAN BOXWOOD	Gossypiospermum praecox	(TT)
WEST INDIAN BOXWOOD	Tabebuia	(TT)
WEST INDIAN CEDAR	Toona odorata	(TT)
WEST INDIAN GHERKIN	Cucumis anguria	(F)
WEST INDIAN HOLLY	Turnera ulmifolia	(TS)
WEST INDIAN JASMINE	Plumeria rubra	(TT)
WEST INDIAN KALE	Colocasia	(V)
WEST INDIAN SILKWOOD	Zanthoxylum flavum	(TT)
WESTERN ARBOR-VITAE	Thuja plicata	(C)
WESTERN BALSAM POPLAR	Populus trichocarpa	(T)
WESTERN CATALPA	Catalpa speciosa	(T)
WESTERN FALSE-ASPHODEL	Tofieldia glutinosa	(H)
WESTERN HEMLOCK	Tsuga heterophylla	(C)
WESTERN JUNIPER	Juniperus occidentalis	(C)
WESTERN LARCH	Larix occidentalis	(C)
WESTERN PLANE	Platanus occidentalis	(T)
WESTERN POLYPODY	Polypodium interjectum	(FN)
WESTERN RED CEDAR	Thuya plicata	(C)
WESTERN REDBUD	Cercis occidentalis	(S)
WESTERN SWORD FERN	Polystichum munitum	(FN)
WESTERN TEA-MYRTLE	Melaleuca nesophylla	(S)
WESTERN TRUMPET HONEYSUCKLE	Lonicera ciliosa	(CL)
WESTERN WHITE PINE	Pinus monticola	(C)
WESTERN YELLOW PINE	Pinus ponderosa	(C)
WESTERN YEW	Taxus brevifolia	(C)
WESTLAND PINE	Dacrydium	(C)
WESTLAND PINE	Dacrydium colensoi	(C)
WESTONBIRT DOGWOOD	Cornus alba 'Sibirica'	(S)
WEYMOUTH PINE	Pinus strobus	(C)
WHEAT	Triticum	(VG)
WHEATLEY ELM	Ulmus minor 'Sarniensis'	(T)
WHEEL OF FIRE	Stenocarpus sinuatus	(HP)
WHIN	Ulex europaeus	(S)
WHINBERRY	Vaccinium myrtillus	(S)
WHITE ALDER	Alnus rhombifolia	(T)
WHITE ALDER	Clethra acuminata	(S)
WHITE AMARANTH	Amaranthus albus	(H)

Common	Botanical	Type
WHITE ANGEL'S TRUMPET	Brugmansia x candida	(TH)
WHITE ASH	Fraxinus americana	(T)
WHITE BALL MUSTARD	Calepina irregularis	(H)
WHITE BALSAM	Gnaphalium polycephalum	(H)
WHITE BANEBERRY	Actaea alba	(H)
WHITE BARK PINE	Pinus albicaulis	(C)
WHITE BASSWOOD	Tilia heterophylla	(T)
WHITE BATCHELORS BUTTONS	Ranunculus aconitifolius	(H)
WHITE BAY	Magnolia virginiana	(S/T)
WHITE BIRCH	Betula pubescens	(T)
WHITE BROOM	Genista raetam	(S)
WHITE BRYONY	Bryonia dioica	(CL)
WHITE BUSH POPPY	Romneya	(S)
WHITE BUTTERBUR	Petasites albus	(H)
WHITE BUTTERCUP	Ranunculus amplexicaulis	(H)
WHITE CAMPION	Silene alba	(H)
WHITE CAMPION	Silene latifolia	(H)
WHITE CEDAR	Melia dubium	(TT)
WHITE CEDAR	Thuya occidentalis	(C)
WHITE CINNAMON	Canella alba	(TS)
WHITE CINNAMON	Canella winterana	(TS)
WHITE CINQUEFOIL	Potentilla alba	(H)
WHITE CLOVER	Trifolium repens	(H)
WHITE COHOSH	Actaea alba	(H)
WHITE COMFREY	Symphytum orientale	(H)
WHITE CYPRESS	Chamaecyparis thyoides	(C)
WHITE CYPRESS PINE	Callitris columellaris	(C)
WHITE DEAD-NETTLE	Lamium album	(H)
WHITE DOGWOOD	Cornus florida	(S)
WHITE DRAGON TREE	Sesbania formosa	(TT)
WHITE EGYPTIAN LOTUS	Nymphaea lotus	(WP)
WHITE ELM	Ulmus americana	(T)
WHITE FALSE HELLEBORE	Veratrum album	(H)
WHITE FIR	Abies concolor	(C)
WHITE FLAX	Linum catharticum	(H)
WHITE FORSYTHIA	Abeliophyllum	(S)
WHITE FUMITORY	Fumaria capreolata	(H)
WHITE GUINEA YAM	Dioscorea rotundata	(V)
WHITE GUM	Eucalyptus rossii	(T)
WHITE HELLEBORINE	Cephalanthera damasonium	(O)
WHITE HENBABE	Hyoscyamus albus	(H)
WHITE HOREHOUND	Marrubim vulgare	(H)
WHITE IPECACUANHA	Ionidium ipecacuanha	(TS)
WHITE IRONBARK	Eucalyptus leucoxylon	(T)
WHITE JEW'S MALLOW	Rhodotypos scandens	(S)
WHITE JUTE	Corchorus capsularis	(TH)
WHITE LAUREL	Magnolia virginiana	(ST)

Know Your Common Plant Names

Common	Botanical	Type
WHITE LILY TURF	Ophiopogon jaburan	(H)
WHITE LUPIN	Lupinus albus	(H)
WHITE MARIPOSA LILY	Calochortus venustus	(BB)
WHITE MELILOT	Melilotus alba	(H)
WHITE MIGNONETTE	Reseda alba	(H)
WHITE MUGWORT	Artemisia lactifilora	(H)
WHITE MULBERRY	Morus alba	(T)
WHITE MULLEIN	Verbascum lychnitis	(H)
WHITE MULLEIN	Verbascum thapsus	(H)
WHITE MUSTARD	Sinapis alba	(V)
WHITE OAK	Quercus alba	(T)
WHITE PASQUE FLOWER	Pulsatilla alba	(R)
WHITE PEPPER	Piper album	(F)
WHITE PINE	Pinus strobus	(C)
WHITE PINE	Podocarpus elatus	(C)
WHITE POPLAR	Populus alba	(T)
WHITE POPPY	Papaver somniferum	(A)
WHITE PORTUGAL BROOM	Cytisus multiflorus (albus)	(S)
WHITE PURSLANE	Euphorbia corollata	(H)
WHITE ROCK	Arabis caucasica	(R)
WHITE ROCKET	Diplotaxis erucoides	(H)
WHITE ROSE OF YORK	Rosa x alba	(S)
WHITE SAGE	Artemisia ludoviciana	(H)
WHITE SALLY	Eucalyptus pauciflora	(T)
WHITE SAPOTA	Casimiroa edulis	(TT)
WHITE SEDGE	Carex curta	(G)
WHITE SERINGA	Kirka acuminata	(HP)
WHITE SHINLEAF	Pyrola secunda	(H)
WHITE SNAKE-ROOT	Eupatorium rugosum	(H)
WHITE SPANISH BROOM	Cytisus multiflorus	(S)
WHITE SPRUCE	Picea glauca	(C)
WHITE SQUILL	Urginea maritima	(BB)
WHITE STINKWOOD TREE	Celtis africana	(TT)
WHITE STONECROP	Sedum album	(H)
WHITE TEA TREE	Melaleuca leucadendron	(T)
WHITE TOP PEPPERMINT	Eucalyptus radiata	(T)
WHITE TORCH CACTUS	Trichocereus spachianus	(CS)
WHITE VELVET	Tradescantia sillamontana	(HP)
WHITE VINE	Clematis vitalba	(CL)
WHITE WALNUT	Juglans cinerea	(T)
WHITE WARATAH	Agastachys odorata	(S)
WHITE WATER LILY	Nymphaea alba	(WP)
WHITE WEED	Leucanthemum vulgare	(H)
WHITE WILLOW	Salix alba	(ST)
WHITE WOOD ASTER	Aster divaricatus	(H)
WHITE YAM	Dioscorea alata	(V)
WHITE-BARKED HIMALAYAN BIRCH	Betula jacquemontii	(T)

Common	Botanical	Type
WHITE-LEAVED MARLOCK	Eucalyptus tetragona	(T)
WHITEBEAM	Sorbus aria	(T)
WHITETHORN	Crataegus monogyna	(ST)
WHITEWOOD	Liriodendron tulipfera	(T)
WHITEYWOOD	Melicytus ramiflorus	(S)
WHITLOW GRASS	Draba	(H)
WHITLOW GRASS	Erophila verna	(G)
WHORLFLOWER	Morina longifolia	(H)
WHORL GRASS	Catabrosa aquatica	(G)
WHORL-FLOWER	Morina	(H)
WHORLED CARAWAY	Carum verticilliatum	(H)
WHORLED MINT	Mentha x verticilliata	(H)
WHORLED WATER MILFOIL	Myriophyllum verticilliatum	(WP)
WHORTLE WILLOW	Salix myrsinites	(S)
WHORTLE-LEAVED WILLOW	Salix myrsinites	(S)
WHORTLEBERRY	Vaccineum myrtillus	(F)
WIDOW IRIS	Hermodactylus tuberosus	(H)
WIDOW TEARS	Tradescantia	(H)
WIG KNAPWEED	Centaurea phrygia	(H)
WIG TREE	Cotinus coggygria	(S)
WILD ANGELICA	Angelica sylvestris	(H)
WILD ASPARAGUS	Asparagus officinalis	(H)
WILD BALSAM	Impatiens noli-tangere	(A)
WILD BANANA	Heliconia	(TS)
WILD BANANA	Strelitzia nicolai	(HP)
WILD BARLEY	Hordeum murinum	(G)
WILD BASIL	Clinopodium vulgare	(H)
WILD BERGAMOT	Monarda fistulosa	(HB)
WILD BUCKWHEAT	Eriogonum	(H)
WILD CABBAGE	Brassica oleracea	(H)
WILD CANDYTUFT	Iberis amara	(R)
WILD CARROT	Daucus carota	(H)
WILD CELERY	Apium graveolens	(H)
WILD CHAMOMILE	Matricaria recutita	(A)
WILD CHERRY	Prunus avium	(ST)
WILD CHINA TREE	Sapindus drummondii	(T)
WILD CINNAMON	Canella	(H)
WILD CLARY	Salvia verbenacea	(H)
WILD COFFEE	Polyscias guilfoylei	(TS)
WILD COTTON	Hibiscus diversifolius	(S)
WILD CRAB	Malus sylvestris	(T)
WILD CRANSBILL	Geranium maculatum	(H)
WILD DAFFODIL	Narcissus pseudonarcissus	(BB)
WILD DATE	Yucca baccata	(S)
WILD FESCUE	Festuca altissima	(G)
WILD GARLIC	Allium ursinum	(BB)
WILD GERANIUM	Geranium maculatum	(H)

Common	Botanical	Type
WILD GINGER	Asarum canadense	(H)
WILD HOPS	Bryonia dioica	(CL)
WILD HORSEHOUND	Eupatorium teucrifolium	(H)
WILD HYACINTH	Hyacinthoides non-scripta	(BB)
WILD HYACINTH	Lachenalia contaminata	(BB)
WILD HYSSOP	Pycnanthemum virginianum	(H)
WILD INDIGO	Baptisia tinctoria	(H)
WILD IRISHMAN	Discaria toumatou	(S)
WILD JALOP	Ipomoea pandurata	(H)
WILD JONQUIL	Narcissus jonquilla	(WP)
WILD LEEK	Allium ampeloprasum	(BB)
WILD LEMON	Podophyllum peltatum	(H)
WILD LENTIL	Astragalus cicer	(H)
WILD LILY-OF-THE-VALLEY	Pyrola rotundifolia	(H)
WILD LIQUORICE	Astragalus glycyphyllos	(H)
WILD MADDER	Rubia peregrina	(H)
WILD MARJORAM	Origanum vulgare	(HB)
WILD MIGNONETTE	Reseda lutea	(H)
WILD MINT	Mentha x verticilliata	(HB)
WILD MUSTARD	Sinapis arvensis	(H)
WILD NARD	Asarum europacum	(H)
WILD OAT	Arena fatua	(G)
WILD OLIVE	Olea africana	(TT)
WILD PANSY	Viola tricolor	(H)
WILD PARSNIP	Pastinaca sativa	(H)
WILD PEA	Lathyrus sylvestris	(H)
WILD PEACH	Kiggelaria africana	(TT)
WILD PEAR	Pyrus pyraster	(T)
WILD PETUNIA	Ruellia ciliosa	(H)
WILD PINEAPPLE	Ananas bracteatus	(HP)
WILD PINK	Dianthus plumarius	(R)
WILD PLANTAIN	Heliconia wagneriana	(TH)
WILD PLUM	Prunus domestica	(T)
WILD POINSETTIA	Warszewiczia coccinea	(TS)
WILD POMEGRANATE	Burchellia bubalina	(S)
WILD POTATO	Ipomoea fastigiata	(CL)
WILD POTATO VINE	Ipomoea pandurata	(CL)
WILD PRIDE OF INDIA	Galpinia transvaalica	(TT)
WILD RADISH	Raphanus raphanistrum	(V)
WILD RASPBERRY	Rubus idaeus	(S)
WILD RED CHERRY	Prunus pennsylvanica	(T)
WILD RED RASPBERRY	Rubus strigosus	(S)
WILD RICE	Zizania aquatica	(WP)
WILD ROSEMARY	Croton cascarilla	(S)
WILD ROSEMARY	Ledum palustre	(S)
WILD RYE	Elymus	(G)
WILD SAGE	Salvia horminoides	(H)

Common	Botanical	Type
WILD SAGE	Salvia nemorosa	(H)
WILD SARSAPARILLA	Aralia nudicaulis	(S)
WILD SENNA	Cassia marilandica	(TS)
WILD SERVICE TREE	Sorbus torminalis	(T)
WILD SPANIARD	Aciphylla colensoi	(H)
WILD STRAWBERRY	Fragaria vesca	(H)
WILD SUCCORY	Sabatia angularis	(HB)
WILD SUNFLOWER	Inula helenium	(H)
WILD THYME	Thymus serpyllum	(R)
WILD TULIP	Tulipa sylvestris	(BB)
WILD TURNIP	Arum triphyllum	(H)
WILD VANILLA	Liatris odoratissimum	(H)
WILD YAM	Dioscorea villosa	(F)
WILLOW	Salix	(ST)
WILLOW CHERRY	Prunus incana	(S)
WILLOW GENTIAN	Gentiana asclepiadea	(R)
WILLOW HERB	Epilobium	(HA)
WILLOW MOSS	Foninalis antipyretica	(WP)
WILLOW MOSS	Fontinalis	(WP)
WILLOW MYRTLE	Agonis flexuosa	(T)
WILLOW OAK	Quercus phellos	(T)
WILLOW-LEAF BAY	Laurus nobilis angustifolia	(S)
WILLOW-LEAFED MAGNOLIA	Magnolia salicifolia	(ST)
WILLOW-LEAFED PEAR	Pyrus salicifolia	(T)
WILLOW-LEAVED POPLAR	Populus angustifolia	(T)
WILLOWMORE CEDAR	Widdringtonia schwarzii	(C)
WILSON'S BARBERRY	Berberis wilsoniae	(S)
WIND EYEBRIGHT	Euphrasia nemorosa	(H)
WIND POPPY	Stylomecon heterophylla	(H)
WINDFLOWER	Anemone	(H)
WINDMILL PALM	Trachycarpus fortunei	(P)
WINE PALM	Caryota urens	(P)
WINE PALM	Jubaea chilensis	(P)
WINEBERRY	Rubus phoenicolasius	(CL)
WINECUPS	Babiana rubro-cyanea	(BB)
WING KELP	Alaria esculenta	(SW)
WING NUT	Pterocarya	(T)
WINGED BROOM	Chamaespartium sagittale	(S)
WINGED EVERLASTING	Ammobium alatum	(H)
WINGED SPINDLE	Euonymus alatus	(S)
WINGED WATTLE	Acacia alata	(T)
WINGSEED	Ptelea trifoliata	(S/T)
WINTER ACONITE	Eranthis hyemalis	(BB)
WINTER BEAUTY	Lonicera x purpusii	(S)
WINTER BROCCOLI	Brassica oleracea botrytis cymosa	(V)
WINTER CAULIFLOWER	Brassica oleracea botrytis	(V)
WINTER CHERRY	Physalis alkekengi	(H)

Know Your Common Plant Names

Common	Botanical	Type
WINTER CHERRY	Prunus subhirtella 'Autumnalis'	(S/T)
WINTER CHERRY	Solanum capsicastrum	(HP)
WINTER DAFFODIL	Strenbergia lutea	(BB)
WINTER DAPHNE	Daphne odora	(S)
WINTER GREEN	Chimaphila umbellata	(H)ˈ
WINTER HAZEL	Corylopsis	(S)
WINTER HEATH	Erica carnea	(S)
WINTER HELIOTROPE	Petasites fragrans	(H)
WINTER HONEYSUCKLE	Lonicera fragrantissima	(S)
WINTER HONEYSUCKLE	Lonicera standishii	(S)
WINTER HONEYSUCKLE	Lonicera x purpusii	(S)
WINTER JASMINE	Jasminium nudiflorum	(S)
WINTER PURSLANE	Claytonia perfoliata	(H)
WINTER SAVOURY	Satureia montana	(HB)
WINTER WILD OAT	Avena sterilis	(G)
WINTER'S BARK	Drimys winteri	(S)
WINTER-CRESS	Barbarea vulgaris	(H)
WINTER-FLOWERING CHERRY	Prunus subhirtella 'Autumnalis'	(T)
WINTERBERRY	Ilex verticilliata	(ST)
WINTERBLOOM	Hamamelis	(S)
WINTERGREEN	Gaultheria procumbens	(S)
WINTERGREEN	Pyrola minor	(H)
WINTERSWEET	Chimonanthus	(S)
WIRE MESH PLANT	Calocephalus brownii	(H)
WIRE NETTING BUSH	Corokia cotoneaster	(S)
WIRE-PLANT	Muehlenbeckia complexa	(CL)
WIRILDA	Acacia retinodes	(T)
WIRY HONEYMYRTLE	Melaleuca nematophylla	(S)
WISCONSIN WEEPING WILLOW	Salix blanda	(T)
WISHBONE FLOWER	Torenia fourneri	(H)
WISTERIA	Wisteria	(CL)
WISTERIA TREE	Sesbania tripetii	(TT)
WITCH GRASS	Panicum capillare	(G)
WITCH HAZEL	Hamamelis	(S)
WITCH HOBBLE	Viburnum lantanoides	(S)
WITCH-GRASS	Agropyron repens	(G)
WITCH-GRASS	Elymus repens	(G)
WITCH-HOBBLE	Viburnum lantanoides	(S)
WITCHES GLOVES	Digitalis purpurea	(B)
WITCHWEED	Striga	(H)
WITHE-ROD	Viburnum cassinoides	(S)
WITHYWIND	Convolvulus arvensis	(CL)
WOAD	Isatis tinctoria	(HB)
WOAD WAXEN	Genista tinctoria	(S)
WOLF'S BANE	Aconitum lycoctonum vulgaria	(H)
WOLF'S MILK	Euphorbia	(H)
WOLFBERRY	Symphoricarpos occidentalis	(S)

Know Your Common Plant Names

Common	Botanical	Type
WOLFCHOP	Faucaria	(CS)
WOLLEY-DODS ROSE	Rosa villosa 'Duplex'	(S)
WOMAN'S CAP ORCHID	Thelymitra	(O)
WOMAN'S TONGUE TREE	Albizzia lebbek	(TT)
WONDERBOOM	Ficus pretoriae	(HP)
WONGA WONGA VINE	Pandorea pandorana	(CHP)
WOOD ANEMONE	Anemone nemorosa	(H)
WOOD APPLE	Feronia limonia	(S)
WOOD AVENS	Geum urbanum	(H)
WOOD BARLEY	Hordelymus europaeus	(G)
WOOD BEDSTRAW	Galium sylvaticum	(H)
WOOD BELLS	Hyacinthoides non-scripta	(BB)
WOOD BITTER VETCH	Vicia orobus	(H)
WOOD BLEWIT	Lepista nuda	(FU)
WOOD CALAMINT	Calamintha sylvatica	(H)
WOOD CLUB-RUSH	Scirpus sylvaticus	(G)
WOOD CRANESBILL	Geranium sylvaticum	(H)
WOOD CUDWEED	Omalotheca sylvatica	(H)
WOOD DOCK	Rumex sanguineus	(H)
WOOD FERN	Dryopteris	(F)
WOOD FESCUE	Festuca altissima	(G)
WOOD FORGET-ME-NOT	Myosotis sylvatica	(H)
WOOD GROUNDSEL	Senecio sylvaticus	(H)
WOOD HORSETAIL	Equisetum sylvaticum	(H)
WOOD HYACINTH	Hyacinthoides non-scripta	(BB)
WOOD LILY	Trillium	(H)
WOOD MEADOW GRASS	Poa nemoralis	(G)
WOOD MELICK	Melica uniflora	(G)
WOOD MILLET	Milium effusum	(G)
WOOD MUSHROOM	Psalliota silvicola	(FU)
WOOD PIMPERNEL	Lysimachia nemorum	(H)
WOOD PIMPERNEL	Lysimachia vulgaris	(H)
WOOD RAGWORT	Senecio nemorensis	(H)
WOOD ROSE	Meremia tuberosa	(S)
WOOD SAGE	Teucrium scorodonia	(H)
WOOD SEDGE	Carex sylvatica	(G)
WOOD SMALL-REED	Calamagrostis epigeios	(G)
WOOD SPEEDWELL	Veronica montana	(H)
WOOD SPURGE	Euphorbia angydaloides	(H)
WOOD STITCHWORT	Stellaria nemorum	(H)
WOOD VETCH	Vicia sylvatica	(H)
WOOD WOUNDWORT	Stachys sylvatica	(H)
WOOD-APPLE	Feronia limonia	(H)
WOOD-BETONY	Pedicularis	(H)
WOOD-SORREL	Oxalis acetosella	(H)
WOODBINE	Lonicera periclymenum	(CL)
WOODRUFF	Asperula odorata	(H)

Common	Botanical	Type
WOODRUSH	Luzula	(G)
WOODSAGE	Teucrium scorodonia	(HB)
WOODY NIGHTSHADE	Solanum dulcamara	(H)
WOOLLY BLUE-CURLS	Trichostema lanatum	(S)
WOOLLY FOXGLOVE	Digitalis lanata	(H)
WOOLLY HAWKWEED	Hieracium lanatum	(H)
WOOLLY MILK-VETCH	Oxytropis pilosa	(H)
WOOLLY ROCK FERN	Cheilanthes distans	(FN)
WOOLLY THISTLE	Cirsium eriophorum	(H)
WOOLLY THISTLE	Onopordon acanthium	(B)
WOOLLY TREE FERN	Dicksonia antarctica	(FN)
WOOLLY WILLOW	Salix lanata	(S)
WOOLLY WOUNDWORT	Stachys byzantina	(H)
WOOLLY-PODDED BROOM	Cytisus grandiflorus	(S)
WORM GRASS	Spigelia	(G)
WORM GRASS	Spigelia marilandica	(H)
WORMSEED	Chenopodium ambrosioides anthelminticum	(H)
WORMWOOD	Artemisia absinthium	(H)
WOUNDWORT	Solidago virgaurea	(H)
WOUNDWORT	Stachys	(H)
WYCH ELM	Ulmus glabra	(T)
YAM	Dioscorea	(F)
YAM BEAM	Pachyrhizus erosus	(V)
YANGTOA	Actinidia deliciosa	(F)
YARROW	Achillea millefolium	(H)
YARROW BROOMRAPE	Orobanche purpurea	(PE/H)
YATAY PALM	Butia yatay	(P)
YATE	Eucalyptus cornuta	(T)
YAUPON	Ilex vomitoria	(S)
YAUTIA	Xanthosoma sagittifolium	(F)
YAWROOT	Stillingia sylvatica	(H)
YELLOW ACONITE	Aconitum napellus lycotonum	(H)
YELLOW ARCHANGEL	Lamium galeobdolon	(H)
YELLOW ASPHODEL	Asphodeline lutea	(H)
YELLOW BACHELORS BUTTONS	Ranunculus acris "Flora Pleno"	(H)
YELLOW BANKSIAN ROSE	Rosa banksiae 'lutea'	(S)
YELLOW BARK	Cinchona calisaya	(TT)
YELLOW BARTSIA	Parentucellia viscosa	(H)
YELLOW BELL	Allamanda cathantica	(TS)
YELLOW BELLFLOWER	Campanula thyrsoides	(H)
YELLOW BELLS	Tecoma stans	(TT)
YELLOW BIGNONIA	Tecoma stans	(TT)
YELLOW BIRCH	Betula lutea	(T)
YELLOW BIRD'S NEST	Monotropa hypophega	(H)
YELLOW BOX	Eucalyptus melliodora	(T)
YELLOW BUCKEYE	Aesculus flava	(T)
YELLOW BUGLE	Ajuga chamaepitys	(H)

Know Your Common Plant Names

Common	Botanical	Type
YELLOW CARABEEN	Sloanea woolsii	(MS)
YELLOW CATALPA	Catalpa ovata	(T)
YELLOW CEDAR	Thuja occidentalis	(C)
YELLOW CENTAURY	Cicendia filiformis	(A)
YELLOW CHAMOMILE	Anthemis tinctoria	(H)
YELLOW CHESTNUT OAK	Quercus muhlenbergii	(T)
YELLOW CORIS	Hypericum coris	(R)
YELLOW COTTON TREE	Cochlospermum religiosum	(TT)
YELLOW COW-WHEAT	Melampyrum pratense	(H)
YELLOW CUCUMBER TREE	Magnolia cordata	(T)
YELLOW CYPRESS	Chamaecyparis nootkatensis	(C)
YELLOW DAISY	Rudbeckia hirta	(H)
YELLOW DAY LILY	Hemerocallis flava	(H)
YELLOW DOCK	Rumex crispus	(H)
YELLOW EDGING DAISY	Chrysocoma coma-aurea	(H)
YELLOW ELDER	Tecoma stans	(TT)
YELLOW FIGWORT	Scrophularia vernalis	(H)
YELLOW FLAG IRIS	Iris pseudacorus	(WP)
YELLOW FLAME	Peltophorum pterocarpum	(TT)
YELLOW FLAX	Linum flavum	(R)
YELLOW FLAX	Reinwardtia indica	(S)
YELLOW FORGET-ME-NOT	Myosotis discolor	(H)
YELLOW FRITILLARY	Fritillaria pudica	(BB)
YELLOW FUMITORY	Corydalis lutea	(H)
YELLOW GENTIAN	Gentiana lutea	(H)
YELLOW GOATSBEARD	Tragopogon pratensis	(H)
YELLOW GUM	Eucalyptus johnstonii	(T)
YELLOW HAW	Crataegus flava	(T)
YELLOW HORNED-POPPY	Glaucum flavum	(H)
YELLOW INDIGO	Baptisia tinctoria	(H)
YELLOW JASMINE	Gelsemium sempervirens	(CL)
YELLOW JASMINE	Jasminum odoratissimum	(CL)
YELLOW JESSAMINE	Gelsemium sempervirens	(CL)
YELLOW LOBELIA	Monopsis lutea	(A)
YELLOW LOCUST	Robinia pseudoacacia	(T)
YELLOW LOOSESTRIFE	Lysimachia vulgaris	(H)
YELLOW LUPIN	Lupinus luteus	(A)
YELLOW MARSH AFRIKANDER	Gladiolus tristis	(BB)
YELLOW MEADOW-RUE	Thalictrum flavum	(H)
YELLOW MEDICK	Medicago falcata	(H)
YELLOW MELILOT	Melilotus altissima	(H)
YELLOW MOMBIN	Spondias lutea	(TT)
YELLOW MOMBIN	Spondias mombin	(T)
YELLOW MONKSHOOD	Aconitum anthora	(H)
YELLOW MORNING GLORY	Merremia tuberosa	(CL)
YELLOW MOUNTAIN SAXIFRAGE	Saxifraga aizoides	(R)
YELLOW MUSTARD	Sinapis alba	(V)

Common	Botanical	Type
YELLOW OAT GRASS	Trisetum flavescens	(G)
YELLOW OLEANDER	Thevetia peruviana	(TS)
YELLOW ONION	Allium flavum	(BB)
YELLOW OX-EYE	Bupthalmum salicifolum	(H)
YELLOW OXYTROPIS	Oxytropis campestris	(H)
YELLOW PALM	Chrysalidocarpos lutescens	(P)
YELLOW PARILLA	Menisperum canadense	(CL)
YELLOW PASSION FRUIT	Passiflora edulis flaviocarpa	(F)
YELLOW PHEASANT'S EYE	Adonis vernalis	(H)
YELLOW PIMPERNEL	Lysimachia nemorum	(H)
YELLOW POND LILY	Nuphar advena	(WP)
YELLOW POPLAR	Liriodendron tulipifera	(T)
YELLOW POUI	Tabebuia serratifolia	(TT)
YELLOW PUCCOON	Hydrastis canadensis	(H)
YELLOW RATTLE	Rhinanthus minor	(A)
YELLOW ROCKET	Barbarea vulgaris	(H)
YELLOW SACRED BEAN	Nelumbo	(WP)
YELLOW SAGE	Lantana camara	(HP)
YELLOW SCABIOUS	Scabiosa columbaria ochraleuca	(H)
YELLOW SEDGE	Carex flava	(G)
YELLOW SILVER PINE	Dacrydium intermedium	(C)
YELLOW SNOWDROP	Erythronium americanum	(BB)
YELLOW SORREL	Oxalis corniculata	(H)
YELLOW STAR ANISE	Illicium parviflorum	(T)
YELLOW STAR FLOWER	Sternbergia lutea	(BB)
YELLOW STAR OF BETHLEHEM	Gagea lutea	(BB)
YELLOW STAR OF BETHLEHEM	Gagea sylvatica	(H)
YELLOW STAR-THISTLE	Centaurea solstitalis	(H)
YELLOW STRINGY-BARK	Eucalyptus muelleriana	(T)
YELLOW TOADFLAX	Linaria vulgaris	(H)
YELLOW TREE LUPIN	Lupinus arboreus	(S)
YELLOW TREE TOBACCO	Nicotiana glauca	(H)
YELLOW TRUMPET-TREE	Tecoma stans	(TT)
YELLOW VETCH	Vicia lutea	(H)
YELLOW VETCHLING	Lathyrus aphaca	(A)
YELLOW WATER LILY	Nuphar lutea	(WP)
YELLOW WHITLOW GRASS	Draba aizoides	(H)
YELLOW WILLOW HERB	Lysimachia vulgaris	(H)
YELLOW WOOD	Cladrastis lutea	(S/T)
YELLOW WOOD	Zanthoxylum	(S/T)
YELLOW WOOD ANEMONE	Anemone ranunculoides	(H)
YELLOW WOOD VIOLET	Viola biflora	(H)
YELLOW WOUNDWORT	Stachys recta	(H)
YELLOW YAM	Dioscorea cayenensis	(F)
YELLOW-BARK ASH	Fraxinus excelsior 'Jaspidea'	(T)
YELLOW-BARK OAK	Quercus velutina	(T)
YELLOW-BERRIED HOLLY	Ilex aquifolium 'Bacciflava'	(ST)

Common	Botanical	Type
YELLOW-BERRIED MOUNTAIN ASH	Sorbus aucuparia 'Xanthocarpa'	(T)
YELLOW-BERRIED YEW	Taxus baccata 'Fructo-luteo'	(C)
YELLOW-BIRD'S NEST	Monotropa hypopitys	(H)
YELLOW-EYED FLAME PEA	Chorizema dicksonii	(S)
YELLOW-FRUITED HOLLY	Ilex aquifilium 'Bacciflava'	(ST)
YELLOW-ROOT	Xanthorrniza simplicissima	(S)
YELLOW-STAINING MUSHROOM	Agaricus xanthodermus	(FU)
YELLOW-STEMMED DOGWOOD	Cornus stolonifera 'Flaviramea'	(S)
YELLOW-WOOD	Rhodosphaera rhodanthema	(TT)
YELLOW-WORT	Blackstonia perfoliata	(H)
YELLOWCRESS	Rorippa	(H)
YERBA BUENA	Satureja douglasii	(S)
YERBA DULCE	Lippia dulcis	(TS)
YERBA MANSA	Anemopsis californica	(TS)
YERBA MATE	Ilex paraguensis	(VT)
YERBA SANTA	Eriodictyon glutinosum	(TS)
YESTERDAY-TODAY-AND-TOMORROW	Brunfelsia	(HP)
YEW	Taxus	(C)
YEW CYPRESS	Taxodium	(C)
YEW-LEAVED TORREYA	Torreya taxifolia	(C)
YEZO SPRUCE	Picea jezoensis	(C)
YLANG-YLANG	Cananga odorata	(TS)
YOLK-OF-EGG WILLOW	Salix alba 'Vitellina'	(S/T)
YORK AND LANCASTER ROSE	Rosa damascena 'Versicolor'	(S)
YORKSHIRE FOG	Holcus lanatus	(G)
YORUBA EBONY	Diospyros monbuttensis	(TT)
YOSHINO CHERRY	Prunus x yedoensis	(T)
YOUNG'S WEEPING BIRCH	Betula pendula 'Youngii'	(T)
YOUTH AND OLD AGE	Zinnia elegans	(A)
YOUTH-ON-AGE	Tolmiea menziesii	(HP)
YULAN	Magnolia denudata	(ST)
YUNNAN LILAC	Syringa yunnanensis	(S)
ZAMBAK	Jasminum sambac	(CL)
ZANONA PALM	Socratea exorhiza	(P)
ZEBRA GRASS	Miscanthus sin. 'zebrina'	(G)
ZEBRA PLANT	Aphelandra squarrosa	(HP)
ZEBRA PLANT	Calathea zebrina	(HP)
ZEBRA RUSH	Scirpus tabernaemontani 'Zebrinus'	(H)
ZEBRA WOOD	Connarus guianensis	(TT)
ZEBRA WOOD	Diospyros kurzii	(TT)
ZEDOARY	Curcuma zedoaria	(H)
ZEPHYR LILY	Zephyranthes	(BB)
ZIGZAG BAMBOO	Phyllostachys flexuosa	(G)
ZIGZAG CLOVER	Trifolium medium	(H)
ZIMMER LINDEN	Sparmannia africana	(HP)
ZITHER WOOD	Citharexylum	(TT)
ZOESCHEN MAPLE	Acer x zoeschense	(T)

Common	Botanical	Type
ZONAL PELARGONIUM	Pelargonium x hortorum	(HP)
ZULU GIANT	Stapelia gigantea	(HP)

Key To Plant Type

A	-	Annual
B	-	Biennial
BB	-	Bulb or Corm
C	-	Conifer
CL	-	Climber
CS	-	Cactus
FU	-	Fungi
F	-	Fruit
FN	-	Fern
G	-	Grass or Bamboo
H	-	Herbaceous Perennial
HB	-	Herb
HP	-	House Plant
MB	-	Moss
O	-	Orchid
P	-	Palm
PE	-	Parasite
R	-	Rockery or Alpine Plant
S	-	Shrub
ST	-	Shrub or Tree
SW	-	Sea Weed
T	-	Tree
TCL	-	Tropical Climber
TH	-	Tropical Herb
TS	-	Tropical Shrub
TT	-	Tropical Tree
V	-	Vegetable
WP	-	Water Plant

Botanical
to
Common

Know Your Common Plant Names

Botanical	Common	Type
Abeliophyllum	WHITE FORSYTHIA	(S)
Abelmoschus esculentus	GOMBO	(V)
Abelmoschus esculentus	GUMBO	(V)
Abelmoschus esculentus	LADY'S FINGERS	(V)
Abelmoschus esculentus	OKRA	(V)
Abelmoschus moschatus	MUSK SEED	(V)
Abies	FIR	(C)
Abies alba	COMMON SILVER FIR	(C)
Abies alba	EUROPEAN SILVER FIR	(C)
Abies alba	SILVER FIR	(C)
Abies alba	SILVER FIR	(C)
Abies amabilis	PACIFIC SILVER FIR	(C)
Abies amabilis	RED SILVER FIR	(C)
Abies balsamea	BALM OF GILEAD	(C)
Abies balsamea	BALSAM FIR	(C)
Abies borisii-regis	BULGARIAN FIR	(C)
Abies borisii-regis	KING BORIS FIR	(C)
Abies bornmuelleriana	TURKISH FIR	(C)
Abies bracteata	BRISTLECONE FIR	(C)
Abies bracteata	SANTA LUCIA FIR	(C)
Abies cephalonica	GRECIAN FIR	(C)
Abies cephalonica	GREEK FIR	(C)
Abies chensiensis	SHENSI FIR	(C)
Abies cilicica	CILICIAN FIR	(C)
Abies concolor	COLORADO FIR	(C)
Abies concolor	WHITE FIR	(C)
Abies concolor lowiana	PACIFIC WHITE FIR	(C)
Abies concolor lowiana	SIERRA FIR	(C)
Abies delavayi forrestii	FORREST FIR	(C)
Abies delavayi forrestii	FORREST'S SILVER FIR	(C)
Abies fargesii	FARGES FIR	(C)
Abies firma	JAPANESE FIR	(C)
Abies grandis	GIANT FIR	(C)
Abies grandis	GRAND FIR	(C)
Abies holophylla	MANCHURIAN FIR	(C)
Abies homolepis	NIKKO FIR	(C)
Abies koreana	KOREAN FIR	(C)
Abies lasiocarpa	ALPINE FIR	(C)
Abies lasiocarpa	ROCKY MOUNTAIN FIR	(C)
Abies lasiocarpa	SUBALPINE FIR	(C)
Abies lasiocarpa arizonica	ARIZONA CORK FIR	(C)
Abies lasiocarpa arizonica	CORK FIR	(C)
Abies macrocana	MOROCCAN FIR	(C)
Abies magnifica	CALIFORNIAN RED FIR	(C)
Abies magnifica	RED FIR	(C)
Abies marocana	MAROC FIR	(C)
Abies nephrolepis	KHINGAN FIR	(C)

Know Your Common Plant Names

Botanical	Common	Type
Abies nordmanniana	CAUCASIAN FIR	(C)
Abies numidica	ALGERIAN FIR	(C)
Abies pindrow	WEST HIMALAYAN FIR	(C)
Abies pinsapo	SPANISH FIR	(C)
Abies pinsapo glauca	BLUE SPANISH FIR	(C)
Abies procera	NOBLE FIR	(C)
Abies religiosa	SACRED FIR	(C)
Abies spectabilis	HIMALAYAN FIR	(C)
Abies squamata	FLAKY FIR	(C)
Abies sutchuenensis	SZECHWAN FIR	(C)
Abies veitchii	VEITCH'S SILVER FIR	(C)
Abobra	CRANBERRY GOURD	(S)
Abronia latifolia	SAND VERBENA	(H)
Abronia umbellata	PINK SAND VERBENA	(H)
Abrus precatorius	CRAB'S EYE VINE	(CL)
Abrus precatorius	INDIAN LIQUORICE	(TS)
Abrus precatorius	PRAYER BEADS	(H)
Abrus precatorius	PRECATORY BEAN	(H)
Abrus precatorius	ROSARY PEA	(H)
Abrus precatorius	WEATHER PLANT	(CL)
Abutilon	FLOWERING MAPLE	(S)
Abutilon	PARLOUR MAPLE	(S/CL)
Abutilon avicennae	CHINA JUTE	(TS)
Acacia	MIMOSA	(ST)
Acacia alata	WINGED WATTLE	(T)
Acacia arabica	GUM ARABIC	(TT)
Acacia arabica	INDIAN GUM	(TT)
Acacia armata	HEDGE WATTLE	(T)
Acacia armata	KANGAROO THORN	(ST)
Acacia berteriana	BASTARD LOGWOOD	(T)
Acacia botrycephala	SUNSHINE WATTLE	(T)
Acacia calamifolia	BROOM WATTLE	(T)
Acacia cultriformis	KNIFE-LEAF WATTLE	(T)
Acacia cynanophylla	BLUE WATTLE	(T)
Acacia dealbata	SILVER WATTLE	(ST)
Acacia decurrens	GREEN WATTLE	(T)
Acacia dunnii	ELEPHANT EAR WATTLE	(T)
Acacia elata	CEDAR WATTLE	(T)
Acacia elongata	SWAMP WATTLE	(T)
Acacia farnesiana	POPINAC	(T)
Acacia giraffae	CAMEL THORN	(T)
Acacia gummifera	MOGADORE GUM	(T)
Acacia karroo	SWEET THORN	(T)
Acacia longifolia	SYDNEY GOLDEN WATTLE	(T)
Acacia melanoxylon	BLACK-WOOD ACACIA	(T)
Acacia melonoxylon	AUSTRALIAN BLACKWOOD	(T)
Acacia nilotica	GUM ACACIA	(TT)

Know Your Common Plant Names

Botanical	Common	Type
Acacia nilotica	GUM ARABIC	(T.T)
Acacia nilotica	SHITTIM WOOD	(TT)
Acacia nudicaulis	BAMBOO BRIER	(T)
Acacia pendula	WEEPING MYALL	(T)
Acacia penninervis	MOUNTAIN HICKORY	(T)
Acacia podalyriifolia	QUEENSLAND WATTLE	(T)
Acacia pravissima	OVENS WATTLE	(T)
Acacia pubescens	HAIRY WATTLE	(T)
Acacia pycnantha; Longifolia	GOLDEN WATTLE	(ST)
Acacia retinodes	WIRILDA	(T)
Acacia saileyana	COOTAMUNDRA WATTLE	(T)
Acacia senegal	CAPE GUM	(T)
Acacia senegal	EGYPTIAN THORN	(T)
Acacia senegal	GUM ACACIA	(TT)
Acacia senegal	GUM ARABIC	(T.T)
Acacia senegal	SENEGAL GUM	(TT)
Acacia seyal	GUM ARABIC	(T.T)
Acacia spadicigera	BULL'S HORN ACACIA	(T)
Acacia species	WATTLE	(ST)
Acacia spectabilis	MUDGEE WATTLE	(T)
Acacia verniciflua	VARNISH WATTLE	(T)
Acacia verticilliata	PRICKLY MOSES	(T)
Acacia verticilliata	STAR ACACIA	(T)
Acacia verticilliata	STAR WATTLE	(T)
Acaena	BIDI-BIDI	(R)
Acaena	BIDIDY-BID	(R)
Acaena anserinifolia	BIDGEE-WIDGEE	(R)
Acaena inermis	BLUE MOUNTAIN BIDI-BIDI	(R)
Acaena microphylla	BLUE MOUNTAIN BIDI-BIDI	(R)
Acaena microphylla	NEW ZEALAND BURR	(R)
Acaena microphylla	SCARLET BIDI-BIDI	(R)
Acaena novae-zealandiae	RED BIDI-BIDI	(R)
Acalypha hispida	CHENILLE PLANT	(HP)
Acalypha hispida	MONKEY TAIL	(HP)
Acalypha hispida	PHILLIPINE MEDUSA	(HP)
Acalypha hispida	RED HOT CAT'S TAIL	(HP)
Acalypha hispida	RED-HOT CAT TAIL	(HP)
Acalypha hispida	RED-HOT CAT'S TAIL	(HP)
Acalypha wilkesiana	BEEFSTEAK PLANT	(HP)
Acalypha wilkesiana	COPPER LEAF	(HP)
Acalypha wilkesiana	FIRE DRAGON PLANT	(HP)
Acalypha wilkesiana	JACOB'S COAT	(HP)
Acalypha wilkesiana	MATCH-ME-IF-YOU-CAN	(HP)
Acanthocereus	CLIMBING CACTUS	(CS)
Acantholimon	PRICKLY THRIFT	(R)

Know Your Common Plant Names

Botanical	Common	Type
Acanthophoonix	PRICKLY DATE PALM	(P)
Acanthus	BEARS BREECHES	(H)
Acanthus mollis	BRANK-URSINE	(H)
Acca sellowiona	PINEAPPLE GUAVA	(S)
Acer	MAPLE	(ST)
Acer buergeranum	TRIDENT MAPLE	(T)
Acer campestre	COMMON MAPLE	(ST)
Acer campestre	FIELD MAPLE	(ST)
Acer campestre	HEDGE MAPLE	(S.T)
Acer capillipes	RED SNAKE-BARK MAPLE	(T)
Acer capillipes	SNAKEBARK MAPLE	(T)
Acer cappadocicum	CAUCASIAN MAPLE	(T)
Acer cappadocium	CAPPADOCIAN MAPLE	(T)
Acer carpinifolia	HORNBEAM MAPLE	(T)
Acer circinatum	VINE MAPLE	(T)
Acer cissifolium	VINE-LEAFED MAPLE	(T)
Acer crataegifolium	HAWTHORN-LEAVED MAPLE	(T)
Acer crataegifolium	SNAKEBARK MAPLE	(T)
Acer davidii	PERE DAVID'S MAPLE	(T)
Acer davidii cvs	SNAKEBARK MAPLE	(T)
Acer diabolicum	HORNED MAPLE	(T)
Acer distylum	LIME-LEAVED MAPLE	(T)
Acer forrestii	SNAKEBARK MAPLE	(T)
Acer glabrum	ROCK MAPLE	(T)
Acer glabrum douglasii	DOUGLAS MAPLE	(T)
Acer griseum	PAPERBARK MAPLE	(T)
Acer hersii	SNAKEBARK MAPLE	(T)
Acer hyrcanum	BALKAN MAPLE	(T)
Acer japonicum	DOWNY JAPANESE MAPLE	(ST)
Acer japonicum	FULLMOON MAPLE	(S.T)
Acer japonicum	SMOOTH JAPANESE MAPLE	(C)
Acer japonicum/palmatum	JAPANESE MAPLE	(S)
Acer laxiflorum	SNAKEBARK MAPLE	(T)
Acer leucoderme	CHALK MAPLE	(T)
Acer macrophyllum	OREGON MAPLE	(T)
Acer maximowicziana	NIKKO MAPLE	(T)
Acer monspessulanum	MONTPELIER MAPLE	(T)
Acer negundo	ASH LEAFED MAPLE	(T)
Acer negundo	BOX ELDER	(T)
Acer negundo	WATER ASH	(T)
Acer nigrum	BLACK MAPLE	(T)
Acer opalus	ITALIAN MAPLE	(T)
Acer palmatum 'Atropurpureum'	BLOOD-LEAF JAPANESE MAPLE	(S)
Acer palmatum 'senkaki'	CORAL-BARK MAPLE	(ST)
Acer pensylvanicum	MOOSE BARK	(T)
Acer pensylvanicum	MOOSEWOOD	(T)
Acer pensylvanicum	SNAKEBARK MAPLE	(T)

Know Your Common Plant Names

Botanical	Common	Type
Acer platanoides	NORWAY MAPLE	(T)
Acer platanoides 'Laciniatum'	EAGLE'S CLAW MAPLE	(T)
Acer pseudoilatanus 'Worlei'	GOLDEN SYCAMORE	(T)
Acer pseudoplatanus	MOCK PLANE	(T)
Acer pseudoplatanus	SCOTS PLANE	(T)
Acer pseudoplatanus	SYCAMORE	(T)
Acer pseudoplatanus 'Atropurpureum'	PURPLE-LEAVED SYCAMORE	(T)
Acer pseudoplatanus 'Costorphinense'	COSTORPHINE PLANE	(T)
Acer rubrum	CANADIAN MAPLE	(T)
Acer rubrum	RED MAPLE	(T)
Acer rubrum	SCARLET MAPLE	(T)
Acer rufinerve	GREY-BUDDED SNAKE-BARK MAPLE	(T)
Acer rufinerve	SNAKEBARK MAPLE	(T)
Acer saccharinum	BIRD'S EYE MAPLE	(T)
Acer saccharinum	SILVER MAPLE	(T)
Acer saccharum	SUGAR MAPLE	(T)
Acer sempervirens	CRETAN MAPLE	(T)
Acer shirasawanum 'Aureum'	GOLDEN-LEAVED JAPANESE MAPLE	(S)
Acer spicatum	MOUNTAIN MAPLE	(T)
Acer tataricum	TATARIAN MAPLE	(T)
Acer tataricum ginnala	AMUR MAPLE	(ST)
Acer tetramerum	BIRCH-LEAF MAPLE	(T)
Acer trautvetteri	RED-BUD MAPLE	(T)
Acer trautvetteri	REDBUD MAPLE	(T)
Acer triflorum	ROUGH-BARKED MAPLE	(T)
Acer x lobelii	LOBEL'S MAPLE	(T)
Acer x zoeschense	ZOESCHEN MAPLE	(T)
Aceras anthropophorum	MAN ORCHID	(O)
Aceras anthropothora	GREEN MAN ORCHID	(O)
Achillea ageratum	SWEET NANCY	(H)
Achillea millefolium	MILFOIL	(H)
Achillea millefolium	NOSEBLEED	(H)
Achillea millefolium	THOUSAND WEED	(H)
Achillea millefolium	YARROW	(H)
Achillea ptarmica	GOOSEWORT	(H)
Achillea ptarmica	SNEEZEWORT	(H)
Achillea tomentosa	ALPINE YARROW	(H)
Achimenes	CUPID'S BOWER	(BB)
Achimenes	HOT WATER PLANT	(HP)
Achimenes	MAGIC FLOWER	(HP)
Achimenes	NUT ORCHID	(HP)
Achlys	DEER-FOOT	(H)
Achlys triphylla	VANILLA LEAF	(H)
Achras zapota	CHICLE	(TT)
Achras zapota	SAPODILLA PLUM	(TT)
Acinos arvensis	BASIL THYME	(HB)
Aciphylla aurea	GOLDEN SPANIARD	(H)

Know Your Common Plant Names

Botanical	Common	Type
Aciphylla colonooi	SPANIARD	(H)
Aciphylla colensoi	WILD SPANIARD	(H)
Aciphylla scott-thomsonii	GIANT SPANIARD	(H)
Aciphylla squarrosa	BAYONET PLANT	(H)
Aciphylla squarrosa	SPEARGRASS	(H)
Acokanthera	KAFFIA PLUM	(TT)
Aconitum	ACONITE	(H)
Aconitum anthora	YELLOW MONKSHOOD	(H)
Aconitum lycoctonum vulgaria	WOLF'S BANE	(H)
Aconitum lycotonum lycotonum	NORTHERN WOLFSBANE	(H)
Aconitum lycotonum vulparia	FOXBANE	(H)
Aconitum napellus	FRIAR'S CAP	(H)
Aconitum napellus	MONK'S HOOD	(H)
Aconitum napellus lycotonum	YELLOW ACONITE	(H)
Aconitum orientale	RUSSIAN ACONITE	(H)
Acorus calamus	MYRTLE FLAG	(H)
Acorus calamus	MYRTLE GRASS	(H)
Acorus calamus	MYRTLE SEDGE	(H)
Acorus calamus	SWEET CANE	(H)
Acorus calamus	SWEET FLAG	(WP)
Acorus calamus	SWEET SEDGE	(H)
Acridocarpus natalitius	FEATHER CLIMBER	(CL)
Acroclinium	EVERLASTING FLOWER	(A)
Acrostichum aureum	LEATHER FERN	(FN)
Actaea	COHOSH	(H)
Actaea alba	WHITE BANEBERRY	(H)
Actaea alba	WHITE COHOSH	(H)
Actaea erythocarpa	RED BANEBERRY	(H)
Actaea spicata	BANEBERRY	(H)
Actaea spicata	BUGBANE	(H)
Actaea spicata	COMMON BANEBERRY	(H)
Actaea spicata	HERB CHRISTOPHER	(H)
Acthionema saxatile	CANDY MUSTARD	(R)
Actinea grandiflora	PIGMY SUNFLOWER	(H)
Actinidia deliciosa	CHINESE GOOSEBERRY	(CL)
Actinidia deliciosa	KIWI FRUIT	(F.CL)
Actinidia deliciosa	YANGTOA	(F)
Actinidia polygama	CHINESE CAT POWDER	(CL)
Actinidia polygama	SILVER VINE	(CL)
Actinomeris	NORTH AMERICAN SUNFLOWER	(H)
Actinotus helianthi	FLANNEL FLOWER	(A)
Adansonia digitata	BAOBAB	(T)
Adansonia digitata	MONKEY-BREAD TREE	(F)
Adenandra fragrans	BREATH OF HEAVEN	(S)
Adenandra fragrans	DWARF CHINA FLOWER	(S)
Adenanthera pavonina	RED SANDALWOOD TREE	(TT)
Adenium obesum	DESERT ROSE	(TH)

Know Your Common Plant Names

Botanical	Common	Type
Adenophora	GRAND BELLFLOWER	(H)
Adenophora lilifolia	COMMON LADYBELL	(H)
Adenostyles alliariae	ADENOSTYLES	(H)
Adensonia digitata	LEMONADE TREE	(TT)
Adhatoda vasica	MALABAR NUT	(TS)
Adiantum capillus-veneris	VENUS' HAIR	(FN)
Adiantum formosum	AUSTRALIAN MAIDENHAIR FERN	(FN)
Adiantum pedatum.	MAIDENHAIR FERN	(FN)
Adiantum raddianum	DELTA MAIDENHAIR FERN	(FN)
Adiantum venustum	KASHMIR MAIDENHAIR FERN	(FN)
Adlumia	CLIMBING FUMITORY	(H)
Adlumia fungosa	ALLEGHANY VINE	(CL)
Adlumia fungosa	ALLEGHENY VINE	(CL)
Adlumia fungosa	MOUNTAIN FRINGE	(CL)
Adonis aestivalis	SUMMER ADONIS	(H)
Adonis aestivalis	SUMMER PHEASANT'S EYE	(H)
Adonis annua	PHEASANT'S EYE	(A)
Adonis vernalis	SPRING ADONIS	(H)
Adonis vernalis	YELLOW PHEASANT'S EYE	(H)
Adoxa moschatellina	FIVE-FACED BISHOP	(H)
Adoxa moschatellina	MOSCHATEL	(H)
Adoxa moschatellina	TOWN HALL CLOCK	(H)
Adromischus cooperi	PLOVER EGGS	(HP)
Adromischus maculatus	CALICO HEARTS	(HP)
Aechmea fasciata	URN PLANT	(HP)
Aechmea fasciata	VASE PLANT	(HP)
Aechmea racineae	CHRISTMAS JEWELS	(HP)
Aegle marmelos	BAEL FRUIT	(F)
Aegle marmelos	BENGAL QUINCE	(S)
Aegopodium podagaria	PIGWEED	(H)
Aegopodium podagraria	BISHOP'S WEED	(H)
Aegopodium podagraria	GOUTWEED	(H)
Aegopodium podagraria	GROUND ELDER	(H)
Aegopodium podograri	ASHWEED	(H)
Aeonium canariense	GIANT VELVET ROSE	(HP)
Aeonium haworthii	PIN-WHEEL	(HP)
Aeonium undulatum	SAUCER PLANT	(HP)
Aerides	AIR-PLANT	(HP)
Aerides	FOX-TAIL ORCHID	(O)
Aeschynanthus	BASKET PLANT	(HP)
Aeschynanthus	LIPSTICK VINE	(HP)
Aesculus	BUCKEYE	(S.T.)
Aesculus californica	CALIFORNIA BUCKEYE	(S)
Aesculus carnea	PINK HORSE CHESTNUT	(T)
Aesculus carnea 'Brioti'	RED HORSECHESTNUT	(T)
Aesculus flava	SWEET BUCKEYE	(T)
Aesculus flava	YELLOW BUCKEYE	(T)

Botanical	Common	Type
Aesculus glabra	OHIO BUCKEYE	(T)
Aesculus hippocastanum	COMMON HORSE CHESTNUT	(T)
Aesculus hippocastanum	CONKER TREE	(T)
Aesculus hippocastanum	HORSE CHESTNUT	(ST)
Aesculus indica	INDIAN HORSE CHESTNUT	(T)
Aesculus neglecta 'Erythroblastos'	SUNRISE HORSE CHESTNUT	(T)
Aesculus parviflora	DWARF BUCKEYE	(S)
Aesculus parviflora	SHRUBBY PAVIA	(S)
Aesculus pavia	RED BUCKEYE	(S)
Aesculus 'Plantierensis'	DAMASK HORSE CHESTNUT	(T)
Aesculus turbinata	JAPANESE HORSE-CHESTNUT	(T)
Aethionema	STONECRESS	(R)
Aethionema grandiflorum	PERSIAN STONE CRESS	(R)
Aethusa cynapium	DOG POISON	(A)
Aethusa cynapium	FOOL'S PARSLEY	(H)
Agalmyla	SCARLET ROOT BLOSSOM	(HP)
Agapanthus	AFRICAN LILY	(H)
Agapanthus	LILY-OF-THE-NILE	(H)
Agapanthus	LOVE FLOWER	(H)
Agaricus arvensis	HORSE MUSHROOM	(FU)
Agaricus bisporus	CULTIVATED MUSHROOM	(F)
Agaricus bisporus	MUSHROOM	(FU)
Agaricus campestris	FIELD MUSHROOM	(FU)
Agaricus xanthodermus	YELLOW-STAINING MUSHROOM	(FU)
Agastache anisata	ANISE HYSSOP	(H)
Agastache foeniculum	ANISE HYSSOP	(HB)
Agastache rugosa	KOREAN MINT	(HB)
Agastache urticifolia	GIANT HYSSOP	(H)
Agastachys odorata	WHITE WARATAH	(S)
Agathis	DAMMAR PINE	(C)
Agathis	KAURI PINE	(C)
Agathis	MANILA COPAL	(C)
Agathis alba	AMBOYNA PITCH TREE	(C)
Agathis australis	KAURI PINE	(C)
Agathis brownii	QUEENSLAND KAURI	(C)
Agathis dammara	DAMMAR	(C)
Agathis microstachys	BLACK KAURI PINE	(C)
Agathis vitiensis	FIJIAN KAURI PINE	(C)
Agathosma betulina	ROUND BUCHU	(TS)
Agathosma crenulata	LONG BUCHU	(TS)
Agave americana	CENTURY PLANT	(V)
Agave americana	PULQUE	(CS)
Agave cantala	CANTALA	(CS)
Agave filifera	THREAD AGAVE	(CS)
Agave fourcroydes	HENEQUEN	(CS)
Agave fourcroydes	SISAL HEMP	(CS)
Agave lophantha poselgeri	LECHUGUILLA	(CS)

Know Your Common Plant Names

Botanical	Common	Type
Agave pelmeri	BLUE CENTURY PLANT	(CS)
Agave sisalina	SISAL	(CS)
Agave spp.	MESCAL	(CS)
Agave victoriae-reginae	ROYAL AGAVE	(CS)
Ageratum	FLOSS FLOWER	(A)
Aglaonema crispum 'Silver Queen'	PAINTED DROP-TONGUE	(HP)
Aglaonema simplex	MALAYAN SWORD	(WP)
Agonis flexuosa	PEPPERMINT TREE	(T)
Agonis flexuosa	WILLOW MYRTLE	(T)
Agrimonia eupatoria	AGRIMONY	(H)
Agrimonia eupatoria	CHURCH STEEPLES	(H)
Agrimonia eupatoria	COMMON AGRIMONY	(H)
Agrimonia eupatoria	STICKLEWORT	(H)
Agropyron pungens	SEA TWITCH	(G)
Agropyron repens	WITCH-GRASS	(G)
Agrostemma githago	CORN CAMPION	(A)
Agrostemma githago	CORN COCKLE	(A)
Agrostemma githago	CORN PINK	(A)
Agrostis	BENT GRASS	(G)
Agrostis canina	BROWN BENT GRASS	(G)
Agrostis canina	VELVET BENT	(G)
Agrostis curtisii	BRISTLE BENT	(G)
Agrostis gigantea	BLACK BENT	(G)
Agrostis nebulosa	CLOUD GRASS	(G)
Agrostis stolonifera	CREEPING BENT	(G)
Agrostis stolonifera	CREEPING-BENT	(G)
Agrostis tenuis	COMMON BENT	(G)
Ahnfeltia plicata	LANLADY'S WIG	(SW)
Aichryson x domesticum	CLOUD GRASS	(CS)
Ailanthus	TREE OF HEAVEN	(T)
Ailanthus glandulosa	AILANTO	(T)
Aira caryophylla	SILVER HAIR GRASS	(G)
Aira; Deschampsia	HAIR GRASS	(G)
Aira praecox	EARLY HAIR GRASS	(G)
Ajuga	BUGLE	(H)
Ajuga chamaepitys	GROUND-PINE	(H)
Ajuga chamaepitys	YELLOW BUGLE	(H)
Ajuga genevensis	BLUE BUGLE	(H)
Ajuga pyramidalis	PYRAMIDAL BUGLE	(H)
Ajugareptons	CARPENTERS HERB	(H)
Akebia quinata	CHOCOLATE VINE	(CL)
Alaria esculenta	DABBERLOCKS	(SW)
Alaria esculenta	WING KELP	(SW)
Albizia	SILK TREE	(S)
Albizia julibrissin	PERSIAN ACACIA	(T)
Albizia julibrissin	PINK SIRIS	(ST)
Albizzia	NEMU TREE	(TT)

Botanical	Common	Type
Albizzia lebbeck	EAST INDIAN WALNUT	(TT)
Albizzia lebbek	WOMAN'S TONGUE TREE	(TT)
Albizzia odoratissima	CEYLON ROSEWOOD	(TS)
Albizzia toona	RED SIRIS	(T)
Alcea rosea	HOLLYHOCK	(H)
Alchemilla alpina	ALPINE LADY'S MANTLE	(R)
Alchemilla vulgaris	BEAR'S FOOT	(H)
Alchemilla vulgaris	LION'S FOOT	(H)
Alchemilla vulgaris etc.	LADY'S MANTLE	(H)
Alectryon excelsum	TITOKI	(S)
Aletris	STAR-GRASS	(H)
Aletris farinosa	AGUE ROOT	(H)
Aletris farinosa	BLAZING STAR	(H)
Aletris farinosa	COLIC ROOT	(H)
Aletris farinosa	STARWORT	(H)
Aletris farinosa	UNICORN ROOT	(S)
Aleurites	TUNG TREE	(TT)
Aleurites fordii	TUNG OIL	(TT)
Aleurites molluccana	VARNISH TREE	(TT)
Aleurites moluccana	CANDLEBERRY TREE	(TT)
Aleurites moluccana	CANDLENUT	(T)
Alhagi camelorum	CAMEL THORN	(TT)
Alhagi maurorum	MANNA TREE	(TT)
Alisma plantago-aquatica	GREAT WATER PLANTAIN	(WP)
Alisma plantago-aquatica	MAD-DOG WEED	(WP)
Alisma plantago-aquatica	WATER PLANTAIN	(WP)
Alkanna tinctoria	ALKANET	(H)
Allamanda cathantica	YELLOW BELL	(TS)
Allamanda cathartica	ALLAMANDA	(TS)
Allamanda cathartica	BUTTERCUP FLOWER	(TS)
Allamanda cathartica	GOLDEN TRUMPET	(HP)
Alliaria petiolata	JACK-BY-THE-HEDGE	(H)
Alliaria sativa	HEDGEHOG GARLIC	(H)
Alliaria sativum	GARLIC MUSTARD	(H)
Allium ampeloprasum	WILD LEEK	(BB)
Allium carinatum	KEELED GARLIC	(BB)
Allium cepa	ONION	(V)
Allium cepa aggregatum	EGYPTIAN ONION	(V)
Allium cepa agregatum	POTATO ONION	(V)
Allium cepa ascalonicum	SHALLOT	(V)
Allium cepa perutile	EVER-READY ONION	(V)
Allium cepa proliferum	TREE ONION	(HB)
Allium chinense	RAKKYO	(BB)
Allium fistulosum	JAPANESE BUNCHING ONION	(V)
Allium fistulosum	SCALLION	(BB)
Allium fistulosum	WELSH ONION	(HB)
Allium flavum	YELLOW ONION	(BB)

Know Your Common Plant Names

Botanical	Common	Type
Allium moly	GOLDEN GARLIC	(BB)
Allium moly	LILY LEEK	(BB)
Allium moly	MOLY	(BB)
Allium oleraceum	FIELD GARLIC	(BB)
Allium paradoxum	FEW-FLOWERED LEEK	(BB)
Allium perutile	EVERLASTING ONION	(HB)
Allium porrum	LEEK	(V)
Allium roseum	ROSY GARLIC	(BB)
Allium sativum	GARLIC	(HB)
Allium schoenoprasum	CHIVES	(HB)
Allium scordoprasum	ROCAMBOLE	(BB)
Allium scorodoprasum	SAND LEEK	(BB)
Allium senescens	GERMAN GARLIC	(BB)
Allium sphaerocephalon	ROUND-HEADED LEEK	(BB)
Allium triquetrum	TRIANGULAR-STALKED GARLIC	(BB)
Allium triquetrum	TRIQUETROS LEEK	(BB)
Allium tuberosum	CHINESE CHIVES	(BB)
Allium ursinum	BEAR'S GARLIC	(HB)
Allium ursinum	RAMSONS	(H)
Allium ursinum	RAMSONS WOOD GARLIC	(BB)
Allium ursinum	WILD GARLIC	(BB)
Allium vineale	CROW GARLIC	(BB)
Alloplectus nummularia	CLOG PLANT	(HP)
Alnus	ALDER	(T)
Alnus cordata	ITALIAN ALDER	(T)
Alnus crispa	AMERICAN GREEN ALDER	(T)
Alnus glutinosa	BLACK ALDER	(T)
Alnus glutinosa	COMMON ALDER	(T)
Alnus incana	EUROPEAN ALDER	(T)
Alnus incana	GREY ALDER	(T)
Alnus incana 'Pendula'	WEEPING ALDER	(T)
Alnus maritima	SEASIDE ALDER	(T)
Alnus nitida	HIMALAYAN ALDER	(T)
Alnus rhombifolia	WHITE ALDER	(T)
Alnus rubra	OREGON ALDER	(T)
Alnus rubra	RED ALDER	(T)
Alnus rugosa	SPECKLED ALDER	(T)
Alnus serrulata	SMOOTH ALDER	(T)
Alnus serrulata	TAG ALDER	(T)
Alnus sinuata	SITKA ALDER	(T)
Alnus subcordata	CAUCASIAN ALDER	(T)
Alnus viridis	EUROPEAN GREEN ALDER	(T)
Alnus viridis	GREEN ALDER	(T)
Alnuscrispa mollis	AMERICAN GREEN ALDER	(T)
Alocasia sanderiana	KRIS PLANT	(H)
Aloe arborescens	CANDELABRA ALOE	(HP)
Aloe arborescens	OCTOPUS PLANT	(HP)

Botanical	Common	Type
Aloe arborooonc	TORCH PLANT	(HP)
Aloe aristata	LACE ALOE	(CS)
Aloe brevifolia	SHORT-LEAVED ALOE	(HP)
Aloe ferox	BITTER ALOE	(CS)
Aloe ferox	CAPE ALOE	(CS)
Aloe ferox	RED ALOE	(CS)
Aloe variegata	KANNIEDOOD ALOE	(HP)
Aloe variegata	PARTRIDGE-BREASTED ALOE	(HP)
Aloe variegata	PHEASANT'S WINGS	(HP)
Aloe variegata	TIGER ALOE	(HP)
Aloe vera	BITTER ALOES	(CS)
Aloe vera	FIRST-AID PLANT	(CS)
Aloe vera	MEDICINE PLANT	(CS)
Alonsoa warscewiczii	MASK FLOWER	(A)
Alopecurus	FOXTAIL GRASS	(G)
Alopecurus	LAMB'S TAIL GRASS	(G)
Alopecurus aequalis	ORANGE FOXTAIL	(G)
Alopecurus bulbosus	BULBOUS FOXTAIL	(G)
Alopecurus geniculatus	MARSH FOXTAIL	(G)
Alopecurus myosuroides	BLACK GRASS	(G)
Alopecurus pratensis	MEADOW FOXTAIL	(G)
Alopecurus pratensis 'Aureo-variegatus'	GOLDEN FOXTAIL	(G)
Aloysia triphylla	LEMON PLANT	(S)
Aloysia triphylla	LEMON VERBENA	(S)
Aloysia triphylla	LEMON-SCENTED VERBENA	(S)
Alpina	INDIAN SHELL FLOWER	(H)
Alpinia calcarata	INDIAN GINGER	(H)
Alpinia officinarum	GALANGAL	(TS)
Alpinia purpurata	RED GINGER	(TH)
Alpinia zerumbet	SHELL FLOWER	(H)
Alpinia zerumbet	SHELL GINGER	(TH)
Alsophila	GROVE FERN	(FN)
Alsophila	NORFOLK ISLAND TREE FERN	(FN)
Alstonia constricta	AUSTRALIAN QUININE	(S)
Alstonia scholaris	AUSTRALIAN FEVER BUSH	(TT)
Alstonia scholaris	BITTER BARK	(TT)
Alstonia scholaris	DEVIL TREE	(TT)
Alstonia scholaris	DEVIL'S BIT	(TT)
Alstonia scholaris	DITA BARK	(S)
Alstroemeria	PERUVIAN LILY	(H)
Alstroemeria	ST. MARTIN'S FLOWER	(H)
Alstroemeria psittacina	PARROT LILY	(H)
Alternanthera	JOY WEED	(H)
Alternanthera	JOY-WEED	(H)
Althaea hirsuta	ROUGH MARSH MALLOW	(H)
Althaea officinalis	MARSH MALLOW	(H)

Botanical	Common	Type
Altingia excelsa	RASAMALA	(S)
Alyssum	ALISON	(R)
Alyssum; Asperugo procumbens	MADWORT	(R)
Alyssum montanum	MOUNTAIN ALISON	(R)
Alyssum saxatile	GOLD DUST	(R)
Alyssum saxatile	GOLDEN ALYSSUM	(R)
Alyssum saxatile	GOLDEN TUFT	(R)
Amanita citrina	FALSE DEATH CAP	(FU)
Amanita fulva	TAWNY GRISETTE	(FU)
Amanita muscaria	FLY AGARIC	(FU)
Amanita pantherina	PANTHER CAP	(FU)
Amanita phalloides	DEATH CAP	(FU)
Amanita phalloides	DEATHCAP	(FU)
Amanita verna	FOOL'S MUSHROOM	(FU)
Amanita virosa	DESTROYING ANGEL	(FU)
Amaracus dictamnus	CRETAN DITTANY	(H)
Amaranthus	AMARANTH	(A)
Amaranthus albus	WHITE AMARANTH	(H)
Amaranthus caudatus	LOVE-LIES-BLEEDING	(A)
Amaranthus graecizans	TUMBLEWEED	(H)
Amaranthus hybridus	GREEN AMARANTH	(H)
Amaranthus hypochondriacus	PRINCE'S FEATHER	(A)
Amaranthus retroflexus	COMMON AMARANTH	(H)
Amaranthus tricolor	JOSEPH'S COAT	(A)
Amaryllis belladonna	BELLADONNA LILY	(BB)
Ambrosia	RAGWEED	(H)
Ambrosia artemisiifolia	RAGWEED	(A)
Amelanchier	JUNE BERRY	(S)
Amelanchier	SERVICE BERRY	(ST)
Amelanchier	SHADBLOW	(ST)
Amelanchier	SHADBUSH	(ST)
Amelanchier arborea	JUNE BERRY	(S)
Amelanchier laevis	ALLEGHENY SERVICE BERRY	(ST)
Amelanchier lamarckii	SNOWY MESPILUS	(ST)
Amhertsia nobilis	PRIDE OF BURMA	(TT)
Ammi majus	BISHOP'S FLOWER	(H)
Ammi majus	FALSE BISHOP'S WEED	(H)
Ammobium	EVERLASTING SAND FLOWER	(H)
Ammobium alatum	WINGED EVERLASTING	(H)
Ammophila	BEACH GRASS	(G)
Ammophila arenaria	MARRAM GRASS	(G)
Amomum compaetum	ROUND CARDAMON	(H)
Amorpha canescens	LEAD PLANT	(S)
Amorpha fruticosa	BASTARD INDIGO	(S)
Amorpha fruticosa	FALSE INDIGO	(H)
Ampelopsis arborea	PEPPER VINE	(CL)
Amsinckia micrantha	AMSINCKIA	(H)

Know Your Common Plant Names

Botanical	Common	Type
Anacamptis pyramidalis	PYRAMIDAL ORCHID	(O)
Anacardium	MARKING NUT	(F)
Anacardium occidentale	CASHEW NUT	(V)
Anacharis	WATER THYME	(WP)
Anacyclus depressus	MOUNT ATLAS DAISY	(A)
Anacyclus pyrethrum	PELLITORY	(R)
Anacyclus pyrethrum	PELLITORY OF SPAIN	(H)
Anagalis arvensis	SHEPHERD'S BAROMETER	(A)
Anagallis arvensis	POOR MAN'S WEATHER GLASS	(A)
Anagallis arvensis	SCARLET PIMPERNEL	(H)
Anagallis foemina	BLUE PIMPERNEL	(H)
Anagallis minima	CHAFF WEED	(H)
Anagallis tenella	BOG PIMPERNEL	(H)
Ananas bracteatus	RED PINEAPPLE	(HP)
Ananas bracteatus	WILD PINEAPPLE	(HP)
Ananas comosus	PINEAPPLE	(F)
Anaphalis	PEARLY EVERLASTING FLOWER	(H)
Anarrhinum bellidifolium	ANARRHINUM	(H)
Anastatica hierochuntica	RESURRECTION PLANT	(H)
Anastatica hierochuntica	ROSE OF JERICHO	(H)
Anchusa arvensis	BUGLOSS	(H)
Anchusa azurea	LARGE BLUE ALKANET	(H)
Anchusa capensis	ANNUAL ANCHUSA	(A)
Anchusa capensis	CAPE FORGET-ME-NOT	(A)
Anchusa officinalis	ALKANET	(H)
Andira	CABBAGE TREE	(TT)
Andira araroba	ARAROBA	(TT)
Andira araroba	RINGWORM POWDER	(TT)
Andromeda polifolia	BOG ROSEMARY	(S)
Andromeda polifolia	MARSH ROSEMARY	(S)
Andropogon	BEARD GRASS	(H)
Andropogon	SHEPHERD'S BEARD	(H)
Androsace	ROCK JASMINE	(R)
Androsace	ROCK JESSAMINE	(R)
Androsace carnea	PINK ROCK-JASMINE	(R)
Androsace chamaejasme	BASTARD JASMINE	(R)
Androsace lactea	MILKWHITE ROCK-JASMINE	(R)
Aneimia	FLOWER FERN	(FN)
Aneimia	FLOWERING FERNS	(FN)
Aneimia adiantifolia	PINE FERN	(FN)
Anemone	ANEMONE	(H) (BB)
Anemone	WINDFLOWER	(H)
Anemone appennina	BLUE ANEMONE	(BB)
Anemone blanda	GREEK WINDFLOWER	(BB)
Anemone coronaria	CROWN ANEMONE	(H)
Anemone coronaria	DE CAEN ANEMONE	(BB)
Anemone coronaria	POPPY ANEMONE	(BB)

Know Your Common Plant Names

Botanical	Common	Type
Anemone fulgens	SCARLET ANEMONE	(BB)
Anemone fulgens	SCARLET WINDFLOWER	(BB)
Anemone hepatica	AMERICAN LIVERWORT	(H)
Anemone hybrida	JAPANESE WINDFLOWER	(H)
Anemone nemorosa	WOOD ANEMONE	(H)
Anemone ranunculoides	YELLOW WOOD ANEMONE	(H)
Anemone rupicola	ROCK WINDFLOWER	(R)
Anemone stellata	STAR WINDFLOWER	(H)
Anemone sylvestris	SNOWDROP ANEMONE	(BB)
Anemone sylvestris	SNOWDROP WINDFLOWER	(BB)
Anemone virginiana	THIMBLEWEED	(H)
Anemone x hybrida	JAPANESE ANEMONE	(H)
Anemopsis californica	APACHE BEADS	(A)
Anemopsis californica	YERBA MANSA	(TS)
Anethum graveolens	DILL	(A/HB)
Angelica archangelica	ANGELICA	(HB)
Angelica archangelica	HOLY GHOST	(HB)
Angelica sylvestris	WILD ANGELICA	(H)
Angemone coronaria	ST BRIGID ANEMONE	(BB)
Angophora	GUM MYRTLE	(S)
Angraecum sesquipedale	STAR OF BETHLEHEM ORCHID	(O)
Anguloa clowesii	CRADLE ORCHID	(O)
Anigozanthos	AUSTRALIAN SWORD LILY	(S)
Anigozanthus	KANGAROO PAW	(HP)
Anigozanthus humilis	CAT'S PAW	(S)
Anigozanthus manglesii	MANGLE'S KANGAROO PAW	(H)
Anigozanthus preissii	ALBANY CAT'S PAW	(H)
Anigozanthus rufus	RED KANGAROO PAW	(H)
Annona cherimola	CHERIMOYA	(TS)
Annona glabra	ALLIGATOR APPLE	(TT)
Annona muricata	SOUR SOP	(TT)
Annona muricata	SOURSOP	(TT)
Annona palustris	ALLIGATOR APPLE	(TT)
Annona reticulata	BULLOCK'S HEART	(S)
Annona reticulata	CUSTARD APPLE	(F)
Annona squamosa	SUGAR-APPLE	(V)
Annona squamosa	SWEETSOP	(TT)
Anoechtochilus	JEWEL ORCHID	(O)
Anogramma leptophylla	JERSEY FERN	(FN)
Anopterus glandulosa	TASMANIAN LAUREL	(S)
Antennaria	PUSSY'S TOES	(R)
Antennaria alpina	ALPINE CAT'S FOOT	(R)
Antennaria dioica	CAT'S FOOT	(R)
Antennaria dioica	MOUNTAIN EVERLASTING	(R)
Anthemis	MAYWEED	(AH)
Anthemis arvensis	CORN CHAMOMILE	(H)
Anthemis cotula	DOG'S FENNEL	(H)

Botanical	Common	Type
Anthemis cotula	STINKING CHAMOMILE	(AH)
Anthemis cotula	STINKING MAYWEED	(AH)
Anthemis tinctoria	DYER'S CHAMOMILE	(H)
Anthemis tinctoria	GOLDEN MARGUERITE	(H)
Anthemis tinctoria	OX-EYE CHAMOMILE	(H)
Anthemis tinctoria	YELLOW CHAMOMILE	(H)
Anthericum liliago	ST. BERNARD'S LILY	(H)
Anthockistazam besiaca	FOREST FEVER TREE	(TT)
Anthoxanthum aristatum	ANNUAL VERNAL GRASS	(G)
Anthoxanthum odoratum	SCENTED VERNAL GRASS	(G)
Anthoxanthum odoratum	SWEET VERNAL GRASS	(G)
Anthriscus	SALAD CHERVIL	(HB)
Anthriscus caucalis	BUR CHERVIL	(H)
Anthriscus cerefolium	CHERVIL	(HB)
Anthriscus cerefolium	GARDEN CHERVIL	(HB)
Anthriscus sylvestris	COW PARSLEY	(H)
Anthriscus sylvestris	QUEEN ANNE'S LACE	(H)
Anthurium	FLAMINGO FLOWER	(HP)
Anthurium	HEART FLOWER	(HP)
Anthurium andraenum	OILCLOTH FLOWER	(HP)
Anthurium andreanum	PAINTER'S PALETTE	(HP)
Anthurium crystallinum	CRYSTAL ANTHURIUM	(TH)
Anthurium crystallinum	STRAP FLOWER	(HP)
Anthyliis barba-jovis	JUPITER'S BEARD	(H)
Anthyllis velneraria	KIDNEY VETCH	(H)
Anthyllis vulneraria	LADY'S FINGERS	(H)
Antiaris toxicaria	UPAS TREE	(TT)
Antigonon	CONFEDERATE VINE	(CL)
Antigonon leptopus	CHAIN OF LOVE	(TCL)
Antigonon leptopus	CORAL VINE	(CL)
Antigonon leptopus	MEXICAN CREEPER	(TCL)
Antigonon leptopus	PINK VINE	(TCL)
Antigonon leptopus	QUEEN'S JEWELS	(TCL)
Antirrhinum	WEASEL'S SNOUT	(A)
Antirrhinum asarina	CREEPING MOUNTAIN ASH	(H)
Antirrhinum majus	SNAPDRAGON	(A)
Apera interrupta	DENSE SILKY BENT	(G)
Apera spica-venti	LOOSE SILKY BENT	(G)
Aphanes armensis	PARSLEY PIERT	(H)
Aphelandra squarrosa	SAFFRON SPIKE	(HP)
Aphelandra squarrosa	ZEBRA PLANT	(HP)
Aphyllanthes monspeliensis	BLUE GRASS LILY	(H)
Apios americana	CINNAMON VINE	(CL)
Apios americana	POTATO BEAN	(H)
Apios americana	POTATO-BEAN	(H)
Apios tuberosa	GROUND NUT	(H)
Apium graveolens	CELERY	(V)

Know Your Common Plant Names

Botanical	Common	Type
Apium graveolens	WILD CELERY	(H)
Apium graveolens rapaceum	CELERIAC	(V)
Apium inundatum	FLOATING MARSH-WORT	(WP)
Apium nodiflorum	FOOL'S WATER-CRESS	(WP)
Aplectrum hyemale	PUTTYROOT	(O)
Apocymun venetum	DOGBANE	(H)
Apocynum androsaemifolium	BITTER ROOT	(H)
Apocynum cannabinum	AMERICAN HEMP	(H)
Apocynum cannabinum	BLACK INDIAN HEMP	(H)
Apocynum cannabinum	BOWMAN'S ROOT	(H)
Apocynum cannabinum	CANADIAN HEMP	(H)
Apocynum cannabinum	CHOC TAW ROOT	(H)
Aponogeton distachyos	CAPE PONDWEED	(WP)
Aponogeton distachyum	WATER HAWTHORN	(WP)
Aponogeton fenestralis	LACE-LEAF	(WP)
Aponogeton fernestralis	LATTICE LEAF	(WP)
Aporocactus flagelliformis	RAT'S TAIL CACTUS	(CS)
Aporocactus flagelliformis	RAT'S-TAIL CACTUS	(O)
Aquilaria	EAGLEWOOD	(TT)
Aquilegia	COLUMBINE	(H)
Aquilegia	GRANNY'S BONNET	(H)
Aquilegia atrata	DARK COLUMBINE	(H)
Aquilegia caerulea	ROCKY MOUNTAIN COLUMBINE	(H)
Aquilegia canadensis	ROCK BELLS	(R)
Aquilegia vulgaris	CULVERWORT	(H)
Arabidopsis thaliana	THALE CRESS	(A)
Arabis	ROCK CRESS	(B)
Arabis	WALL CRESS	(R)
Arabis albida	SNOW-ON-THE-MOUNTAIN	(R)
Arabis alpina	ALPINE ROCK-CRESS	(R)
Arabis caucasica	GARDEN ARABIS	(R)
Arabis caucasica	WHITE ROCK	(R)
Arabis glabra	TOWER MUSTARD	(H)
Arabis hirsuta	HAIRY ROCK-CRESS	(R)
Arabis turrita	TOWER CRESS	(H)
Arachis hypogaea	EARTH NUT	(H)
Arachis hypogaea	GROUNDNUT	(F)
Arachis hypogaea	MONKEY NUT	(V)
Arachis hypogaea	PEANUT	(V)
Aralia chinensis	CHINESE ANGELICA TREE	(S/T)
Aralia cordata	UDO	(S)
Aralia elata	ANGELICA TREE	(ST)
Aralia elata	JAPANESE ANGELICA TREE	(ST)
Aralia nudicaulis	AMERICAN SARSAPARILLA	(S)
Aralia nudicaulis	RABBIT ROOT	(S)
Aralia nudicaulis	SARSAPARILLA	(S)
Aralia nudicaulis	SPIKENARD	(H)

Know Your Common Plant Names

Botanical	Common	Type
Aralia nudicaulis	WILD SARSAPARILLA	(S)
Aralia racemosa	AMERICAN SPIKENARD	(S)
Aralia racemosa	SPIGNET	(S)
Aralia racemosa	SPIKENARD	(H)
Aralia spinosa	CLUB OF HERCULES	(S)
Aralia spinosa	DEVIL'S WALKING STICK	(S)
Aralia spinosa	HERCULES' CLUB	(S)
Araucaria angustifolia	BRAZILIAN ARAUCARIA	(C)
Araucaria angustifolia	BRAZILIAN PINE	(C)
Araucaria angustifolia	CANDELABRA TREE	(C)
Araucaria angustifolia	PARANA TREE	(C)
Araucaria araucana	CHILE PINE	(C)
Araucaria araucana	MONKEY PUZZLE	(C)
Araucaria bidwillii	BUNYA-BUNYA	(C)
Araucaria cunninghamii	HOOP PINE	(C)
Araucaria cunninghamii	MORETON BAY PINE	(C)
Araucaria heterophylla	NORFOLK ISLAND PINE	(C)
Araucaria hunsteinii	KLINKI PINE	(C)
Araujia sericofera	CRUEL PLANT	(CL)
Arbutus	STRAWBERRY TREE	(ST)
Arbutus andrachne	CYPRUS STRAWBERRY TREE	(S)
Arbutus andrachne	GRECIAN STRAWBERRY TREE	(T)
Arbutus menziesii	MADRONA	(T)
Arbutus unedo	KILLARNEY STRAWBERRY TREE	(ST)
Arbutus x andrachnoides	HYBRID STRAWBERRY TREE	(T)
Archontiphoenix cunninghamiana	ILLAWARRA PALM	(P)
Archontophoenix	KING PALM	(P)
Archontophoenix alexandrae	ALEXANDRA PALM	(P)
Archontophoenix cunninghamiana	PICCABEEN PALM	(P)
Arctium lappa	BEGGAR'S BUTTONS	(H)
Arctium lappa	BURDOCK	(H)
Arctium lappa	CLOT-BUR	(H)
Arctium lappa	GREAT BURDOCK	(B)
Arctium lappa anagyroides	GOBO	(H)
Arctium minus	LESSER BURDOCK	(H)
Arctostaphylos	BEARBERRY	(S)
Arctostaphylos andersonii	HEARTLEAF MANZANITA	(S)
Arctostaphylos canescens	HOARY MANZANITA	(S)
Arctostaphylos glauca	BIG BERRY MANZANITA	(S)
Arctostaphylos manzanita	MANZANITA	(S)
Arctostaphylos nevadensis	PINE-MAT MANZANITA	(S)
Arctostaphylos patula	GREENLEAF MANZANITA	(S)
Arctostaphylos tomentosa	SHAGGY-BARKED MANZANITA	(S)
Arctostaphylos uva-ursi	KINNIKINICK	(S)
Arctostaphylos uva-ursi	MOUNTAIN BOX	(S)
Arctostaphylos uva-ursi	RED BEARBERRY	(S)
Arctotheca calendula	CAPE DANDELION	(H)

Know Your Common Plant Names

Botanical	Common	Type
Arctotis	AFRICAN DAISY	(A)
Arctous alpinus	BLACK BEANBERRY	(S)
Ardisia	CORAL BERRY	(S)
Ardisia	MARLBERRY	(S)
Ardisia	SPEAR FLOWER	(S)
Ardisia	SPEARFLOWER	(S)
Areca aleracae	CABBAGE PALM	(P)
Areca catechu	ARECA NUT	(TT)
Areca catechu	BETEL NUT	(F)
Areca lutescens	BUTTERFLY PALM	(P)
Areca sp.	BETEL NUT	(P)
Arecastrum romanzoffianum	QUEEN PALM	(P)
Aremonia agrimonoides	BASTARD AGRIMONY	(H)
Arena fatua	WILD OAT	(G)
Arena strigosa	BRISTLE OAT	(G)
Arenaria	SANDWORT	(R)
Arenaria ciliata	FRINGED SANDWORT	(R)
Arenaria leptoclados	SLENDER SANDWORT	(R)
Arenaria montana	ALPINE SANDWORT	(R)
Arenaria norvegica	ARCTIC SANDWORT	(R)
Arenaria serpyllifolia	THYME-LEAVED SANDWORT	(R)
Arenga pinnata	GOMUTI	(P)
Arenga pinnata	SUGAR PALM	(P)
Arenula pratensis	MEADOW OAT GRASS	(G)
Arethusa bulbosa	BOG ORCHID	(O)
Arethusa bulbosa	SWAMP PINK	(H)
Argania	IRON-WOOD	(TS)
Argemone	CRESTED POPPY	(H)
Argemone	PRICKLY-POPPY	(H)
Argemone mexicana	DEVIL'S FIG	(TS)
Argemone mexicana	MEXICAN POPPY	(H)
Argemone mexicana	PRICKLY POPPY	(H)
Argemone platyceras	CRESTED POPPY	(H)
Argyranthemum frutescens	MARGUERITE	(A)
Argyranthemum frutescens	PARIS DAISY	(H)
Argyreia nervosa	SILVER MORNING GLORY	(H)
Arisaema	DRAGON ARUM	(H)
Arisaema	DRAGON-ROOT	(H)
Arisaema dracontium	DRAGON ROOT	(H)
Arisaema dracontium	GREEN DRAGON	(H)
Arisaema nepenthoides	COBRA PLANT	(H)
Arisaema triphyllum	AMERICAN WAKE ROBIN	(H)
Arisaema triphyllum	INDIAN TURNIP	(H)
Arisaema triphyllum	JACK-IN-THE-PULPIT	(H)
Arisarum probiscideum	MOUSE TAIL PLANT	(H)
Aristolochia	DUTCHMAN'S PIPE	(CL)
Aristolochia clematis	BIRTHWORT	(CL)

Know Your Common Plant Names

Botanical	Common	Type
Aristolochia elegans	CALICO FLOWER	(CL)
Aristolochia grandiflora	PELICAN FLOWER	(CL)
Aristolochia macrophylla	PIPE-VINE	(CL)
Aristolochia serpentaria	AMERICAN SNAKE-ROOT	(CL)
Aristolochia serpentaria	SNAKEROOT	(CL)
Aristolochia serpentaria	VIRGINIA SNAKEROOT	(H)
Armeria	THRIFT	(R)
Armeria alliacea	JERSEY THRIFT	(R)
Armeria maritima	SEA PINK	(R)
Armillariella mellea	BOOTLACE FUNGUS	(FU)
Armillariella mellea	HONEY FUNGUS	(FU)
Armoracia rusticana	HORSE RADISH	(HB)
Arnebia echiodes	PROPHET FLOWER	(R)
Arnica	LAMB'S SKIN	(H)
Arnica montana	ARNICA	(H)
Arnica montana	MOUNTAIN TOBACCO	(H)
Arnoseris minima	LAMBS SUCCORY	(H)
Arnoseris minima	SWINE'S SUCCORY	(H)
Aronia	CHOKEBERRY	(T)
Aronia arbutifolia	RED CHOKEBERRY	(S)
Aronia melanocarpa	BLACK CHOKEBERRY	(S)
Aronia prunifolia	PURPLE CHOKEBERRY	(S)
Arrhenatherum elatius	FALSE OAT GRASS	(G)
Arrhenatherum elatius	OAT GRASS	(G)
Artemisia abrotanum	BOY'S LOVE	(S)
Artemisia abrotanum	LAD'S LOVE	(HB)
Artemisia abrotanum	OLD MAN	(H)
Artemisia abrotanum	SOUTHERNWOOD	(HB)
Artemisia absinthium	ABSINTHE	(HB)
Artemisia absinthium	COMMON WORMWOOD	(HB)
Artemisia absinthium	GREEN GINGER	(H)
Artemisia absinthium	WORMWOOD	(H)
Artemisia campestris	FIELD SOUTHERNWOOD	(H)
Artemisia campestris	FIELD WORMWOOD	(H)
Artemisia cana	SILVER SAGE	(H)
Artemisia chamaemelifolia	LADY'S MAID	(H)
Artemisia chamaemelifolia	LEVANT WORMSEED	(H)
Artemisia chamaemelifolia	SEA WORMWOOD	(H)
Artemisia dracunculus	ESTRAGON	(HB)
Artemisia dracunculus	FRENCH TARRAGON	(HB)
Artemisia dracunculus	TARRAGON	(HB)
Artemisia dracunculus 'Inodora'	RUSSIAN TARRAGON	(H)
Artemisia glacidis	GLACIER WORMWOOD	(H)
Artemisia lactifilora	WHITE MUGWORT	(H)
Artemisia ludoviciana	WHITE SAGE	(H)
Artemisia maritima	SEA WORMWOOD	(H)
Artemisia pontica	OLD WARRIOR	(HB)

Know Your Common Plant Names

Botanical	Common	Type
Artemisia pontica	ROMAN WORMWOOD	(H)
Artemisia stellerana	HOARY MUGWORT	(H)
Artemisia stellerana	OLD WOMAN	(H)
Artemisia stelleriana	DUSTY MILLER	(H)
Artemisia tridentata	BASIN SAGEBRUSH	(H)
Artemisia tridentata	SAGE BRUSH	(H)
Artemisia verlotiorum	CHINESE MUGWORT	(H)
Artemisia vulgaris	MUGWORT	(HA)
Artemisia vulgaris	ST. JOHN'S HERB	(H)
Artemisia vulgaris	ST. JOHNS PLANT	(H)
Arthrocnemum perenne	PERENNIAL GLASSWORT	(H)
Arthropodium candidum	STAR LILY	(H)
Arthropodium cirrhatum	RENGARENGA	(H)
Arthropodium cirrhatum	RIENGA LILY	(H)
Arthropodium cirrhatum	ROCK LILY	(H)
Artocarpus altilis	BREADFRUIT	(F)
Artocarpus scortechinii	JACK FRUIT	(F)
Arum italicum	ITALIAN ARUM	(H)
Arum italicum	LARGE CUCKOO-PINT	(H)
Arum maculatum	ADDER'S ROOT	(H)
Arum maculatum	COCKY BABY	(H)
Arum maculatum	CUCKOO PINT	(H)
Arum maculatum	FRIARS COWL	(H)
Arum maculatum	LORDS AND LADIES	(H)
Arum maculatum	PARSON AND CLERK	(H)
Arum palaestinum	BLACK CALLA	(H)
Arum triphyllum	AMERICAN ARUM	(H)
Arum triphyllum	AMERICAN WAKE ROBIN	(H)
Arum triphyllum	DRAGON ROOT	(H)
Arum triphyllum	WILD TURNIP	(H)
Aruncus, Tragopogon	GOAT'S BEARD	(H)
Arundinaria	BAMBOO	(G)
Arundinaria anceps	HIMALAYAN BAMBOO	(G)
Arundinaria anceps	RINGAL	(G)
Arundinaria gigantea	CANE REED	(G)
Arundinaria gigantea	GIANT CANE	(G)
Arundinaria quadrangularis	SQUARE-STEMMED BAMBOO	(G)
Arundinaria tecta	SMALL CANE	(G)
Arundinaria tecta	SWITCH CANE	(G)
Arundo	INDIAN GRASS	(G)
Arundo donax	GIANT REED	(G)
As hedging, 2 Prunus cerasifera "Pissardii" to 1 Prunus cerasifera (S)		FLAMBOYANT
Asarum canadense	WILD GINGER	(H)
Asarum caudatum	BRITISH COLOMBIA WILD GINGER	(H)
Asarum europacum	WILD NARD	(H)
Asarum europaeum	ASARABACCA	(R)

227

Botanical	Common	Type
Asarum europaeum	EUROPEAN GINGER	(H)
Asarum europaeum	HAZELWORT	(H)
Asclepias	MILKWEED	(H)
Asclepias curassavica	BLOOD FLOWER	(TH)
Asclepias incarnata	SWAMP MILKWEED	(H)
Asclepias syriaca	SILKWEED	(H)
Asclepias tuberosa	BUTTERFLY WEED	(H)
Asclepias tuberosa	CANADA ROOT	(H)
Asclepias tuberosa	ORANGE MILKWEED	(H)
Asclepias tuberosa	PLEURISY ROOT	(H)
Ascophyllum nodosum	KNOTTED WRACK	(SW)
Ascophyllum nodosum	MUSSEL WRACK	(SW)
Ascyrum	ST. PETER'S WORT	(S)
Ascyrum hypericoides	ST. ANDREWS CROSS	(H)
Asimina triloba	PAWPAW	(ST)
Asparagus officinalis	COMMON ASPARAGUS	(V)
Asparagus officinalis	SPARROW GRASS	(V)
Asparagus officinalis	WILD ASPARAGUS	(H)
Asparagus plumosus	ASPARAGUS FERN	(F)
Asperula arvensis	BLUE WOODRUFF	(H)
Asperula cynanchica	SQUINANCY WORT	(H)
Asperula odorata	SWEET WOODRUFF	(H)
Asperula odorata	WOODRUFF	(H)
Asperula tinctoria	DYER'S WOODRUFF	(H)
Asphodeline	JACOB'S ROD	(H)
Asphodeline lutea	KING'S SPEAR	(H)
Asphodeline lutea	YELLOW ASPHODEL	(H)
Asphodelus	KING'S SPEAR	(H)
Asphodelus albus	ROYAL STAFF	(H)
Asphodelus alpus	ASPHODEL	(H)
Asphodelus cerasiferus	SILVER ROD	(H)
Asphodelus ramosus	BRANCHED ASPHODEL	(H)
Aspidistra	CAST IRON PLANT	(HP)
Aspidosperma quebracho-blanco	QUEBRACHO	(TS)
Asplenium	SPLEENWORT	(FN)
Asplenium adiantum nigrum	BLACK SPLEENWORT	(FN)
Asplenium bulbiferum	HEN AND CHICKEN FERN	(FN)
Asplenium forisiense	ROCK SPLEENWORT	(FN)
Asplenium marinum	SEA SPLEENWORT	(FN)
Asplenium nidus	BIRD'S NEST FERN	(FN)
Asplenium ruta-muraria	WALL-RUE	(FN)
Asplenium septentrionale	FORKED SPLEENWORT	(FN)
Asplenium trichomanes	MAIDENHAIR SPLEENWORT	(FN)
Asplenium viride	GREEN SPLEENWORT	(FN)
Aster	FROST FLOWER	(H)
Aster	STARWORT	(H)
Aster albescens	SHRUBBY ASTER	(S)

Botanical	Common	Type
Aster alpinus	ALPINE ASTER	(R)
Aster alpinus	BLUE ALPINE DAISY	(R)
Aster amellus	EUROPEAN MICHAELMAS DAISY	(H)
Aster amellus	ITALIAN STARWORT	(H)
Aster divaricatus	WHITE WOOD ASTER	(H)
Aster linosyris	GOLDILOCKS ASTER	(H)
Aster novi-belgii	MICHAELMAS DAISY	(H)
Aster tripolium	SEA ASTER	(H)
Astilbe	FALSE GOATSBEARD	(H)
Astragalus	GOAT'S THORN	(S)
Astragalus	LOCOWEED	(H)
Astragalus alpinus	ALPINE MILK-VETCH	(H)
Astragalus cicer	WILD LENTIL	(H)
Astragalus danicus	PURPLE MILK-VETCH	(H)
Astragalus glycyphyllos	MILK-VETCH	(H)
Astragalus glycyphyllos	WILD LIQUORICE	(H)
Astragalus gummifer	GUM TRAGACANTH	(TT)
Astragalus, oxytropis	MILK VETCH	(S)
Astrantia;	MASTERWORT	(H)
Astrantia major	MELANCHOLY GENTLEMAN	(H)
Astroloma ciliatum	CANDLE CRANBERRY	(S)
Astrophytum asterias	SAND DOLLAR	(CS)
Astrophytum asterias	SILVER DOLLAR CACTUS	(CS)
Astrophytum capricorne	GOAT'S HORN CACTUS	(CS)
Astrophytum myriostigma	BISHOP'S CAP CACTUS	(CS)
Astrophytum myriostigma	BISHOP'S HOOD	(CS)
Astrophytum ornatum	ORNAMENTAL MONK'S HOOD	(CS)
Astrophytum ornatum	STAR CACTUS	(CS)
Athamanta cretensis	ATHAMANTA	(H)
Athamanta matthioli	CANDY CARROT	(TS)
Atherosperma moschata	PLUME NUTMEG	(S)
Atherosperma moschatum	AUSTRALIAN SASSAFRAS	(CT)
Atherosperma moschatum	BLACK SASSAFRAS	(T)
Atherosperma moschatum	SOUTHERN SASSAFRAS	(T)
Athrotaxis	PENCIL PINE	(C)
Athrotaxis	TASMANIAN CEDAR	(C)
Athrotaxis cupressoides	SMOOTH TASMANIAN CEDAR	(C)
Athrotaxis laxifolia	SUMMIT CEDAR	(C)
Athrotaxis selaginoides	KING WILLIAM PINE	(C)
Athyrium filix-foemina	LADY FERN	(FN)
Athyrium nipponicum 'Pictum'	JAPANESE PAINTED FERN	(FN)
Atraphaxis	SHRUBBY BUCKWHEAT	(S)
Atriplex	SALT BUSH	(S)
Atriplex canescens	FOUR WING SALTBUSH	(S)
Atriplex canescens	FOUR-WING SALT BUSH	(S)
Atriplex canescens	GREY SAGE BRUSH	(S)
Atriplex canescens	GREY SAGE BUSH	(S)

Botanical	Common	Type
Atriplex halimus	TREE PURSLANE	(S)
Atriplex hastata	HASTATE ORACHE	(H)
Atriplex hortensis	ORACHE	(AH)
Atriplex hortensis rubra	RED ORACHE	(HB)
Atriplex lentiformis breweri	BREWER'S SALTBUSH	(S)
Atriplex lociniata	FROSTED ORACHE	(H)
Atriplex patula	COMMON ORACHE	(A)
Atriplex portulacoides	SEA PURSLANE	(S)
Atropa belladonna	BELLADONNA	(H)
Atropa belladonna	BLACK CHERRY	(H)
Atropa belladonna	DEADLY NIGHTSHADE	(A)
Atropa belladonna	DWALE	(A)
Attalea funifira	PIASSABA	(P)
Aucomea klainiana	GABOON	(TT)
Aucuba	HIMALAYAN LAUREL	(S)
Aucuba	JAPANESE LAUREL	(S)
Aucuba japonica 'Variegata'	SPOTTED LAUREL	(S)
Aucuba japonica 'Variegata'	VARIEGATED LAUREL	(S)
Austrocedrus chilensis	CHILEAN CEDAR	(C)
Austrocedrus chilensis	CHILEAN INCENSE CEDAR	(C)
Avena sativa	OATS	(V)
Avena sterilis	WINTER WILD OAT	(G)
Averrhoa bilimbi	BILIMBI	(TT)
Averrhoa caranbola	CARAMBOLA	(H)
Avicennia nitida	BLACK MANGROVE	(TT)
Azima tetracantha	NEEDLE BUSH	(S)
Azolla	FAIRY MOSS	(MS)
Babiana	BABOON ROOT	(BB)
Babiana rubro-cyanea	WINECUPS	(BB)
Baccharis	GROUNDSEL TREE	(S)
Baccharis halimfolia	TREE GROUNDSEL	(S)
Baccharis halirrifolia	BUSH GROUNDSEL	(S)
Baccharis pilularis	COYOTE BRUSH	(S)
Backhousia citriodora	SWEET VERBENA TREE	(T)
Bacopa monnieri	BABY TEARS	(WP)
Bactris	MARAJA PALM	(P)
Baileya multiradiata	DESERT MARIGOLD	(TS)
Balaustion microphyllum	BUSH POMEGRANATE	(TS)
Baldellia ranunculoides	LESSER WATER PLANTAIN	(WP)
Ballota frutescens	SHRUBBY HOREHOUND	(S)
Ballota nigra	BLACK HOREHOUND	(H)
Ballota nigra	HOREHOUND	(H)
Balsamita major	ALECOST	(HB)
Balsamita major	COSTMARY	(HB)
Balsamita major	MINT GERANIUM	(HB)
Balsamita major tomentosum	CAMPHOR PLANT	(HB)
Balsamorhiza sagittata	ARROWLEAF BALSAMROOT	(TS)

Know Your Common Plant Names

Botanical	Common	Type
Bambusa	BAMBOO	(G)
Bambusa multiplex	HEDGE BAMBOO	(G)
Banksia	AUSTRALIAN HONEYSUCKLE	(S)
Banksia grandis	BULL BANKSIA	(S)
Banksia integrifolia	COAST BANKSIA	(S)
Banksia littoralis	SWAMP BANKSIA	(S)
Baphia	BARWOOD	(P)
Baphia nitida	CAMWOOD	(P)
Baptisia	FALSE INDIGO	(H)
Baptisia tinctoria	HORSE-FLY WEED	(H)
Baptisia tinctoria	INDIGO-WEED	(H)
Baptisia tinctoria	WILD INDIGO	(H)
Baptisia tinctoria	YELLOW INDIGO	(H)
Barbarea stricta	LESSER YELLOW ROCKET	(H)
Barbarea verna	AMERICAN CRESS	(H)
Barbarea verna	AMERICAN WINTERCRESS	(H)
Barbarea verna	LAND CRESS	(V)
Barbarea vulgaris	COMMON WINTERCRESS	(H)
Barbarea vulgaris	COMMON YELLOW ROCKET	(H)
Barbarea vulgaris	WINTER-CRESS	(H)
Barbarea vulgaris	YELLOW ROCKET	(H)
Barleria cristata	PHILLIPINE VIOLET	(S)
Barosma betulina	BUCHU	(S)
Basella alba	MALABAR NIGHTSHADE	(THB)
Basella rubra	MALABAR NIGHTSHADE	(THB)
Bassia hirsuta	HAIRY SEABLITE	(H)
Batis maritima	SALTWORT	(S)
Bauhinia	MOUNTAIN EBONY	(T/CS)
Bauhinia cumanensis	TURTLE VINE	(S)
Bauhinia monandra	BUTTERFLY FLOWER	(H)
Bauhinia purpurea	BULL HOOF TREE	(TT)
Bauhinia purpurea	BUTTERFLY TREE	(TT)
Bauhinia purpurea	CAMEL'S FOOT	(TT)
Bauhinia purpurea	ORCHID TREE	(TT)
Bauhinia purpurea	OX HOOF TREE	(TT)
Bauhinia variegata	EBONYWOOD	(S)
Bauhinia variegata	PURPLE ORCHID TREE	(TT)
Beaucarnea recurvata	ELEPHANT'S FOOT	(T)
Beaucarnea recurvata	PONY-TAIL	(T)
Beaumontia	HERALD'S TRUMPET	(S)
Beaumontia	TRUMPET FLOWER	(H)
Begonia	ELEPHANT'S EAR	(HP)
Begonia albo-picta	GUINEA-WING BEGONIA	(HP)
Begonia boweri	EYELASH BEGONIA	(HP)
Begonia coccinea	ANGELWING BEGONIA	(HP)
Begonia dregei	MAPLE-LEAF BEGONIA	(HP)
Begonia 'Erythrophylla'	KIDNEY BEGONIA	(HP)

Know Your Common Plant Names

Botanical	Common	Type
Begonia 'Erythrophylla'	POND-LILY BEGONIA	(HP)
Begonia fuchsoides	FUCHSIA BEGONIA	(HP)
Begonia gracilis	HOLLYHOCK BEGONIA	(HP)
Begonia luxurians	PALM-LEAF BEGONIA	(HP)
Begonia masoniana	IRON CROSS BEGONIA	(HP)
Begonia metallica	METALLIC LEAF BEGONIA	(HP)
Begonia rex	REX BEGONIA	(HP)
Begonia scharffii	ELEPHANT'S EAR BEGONIA	(HP)
Begonia semperflorens	BEDDING BEGONIA	(A)
Begonia semperflorens	FIBROUS-ROOTED BEGONIA	(A)
Begonia x cheimantha	CHRISTMAS BEGONIA	(HP)
Begonia x cheimantha	LORRAINE BEGONIA	(HP)
Begonia x tuberhybrida	PENDULOUS BEGONIA	(BB)
Begonia x tuberhybrida	TUBEROUS BEGONIA	(BB)
Begonia xerythrophylla	BEEFSTEAK BEGONIA	(HP)
Belamcanda	BLACKBERRY LILY	(BB)
Belamcanda chinensis	BLACKBERRY LILY	(BB)
Belamcanda chinensis	LEOPARD'S FLOWER	(I)
Bellendena montana	MOUNTAIN ROCKET	(R)
Bellevalia romana	ROMAN HYACINTH	(BB)
Bellis	ENGLISH DAISY	(H)
Bellis	TRUE DAISY	(H)
Bellis perennis	COMMON DAISY	(H)
Bellis perennis	DAISY	(H)
Bellium minutum	LITTLE MARY	(H)
Benincasa hispida	WAX GOURD	(F)
Benincasa hispida	WAX GOURD	(F)
Berberidopsis	CORAL PLANT	(S)
Berberis	BARBERRY	(S)
Berberis aristata	NEPAL BARBERRY	(S)
Berberis hypokerina	SILVER HOLLY	(S)
Berberis morrisonensis	MOUNT MORRISON BERDERIS	(S)
Berberis thunbergii	JAPANESE BARBERRY	(S)
Berberis thunbergii 'Atropurpurea'	PURPLE-LEAF BARBERRY	(S)
Berberis thunbergii 'Aurea'	GOLDEN-LEAVED BERBERIS	(S)
Berberis vulgaris	COMMON BARBERRY	(S)
Berberis vulgaris	PIPPERIDGE	(S)
Berberis wilsoniae	WILSON'S BARBERRY	(S)
Berchemia	RATTAN VINE	(CL)
Bergenia	ELEPHANT'S EAR	(H/A)
Bergenia	MEGASEA	(H)
Berkheya	SOUTH AFRICAN THISTLE	(S)
Berteroa incana	HOARY ALISON	(R)
Bertholletia excelsa	BRAZIL NUT	(F)
Berula erecta	LESSER WATER PARSNIP	(H)
Bessera	CORAL DROPS	(H)
Bessera elegans	CORAL DROPS	(H)

Botanical	Common	Type
Beta vulgaris	BEET	(V)
Beta vulgaris	BEETROOT	(V)
Beta vulgaris	MANGEL	(V)
Beta vulgaris	MANGEL WURZEL	(V)
Beta vulgaris	MANGOLD	(V)
Beta vulgaris	SUGAR BEET	(V)
Beta vulgaris cicla	CHARD	(V)
Beta vulgaris cicla	LEAF BEET	(V)
Beta vulgaris cicla	SPINACH BEET	(V)
Beta vulgaris cicla	SWISS CHARD	(V)
Beta vulgaris maritima	SEA BEET	(V)
Betula	BIRCH	(T)
Betula albosinensis	CHINESE RED-BARKED BIRCH	(T)
Betula coerulea-grandis	BLUE BIRCH	(T)
Betula ermanii	RUSSIAN ROCK BIRCH	(T)
Betula grossa	JAPANESE CHERRY BIRCH	(T)
Betula jacquemontii	WHITE-BARKED HIMALAYAN BIRCH	(T)
Betula lenta	CHERRY BIRCH	(T)
Betula lenta	SWEET BIRCH	(T)
Betula lutea	YELLOW BIRCH	(T)
Betula maximowicziana	MONARCH BIRCH	(T)
Betula medwediewii	TRANSCAUCASIAN BIRCH	(T)
Betula nana	DWARF BIRCH	(S)
Betula nana	ROCK BIRCH	(S)
Betula nigra	BLACK BIRCH	(T)
Betula nigra	RED BIRCH	(T)
Betula nigra	RIVER BIRCH	(T)
Betula occidentalis	WATER BIRCH	(T)
Betula papyrifera	CANOE BIRCH	(T)
Betula papyrifera	PAPER BIRCH	(T)
Betula pendula	COMMON SILVERBIRCH	(T)
Betula pendula	EUROPEAN WHITE BIRCH	(T)
Betula pendula	LADY OF THE WOODS	(T)
Betula pendula	SILVER BIRCH	(T)
Betula pendula 'Dalecarlica'	SWEDISH BIRCH	(T)
Betula pendula 'Purpurea'	PURPLE BIRCH	(T)
Betula pendula 'Purpurea'	PURPLE-LEAF BIRCH	(T)
Betula pendula 'Tristis'	WEEPING BIRCH	(T)
Betula pendula 'Youngii'	WEEPING BIRCH	(T)
Betula pendula 'Youngii'	YOUNG'S WEEPING BIRCH	(T)
Betula platyphylla japonica	JAPANESE WHITE BIRCH	(T)
Betula populifolia	GREY BRICH	(T)
Betula pubescens	COMMON WHITE BIRCH	(T)
Betula pubescens	DOWNY BIRCH	(T)
Betula pubescens	WHITE BIRCH	(T)
Betula utilis	HIMALAYAN BIRCH	(T)
Bidens	BEGGAR'S TICKS	(H)

Know Your Common Plant Names

Botanical	Common	Type
Bidens	STICK-TIGHT	(H)
Bidens cernua	NODDING BUR-MARIGOLD	(WP)
Bidens frondosa	BEGGARTICKS	(H)
Bidens pilosa	BLACK JACK	(H)
Bidens tripartita	BUR MARIGOLD	(H)
Bidens tripartita	BUR-MARIGOLD	(H)
Bignonia, campsis	TECOMA	(CL)
Bignonia capreolata	CROSS VINE	(CL)
Bilbergia nutans	QUEEN'S TEARS	(HP)
Billardiera	APPLE-BERRY	(CL)
Billardiera longiflora	APPLE BERRY	(CL)
Billardiera longiflora	PURPLE APPLE-BERRY	(CL)
Billbergia nutans	ANGEL'S TEARS	(HP)
Billbergia nutans	SUMMER TORCH	(HP)
Biscutella laevigata	BUCKLER MUSTARD	(H)
Bixa orellana	ANNATTO	(T)
Bixa orellana	ANNATTO TREE	(T)
Blackstonia perfoliata	CENTURY	(H)
Blackstonia perfoliata	YELLOW-WORT	(H)
Blandfordia grandiflora	CHRISTMAS BELL	(H)
Blandfordia grandiflora	CHRISTMAS TREE	(H)
Blechnum capense	PALM-LEAF FERN	(FN)
Blechnum discolor	CROWN FERN	(FN)
Blechnum occidentale	HAMMOCK FERN	(FN)
Blechnum spicant	DEER FERN	(FN)
Blechnum spicant	HARD FERN	(FN)
Blighia sapida	AKEE TREE	(TT)
Blysmus compressus	FLAT SEDGE	(G)
Bochmeria nivea	RAMIE FIBRE	(G)
Boehmeria nivea	CHINA GRASS	(G)
Boehmeria nivea	CHINA-GRASS	(G)
Boehmeria nivea	RAMIE	(S)
Boletus edulis	CEP	(FU)
Bolusanthus speciosus	TREE WISTERIA	(T)
Bombax	COTTON TREE	(TT)
Bombax malaboricum	INDIAN SILK-COTTON TREE	(TT)
Borago officinalis	BORAGE	(HB)
Borzicactus celsianus	OLD MAN OF THE ANDES	(CS)
Boswellia	OLIBANUS TREE	(TT)
Boswellia thurifera	FRANKINCENSE	(T)
Bothriochloa saccharoides	SILVER BEARD GRASS	(G)
Botrychium	GRAPE FERN	(FN)
Botrychium	MOONWORT	(FN)
Botrychium lunaria	MOONWORT FERN	(FN)
Botrychium multifidum	LEATHERY MOONWORT	(FN)
Botrychium virginianum	RATTLESNAKE FERN	(FN)
Botrychium virginianum	VIRGINIAN MOONWORT	(FN)

Botanical	Common	Type
Bougainvillea	PAPER FLOWER	(HP)
Boussingaultia	MADEIRA VINE	(CL)
Boussingaultia gracilis	MADEIRA VINE	(CL)
Bouteloua gracilis	BLUE GRAMA	(G)
Bouteloua gracilis	MOSQUITO GRASS	(G)
Bouvardia ternifolia	SCARLET TRUMPETILLA	(S)
Brabeium	AFRICAN ALMOND	(H)
Brachychiton	BOTTLE TREE	(TT)
Brachychiton acerfolium	FLAME BOTTLE TREE	(TT)
Brachychiton acerfolium	FLAME TREE	(TT)
Brachychiton acerifolius	ILLAWARRA FLAME TREE	(T)
Brachycome beridifolia	SWAN RIVER DAISY	(A)
Brachyglottis	SHRUBBY RAGWORT	(S)
Brachyglottis repanda	PUKAPUKA	(S)
Brachyglottis repanda	RANGIORA	(S)
Brachylaena huillensis	MUHUGU	(TS)
Brachypodium sylvaticum	FALSE BROME	(G)
Brachypodium sylvaticum	TOR GRASS	(G)
Brasenia	WATER SHIELD	(WP)
Brasenia schreberi	WATER-SHIELD	(WP)
Brassavola	LADY-OF-THE-NIGHT-ORCHID	(O)
Brassica chinensis	PAK-CHOI	(V)
Brassica fimbriata	BORECOLE	(V)
Brassica juncea	INDIAN MUSTARD	(V)
Brassica napobrassica	RUTABAGA	(V)
Brassica napobrassica	SWEDE	(V)
Brassica napus	COLZA	(V)
Brassica napus	RAPE	(V)
Brassica napus napobrassica	TURNIP CABBAGE	(V)
Brassica napus oleifera	COLE	(V)
Brassica napus oleifera	OILSEED RAPE	(F)
Brassica nigra	BLACK MUSTARD	(V)
Brassica nigra	MUSTARD	(V)
Brassica olearacea botrytis	CAULIFLOWER	(V)
Brassica oleracea	SPRING GREENS	(V)
Brassica oleracea	WILD CABBAGE	(H)
Brassica oleracea acephala	COLLARD	(V)
Brassica oleracea acephala	ORNAMENTAL CABBAGE	(A)
Brassica oleracea botrytis	BROCCOLI	(V)
Brassica oleracea botrytis	WINTER CAULIFLOWER	(V)
Brassica oleracea botrytis cymosa	WINTER BROCCOLI	(V)
Brassica oleracea bullata	SAVOY	(V)
Brassica oleracea capitata	CABBAGE	(V)
Brassica oleracea costata	COUVE TRONCHUDA	(V)
Brassica oleracea costata	PORTUGUESE CABBAGE	(V)
Brassica oleracea gemmifera	BRUSSEL SPROUT	(V)
Brassica oleracea gongylodes	KOHL RABI	(V)

Know Your Common Plant Names

Botanical	Common	Type
Brassica oleracea gongylodes	TURNIP CABBAGE	(V)
Brassica oleracea italica	CALABRESSE	(V)
Brassica oleracea italica	SPROUTING BROCCOLI	(V)
Brassica oleracea longata	JERSEY KALE	(V)
Brassica oleracea longata	TREE CABBAGE	(V)
Brassica oleracea longata	WALKING-STICK CABBAGE	(V)
Brassica oleracea sabellica	KALE	(V)
Brassica oleracea sabellica	SCOTCH KALE	(V)
Brassica pekinensis	CHINESE CABBAGE	(V)
Brassica pekinensis	PE-TSAI	(V)
Brassica rapa	TURNIP	(V)
Bravoa	SCARLET TWINFLOWER	(H)
Bravoa geminiflora	TWIN-FLOWER	(H)
Braya lineoris	BRAYA	(H)
Brevoortia	FLORAL FIRECRACKER	(HP)
Breynia disticha	SNOW BUSH	(S)
Briza maxima	PEARL GRASS	(G)
Briza media	COMMON QUAKING GRASS	(G)
Briza media	DODDERING DILLIES	(G)
Briza media	QUAKING GRASS	(G)
Brodiaea	CALIFORNIAN HYACINTH	(BB)
Brodiaea	TRITELIA	(BB)
Bromelia balansae	HEART OF FLAME	(HP)
Bromelia pinguin	PINGUIN	(H)
Bromus	BROME GRASS	(G)
Bromus arvensis	FIELD BROME	(G)
Bromus commutatus	MEADOW BROME	(G)
Bromus diandrus	GREAT BROME	(G)
Bromus erectus	UPRIGHT BROME	(G)
Bromus hordeaceus	SOFT BROME	(G)
Bromus inermis	HUNGARIAN BROME	(G)
Bromus japonicus	JAPANESE BROME	(G)
Bromus lepidus	SLENDER BROME	(G)
Bromus mollis	SOFT BROME	(G)
Bromus racemosus	SMOOTH BROME	(G)
Bromus ramosus	HAIRY BROME	(G)
Bromus rigidus	STIFF BROME	(G)
Bromus secalinus	RYE BROME	(G)
Bromus sterilis	BARREN BROME	(G)
Bromus tectorum	DROOPING BROME	(G)
Bromus willdenowii	RESCUE BROME	(G)
Brosimum	COW TREE	(TT)
Brosimum alicastrum	BREAD-NUT	(TT)
Broussonetia papyrifera	PAPER MULBERRY	(S)
Browalia speciosa	SAPPHIRE FLOWER	(HP)
Browallia	BUSH VIOLET	(HP)
Brownea grandiceps	ROSE OF VENEZUELA	(TT)

Botanical	Common	Type
Bruckenthalia spiculifolia	SPIKE HEATH	(S)
Brugmansia aurea	GOLDEN ANGEL'S TRUMPET	(TH)
Brugmansia cornigera	ANGEL'S TRUMPET	(H)
Brugmansia suaveolens	ANGELS TRUMPET	(S)
Brugmansia x candida	WHITE ANGEL'S TRUMPET	(TH)
Brunfelsia	YESTERDAY-TODAY-AND-TOMORROW	(HP)
Brunfelsia americana	LADY-OF-THE-NIGHT	(S)
Brunfelsia hopeana	MANACA ROOT	(TS)
Brunfelsia latifolia	KISS-ME-QUICK	(S)
Brunia nodiflora	STOMPIE	(S)
Brunnera	CHATHAM ISLAND FORGET-ME-NOT	(H)
Brunnera	PERENNIAL FORGET-ME-NOT	(H)
Brunnera macrophylla	SIBERIAN BUGLOSS	(H)
Brunonia australis	BLUE PINCUSHION	(H)
Brunsvigia josephinae	JOSEPHINE'S LILY	(BB)
Bryonia	BRYONY	(CL)
Bryonia dioica	WHITE BRYONY	(CL)
Bryonia dioica	WILD HOPS	(CL)
Bryopsis plumosa	HEN PEN	(SW)
Buchloc dactyloides	BUFFALO GRASS	(GS)
Buddleia alternifolia	FOUNTAIN BUDDLEIA	(S)
Buddleia davidii	SUMMER LILAC	(S)
Buddleia globosa	ORANGE BALL TREE	(S)
Buddleja davidii	BUTTERFLY BUSH	(S)
Buddleja salviifolia	SOUTH AFRICAN SAGE WOOD	(S)
Buglossoides arvensis	CORN GROMWELL	(H)
Buglossoides purpurocaerulea	PURPLE GROMWELL	(H)
Bulbocodium	SPRING MEADOW SAFFRON	(H)
Bumelia hycioides	SOUTHERN BUCKTHORN	(S)
Bunias erucago	BUNIAS	(H)
Bunias orientalis	WARTY CABBAGE	(H)
Bunium bulbocastanum	GREAT EARTHNUT	(H)
Bunium bulbocastanum	GREAT PIGNUT	(H)
Bunium bulbocastanum	TUBEROUS CARAWAY	(H)
Bupleurum baldense	SMALL HARE'S EAR	(H)
Bupleurum falcatum	SICKLE HARE'S EAR	(H)
Bupleurum fruticosum	SHRUBBY HARE'S EAR	(S)
Bupleurum longifolium	LONG-LEAVED HARE'S EAR	(H)
Bupleurum rotundifolium	HARE'S EAR	(H)
Bupleurum rotundifolium	THOROW-WAX	(H)
Bupleurum tenuissimum	SLENDER HARE'S EAR	(H)
Bupthalmum salicifolum	YELLOW OX-EYE	(H)
Burchellia bubalina	WILD POMEGRANATE	(S)
Bursera simaroba	GUMBO-LIMBO	(S/T)
Bursera simaruba	WEST INDIAN BIRCH	(S/T)
Burtonia hendersonii	RED BONNETS	(S)
Butea superba	CLIMBING PALAS	(TS)

Know Your Common Plant Names

Botanical	Common	Type
Butia	PINDO PALM	(P)
Butia capitata	JELLY PALM	(P)
Butia capitata	JELLY PALM	(P)
Butia yatay	YATAY PALM	(P)
Butomus umbellatus	FLOWERING RUSH	(G)
Butyrospermum paradoxum	SHEA BUTTER TREE	(TT)
Butyrospermum parkii	SHEA BUTTER TREE	(TT)
Buxus	BOX	(S)
Buxus balearica	BALEARIC BOX	(S)
Buxus macowani	CAPE BOX	(TS)
Buxus semperrirens 'Suffruticosa'	EDGING BOX	(S)
Buxus sempervirens	BOXWOOD	(S)
Buxus sempervirens	COMMON BOX	(TS)
Buxus sempervirens	DUDGEON	(S/T)
Byblis liniflora	RAINBOW PLANT	(S)
Cabomba caroliniana	FANWORT	(WP)
Cabomba caroliniana	FISH GRASS	(G)
Cabomba caroliniana	WASHINGTON PLANT	(WP)
Caesalpinia	NICKER-BEAN	(S)
Caesalpinia brasiliensis	BRAZILWOOD	(TS)
Caesalpinia coriarian	DIVI-DIVI	(S)
Caesalpinia echinata	PEACH WOOD	(TS)
Caesalpinia pulcherrima	BARBADOS-PRIDE	(TS)
Caesalpinia pulcherrima	DWARF POINCIANA	(TT)
Caesalpinia pulcherrima	PEACOCK FLOWER	(TT)
Caesalpinia pulcherrima	PRIDE OF BARBADOS	(TT)
Caesalpinia sappon	SAPPAN	(TS)
Caesalpinia vesicaria	BRASILETTO	(TT)
Cajanas cajan	PIGEON PEA	(V)
Cakile maritima	SEA ROCKET	(H)
Caladium	ANGEL WINGS	(HP)
Caladium	ANGEL'S WINGS	(HP)
Caladium	ELEPHANT'S EARS	(HP)
Caladium	HEART OF JESUS	(HP)
Calamagrostis	SMALL-REED	(G)
Calamagrostis canescens	PURPLE SMALL-REED	(G)
Calamagrostis epigeios	WOOD SMALL-REED	(G)
Calamintha	CALAMINT	(H)
Calamintha ascendens	COMMON CALAMINT	(H)
Calamintha nepeta	LESSER CALAMINT	(H)
Calamintha sylvatica	WOOD CALAMINT	(H)
Calamus	CANE PALM	(G)
Calamus	RATTAN	(G)
Calamus scipionum	MALACCA CANE	(G)
Calandrinia	ROCK PURSLANE	(R)
Calandrinia menziesii	RED MAIDS	(A)
Calathea makoyana	PEACOCK PLANT	(HP)

Botanical	Common	Type
Calathea maxoyana	CATHEDRAL WINDOWS	(HP)
Calathea zebrina	ZEBRA PLANT	(HP)
Calceolaria	SLIPPER-WORT	(H)
Calendula	SCOTCH MARIGOLD	(A)
Calendula officinalis	GOLDS	(A)
Calendula officinalis	POT MARIGOLD	(A)
Calendula officinalis prolifera	HEN AND CHICKENS MARIGOLD	(H)
Calendula, Tagetes	MARIGOLD	(A)
Caleolaria	SLIPPER FLOWER	(AS)
Calepina irregularis	WHITE BALL MUSTARD	(H)
Calla palustris	BOG ARUM	(WP)
Calla palustris	WATER ARUM	(WP)
Calliandra eriophylla	FAIRY DUSTER	(S)
Calliandra haematocephala	POWDER-PUFF BUSH	(S)
Calliandra inaequilatera	POWDER-PUFF TREE	(TT)
Callicarpa	BEAUTY BERRY	(S)
Callicarpa	FRENCH MULBERRY	(S)
Callirhoe	POPPY MALLOW	(H)
Callisia	INCH PLANT	(H)
Callisia	STRIPED INCH PLANT	(HP)
Callistemon	BOTTLEBRUSH	(S)
Callistemon citrinus	LEMON BOTTLEBRUSH	(S)
Callistemon speciosus	ALBANY BOTTLEBRUSH	(S)
Callistephus	ANNUAL ASTER	(A)
Callistephus chinensis	CHINA ASTER	(A)
Callitriche hermaphroditum	AUTUMNAL WATER-STARWORT	(WP)
Callitriche obtusangula	BLUNT-FRUITED WATER-STARWORT	(WP)
Callitriche stagnalis	WATER STARWORT	(WP)
Callitris	CYPRESS PINE	(C)
Callitris	CYPRESS-PINE	(C)
Callitris calcarata	BLACK CYPRESS PINE	(C)
Callitris columellaris	MURRAY RIVER PINE	(C)
Callitris columellaris	WHITE CYPRESS PINE	(C)
Callitris endlicheri	RED CYPRESS PINE	(C)
Callitris glauca	MURRAY RIVER PINE	(C)
Callitris macleayana	PORT MACQUARIE PINE	(C)
Callitris oblonga	TASMANIAN CYPRESS PINE	(C)
Callitris oblonga preissii	COMMON CYPRESS PINE	(C)
Callitris oblonga preissii	ROTTNEST ISLAND PINE	(C)
Callitris oblonga verrucosa	TURPENTINE PINE	(C)
Callitris verrucosa	TURPENTINE PINE	(C)
Calluna, Erica	HEATHER	(S)
Calluna vulgaris	LING	(S)
Calluna vulgaris	SCOTCH HEATHER	(S)
Calocedrus decurrens	INCENSE CEDAR	(C)
Calocephalus brownii	SILVER WIRE NETTING PLANT	(H)
Calocephalus brownii	WIRE MESH PLANT	(H)

Know Your Common Plant Names

Botanical	Common	Type
Calochortus	BUTTERFLY LILY	(BB)
Calochortus	BUTTERFLY TULIP	(BB)
Calochortus	GLOBE TULIP	(BB)
Calochortus	MARIPOSA LILY	(BB)
Calochortus albus	FAIRY LANTERN	(BB)
Calochortus albus	GLOBE LILY	(BB)
Calochortus amabilis	GOLDEN FAIRY LANTERN	(BB)
Calochortus nitidus	BIG POD SEGO LILY	(B)
Calochortus venustus	WHITE MARIPOSA LILY	(BB)
Calocybe gambosa	ST GEORGE'S MUSHROOM	(FU)
Calodendron capense	CAPE CHESTNUT	(T)
Calomeria amaranthoides	INCENSE PLANT	(H)
Calomeria amaranthoides	PLUME BUSH	(S)
Calonyction aculeatum	MOONFLOWER	(CL)
Calophyllum	CALABA TREE	(TT)
Calophyllum	SAINT MARY'S WOOD	(S)
Calophyllum	ST. MARY'S WOOD	(T)
Calophyllum brasiliense	JACAREUBA	(TT)
Calopogon	SWAMP PINK	(H)
Calothamnus validus	BARRENS CLAWFLOWER	(S)
Calotropis procera	CALOTROPIS	(TT)
Calotropis procera	GIANT MILKWEED	(TH)
Caltha palustris	KINGCUP	(WP)
Caltha palustris	MARSH MARIGOLD	(WA)
Caltha palustris	MOLLY BLOBS	(WP)
Caltha palustris	WATER BLOBS	(WP)
Caltha palustris	WATER COWSLIP	(WP)
Calycanthus floridus	ALLSPICE	(S)
Calycanthus floridus	CAROLINA ALLSPICE	(S)
Calycanthus occidentalis	CALIFORNIAN ALLSPICE	(C)
Calypso bulbosa	BOG ORCHID	(O)
Calypso bulbosa	CALYPSO	(O)
Calystegia	BELLBINE	(H)
Calystegia	BINDWEED	(H)
Calystegia sepium	GRANNY POP OUT OF BED	(HCL)
Calystegia sepium	HEDGE BINDWEED	(CL)
Calystegia sepium	LARGER BINDWEED	(H)
Calystegia sepium	OLD MANS NIGHT CAP	(CL)
Calystegia silvatica	GREAT BINDWEED	(CL)
Calystegia soldanella	SEA BINDWEED	(H)
Calytrix tetragona	FRINGE MYRTLE	(S)
Camassia	QUAMASH	(BB)
Camelina sativa	GOLD-OF-PLEASURE	(H)
Camellia japonica	COMMON CAMELLIA	(S)
Camellia japonica rusticana	SNOW CAMELLIA	(S)
Camellia sinensis	TEA	(VT)
Camellia sinensis assamensis	ASSAM TEA	(S)

Botanical	Common	Type
Campanula	BELLFLOWER	(H)
Campanula barbata	BEARDED BELLFLOWER	(H)
Campanula carpatica	CARPATHIAN HAREBELL	(R)
Campanula cochlearifolia	FAIRY'S THIMBLE	(H)
Campanula glomerata	CLUSTERED BELLFLOWER	(H)
Campanula isophylla	ITALIAN BELLFLOWER	(HP)
Campanula isophylla	STAR OF BETHLEHEM	(HP)
Campanula latifolia	GIANT BELLFLOWER	(H)
Campanula media	CANTERBURY BELL	(S)
Campanula medium calycanthema	CUP AND SAUCER CANTERBURY BELL	(B)
Campanula patula	SPREADING BELLFLOWER	(H)
Campanula persicifolia	PEACH-LEAVED BELLFLOWER	(H)
Campanula portenschlagiana	WALL HAREBELL	(R)
Campanula pyramidalis	CHIMNEY BELLFLOWER	(H)
Campanula pyramidalis	STEEPLE BELLFLOWER	(H)
Campanula rapunculoides	CREEPING BELLFLOWER	(H)
Campanula rapunculus	RAMPION	(H)
Campanula rapunculus	RAMPION BELLFLOWER	(H)
Campanula rotundifolia	ENGLISH HAREBELL	(H)
Campanula rotundifolia	HAREBELL	(H)
Campanula rotundifolia	HAREBELL BELLFLOWER	(H)
Campanula rotundifolia	SCOTTISH BLUEBELL	(H)
Campanula thyrsoides	YELLOW BELLFLOWER	(H)
Campanula trachelium	BATS-IN-THE-BELFRY	(H)
Campanula trachelium	NETTLE-LEAVED BELLFLOWER	(H)
Campsis	TRUMPET CREEPER	(CL)
Campsis	TRUMPET VINE	(CL)
Campsis chinensis	CHINESE TRUMPET VINE	(CL)
Camptosorus	WALKING LEAF	(H)
Camptosorus rhizophyllus	WALKING FERN	(FN)
Cananga odorata	YLANG-YLANG	(TS)
Canaralia ensiformis	JACK BEAN	(TS)
Canarina canariensis	CANARY ISLAND BELLFLOWER	(CL)
Canarium commune	KENARI	(TT)
Canella	WILD CINNAMON	(H)
Canella alba	WHITE CINNAMON	(TS)
Canella winterana	WHITE CINNAMON	(TS)
Canna edulis	QUEENSLAND ARROWROOT	(TS)
Canna indica	INDIAN SHOT	(BB)
Cannabis sativa	BHANG	(HB)
Cannabis sativa	GANJA	(H)
Cannabis sativa	HASHISH	(H)
Cannabis sativa	HEMP	(A)
Cannabis sativa	INDIAN HEMP	(A)
Cannabis sativa	MARIHUANA	(HB)
Cannabis sativa	POT	(H)
Cantharellus cibarius	CHANTERELLE	(FU)

Know Your Common Plant Names

Botanical	Common	Type
Capsicum frutescens	PIMENTO	(HB)
Capparis spinosa	CAPER PLANT	(S)
Capsella bursa-pastoris	CASE-WEED	(A)
Capsella bursa-pastoris	LADY'S PURSE	(A)
Capsella bursa-pastoris	PEPPER AND SALT	(A)
Capsella bursa-pastoris	SHEPHERD'S PURSE	(A)
Capsicum	PEPPER	(F)
Capsicum annuum	BELL PEPPER	(F)
Capsicum annuum	CHRISTMAS PEPPER	(F)
Capsicum annuum	GREEN PEPPER	(F)
Capsicum annuum	GREEN PEPPER	(F)
Capsicum annuum	ORNAMENTAL PEPPER	(F)
Capsicum annuum	RED PEPPER	(F)
Capsicum annuum	SWEET PEPPER	(F)
Capsicum frutescens	BIRDPEPPER	(F)
Capsicum frutescens	CAYENNE PEPPER	(F)
Capsicum frutescens	CHILI	(F)
Capsicum frutescens	CHILI PEPPER	(F)
Capsicum frutescens	TABASCO	(F)
Capsicum spp.	PAPRIKA	(F)
Caragana arborescens	PEA TREE	(T)
Caragana arborescens	SIBERIAN PEA TREE	(ST)
Cardamine	BITTERCRESS	(H)
Cardamine amara	LARGE BITTER CRESS	(H)
Cardamine bulbifera	CORAL ROOT	(H)
Cardamine bulbifera	CORALROOT BITTERCRESS	(H)
Cardamine enneaphyllos	DROOPING BITTERCRESS	(H)
Cardamine flexuosa	GREATER BITTER CRESS	(H)
Cardamine flexuosa	WAVY BITTERCRESS	(A)
Cardamine impatiens	NARROW-LEAVED BITTER CRESS	(H)
Cardamine pratensis	CUCKOO FLOWER	(R)
Cardamine pratensis	LADY'S SMOCK	(R)
Cardamine trifolia	TRIFOLIATE BITTERCRESS	(H)
Cardaminopsis arenosa	TALL ROCKCRESS	(H)
Cardaminopsis petraea	NORTHERN ROCKCRESS	(H)
Cardaria draba	HOARY CRESS	(H)
Cardaria hirsuta	HAIRY BITTER CRESS	(H)
Cardiocrinum giganteum	GIANT HIMALAYAN LILY	(BB)
Cardiospermum halicacabum	BALLOON VINE	(CL)
Cardiospermum halicacabum	HEART PEA	(CL)
Cardiospermum halicacabum	HEART SEED	(CL)
Cardiospermum halicacabum	LOVE-IN-A-PUFF	(CL)
Cardomine hirsuta	HAIRY BITTER CRESS	(R)
Carduus	THISTLE	(H)
Carduus acanthoides	WELTED THISTLE	(H)
Carduus defloratus	ALPINE THISTLE	(H)
Carduus nutans	MUSK THISTLE	(H)

Know Your Common Plant Names

Botanical	Common	Type
Carduus nutans	NODDING THISTLE	(H)
Carduus personata	GREAT MARSH THISTLE	(H)
Carduus tenuiflorus	SLENDER THISTLE	(H)
Carex	SEDGE	(G)
Carex acuta	SLENDER-SPIKED SEDGE	(G)
Carex aquatilis	WATER SEDGE	(G)
Carex arenaria	SAND SEDGE	(G)
Carex atrata	BLACK SEDGE	(G)
Carex bigelowii	STIFF SEDGE	(G)
Carex binervis	GREEN-RIBBED SAGE	(G)
Carex buxbaumii	CLUB SEDGE	(G)
Carex buxbaumii	DARK SEDGE	(G)
Carex capillaris	HAIR SEDGE	(G)
Carex caryophyllea	SPRING SEDGE	(G)
Carex curta	PALE SEDGE	(G)
Carex curta	WHITE SEDGE	(G)
Carex diandra	LESSER TUSSOCK SEDGE	(G)
Carex digitata	FINGERED SEDGE	(G)
Carex dioica	DIOECIOUS SEDGE	(G)
Carex distans	DISTANT SEDGE	(G)
Carex disticha	BROWN SEDGE	(G)
Carex divulsa	GREY SEDGE	(G)
Carex echinata	STAR SEDGE	(G)
Carex elata	TUFTED SEDGE	(G)
Carex elongata	ELONGATED SEDGE	(G)
Carex ericetorum	HEATH SEDGE	(G)
Carex flava	YELLOW SEDGE	(G)
Carex grayi	MACE SEDGE	(G)
Carex hirta	HAIRY SEDGE	(G)
Carex hostiana	TAWNY SEDGE	(G)
Carex humilis	DWARF SEDGE	(G)
Carex kiparia	GREAT POND SEDGE	(G)
Carex lachenalii	HARESFOOT SEDGE	(G)
Carex laevigata	SMOOTH SEDGE	(G)
Carex limosa	BOG SEDGE	(G)
Carex loliacea	DARNEL SEDGE	(G)
Carex maritima	CURVED SEDGE	(G)
Carex montana	MOUNTAIN SEDGE	(G)
Carex muricata	PRICKLY SEDGE	(G)
Carex nigra	COMMON SEDGE	(G)
Carex ornithopoda	BIRDS-FOOT SEDGE	(G)
Carex otrubae	FALSE FOX SEDGE	(G)
Carex ovalis	OVAL SEDGE	(G)
Carex pallescens	PALE SEDGE	(G)
Carex panicea	CARNATION GRASS	(G)
Carex panicea	CARNATION SEDGE	(G)
Carex paniculata	GREATER TUSSOCK SEDGE	(G)

Know Your Common Plant Names

Botanical	Common	Type
Carex pauciflora	FEW-FLOWERED SEDGE	(G)
Carex pendula	PENDULOUS SEDGE	(G)
Carex pilulifera	PILL SEDGE	(G)
Carex pseudocyperus	CYPERUS SEDGE	(G)
Carex pulicaris	FLEA SEDGE	(G)
Carex punctata	DOTTED SEDGE	(G)
Carex remota	DISTANT-FLOWERED SEDGE	(G)
Carex riparia	GREATER POND SEDGE	(G)
Carex riparia	POND SEDGE	(G)
Carex rupestris	ROCK SEDGE	9G)
Carex saxatilis	RUSSET SEDGE	(G)
Carex spicata	SPIKED SEDGE	(G)
Carex strigosa	THIN-SPIKED WOOD SEDGE	(G)
Carex sylvatica	WOOD SEDGE	(G)
Carex vesicaria	BLADDER SEDGE	(G)
Carex vulpina	FOX SEDGE	(G)
Careya	TUMMY WOOD	(TT)
Carica cundinamarcensis	MOUNTAIN PAPAW	(F)
Carica papaya	COMMON PAPAW	(F)
Carica papaya	PAPAYA	(T)
Carica papaya	PAWPAW	(TT)
Cariniana	JEQUITIBA	(TT)
Carissa grandiflora	NATAL PLUM	(S)
Carissa macrocarpa	AMATUNGULU	(TS)
Carlina vulgaris	CARLINE THISTLE	(H)
Carludovica palmata	PANAMA HAT PLANT	(TS)
Carnegiea gigantea	SAGUARO	(CS)
Carpinus	HORNBEAN	(ST)
Carpinus betulus	COMMON HORNBEAM	(T)
Carpinus caroliniana	AMERICAN HORNBEAM	(T)
Carpinus caroliniana	BLUE BEECH	(T)
Carpinus japonica	JAPANESE HORNBEAM	(T)
Carpobrotus edulis	HOTTENTOT FIG	(H)
Carthamus	FALSE SAFFRON	(A)
Carthamus tinctorius	AMERICAN SAFFRON	(H)
Carthamus tinctorius	DYER'S SAFFRON	(H)
Carthamus tinctorius	FAKE SAFFRON	(H)
Carthamus tinctorius	SAFFLOWER	(A)
Carthamus tinctorius	SAFFRON THISTLE	(H)
Carum carvi	CARAWAY	(HB)
Carum petroselinum tuberosum	HAMBURG PARSLEY	(HB)
Carum verticilliatum	WHORLED CARAWAY	(H)
Carya	HICKORY	(T)
Carya aquatica	WATER HICKORY	(T)
Carya cordiformis	BITTERNUT	(T)
Carya cordiformis	SWAMP HICKORY	(T)
Carya glabra	HOG NUT	(T)

Know Your Common Plant Names

Botanical	Common	Type
Carya glabra	PIG NUT HICKORY	(T)
Carya illinoensis	PECAN	(T)
Carya laciniosa	KING-NUT	(T)
Carya laciniosa	SHELLBARK HICKORY	(T)
Carya myristiciformis	NUTMEG HICKORY	(T)
Carya ovalis	RED HICKORY	(T)
Carya ovata	SHAGBARK HICKORY	(T)
Carya tomentosa	BIG-BUD HICKORY	(T)
Carya tomentosa	MOCKERNUT	(T)
Caryopteris	BLUE BEARD	(S)
Caryopteris	BLUE SPIRAEA	(S)
Caryopteris	BLUEBEARD	(S)
Caryota mitis	BURMESE FISHTAIL PALM	(P)
Caryota spp	FISHTAIL PALMS	(P)
Caryota urens	JAGGERY PALM	(P)
Caryota urens	SAGO PALM	(P)
Caryota urens	TODDY PALM	(P)
Caryota urens	WINE PALM	(P)
Casimiroa edulis	WHITE SAPOTA	(TT)
Cassia acutifolia	SENNA	(S)
Cassia alata	RINGWORM SENNA	(TS)
Cassia angustifolia	INDIAN SENNA	(TS)
Cassia angustifolia	TINNEVELLY SENNA	(TS)
Cassia auriculata	TANNER'S CASSIA	(TS)
Cassia chamaecrista	GROUND SENNA	(S)
Cassia didymobotrya	CANDLE BUSH	(TS)
Cassia didymobotrya	GOLDENWONDER	(S)
Cassia fasciculata	PARTRIDGE PEA	(TS)
Cassia fistula	GOLDEN SHOWER TREE	(TT)
Cassia fistula	INDIAN LABURNUM	(TT)
Cassia fistula	PUDDING PIPE TREE	(TT)
Cassia fistula	PURGING CASSIA	(S)
Cassia fistula	SHOWER OF GOLD	(TT)
Cassia grandis	PINK SHOWER	(T)
Cassia javanica	APPLE BLOSSOM CASSIA	(TT)
Cassia javanica	PINK CASSIA	(TT)
Cassia laevigata	SMOOTH SENNA	(T)
Cassia marilandica	WILD SENNA	(TS)
Cassia occidentalis	COFFEE SENNA	(T)
Cassia senna	ALEXANDRIAN SENNA	(S)
Cassia tora	SICKLE SENNA	(TS)
Cassinia fulvida	GOLDEN HEATHER	(S)
Castanea	CHESTNUT	(T)
Castanea crenata	JAPANESE CHESTNUT	(T)
Castanea dentata	AMERICAN CHESTNUT	(T)
Castanea mollissima	CHINESE CHESTNUT	(T)
Castanea pumila	CHINQUAPIN	(T)

Know Your Common Plant Names

Botanical	Common	Type
Castanea sativa	SPANISH CHESTNUT	(T)
Castanea sativa	SWEET CHESTNUT	(T)
Castanopsis cuspidata	JAPANESE CHINQUAPIN	(T)
Castanospermum australe	BLACK BEAN TREE	(TT)
Castanospermum australe	MORETON BAY CHESTNUT	(TT)
Castilleja	INDIAN PAINT-BRUSH	(S)
Castilleja	PAINTED CUP	(H)
Castilleja miniata	SCARLET PAINTBRUSH	(S)
Castilloa elastica	PANAMA RUBBER	(TT)
Castonopsis megacarpa	GREATER MALAYAN CHESTNUT	(TT)
Casuarina	BEEFWOOD	(T)
Casuarina cunninghamiana	RIVER OAK	(T)
Casuarina equisetifolia	AUSTRALIAN BEEFWOOD	(TT)
Casuarina equisetifolia	AUSTRALIAN PINE	(TT)
Casuarina equisetifolia	BEECHWOOD	(T/S)
Casuarina equisetifolia	HORSETAIL TREE	(T)
Casuarina equisetifolia	RED BEEFWOOD	(T)
Casuarina equisetifolia	SOUTH SEA IRONWOOD	(TT)
Casuarina stricta	SHE OAK	(T)
Catabrosa	REED MANNA-GRASS	(G)
Catabrosa aquatica	WHORL GRASS	(G)
Catalpa bignonioides	INDIAN BEAN TREE	(T)
Catalpa bignonioides	SOUTHERN CATALPA	(T)
Catalpa bignonioides 'Aurea'	GOLDEN-LEAVED CATALPA	(T)
Catalpa ovata	YELLOW CATALPA	(T)
Catalpa speciosa	WESTERN CATALPA	(T)
Catalpa x erubescens	HYBRID CATALPA	(T)
Catananche	BLUE CUPIDONE	(H)
Catananche	CUPID'S DART	(H)
Catananche	CUPIDONE	(H)
Catechu nigrum	CUTCH	(TT)
Catesbaea spinosa	LILY THORN	(H)
Catesbaea spinosa	LILY-THORN	(H)
Catha edulis	KHAT TREE	(TT)
Catharanthus	OLD MAID	(HP)
Catharanthus roeus	RAMGOAT ROSE	(HP)
Catharanthus rosea	MADAGASCAR PERIWINKLE	(HP)
Caucalis latifolia	GREAT BUR-PARSLEY	(H)
Caucalis platycarpos	SMALL BUR-PARSLEY	(H)
Caulophyllum thalictroides	BLUE COHOSH	(H)
Caulophyllum thalictroides	BLUE GENSENG	(H)
Caulophyllum thalictroides	BLUEBERRY ROOT	(H)
Caulophyllum thalictroides	PAPOOSE ROOT	(S)
Caulophyllum thalictroides	SQUAW ROOT	(S)
Ceanothus	CALIFORNIAN LILAC	(S)
Ceanothus	REDROOT	(S)
Ceanothus americanus	NEW JERSEY TEA PLANT	(S)

Know Your Common Plant Names

Botanical	Common	Type
Ceanothus americanus	RED ROOT	(S)
Ceanothus arboreus	CATALINA CEANOTHUS	(S)
Ceanothus cordulatus	SNOW-BUSH	(S)
Ceanothus crassifolius	HOARYLEAF CEANOTHUS	(S)
Ceanothus cuneatus	BUCK BRUSH	(S)
Ceanothus dentatus	SANTA BARBARA CEANOTHUS	(S)
Ceanothus griseus	CARMEL CEANOTHUS	(S)
Ceanothus integerrimus	DEER BRUSH	(S)
Ceanothus integerrimus	DEER BUSH	(S)
Ceanothus prostratus	SQUAW CARPET	(S)
Ceanothus sanguineus	OREGON TEA	(S)
Ceanothus sorediatus	JIM BRUSH	(S)
Ceanothus thyrsiflorus 'Repens'	CREEPING BLUE BLOSSOM	(S)
Cebtaurea scabiosa	BOTTLEWEED	(H)
Cecropia peltata	TRUMPET TREE	(TT)
Cedronella triphylla	BALM OF GILEAD	(HB)
Cedrus	CEDAR	(C)
Cedrus atlantica	ATLAS CEDAR	(C)
Cedrus atlantica 'Aurea'	GOLDEN ATLAS CEDAR	(C)
Cedrus atlantica 'Glauca'	BLUE ATLAS CEDAR	(C)
Cedrus atlantica 'Glauca'	BLUE CEDAR	(C)
Cedrus atlantica 'Pendula'	WEEPING ATLAS CEDAR	(C)
Cedrus brevifolia	CYPRIAN CEDAR	(C)
Cedrus brevifolia	CYPRUS CEDAR	(C)
Cedrus deodara	DEODAR	(C)
Cedrus deodora	HIMALAYAN CEDAR	(C)
Cedrus deodora	INDIAN CEDAR	(C)
Cedrus deodora 'Aurea'	GOLDEN DEODAR CEDAR	(C)
Cedrus libani	CEDAR OF LEBANON	(C)
Ceiba	COTTON TREE	(TT)
Ceiba pentandra	KAPOK	(TT)
Ceiba pentandra	KAPOK TREE	(TT)
Ceiba pentandra	SILK COTTON TREE	(TT)
Celastrus	CLIMBING BITTERSWEET	(CL)
Celastrus scandens	STAFF TREE	(CL)
Celastrus scandens	WAXWORK	(CL)
Celmisia	NEW ZEALAND DAISY	(H)
Celmisia spectabilis	COTTON DAISY	(H)
Celosia argentea pyramidalis	PRINCE OF WALES FEATHERS	(A)
Celosia cristata	COCKSCOMB	(A)
Celosia plumosa	PLUME FLOWER	(A)
Celsia	CRETAN MULLEIN	(A)
Celsia arcturus	CRETAN BEAR'S TAIL	(B)
Celtis africana	WHITE STINKWOOD TREE	(TT)
Celtis australis	SOUTHERN NETTLE TREE	(T)
Celtis iguanaea	GRANJENO	(TT)
Celtis kraussiana	STINKWOOD	(TT)

Know Your Common Plant Names

Botanical	Common	Type
Celtis laevigata	MISSISSIPPI HACKBERRY	(T)
Celtis laevigata	SUGARBERRY	(T)
Celtis occidentalis	HACKBERRY	(T)
Celtis species	NETTLE TREES	(T)
Centaurea americana	BASKET FLOWER	(H)
Centaurea calcitrapa	RED STAR-THISTLE	(H)
Centaurea calcitrapa	STAR THISTLE	(H)
Centaurea cyanus	BLUE BOTTLE	(H)
Centaurea cyanus	BLUE CORNFLOWER	(A)
Centaurea cyanus	CORNFLOWER	(AH)
Centaurea jacea	BROWN KNAPWEED	(H)
Centaurea macrocephala	GREAT GOLDEN KNAPWEED	(H)
Centaurea montana	MOUNTAIN KNAPWEED	(H)
Centaurea montana	PERENNIAL CORNFLOWER	(H)
Centaurea moschata	SWEET SULTAN	(H)
Centaurea nigra	BLACK KNAPWEED	(H)
Centaurea nigra	HARDHEADS	(H)
Centaurea nigra	KNAPWEED	(H)
Centaurea nigra	LESSER KNAPWEED	(H)
Centaurea phrygia	WIG KNAPWEED	(H)
Centaurea scabiosa	GREAT KNAPWEED	(H)
Centaurea scabiosa	GREATER KNAPWEED	(H)
Centaurea scabiosa	IRONHEAD	(H)
Centaurea solstitalis	YELLOW STAR-THISTLE	(H)
Centaurea solstitialis	ST. BARNABY'S THISTLE	(H)
Centaurium erythraea	COMMON CENTAURY	(A)
Centaurium erythraea	RED CENTAURY	(H)
Centaurium littorale	SEASIDE CENTAURY	(A)
Centaurium pulchellum	SLENDER CENTAURY	(A)
Centaurium scilloides	PERENNIAL CENTAURY	(H)
Centaurum erythraea	CENTAURY	(H)
Centaurum littorale	SEA CENTAURY	(H)
Centaurum pulchellum	LESSER CENTAURY	(H)
Centranthus ruber	BOUNCING BESS	(H)
Centranthus ruber	DRUNKEN SAILOR	(H)
Centranthus ruber	JUPITER'S BEARD	(H)
Centranthus ruber	PRETTY BETSY	(H)
Centranthus ruber	RED VALERIAN	(H)
Centratherum intermedium	MANAOS BEAUTY	(TS)
Cephaelis ipecacuanha	IPECACUANHA	(TT)
Cephalanthera damasonium	WHITE HELLEBORINE	(O)
Cephalanthera rubra	RED HELLEBORINE	(O)
Cephalanthera/Epipactis	HELLEBORINE	(O)
Cephalanthus occidentalis	BUTTON BUSH	(S)
Cephalaria	GIANT SCABIOUS	(H)
Cephalocereus senilis	OLD MAN CACTUS	(CS)
Cephalocereus senilis	OLD-MAN CACTUS	(CS)

Know Your Common Plant Names

Botanical	Common	Type
Cephalophyllum alstonii	RED SPIKE	(CS)
Cephalotaxus	COWS TAIL PINE	(C)
Cephalotaxus	PLUM YEW	(C)
Cephalotaxus fortunei	CHINESE PLUM YEW	(C)
Cephalotaxus harringtonia drupacea	JAPANESE PLUM YEW	(C)
Cephalotus	AUSTRALIAN PITCHER PLANT	(H)
Cephalotus follicularis	AUSTRALIAN FLYCATCHER PLANT	(H)
Cerastium	MOUSE-EAR	(H)
Cerastium alpinum	ALPINE MOUSE-EAR	(H)
Cerastium articum	ARCTIC MOUSE-EAR	(H)
Cerastium arvense	FIELD MOUSE-EAR	(H)
Cerastium cerastoides	STARWORT MOUSE-EAR	(H)
Cerastium fontanum	COMMON MOUSE-EAR	(H)
Cerastium glomeratum	STICKY MOUSE-EAR	(H)
Cerastium tomentosum	DUSTY MILLER	(H)
Cerastium tomentosum	SNOW-IN-SUMMER	(H)
Ceratonia siliqua	CAROB	(T)
Ceratonia siliqua	LOCUST PODS	(T)
Ceratonia siliqua	ST. JOHN'S BREAD	(T)
Ceratopetalum apetalum	LIGHTWOOD	(TT)
Ceratopetalum gummiferum	RED GUM	(TT)
Ceratophyllum demersum	HORNWORT	(WP)
Ceratophyllum demursum	RIGID HORNWORT	(WP)
Ceratophyllum submersum	SOFT HORNWORT	(WP)
Ceratopteris thalictroides	WATER FERN	(WP)
Ceratostigma	HARDY PLUMBAGO	(H)
Ceratostigma	SHRUBBY PLUMBAGO	(S)
Cercidiphyllum	KATSURA TREE	(T)
Cercis canadensis	AMERICAN JUDAS TREE	(T)
Cercis canadensis	REDBUD	(S.T)
Cercis chinensis	CHINESE RED BUD	(T)
Cercis occidentalis	WESTERN REDBUD	(S)
Cercis siliquastrum	JUDAS TREE	(S/T)
Cercocarpus montanus	MOUNTAIN MAHOGANY	(S)
Cereus	DILDO	(CS)
Cereus peruvianus	PERUVIAN APPLE CACTUS	(CS)
Cerinthe glabra	SMOOTH HONEYWORT	(H)
Cerinthe major	HONEYWORT	(H)
Ceropegia sandersonii	FOUNTAIN FLOWER	(S)
Ceropegia sandersonii	PARACHUTE PLANT	(S)
Ceropegia woodii	ROSARY VINE	(HP)
Ceroxylon	WAX PALM	(P)
Certatopteris thalictroides	WATER SPRITE	(WP)
Cestrum	BASTARD JASMINE	(S)
Cestrum nocturnum	NIGHT JASMINE	(S/T)
Cestrum nocturnum	NIGHT-BLOOMING JESSAMINE	(S)
Ceterach aureum	RUSTY-BACK FERN	(FN)

Botanical	Common	Type
Cetraria islandica	ICELAND MOSS	(MS)
Chaenomeles	JAPANESE QUINCE	(S)
Chaenomeles	JAPONICA	(S)
Chaenomeles	ORNAMENTAL QUINCE	(S)
Chaenorhinum minus	SMALL TOADFLAX	(H)
Chaerophyllum	BULBOUS CHERVIL	(H)
Chaerophyllum hirsutum	HAIRY CHERVIL	(H)
Chaerophyllum temulentum	CHERVIL	(HB)
Chaerophyllum temulentum	ROUGH CHERVIL	(H)
Chaetomorpha linum	GREEN HAIR-WEED	(SW)
Chamaecereus sylvestri	PEANUT CACTUS	(CS)
Chamaecrista fasciculata	PARTRIDGE PEA	(V)
Chamaecrista fasciculata	PRAIRIE SENNA	(S)
Chamaecrista fasciculata	SENSITIVE PEA	(S)
Chamaecyparis	FALSE CYPRESS	(C)
Chamaecyparis lawsoniana	LAWSON CYPRESS	(C)
Chamaecyparis lawsoniana	PORT ORFORD CEDAR	(C)
Chamaecyparis nootkatensis	ALASKA CEDAR	(C)
Chamaecyparis nootkatensis	NOOTKA CYPRESS	(C)
Chamaecyparis nootkatensis	YELLOW CYPRESS	(C)
Chamaecyparis obtusa	HINOKI CYPRESS	(C)
Chamaecyparis pisifera	SAWARA CYPRESS	(C)
Chamaecyparis thyoides	WHITE CYPRESS	(C)
Chamaecytisus supinus	CLUSTERED BROOM	(S)
Chamaedaphne calyculata	LEATHER LEAF	(S)
Chamaedorea elegans	PARLOUR PALM	(P)
Chamaedorea erumpens	BAMBOO PALM	(P)
Chamaedorea seifrizii	REED PALM	(P)
Chamaelaucium uncinatum	GERALDTON WAX	(TS)
Chamaelirion luteum	FALSE UNICORN ROOT	(H)
Chamaelirion luteum	HELONIAS	(H)
Chamaemelum nobile	CHAMOMILE	(H)
Chamaemelum nobile	GROUND APPLE	(H)
Chamaemelum nobile	ROMAN CHAMOMILE	(H)
Chamaemelum nobile	SWEET CHAMOMILE	(H)
Chamaemelum nobilis 'Treneague'	LAWN CHAMOMILE	(H)
Chamaepericlymenum suecicum	DWARF CORNEL	(S)
Chamaepeuce diacantha	FISH-BONE THISTLE	(H)
Chamaescilla corymbosa	BLUE STAR	(BB)
Chamaespartium sagittale	WINGED BROOM	(S)
Chamerion latifolium	RIVER BEAUTY	(H)
Chamomilla suaveolens	PINEAPPLE WEED	(HA)
Chamomilla suaveolens	RAYLESS MAYWEED	(H)
Chamorchis alpina	FALSE MUSK ORCHID	(O)
Cheilanthes	LIP FERN	(FN)
Cheilanthes distans	WOOLLY ROCK FERN	(FN)
Cheilanthes gracillima	LACE FERN	(FN)

Botanical	Common	Type
Cheilanthes lamosa	HAIRY LIP FERN	(FN)
Cheiranthus allionii	SIBERIAN WALLFLOWER	(H)
Cheiranthus cheiri	GILLYFLOWER	(H)
Cheiranthus cheiri	WALLFLOWER	(B)
Cheirostemon platanoides	HAND PLANT	(S)
Chelidonium	CELANDINE	(H)
Chelidonium majus	GREATER CELANDINE	(H)
Chelone	TURTLEHEAD	(H)
Chelone glabra	BALMONY	(H)
Chenopodium	GOOSEFOOT	(HA)
Chenopodium	LAMB'S QUARTERS	(H)
Chenopodium album	DIRTWEED	(H)
Chenopodium album	FAT HEN	(A)
Chenopodium album	PIGWEED	(H)
Chenopodium album	WATER GOOSEFOOT	(H)
Chenopodium ambrosioides	MEXICAN TEA	(H)
Chenopodium ambrosioides anthelminticum	WORMSEED	(H)
Chenopodium anthelminticum	AMERICAN WORMCRESS	(H)
Chenopodium anthelminticum	AMERICAN WORMSEED	(H)
Chenopodium anthelminticum	JESUIT'S TEA	(H)
Chenopodium bonus-henricus	GOOD KING HENRY	(A)
Chenopodium botrys	AMBROSIA	(HB)
Chenopodium botrys	JERUSALEM OAK	(H)
Chenopodium capitaton	STRAWBERRY SPINACH	(V)
Chenopodium capitatum	STRAWBERRY-BLITE	(H)
Chenopodium ficifolium	FIG-LEAVED GOOSEFOOT	(H)
Chenopodium glaucum	OAK-LEAVED GOOSEFOOT	(H)
Chenopodium hybridum	SOWBANE	(H)
Chenopodium opulifolium	GREY GOOSEFOOT	(H)
Chenopodium quinoa	QUINOA	(H)
Chenopodium rubrum	RED GOOSEFOOT	(H)
Chenopodium vulvaria	STINKING GOOSE-FOOT	(H)
Chenopudium album	BACON WEED	(A)
Chimaphila maculata	SPOTTED WINTERGREEN	(H)
Chimaphila umbellata	KING'S CURE	(H)
Chimaphila umbellata	PIPSISSEWA	(H)
Chimaphila umbellata	PRINCE'S PINE	(H)
Chimaphila umbellata	RHEUMATISM WEED	(H)
Chimaphila umbellata	UMBELLATE WINTERGREEN	(H)
Chimaphila umbellata	WINTER GREEN	(H)
Chimonanthus	WINTERSWEET	(S)
Chiococca	SNOWBERRY	(S)
Chiogenes hispidula	CREEPING SNOWBERRY	(S)
Chionanthus retusus	CHINESE FRINGE TREE	(T)
Chionanthus virginicus	FRINGE TREE	(S)
Chionanthus virginicus	OLD MAN'S BEARD	(S)
Chionanthus virginicus	POISON ASH	(S)

Know Your Common Plant Names

Botanical	Common	Type
Chionanthus virginicus	SNOWFLOWER	(S)
Chionochloa conspicua	HUNANGEMOHO GRASS	(G)
Chionodoxa	GLORY-OF-THE SNOW	(BB)
Chionodoxa	SNOW GLORY	(BB)
Chiranthodendron pentadactylon	HANDFLOWER TREE	(TT)
Chlorophora excelsa	IROKO	(TT)
Chlorophora tinctoria	FUSTIC	(TT)
Chlorophytum	RIBBON PLANT	(HP)
Chlorophytum comosum	SPIDER PLANT	(HP)
Chloroxylon swietenia	SATIN WOOD	(TT)
Choisya ternata	MEXICAN ORANGE BLOSSOM	(S)
Chondrilla juncea	CHONDRILLA	(H)
Chondrilla juncea	SKELETON WEED	(TS)
Chondrodendron tomentosum	CURARE	(TS)
Chondrodendron tomentosum	PAREIRA	(TT)
Chondrostereum purpureum	SILVER LEAF FUNGUS	(FU)
Chondrus crispus	CARRAGEEN	(MS)
Chondrus crispus	IRISH MOSS	(MS)
Chorda filum	BOOTLACE WEED	(SW)
Chorda filum	MERMAID'S HAIR	(SW)
Chorisia speciosa	FLOSS SILK TREE	(T)
Chorizema dicksonii	YELLOW-EYED FLAME PEA	(S)
Chorizema illicifolium	HOLLY FLAME PEA	(S)
Chrysalidocarpos lutescens	YELLOW PALM	(P)
Chrysalidocarpus	GOLDEN-FEATHER PALM	(P)
Chrysalidocarpus lutescens	BUTTERFLY PALM	(P)
Chrysalidocarpus lutescens	MADAGASCAR PALM	(P)
Chrysanthemum carinatum	PAINTED DAISY	(A)
Chrysanthemum coronarium	CROWN DAISY	(A)
Chrysanthemum rubellum	KOREAN CHRYSANTHEMUM	(H)
Chrysanthemum segetum	CORN MARIGOLD	(H)
Chrysobalanus icaco	COCO PLUM	(TT)
Chrysobalanus icaco	COCO-PLUM	(TT)
Chrysocoma coma-aurea	YELLOW EDGING DAISY	(H)
Chrysogonum virginianum	GOLDEN STAR	(R)
Chrysolepis chrysophylla	GOLDEN CHESTNUT	(T)
Chrysolepis sempervirens	BUSH CHINQUAPIN	(T)
Chrysophyllum	STAR APPLE	(S)
Chrysophyllum cainito	STAR APPLE	(TS)
Chrysophyllum cainito	STAR-APPLE	(TS)
Chrysophyllum oliviforme	SATIN LEAF	(H)
Chrysopsis	GOLDEN ASTER	(H)
Chrysosplenium oppositifolium	GOLDEN SAXIFRAGE	(R)
Chrysothamnus	PLUMED GOLDEN ROD	(H)
Chrysothamnus nauseosus	RUBBER RABBIT BUSH	(S)
Chusquea	BAMBOO	(G)
Chusquea culeou	CULEU	(G)

Know Your Common Plant Names

Botanical	Common	Type
Cibotium	SCYTHIAN LAMB	(FN)
Cicendia filiformis	YELLOW CENTAURY	(A)
Cicer arietinum	CHICK PEA	(V)
Cicer arietinum	GARBANZO	(F)
Cicerbita	BLUE SOWTHISTLE	(H)
Cicerbita macrophylla	BLUE SOWTHISTLE	(H)
Cichorium endivia	ENDIVE	(V)
Cichorium intybus	BLUE SAILORS	(H)
Cichorium intybus	CHICORY	(V/HB)
Cicorium intybus	SUCCORY	(H)
Cicuta maculata	AMERICAN COWBEAN	(H)
Cicuta virosa	COWBANE	(H)
Cicuta virosa	WATER HEMLOCK	(WP)
Cimicifuga	BUGBANE	(H)
Cimicifuga	SNAKEROOT	(H)
Cimicifuga racemosa	BLACK SNAKEROOT	(H)
Cimifuga racemosa	BLACK COHOSH	(H)
Cinchona	JESUIT'S BARK	(TT)
Cinchona calisaya	CALISAYA	(TT)
Cinchona calisaya	YELLOW BARK	(TT)
Cinchona cordifolia	CARTAGENA BARK	(TT)
Cinchona officinalis	QUININE	(T)
Cinchona succirubra	PERUVIAN BARK	(TT)
Cinchona succirula	RED CINCHONA	(TT)
Cinnamodendron corticosum	FALSE WINTER'S BARK	(TS)
Cinnamodendron corticosum	RED CANELLA	(TS)
Cinnamomum camphora	CAMPHOR TREE	(T)
Cinnamomum cassia	CASSIA	(S/T)
Cinnamonum zeylanicum	CINNAMON	(T)
Circaea lutetiana	ENCHANTER'S NIGHTSHADE	(H)
Cirsium	PLUMED THISTLE	(H)
Cirsium	THISTLE	(H)
Cirsium acaule	DWARF THISTLE	(H)
Cirsium acaule	GROUND THISTLE	(H)
Cirsium arvense	CREEPING THISTLE	(H)
Cirsium dissectum	MEADOW THISTLE	(H)
Cirsium eriophorum	WOOLLY THISTLE	(H)
Cirsium heterophyllum	MELANCHOLY THISTLE	(H)
Cirsium oleraceum	CABBAGE THISTLE	(H)
Cirsium palustre	MARSH THISTLE	(H)
Cirsium rivulare	BROOK THISTLE	(H)
Cirsium spinosissimum	SPINIEST THISTLE	(H)
Cirsium vulgare	SPEAR THISTLE	(H)
Cissus antartica	KANGAROO VINE	(HP)
Cissus discolor	REX-BEGONIA VINE	(HP)
Cissus rhombifolia	GRAPE IVY	(HP)
Cissus sicyoides	PRINCESS VINE	(CL)

Know Your Common Plant Names

Botanical	Common	Type
Cissus striata	MINIATURE GRAPE IVY	(HP)
Cistus	ROCK ROSE	(S)
Cistus ladanifer	GUM CISTUS	(S)
Cistus monspeliensis	MONTPELIER ROCK ROSE	(S)
Cistus salviifolius	SAGE-LEAVED ROCK ROSE	(S)
Cithahexylum	FIDDLEWOOD	(T)
Citharexylum	ZITHERWOOD	(TT)
Citrullus colocynthis	BITTER APPLE	(TT)
Citrullus colocynthis	BITTER CUCUMBER	(H)
Citrullus colocynthus	COLOCYNTH	(F)
Citrullus lanatus	WATER MELON	(F)
Citrus aurantifolia	LIME	(F)
Citrus aurantium	BITTER ORANGE	(F)
Citrus aurantium melitensis	BLOOD ORANGE	(F)
Citrus autantium	SEVILLE ORANGE	(F)
Citrus bergamia	BERGAMOT	(F)
Citrus ichangense	ICHANG LEMON	(S)
Citrus limon	LEMON	(F)
Citrus lumia	SWEET LEMON	(F)
Citrus maxima	PUMMELO	(V)
Citrus maxima	SHADDOCK	(F)
Citrus medica	CITRON	(F)
Citrus medica cedra	CEDRAT LEMON	(F)
Citrus paradisi x Citrus reticulata	UGLI FRUIT	(F)
Citrus reticulata	MANDARIN	(F)
Citrus reticulata 'Clementine'	CLEMENTINE	(F)
Citrus reticulata deliciosus	TANGERINE	(F)
Citrus reticulata unshiu	SATSUMA	(F)
Citrus sinensis	ORANGE	(F)
Citrus sinensis	SWEET ORANGE	(F)
Citrus x limonia	MANDARIN LIME	(F)
Citrus x paradisi	GRAPEFRUIT	(F)
Citrus x paradisi	POMELO	(F)
Cladium mariscus	FEN SEDGE	(G)
Cladium mariscus	GREAT FEN SEDGE	(G)
Cladonia rangiferina	REINDEER MOSS	(MS)
Cladrastis lutea	YELLOWWOOD	(S/T)
Cladrastis platycarpa	JAPANESE YELLOW WOOD	(T)
Cladratis sinensis	CHINESE YELLOWWOOD	(T)
Clarkia amoena	SATIN FLOWER	(A)
Clarkia concinna	RED RIBBONS	(A)
Clarkia unguiculata	CLARKIA	(A)
Clarkia unquiculata	MOUNTAIN GARLAND	(A)
Clausena lansium	WAMPEE	(T)
Claviceps purpurea	ERGOT	(PE)
Claytonia	SPRING BEAUTY	(H)
Claytonia perfoliata	MINER'S LETTUCE	(V)

Botanical	Common	Type
Claytonia perfoliata	WINTER PURSLANE	(H)
Cleditsia caspica	CASPIAN LOCUST	(T)
Cleistocactus smaragdiflorus	FIRECRACKER CACTUS	(CS)
Cleistocactus strausii	SILVER TORCH	(CS)
Clematis alpina	ALPINE CLEMATIS	(CL)
Clematis cirrhosa balearica	FERN-LEAVED CLEMATIS	(CL)
Clematis macropetala	DOWNY CLEMATIS	(CL)
Clematis orientalis	ORANGE-PEEL CLEMATIS	(CL)
Clematis recta	ERECT CLEMATIS	(H)
Clematis tangutica	GOLDEN CLEMATIS	(CL)
Clematis virginiana	VIRGIN'S BOWER	(CL)
Clematis vitalba	OLD MAN'S BEARD	(CL)
Clematis vitalba	TRAVELLER'S JOY	(CL)
Clematis vitalba	WHITE VINE	(CL)
Clematopsis stanleyi	SHOCK-HEADED PETER	(H)
Cleome	SPIDER FLOWER	(A)
Cleome	SPIDER-FLOWER	(HP)
Cleome spinosa	GIANT SPIDER PLANT	(BB)
Clerodendrum paniculatum	PAGODA FLOWER	(TS)
Clerodendrum thomsoniae	BLEEDING-HEART VINE	(HP)
Clerodendrum trichotomum	GLORY TREE	(S)
Clethra acuminata	WHITE ALDER	(S)
Clethra alnifolia	SUMMERSWEET	(S)
Clethra alnifolia	SWEET PEPPER BUSH	(S)
Clethra arborea	FOLHADO	(T)
Clethra arborea	LILY-OF-THE-VALLEY TREE	(S)
Clianthus formosus	GLORY PEA	(S)
Clianthus formosus	STURT'S DESERT PEA	(S)
Clianthus puniceus	LOBSTER'S CLAW	(S)
Clianthus puniceus	PARROT'S BILL	(S)
Cliftonia monophylla	BUCKWHEAT TREE	(S)
Clinopodium vulgare	WILD BASIL	(H)
Clintonia	BEAR TONGUE	(H)
Clintonia	BEAR-TONGUE	(H)
Clintonia borealis	BLUEBEAD-LILY	(H)
Clintonia uniflora	QUEENCUP	(H)
Clitoria ternatea	BUTTERFLY PEA	(S)
Clivia	KAFFIR LILY	(HP)
Cneorum tricoccum	SPURGE OLIVE	(S)
Cnicus	THISTLE	(H)
Cnicus benedictus	BLESSED THISTLE	(H)
Cnicus benedictus	HOLY THISTLE	(H)
Cnicus benedictus	ST. BENEDICT'S THISTLE	(A)
Cobaea	CATHEDRAL BELLS	(A.CL)
Cobaea scandens	CUP AND SAUCER	(A)
Coccinia cordifolia	IVY GOURD	(H)
Coccoloba pubescens	LEATHER-COAT TREE	(H)

Know Your Common Plant Names

Botanical	Common	Type
Coccoloba uvifera	SEA GRAPE	(TT)
Coccoloba uvifera	SEASIDE GRAPE	(CL)
Cocculus carolinus	CAROLINA MOONSEED	(CL)
Cocculus carolinus	SNAIL-SEED	(H)
Cocculus carolinus	SNAILSEED	(H)
Cocculus palmatus	COLOMBO	(H)
Cochlearia anglica	ENGLISH SCURVY GRASS	(H)
Cochlearia danica	DANISH SCURVY-GRASS	(A)
Cochlearia officinalis	SCURVY GRASS	(H)
Cochlospermum fraseri	KAPOK BUSH	(TS)
Cochlospermum religiosum	BUTTERCUP TREE	(TT)
Cochlospermum religiosum	YELLOW COTTON TREE	(TT)
Cochlospermum vitifolium	BUTTERCUP TREE	(TT)
Cochlospermum vitifolium	ROSE IMPERIAL	(TT)
Cocos nucifera	COCONUT PALM	(P)
Cocos weddeliana	COCONUT PALM	(P)
Codiaeum variegatum pictum	CROTON	(HP)
Codium tormentosum	VELVET HORN	(SW)
Codonocarpus cotinifolius	BELL-FRUIT TREE	(TT)
Coeloglossum viride	FROG ORCHID	(O)
Coelogyne pandurata	BLACK ORCHID	(O)
Coffea arabica	COFFEE	(FS)
Coffea liberica	LIBERIAN COFFEE	(F)
Coix lacryma-jobi	JOB'S TEARS	(H)
Cola acuminata	ABATA COLA	(TF)
Cola acuminata	COLA	(T)
Cola acuminata	KOLA	(TS)
Cola acuminata	KOLA NUT	(T)
Cola anomala	BAMENDA COLA	(TF)
Cola nitida	GBANJA COLA	(TF)
Cola nitida	KOLA	(TS)
Cola verticilliata	OWE COLA	(TF)
Colchicum	AUTUMN CROCUS	(BB)
Colchicum autumnale	MEADOW SAFFRON	(BB)
Colchicum autumnale	NAKED LADIES	(BB)
Coleonema pulchrum	CONFETTI BUSH	(S)
Coleus	FLAME NETTLE	(HP)
Coleus rotundifolius	HAUSA POTATO	(TS)
Colletia cruciata	ANCHOR PLANT	(S)
Collinsia	BLUE-EYED MARY	(H)
Collinsia bicolor	INNOCENCE	(A)
Collinsia grandiflora	BLUE LIPS	(H)
Collinsonia	CITRONELLA	(H)
Collinsonia	HORSE-BALM	(H)
Collinsonia	HORSE-WEED	(H)
Collinsonia	STONE ROOT	(H)
Collinsonia canadensis	HORSEWEED	(H)

Know Your Common Plant Names

Botanical	Common	Type
Collinsonia canadensis	KNOB ROOT	(H)
Collinsonia canadensis	KNOBWEED	(H)
Collinsonia canadensis	RICHLEAF	(H)
Collinsonia canadensis	RICHWEED	(H)
Collinsonia canadensis	STONE ROOT	(H)
Collybia fusipes	SPINDLE SHANK	(FU)
Collybia maculata	FOXY SPOT	(FU)
Colocasia	COCOYAM	(F)
Colocasia	WEST INDIAN KALE	(V)
Colocasia esculenta	DASHEEN	(F)
Colocasia esculenta	EDDO	(F)
Colocasia esculenta	TARO	(V)
Columnea gloriosa	GOLDFISH PLANT	(HP)
Colutea	BLADDER SENNA	(S)
Comarostaphylis diversifolia	SUMMER HOLLY	(S)
Combretum sundaicum	JUNGLE WEED	(H)
Commelina	BLUE SPIDERWORT	(H)
Commelina	DAY FLOWER	(H)
Commifera abyssinica	MYRRH	(TT)
Commifera molmol	MYRRH	(TT)
Commifera myrrha	MYRRH	(TT)
Commiphora opobalsamum	BALM OF GILEAD	(HB)
Commiphora opobalsmum	BALSAM OF GILEAD	(HB)
Comptonia peregrina	SWEET FERN	(S)
Conium maculatum	HEMLOCK	(H)
Conium maculatum	MUSKRAT WEED	(H)
Conium maculatum	MUSQUASH ROOT	(H)
Conium maculatum	POISON HEMLOCK	(H)
Conium maculatum	POISON PARSLEY	(H)
Conium maculatum	SPOTTED COWBANE	(H)
Connarus guianensis	ZEBRA WOOD	(TT)
Conophytum	CONE PLANT	(A)
Conopodium majus	EARTH NUT	(H)
Conopodium majus	PIG NUT	(H)
Conospermum huegelii	SLENDER SMOKE BUSH	(TS)
Conospermum stoechadis	AUSTRALIAN SMOKE BUSH	(TS)
Conringia orientalis	HARE'S-EAR CABBAGE	(H)
Consolida	LARKSPUR	(A)
Consolida ambigua	LARKSPUR	(A)
Consolida ambigua	ROCKET LARKSPUR	(A)
Consolida regalis	BRANCHED LARKSPUR	(A)
Consolida regalis	FORKING LARKSPUR	(A)
Contoneaster horizontalis	FISH-BONE COTONEASTER	(S)
Contoneaster integerrimus	COMMON COTONEASTER	(S)
Convallaria majalis	LILY-OF-THE-VALLEY	(H)
Convallaria majalis	MAY LILY	(H)
Convallaria majalis	OUR LADY'S TEARS	(H)

Botanical	Common	Type
Convolvulus arvensis	BINDWEED	(H)
Convolvulus arvensis	LESSER BINDWEED	(H)
Convolvulus arvensis	WITHYWIND	(CL)
Convolvulus jalapa	JALAP BINDWEED	(TS)
Convolvulus scammonia	SCAMMONY	(H)
Convolvulus scammonia	SYRIAN BINDWEED	(H)
Convolvulus tricolor	DWARF MORNING GLORY	(A)
Conyza canadensis	CANADIAN FLEABANE	(A)
Conyza canadensis	HORSE WEED	(H)
Cooperia	EVENING STAR	(BB)
Cooperia	PRAIRIE-LILY	(BB)
Cooperia mentzelia	PRAIRIE-LILY	(S)
Copaifera langsdorffii	COPAIBA	(CS)
Copernica cerifera	CARNANBA PALM	(P)
Copernica cerifera	CARNAUBA PALM	(P)
Copernica prunifera	CARNAUBA WAX PALM	(P)
Copernicia macroglossa	PETTICOAT PALM	(P)
Coprifera mopane	TURPENTINE TREE	(TT)
Coprinus comatus	INK CAP	(FU)
Coprinus comatus	LAWYER'S WIG	(FU)
Coprinus comatus	SHAGGY INK CAP	(FU)
Coprinus picaceus	MAGPIE	(FU)
Coprosma repens	MIRROR PLANT	(S)
Coptis	GOLD THREAD	(H)
Coptis	MOUTHROOT	(H)
Coptis trifolia	GOLD THREAD	(H)
Corallorhiza odontorhiza	CRAWLEY ROOT	(O)
Corallorhiza trifida	CORAL ROOT ORCHID	(O)
Corchorus capsularis	JUTE	(TS)
Corchorus capsularis	WHITE JUTE	(TH)
Corchorus olitorius	JEW'S MALLOW	(S)
Corchorus olitorius	JUTE	(TS)
Corchorus olitorius	MELUKHIE	(S)
Corchorus olitorius	TOSSA JUTE	(TH)
Cordia alliadora	ECUADOR LAUREL	(TS)
Cordia sebestana	CORDIA	(TT)
Cordia sebestana	GEIGER TREE	(TT)
Cordia sebestana	GERANIUM TREE	(TT)
Cordia sebestana	SPANISH CORDIA	(TT)
Cordia sebestena	ANACONOA	(TT)
Cordyline	CLUB PALM	(P)
Cordyline australis	CABBAGE PALM	(H)
Cordyline australis	CABBAGE TREE	(S)
Cordyline fruticosa	GOOD LUCK PLANT	(TH)
Cordyline fruticosa	GOOD-LUCK PLANT	(TH)
Cordyline fruticosa	TREE-OF-KINGS	(TH)
Cordyline terminalis	GOOD LUCK PLANT	(S)

Botanical	Common	Type
Corema album	PORTUGUESE CROWBERRY	(S)
Corema conradii	PLYMOUTH CROWBERRY	(S)
Coreopsis	TICKSEED	(H)
Coriandrum sativum	CORIANDER	(HB)
Coriaria myrtifolia	REDOUL	(S)
Cornus	DOGWOOD	(S)
Cornus alba	RED-BARKED DOGWOOD	(S)
Cornus alba	TARTARIAN DOGWOOD	(S)
Cornus alba 'Aurea'	GOLDEN DOGWOOD	(S)
Cornus alba 'Elegantissima'	SILVER VARIEGATED DOGWOOD	(S)
Cornus alba 'Sibirica'	WESTONBIRT DOGWOOD	(S)
Cornus alba 'Spaethii'	GOLDEN VARIEGATED DOGWOOD	(S)
Cornus alternifolia	PAGODA DOGWOOD	(S)
Cornus amomum	SILKY DOGWOOD	(S)
Cornus canadensis	BUNCH BERRY	(S)
Cornus canadensis	CREEPING DOGWOOD	(S)
Cornus capitata	BENTHAM'S CORNEL	(ST)
Cornus controversa	TABLE DOGWOOD	(ST)
Cornus controversa	WEDDING-CAKE TREE	(ST)
Cornus florida	AMERICAN BOXWOOD	(S/T)
Cornus florida	FLOWERING DOGWOOD	(S)
Cornus florida	NEW ENGLAND BOXWOOD	(S/T)
Cornus florida	VIRGINIA DOGWOOD	(S)
Cornus florida	WHITE DOGWOOD	(S)
Cornus florida 'Rainbow'	RAINBOW DOGWOOD	(S)
Cornus florida rubra	PINK DOGWOOD	(S)
Cornus kousa	JAPANESE DOGWOOD	(S)
Cornus kousa chinensis	CHINESE DOGWOOD	(S)
Cornus mas	CORNEL	(S)
Cornus mas	CORNELIAN CHERRY	(S)
Cornus nuttallii	NUTTALL'S DOGWOOD	(T)
Cornus nuttallii	PACIFIC DOGWOOD	(ST)
Cornus racemosa	GREY DOGWOOD	(S)
Cornus sanguinea	DOGBERRY	(S)
Cornus sangutnea	COMMON DOGWOOD	(S)
Cornus stolonifera	RED OSIER DOGWOOD	(S)
Cornus stolonifera 'Flaviramea'	YELLOW-STEMMED DOGWOOD	(S)
Corokia cotoneaster	WIRE NETTING BUSH	(S)
Coronilla coronata	SCORPION VETCH	(H)
Coronilla emerus	SCORPION SENNA	(S)
Coronilla varia	CROWN VETCH	(H)
Coronopus didymus	SWINE CRESS	(H)
Coronopus squamatus	SWINE CRESS	(H)
Correa	AUSTRALIAN FUCHSIA	(S)
Correa alba	BOTANY BAY TEA TREE	(S/T)
Corrigiola litoralis	STRAPWORT	(R)
Cortaderia	PAMPAS GRASS	(G)

Botanical	Common	Type
Cortaderia richardii	TOE-TOE	(G)
Coruphanthus vivpara bisbeerna	HENS AND CHICKEN	(CS)
Coryanthera flava	GOLDEN CASCADES	(S)
Coryanthes	BUCKET ORCHID	(O)
Coryanthes	HELMET FLOWER	(H)
Corydalis cava	BULBOUS CORYDALIS	(H)
Corydalis claviculata	CLIMBING FUMITORY	(H)
Corydalis formosa	TURKEY CORN	(H)
Corydalis lutea	YELLOW FUMITORY	(H)
Corydalis solida	BULBOUS FUMITORY	(H)
Corydalis solida	SOLID-TUBERED CORYDALIS	(H)
Corylopsis	COWSLIP BUSH	(S)
Corylopsis	WINTER HAZEL	(S)
Corylus	HAZEL NUT	(S.T)
Corylus americana	AMERICAN HAZEL	(T)
Corylus avellana	COB-NUT	(S)
Corylus avellana	COMMON HAZEL	(S)
Corylus avellana 'Aurea'	GOLDEN HAZEL	(S)
Corylus avellana 'Contorta'	CONTORTED HAZEL	(S)
Corylus avellana 'Contorta'	CORKSCREW HAZEL	(S)
Corylus avellana 'Contorta'	HARRY LAUDER'S WALKING STICK	(S)
Corylus avellana 'Heterophylla'	CUT-LEAVED HAZEL	(S)
Corylus chinensis	CHINESE HAZEL	(T)
Corylus colurna	TURKISH HAZEL	(T)
Corylus maxima	FILBERT	(F)
Corylus maxima 'Purpurea'	PURPLE-LEAF FILBERT	(S)
Corylus sieboldiana	JAPANESE HAZEL	(T)
Corylus tibetica	TIBETAN HAZEL	(T)
Corynanthera flava	GOLDEN CASCADES	(S)
Corynephorus canescens	GREY HAIR-GRASS	(G)
Corynocarpus	NEW ZEALAND LAUREL	(T)
Corynocarpus laevigata	KARAKA	(T)
Corypha umbraculifera	TALIPOT	(P)
Corypha umbraculifera	TALIPOT PALM	(P)
Coryphampha vivipara arizonica	BEEHIVE CACTUS	(CS)
Coryphantha muehlenfortii	ROBUST PINCUSHION	(CS)
Coryphantha runyonii	BIG NIPPLE CACTUS	(CS)
Coryphantha runyonii	DUMPLING CACTUS	(CS)
Coryphanthus echinus	HEDGEHOG-CORY CACTUS	(CS)
Cosmelia rubra	SPINDLE HEATH	(S)
Cosmos	COSMEA	(A)
Cosmos atrosanguineus	BLACK COSMOS	(H)
Cosmos atrosanguineus	CHOCOLATE COSMOS	(H)
Cosmos bipinnatus	MEXICAN ASTER	(A)
Costus	SPIRAL-FLAG	(H)
Costus afer	SPIRAL GINGER	(TH)
Costus speciosus	CRAPE GINGER	(TH)

Know Your Common Plant Names

Botanical	Common	Type
Costus speciosus	MALAY GINGER	(H)
Cotinus coggygria	SMOKE BUSH	(S)
Cotinus coggygria	SMOKE TREE	(S)
Cotinus coggygria	VENETIAN SUMACH	(S)
Cotinus coggygria	WIG TREE	(S)
Cotinus coggygria follis purpureis	BURNING BUSH	(S)
Cotinus coggygria 'Rubrifolius'	PURPLE SMOKE TREE	(S)
Cotinus obovatus	AMERICAN SMOKETREE	(S)
Cotinus obovatus	CHITAM WOOD	(S)
Cotoneaster	COTONEASTER	(ST)
Cotoneaster adpressus praecox	NAN SHAN	(S)
Cotoneaster apiculatus	CRANBERRY COTONEASTER	(S)
Cotoneaster horizontalis	HERRING-BONE COTONEASTER	(S)
Cotoneaster 'Hybridus Pendulus'	WEEPING COTONEASTER	(T)
Cotoneaster microphyllus	ROSE BOX	(S)
Cotoneaster simonsii	HIMALAYAN COTONEASTER	(S)
Cotula coronopifolia	BRASS BUTTONS	(R)
Cotula coronopifolia	BUTTONWEED	(H)
Cotyledon umbilicus	KIDNEYWORT	(H)
Cotyledon undulata	SILVER CROWN	(H)
Coula edulis	AFRICAN WALNUT	(TT)
Coumarouna odorata	TONKA BEAN	(V)
Couroupita guianensis	CANNON BALL TREE	(TT)
Couroupita guianensis	CARRION TREE	(TT)
Crambe maritima	SEA KALE	(H/V)
Crambe maritima	SEAKALE	(H)
Craspedia incana	SNOWY WOOLLYHEAD	(H)
Crassula falcata	AIRPLANE PROPELLOR PLANT	(HP)
Crassula ovata	FRIENDSHIP TREE	(CS)
Crassula ovata	JADE TREE	(CS)
Crassula ovata	MONEY TREE	(CS)
Crataegomespilus dardari	BRONVAUX MEDLAR	(T)
Crataegus altaica	ALTAI MOUNTAIN THORN	(T)
Crataegus azarolus	AZAROLE	(T)
Crataegus brachyacantha	POMETTE BLEUE	(T)
Crataegus crus-galli	COCKSPUR THORN	(T)
Crataegus douglasii	BLACK HAWTHORN	(T)
Crataegus flava	YELLOW HAW	(T)
Crataegus laciniata	ORIENTAL THORN	(T)
Crataegus laevigata	MAY	(ST)
Crataegus laevigata	MIDLAND HAWTHORN	(T)
Crataegus laevigata	TWO-STYLED HAWTHORN	(S/T)
Crataegus laevigata 'Alba Plena'	DOUBLE WHITE THORN	(T)
Crataegus laevigata 'Paul's Scarlet'	DOUBLE CRIMSON THORN	(T)
Crataegus laevigata 'Paul's Scarlet'	RED MAY	(T)
Crataegus laevigata 'Rosea'	DOUBLE PINK THORN	(T)
Crataegus mollis	DOWNY HAWTHORN	(T)

Know Your Common Plant Names

Botanical	Common	Type
Crataegus mollis	RED HAW	(T)
Crataegus monogyna	BREAD AND CHEESE	(T)
Crataegus monogyna	COMMON HAWTHORN	(ST)
Crataegus monogyna	HAWTHORN	(S.T)
Crataegus monogyna	MAY	(ST)
Crataegus monogyna	QUICK	(S)
Crataegus monogyna	QUICKTHORN	(S.T)
Crataegus monogyna	WHITETHORN	(ST)
Crataegus monogyna 'Biflora'	GLASTONBURY THORN	(T)
Crataegus monogyna 'Compacta'	DWARF HAWTHORN	(S)
Crataegus monogyna 'Pendula'	WEEPING THORN	(T)
Crataegus nigra	HUNGARIAN THORN	(T)
Crataegus pedicellata	SCARLET HAW	(T)
Crataegus phaenopyrum	WASHINGTON THORN	(T)
Crataegus prunifolia	BROAD-LEAVED COCKSPUR THORN	(T)
Crataegus prunifolia	FROSTED THORN	(T)
Crataegus submollis	EMMERSON'S THORN	(T)
Crataegus tanacetifolia	TANSY-LEAVED THORN	(T)
Crataegus tomentosa	PEAR THORN	(T)
Crataegus x lavallei	HYBRID COCKSPUR THORN	(T)
Crataera gynandra	GARLIC PEAR	(T)
Craterellus cornucopioides	HORN OF PLENTY	(FU)
Craterellus cornucopioides	TRUMPET OF DEATH	(FU)
Crepis	HAWK'S BEARD	(H)
Crepis biennis	GREATER HAWK'S BEARD	(H)
Crepis biennis	ROUGH HAWK'S BEARD	(B)
Crepis capillaris	SMOOTH HAWK'S BEARD	(A)
Crepis foetida	STINKING HAWK'S BEARD	(H)
Crepis incana	PINK DANDELION	(H)
Crepis mollis	NORTHERN HAWK'S BEARD	(H)
Crepis nicaeensis	FRENCH HAWK'S BEARD	(H)
Crepis paludosa	MARSH HAWK'S-BEARD	(H)
Crepis pygmaea	PYGMY HAWKSBEARD	(H)
Crepis vesicaria	BEAKED HAWK'S BEARD	(B)
Crescentia cujete	CALABASH TREE	(T)
Crinodendron hookerianum	LANTERN TREE	(S)
Crinum	SPIDER LILY	(BB)
Crinum americanum	SWAMP LILY	(BB)
Crinum asiaticum	ASIATIC POISON BULB	(BB)
Crinum powellii	ELEPHANT LILY	(BB)
Crinum x powellii	CAPE LILY	(BB)
Crinum x powellii	INDIAN ELEPHANT FLOWER	(BB)
Crithmum maritimum	ROCK SAMPHIRE	(R)
Crithmum maritimum	SAMPHIRE	(H)
Crithmum maritimum	SEA FENNEL	(H)
Crocosmia	MONTBRETIA	(BB)
Crocus angustifolius	CLOTH-OF-GOLD CROCUS	(BB)

Botanical	Common	Type
Crocus biflorus	SCOTCH CROCUS	(BB)
Crocus flavus	DUTCH YELLOW CROCUS	(BB)
Crocus korolkowii	CELANDINE CROCUS	(BB)
Crocus sativus	SAFFRON	(BB)
Crossandra	FIRECRACKER FLOWER	(HP)
Crossandra	FIRECRACKER PLANT	(HP)
Crotalaria	RATTLE-BOX	(S)
Crotalaria agatiflora	CANARY-BIRD BUSH	(S)
Crotalaria cunninghamii	GREEN BIRDFLOWER	(S)
Crotalaria cunninghamii	GREENBIRD FLOWER	(S)
Crotalaria juncea	SUNN HEMP	(S)
Croton cascarilla	WILD ROSEMARY	(S)
Croton eleuteria	CASCARILLA	(TS)
Crucianella ciliata	CROSSWORT	(R)
Cruciata ciliata	CROSSWORT	(H)
Cruciata laevipes	CROSSWORT	(H)
Cryptanthus bivittatus	EARTH STAR	(HP)
Cryptocoryne	WATER TRUMPET	(WP)
Cryptogramma crispa	PARSLEY FERN	(FN)
Cryptomeria japonica	JAPANESE CEDAR	(C)
Cryptomeria japonica	JAPANESE RED CEDAR	(C)
Cryptostegia	RUBBER VINE	(HP)
Ctenanthe oppenheimiana	NEVER NEVER PLANT	(HP)
Cucubalus baccifer	BERRY CATCHFLY	(H)
Cucumis anguria	WEST INDIAN GHERKIN	(F)
Cucumis dipsaceus	HEDGEHOG GOURD	(F)
Cucumis dipsaceus	TEASEL GOURD	(F)
Cucumis flexuosum	SERPENT MELON	(V)
Cucumis melo	CANTALOUPE (MELON)	(V)
Cucumis melo	MELON	(F)
Cucumis melo	MUSKMELON	(F)
Cucumis melo dudaim	CANARY MELON	(F)
Cucumis metuliferus	HORNY CUCUMBER	(H)
Cucumis metuliferus	KIWANO	(H)
Cucumis sativus	CUCUMBER	(V)
Cucumis sativus	GHERKIN	(V)
Cucurbita, Lagenaria, Cucumis	GOURD	(V)
Cucurbita pepo	PUMPKIN	(V)
Cucurbita pepo	SQUASH	(V)
Cucurbita pepo ovifera	COURGETTE	(V)
Cucurbita pepo ovifera	MARROW	(V)
Cucurbita pepo ovifera	VEGETABLE MARROW	(V)
Cucurbita pepo styriaca	PUMPKIN NUTS	(V)
Cudrania tricuspidata	CHINESE SILKWORM THORN	(T)
Cudrania tricuspidata	SILK-WORM THORN	(T)
Cuminum cyminum	CUMIN	(HB)
Cunila mariana	DITANY	(H)

Know Your Common Plant Names

Botanical	Common	Type
Cunila origanoides	MARYLAND DITTANY	(H)
Cunila origanoides	STONE MINT	(H)
Cunninghamia lanceolata	CHINA-FIR	(C)
Cunninghamia lanceolata	CHINESE FIR	(C)
Cunonia capensis	AFRICAN RED ALDER	(TT)
Cunonia capensis	ROOIELS	(T)
Cunonia capensis	SPOON TREE	(T)
Cuphea	WAXWEED	(HP)
Cuphea ignea	CIGAR PLANT	(HP)
Cupressocyparis leylandii	LEYLAND CYPRESS	(C)
Cupressus abramsiana	SANTA CRUZ CYPRESS	(C)
Cupressus bakeri	MODOC CYRPRESS	(C)
Cupressus cashmeriana	KASHMIR CYPRESS	(C)
Cupressus duclouxiana	BHUTAN CYPRESS	(C)
Cupressus forbesii	TECATE CYPRESS	(C)
Cupressus funebris	CHINESE WEEPING CYPRESS	(C)
Cupressus funebris	MOURNING CYPRESS	(C)
Cupressus glabra	SMOOTH ARIZONA CYPRESS	(C)
Cupressus goveniana	GOWEN CYPRESS	(C)
Cupressus guadalupensis	TECATE CYPRESS	(C)
Cupressus lusitanica	CEDAR OF GOA	(C)
Cupressus lusitanica	MEXICAN CYPRESS	(C)
Cupressus macrocarpa	MONTEREY CYPRESS	(C)
Cupressus sempervirens	ITALIAN CYPRESS	(C)
Cupressus torulosa	BHUTAN CYPRESS	(C)
Cupressus torulosa	HIMALAYAN CYPRESS	(C)
Cupressus/Chamaecyparis	CYPRESS	(C)
Curcuma	TURMERIC	(F)
Curcuma angustifolia	EAST INDIAN ARROWROOT	(TS)
Curcuma longa	TURMERIC	(V)
Curcuma zedoaria	ZEDOARY	(H)
Cureuligo	WEEVIL PLANT	(H)
Curtisia	ASSEGAI WOOD	(TT)
Curtonus	AUNT ELIZA	(H)
Cuscuta campestris	FIELD DODDER	(CL)
Cuscuta epithymum	COMMON DODDER	(CL)
Cuscuta epithymum	DODDER	(H)
Cuscuta europaea	GREATER DODDER	(CL)
Cusparia febrifuga	ANGOSTURA	(TT)
Cussonia paniculata	MOUNTAIN KIEPERSOL	(S)
Cyanotis kewensis	TEDDY BEAR PLANT	(HP)
Cyanotis somaliensis	PUSSY EARS	(H)
Cyathea	TREE FERN	(FN)
Cyathea dealbata	SILVER KING FERN	(FN)
Cyathodes glauca	CHEESEBERRY	(S)
Cycas circinalis	FERN PALM	(P)
Cycas revoluta	JAPANESE SAGO PALM	(P)

Know Your Common Plant Names

Botanical	Common	Type
Cycas revoluta	SAGO PALM	(P)(F)
Cyclamen	SOWBREAD	(BB)
Cyclamen persicum	FLORIST'S CYCLAMEN	(HP)
Cyclanthera pedata	ACHOCHA	(TS)
Cydonia oblonga	COMMON QUINCE	(T)'
Cydonia oblonga	QUINCE	(T.T)
Cymbalaria	CLIMBIMG SAILOR	(H)
Cymbalaria muralis	IVY-LEAVED TOADFLAX	(H)
Cymbalaria muralis	KENILWORTH IVY	(H)
Cymbalaria muralis	PENNYWORT	(H)
Cymbopogon citratus	LEMON GRASS	(G)
Cymbopogon nardus	CITRONELLA	(G)
Cymbopogon nardus	CITRONELLA GRASS	(G)
Cynara cardunculus	CARDOON	(V)
Cynara scoymus	GLOBE ARTICHOKE	(VH)
Cynodon dactylon	BERMUDA GRASS	(G)
Cynoglossum germanicum	GREEN HOUND'S TONGUE	(H)
Cynoglossum officinale	HOUND'S TONGUE	(H)
Cynosurus	DOG'S TAIL	(G)
Cynosurus cristatus	CRESTED DOG'S TAIL	(G)
Cynura sarmentosa	PURPLE PASSION VINE	(HP)
Cyperus alternifolius	UMBRELLA GRASS	(G)
Cyperus alternifolius	UMBRELLA PALM	(G)
Cyperus articulatus	ADRUE	(G)
Cyperus articulatus	GUINEA RUSH	(G)
Cyperus esculentus	CHUFA	(G)
Cyperus esculentus	CHUFFA	(G)
Cyperus esculentus	TIGER NUT	(G)
Cyperus longus	GALINGALE	(G)
Cyperus longus	SWEET GALINGALE	(G)
Cyperus papyrus	EGYPTIAN PAPER PLANT	(G)
Cyperus papyrus	EGYPTIAN PAPER RUSH	(G)
Cyperus papyrus	PAPER PLANT	(G)
Cyperus papyrus	PAPER REED	(G)
Cyperus papyrus	PAPYRUS	(G)
Cyperus rotundus	NUT GRASS	(G)
Cyperus tagetiformis	CHINESE MAT GRASS	(G)
Cyphomandra betacea	TREE TOMATO	(TT)
Cyphomandra betacea	TREE-TOMATO	(TT)
Cypridium calceolus	LADY'S SLIPPER	(O)
Cypripedium	MOCCASIN FLOWER	(O)
Cypripedium	NERVE ROOT	(O)
Cypripedium japonicum	JAPANESE LADY'S SLIPPER	(O)
Cyrilla racemiflora	LEATHERWOOD	(S)
Cyrtanthus purpureus	SCARBOROUGH LILY	(BB)
Cyrtostachys lakka	SEALING WAX PALM	(P)
Cyrtostachys renda	SEALING-WAX PALM	(P)

Botanical	Common	Type
Cystopteris	BLADDER FERN	(FN)
Cystopteris fragilis	BRITTLE BLADDER FERN	(FN)
Cystopteris montana	MOUNTAIN BLADDER FERN	(FN)
Cytisus battandieri	MOROCCAN BROOM	(S)
Cytisus battandieri	PINEAPPLE BROOM	(S)
Cytisus, Genista	BROOM	(S)
Cytisus grandiflorus	WOOLLY-PODDED BROOM	(S)
Cytisus monspessulanus	MONTPELIER BROOM	(S)
Cytisus multiflorus	WHITE SPANISH BROOM	(S)
Cytisus multiflorus (albus)	WHITE PORTUGAL BROOM	(S)
Cytisus palmensis	TAGASASTE	(S)
Cytisus proliferus	ESCABON	(S)
Cytisus purpureus	PURPLE BROOM	(S)
Cytisus scoparius	COMMON BROOM	(S)
Cytisus x praecox	WARMINSTER BROOM	(S)
Daboecia cantabrica	CONNEMARA HEATH	(S)
Daboecia cantabrica	IRISH HEATH	(S)
Daboecia cantabrica	ST. DABOEC'S HEATH	(S)
Dacrycarpus dacrydioides	KAHIKATEA	(C)
Dacrycarpus dacrydioides	NEW ZEALAND WHITE PINE	(C)
Dacrydium	WESTLAND PINE	(C)
Dacrydium bidwillii	MOUNTAIN PINE	(C)
Dacrydium colensoi	WESTLAND PINE	(C)
Dacrydium cupressinum	RED PINE	(C)
Dacrydium cupressinum	RIMU	(C)
Dacrydium cupressinum	RIMU PINE	(C)
Dacrydium intermedium	YELLOW SILVER PINE	(C)
Dactylis glomerata	COCK'S FOOT GRASS	(G)
Dactylis glomerata	COCKSFOOT	(G)
Dactylis glomerata	ORCHARD GRASS	(G)
Dactylorhiza fuchsii	COMMON SPOTTED ORCHID	(O)
Dactylorhiza incarnata	EARLY MARSH ORCHID	(O)
Dactylorhiza incarnata	MEADOW ORCHID	(O)
Dactylorhiza maculata	HEATH SPOTTED ORCHID	(O)
Dactylorhiza majalis	BROAD-LEAVED MARSH ORCHID	(O)
Dactylorhiza praetermissa	SOUTHERN MARSH ORCHID	(O)
Dactylorhiza purpurella	NORTHERN MARSH ORCHID	(O)
Daemomorops draco	DRAGON'S BLOOD	(TS)
Dahlia juarezii	CACTUS DAHLIA	(A)
Dahlia merckii	BEDDING DAHLIA	(A)
Dais cotonifolia	POSY BUSH	(TS)
Dalbergia	ROSEWOOD	(TT)
Dalbergia latifolia	BLACK WOOD	(TT)
Damasonium alisma	STAR FRUIT	(S)
Danae racemosa	ALEXANDRIAN LAUREL	(S)
Danthonia decumbens	HEATH GRASS	(G)
Daphne aurantiaca	GOLDEN-FLOWERED DAPHNE	(S)

Botanical	Common	Type
Daphne cneorum	GARLAND FLOWER	(S)
Daphne laureleola	SPURGE LAUREL	(S)
Daphne mezereum	MEZEREON	(S)
Daphne odora	WINTER DAPHNE	(S)
Darlingtonia	CALIFORNIAN PITCHER PLANT	(H)
Darlingtonia californica	COBRA LILY	(HP)
Darmera peltatum	UMBRELLA PLANT	(H)
Dartonia	BLAZING STAR	(H)
Dasylirion leiophyllum	DESERT CANDLE	(CS)
Dasylirion leiophyllum	SOTOL	(CS)
Dasylirion leiophyllum	SPOON PLANT	(CS)
Dasypogon bromeliaefolius	PINEAPPLE BUSH	(S)
Datisca	BASTARD HEMP	(H)
Datura	TRUMPET FLOWER	(H)
Datura meteloides	TOLOACHI	(H)
Datura stramonium	DEVIL'S APPLE	(H)
Datura stramonium	JAMESTOWN WEED	(H)
Datura stramonium	JIMSON WEED	(H)
Datura stramonium	MAD APPLE	(S)
Datura stramonium	THORN APPLE	(A)
Daucus carota	QUEEN ANNE'S LACE	(V)
Daucus carota	WILD CARROT	(H)
Daucus carota sativus	CARROT	(V)
Daucus carota sativus	CULTIVATED CARROT	(V)
Davallia bullata	SQUIRREL'S FOOT FERN	(FN)
Davallia canariensis	DEERSFOOT FERN	(FN)
Davallia canariensis	RABBIT'S FOOT FERN	(FN)
Davallia fejeensis	HARE'S FOOT FERN	(FN)
Davallia fejeensis	RABBIT'S FOOT FERN	(FN)
Davidia involucrata	DOVE TREE	(T)
Davidia involucrata	GENTLEMAN'S POCKET HANDKERCHEIF TREE	(T)
Davidia involucrata	GHOST TREE	(T)
Davidia involucrata	HANDKERCHIEF TREE	(T)
Davidia involucrata	LADIES HANDKERCHIEF	(T)
Davidia involucrata	LADY'S POCKET HANDKERCHIEF TREE	(T)
Davidia involucrata	POCKET HANDKERCHIEF TREE	(T)
Davidsonia pruriens	QUEENSLAND ITCH TREE	(T)
Daviesia	AUSTRALIAN HOP	(S)
Daviesia acicularis	OUCH BUSH	(S)
Daviesia pachyphylla	OUCH BUSH	(S)
Decodon	WATER WILLOW	(H)
Delonix regia	FANCY ANNY	(TT)
Delonix regia	FLAMBOYANT	(TT)
Delonix regia	FLAMBOYANT TREE	(T.T)
Delonix regia	FLAME OF THE FOREST	(T.T.)
Delonix regia	FLAME TREE	(T.T.)
Delonix regia	GULMOHUR	(TT)

Know Your Common Plant Names

Botanical	Common	Type
Delonix regia	PEACOCK FLOWER	(TT)
Delonix regia	POINCIANA	(TT)
Delonix regia	ROYAL POINCIANA	(TT)
Delphinium cardinale	SCARLET LARKSPUR	(H)
Delphinium nudicaule	CHRISTMAS-HORNS	(H)
Delphinium staphisagria	STAVESACRE	(H)
Dendranthema	FLORIST'S CHRYSANTHEMUM	(A)
Dendrocalamus	GIANT BAMBOO	(G)
Dendrochilum glumaceum	SILVER CHAIN	(O)
Dendromecon rigidum	TREE POPPY	(S)
Dendroseris macrophylla	TREE DANDELION	(H)
Dendrosicyos socotrana	CUCUMBER TREE OF SOCOTRA	(TT)
Dennstaedtia	CUP FERN	(FN)
Dentaria	PEPPER ROOT	(H)
Dentaria	TOOTHWORT	(H)
Dentaria bulbifera	CORAL-WORT	(S)
Deschampsia caespitosa	TUFTED HAIR-GRASS	(G)
Deschampsia flexuosa	WAVY HAIR-GRASS	(G)
Deschampsia setacea	DOG HAIR-GRASS	(G)
Descurainia sophia	FLIXWEED	(H)
Desmarestia spp	SEA SORREL	(SW)
Desmazeria rigida	FERN GRASS	(G)
Desmodium	TICK CLOVER	(S)
Desmodium	TICK TREFOIL	(S)
Desmodium gyrans	TELEGRAPH PLANT	(A)
Desmodium motorium	TELEGRAPH PLANT	(S)
Deutzia	DEUTZIA	(S)
Deutzia gracilis	JAPANESE SNOW-FLOWER	(S)
Dianella	FLAX LILY	(H)
Dianella	FLAX-LILY	(BB)
Dianthus	FLOWER OF THE GODS	(H/R)
Dianthus	PINK	(HR)
Dianthus allwoodii	MODERN PINK	(H)
Dianthus alpinus	ALPINE PINK	(R)
Dianthus armeria	DEPTFORD PINK	(H)
Dianthus barbatus	SWEET WILLIAM	(B)
Dianthus caryophyllus	BORDER CARNATION	(A)
Dianthus caryophyllus	CARNATION	(H)
Dianthus caryophyllus	CLOVE PINK	(H)
Dianthus caryophyllus	COTTAGE PINK	(H)
Dianthus caryophyllus	GILLY FLOWER	(H)
Dianthus caryophyllus	PICOTEE	(H)
Dianthus chinensis	ANNUAL PINK	(A)
Dianthus chinensis	INDIAN PINK	(A)
Dianthus deltoides	MAIDEN PINK	(R)
Dianthus glacialis	GLACIER PINK	(H)
Dianthus gratianopolitanus	CHEDDAR PINK	(R)

Know Your Common Plant Names

Botanical	Common	Type
Dianthus plumarius	BORDER PINK	(H)
Dianthus plumarius	GRASS PINK	(A)
Dianthus plumarius	WILD PINK	(R)
Dianthus sinensis	CHINESE PINK	(A)
Dianthus superbus	LARGE PINK	(H)
Dicentra	BLEEDING HEART	(H)
Dicentra	DIELYTRA	(H)
Dicentra	DUTCHMAN'S BREECHES	(H)
Dicentra canadensis	SQUIRREL CORN	(H)
Dicentra canadensis	SQUIRREL-CORN	(H)
Dicentra canadensis	STAGGERWEED	(H)
Dicentra canadensis	TURKEY CORN	(H)
Dicentra canadensis	TURKEY PEA	(H)
Dicentra chrysantha	GOLDEN EARDROPS	(H)
Dicentra spectabilis	CHINAMAN'S BREECHES	(H)
Dicentra spectabilis	LADIES LOCKET	(H)
Dicentra spectabilis	LADY'S LOCKET	(H)
Dicentra spectabilis	LYRE FLOWER	(H)
Dichanthium ischaemum	DOGSTOOTH GRASS	(G)
Dichelostemma ida-maia	FLORAL FIRECRACKER	(H)
Dichorisandra reginae	QUEEN'S SPIDERWORT	(HP)
Dichorisandra reginae	QUEENS SPIDERWORT	(HP)
Dicksonia	TREE FERN	(FN)
Dicksonia antarctica	WOOLLY TREE FERN	(FN)
Dicksonia fibrosa	GOLDEN TREE FERN	(FN)
Dicksonia squarrosa	NEW ZEALAND TREE FERN	(FN)
Dictamnus	BURNING BUSH	(H)
Dictamnus	DITTANY	(H)
Dictamnus alpus	FRAXINELLA	(H)
Dictamus	GAS PLANT	(H)
Didiscus caeruleus	BLUE LACE FLOWER	(H/A)
Dieffenbachia	DUMB CANE	(HP)
Dieffenbachia	LEOPARD'S LILY	(HP)
Dierama	ANGELS FISHING ROD	(H)
Dierama	WAND FLOWER	(H)
Diervilla	BUSH-HONEYSUCKLE	(S)
Digitalis	FOX-GLOVE	(H)
Digitalis ferruginea	RUSTY FOXGLOVE	(H)
Digitalis grandiflora	LARGE YELLOW FOXGLOVE	(H)
Digitalis lanata	WOOLLY FOXGLOVE	(H)
Digitalis lutea	SMALL YELLOW FOXGLOVE	(H)
Digitalis purpurea	DEAD MEN'S BELLS	(H)
Digitalis purpurea	FAIRY THIMBLES	(B)
Digitalis purpurea	LADY'S GLOVE	(H)
Digitalis purpurea	WITCHES GLOVES	(B)
Digitaria	FINGER-GRASS	(G)
Digitaria ischaemum	SMOOTH FINGER-GRASS	(G)

Know Your Common Plant Names

Botanical	Common	Type
Dillenia indica	ELEPHANT APPLE	(TT)
Dillenia indica	HONDAPARA	(S)
Dimorphotheca	CAPE MARIGOLD	(H)
Dimorphotheca	STAR OF THE VELDT	(AH)
Dimorphotheca, osteospermum	AFRICAN DAISY	(H)
Dimorphotheca pluvialis	NAMAQUALAND DAISY	(H)
Dimorphotheca pluvialis	RAIN DAISY	(H)
Dimorphotheca sinuata	NAMAQUALAND DAISY	(A)
Dionaea muscipula	VENUS FLY TRAP	(HP)
Dioon edule	VIRGIN'S PALM	(TS)
Dioscorea	YAM	(F)
Dioscorea alata	GREATER YAM	(F)
Dioscorea alata	WHITE YAM	(V)
Dioscorea batatas	CHINESE YAM	(V)
Dioscorea bulbifera	POTATO YAM	(F)
Dioscorea cayenensis	YELLOW YAM	(F)
Dioscorea discolor	ORNAMENTAL YAM	(F)
Dioscorea elephantipes	ELEPHANT'S FOOT	(F)
Dioscorea elephantipes	HOTTENTOT BREAD	(F)
Dioscorea elephantipes	TORTOISE PLANT	(F)
Dioscorea mexicana	MEXICAN YAM	(F)
Dioscorea rotundata	WHITE GUINEA YAM	(V)
Dioscorea villosa	WILD YAM	(F)
Diospyros ebenum	CEYLON EBONY	(TT)
Diospyros ebenum	EAST INDIAN EBONY	(TT)
Diospyros ebenum	EBONY	(T)
Diospyros kaki	CHINESE PERSIMMON	(T)
Diospyros kaki	JAPANESE PERSIMMON	(T)
Diospyros kaki	KAKI	(T)
Diospyros kaki	PERSIMMON	(T)
Diospyros kurzii	ANDAMAN MARBLE	(TT)
Diospyros kurzii	ZEBRA WOOD	(TT)
Diospyros lotus	DATE PLUM	(T)
Diospyros melanoxylon	COROMANDEL EBONY	(TT)
Diospyros mespiliformis	LAGOS EBONY	(TT)
Diospyros mespiliformis	WEST AFRICAN EBONY	(TT)
Diospyros monbuttensis	WALKING STICK EBONY	(TT)
Diospyros monbuttensis	YORUBA EBONY	(TT)
Diospyros virginiana	AMERICAN PERSIMMON	(T)
Diospyros virginiana	PERSIMMON	(T)
Diospyros whyteana	BLACK-BARK	(TT)
Diospyros whyteana	BLADDER-NUT	(TT)
Diotis candidissima	COTTON-WEED	(H)
Diphylleia cymosa	UMBRELLA LEAF	(H)
Diplarrhena moraea	BUTTERFLY FLAG	(H)
Diplotaxis erucoides	WHITE ROCKET	(H)
Diplotaxis muralis	ANNUAL WALL ROCKET	(A)

Botanical	Common	Type
Diplotaxis tenuifolia	PERENNIAL WALL ROCKET	(H)
Diplotaxis tenuifolia	WALL MUSTARD	(H)
Diplotaxis tenuifolia	WALL ROCKET	(H)
Dipsacus fullonum	COMMON TEASEL	(H)
Dipsacus fullonum	TEASEL	(B)
Dipsacus fullonum sativus	FULLER'S TEASEL	(H)
Dipsacus pilosus	SMALL TEASEL	(H)
Dipterocarpus sp.	KERVING	(TT)
Dipterocarpus sp.	OPITONG	(TT)
Dipteryx odorata	TONKA BEAN	(V)
Dipteryx oppositifolia	TONKA BEAN	(V)
Dirca palustris	LEATHERWOOD	(S)
Discaria toumatou	WILD IRISHMAN	(S)
Disporum	FAIRYBELLS	(H)
Disporum trachycarpum	FAIRYBELLS	(H)
Distictis buccinatoria	MEXICAN BLOOD FLOWER	(CL)
Dittrichia graveolens	STINK ASTER	(H)
Dizygotheca	FALSE ARALIA	(HP)
Dizygotheca	FINGER ARALIA	(HP)
Dodecatheon	AMERICAN COWSLIP	(R)
Dodecatheon	SHOOTING STAR	(R)
Dombeya wallichii	PINK BALL TREE	(TS)
Dombeya x cayeuxii	PINK SNOWBALL	(T)
Dorema ammoniacum	AMMONIACUM	(T)
Dorema ammoniacum	GUM AMMONIAC	(S)
Doronicum pardalianches	GREAT LEOPARD'S BANE	(H)
Doronicum pardalianches	LEOPARD'S BANE	(H)
Dorotheanthus bellidiformis	LIVINGSTONE DAISY	(A)
Doryalis caffra	KEI APPLE	(TS)
Doryanthes	SPEAR LILY	(H)
Doryanthes excelsa	AUSTRALIAN GIANT LILY	(BB)
Doxantha unguis-cato	CAT'S CLAW	(S)
Draba	NAILWORT	(R)
Draba	WHITLOW GRASS	(H)
Draba aizoides	YELLOW WHITLOW GRASS	(H)
Draba incana	HOARY WHITLOW GRASS	(H)
Draba norvegica	ROCK WHITLOW GRASS	(R)
Dracaena draco	DRAGON TREE	(HP)
Dracaena marginata	MADAGASCAR DRAGON TREE	(HP)
Dracaena sanderiana	RIBBON PLANT	(S)
Dracocephalum	DRAGONHEAD	(H)
Dracocephalum moldavica	MOLDAVIAN BALM	(H)
Dracocephalum ruyschiana	NORTHERN DRAGONHEAD	(H)
Dracunculus	DRAGON PLANT	(H)
Dracunculus vulgaris	DRAGON ARUM	(H)
Drimys lanceolata	MOUNTAIN PEPPER	(S)
Drimys winteri	WINTER'S BARK	(S)

Know Your Common Plant Names

Botanical	Common	Type
Drosera	SUNDEW	(H)
Drosera anglica	GREAT SUNDEW	(H)
Drosera capensis	CAPE SUNDEW	(H)
Dryas octopetala	MOUNTAIN AVENS	(R)
Dryobalanops	KAPUR	(TT)
Dryopteris	BUCKLER FERN	(FN)
Dryopteris	WOOD FERN	(F)
Dryopteris aemula	HAY-SCENTED BUCKLER FERN	(FN)
Dryopteris borreri	GOLDEN-SCALED MALE FERN	(FN)
Dryopteris cristata	CRESTED BUCKLER FERN	(FN)
Dryopteris dilatata	BROAD BUCKLER FERN	(FN)
Dryopteris dilatata	FLORIST'S FERN	(FN)
Dryopteris erythosora	JAPANESE SHIELD FERN	(FN)
Dryopteris filix-mas	MALE FERN	(FN)
Dryopteris fragrans	FRAGRANT BUCKLER FERN	(FN)
Dryopteris goldiana	GIANT WOOD FERN	(FN)
Dryopteris marginalis	LEATHERWOOD FERN	(FN)
Dryopteris oreades	MOUNTAIN MALE FERN	(FN)
Dryopteris submontana	RIGID BUCKLER FERN	(FN)
Duboisia myoporoides	CORKWOOD TREE	(T)
Duboisia myoporoides	PITURI	(H)
Duchesnea indica	INDIAN STRAWBERRY	(F)
Duchesnea indica	MOCK STRAWBERRY	(H)
Duranta repens	PIGEON BERRY	(S)
Duranta repens	SKYFLOWER	(S)
Durio zibathinus	DURIAN	(F)
Duvernoia adhatodioides	PISTOL BUSH	(S)
Duvernoia adhatodoides	SNAKE BUSH	(S)
Eccremocarpus	CHILEAN GLORY FLOWER	(CL)
Eccremocarpus	GLORY FLOWER	(CL)
Echallium elaterium	SQUIRTING CUCUMBER	(HB)
Echeveria derenbergii	PAINTED LADY	(CS)
Echinacea angustifloria	KANSAS NIGGERHEAD	(H)
Echinacea purpurea	BLACK SAMSON	(H)
Echinacea purpurea	PURPLE CONEFLOWER	(H)
Echinocactus	EAGLES CLAW	(CS)
Echinocactus ferocactus	HEDGEHOG CACTUS	(S)
Echinocactus grunsonii	GOLDEN BARREL CACTUS	(C)
Echinocactus grusonii	BARREL CACTUS	(CS)
Echinocactus grusonii	GOLDEN BALL	(CS)
Echinocactus grusonii	MOTHER-IN-LAWS SEAT	(CS)
Echinocactus pectinatus	HEDGEHOG CACTUS	(S)
Echinocereus	HEDGEHOG CACTUS	(CS)
Echinocereus dasyacanthus	TEXAS RAINBOW CACTUS	(CS)
Echinocereus dubius	PURPLE PITAYA	(CS)
Echinocereus enneacanthus	ARIZONA RAINBOW HEDGEHOG	(CS)
Echinocereus enneacanthus	PITAYA	(CS)

Know Your Common Plant Names

Botanical	Common	Type
Echinocereus enneacanthus	STRAWBERRY CACTUS	(CS)
Echinocereus fendleri robustus	ROBUST HEDGEHOG	(CS)
Echinocereus horizinthalonius	BLUE BARREL	(CS)
Echinocereus pectinatus	RAINBOW CACTUS	(CS)
Echinocereus pentalophus	LADY FINGER CACTUS	(CS)
Echinocereus schmollii	LAMB'S TAIL CACTUS	(CS)
Echinocerous viridiflorous	GREEN-FLOWERED PITAYA	(CS)
Echinocerous viridiflorous	GREEN-FLOWERED TORCH CACTUS	(CS)
Echinochlea crus-galli	JAPANESE MILLET	(G)
Echinochloa	HEDGEHOG GRASS	(G)
Echinochloa crus-galli	COCKSPUR	(G)
Echinocystis lobata	PRICKLY CUCUMBER	(H)
Echinops	GLOBE THISTLE	(H)
Echinopsis	THISTLE GLOBE	(CS)
Echinopsis multiplex	SEA URCHIN CACTUS	(CS)
Echites andrewsii	SAVANNAH FLOWER	(A)
Echium	ANNUAL BORAGE	(A)
Echium fastuosum	PRIDE OF MADEIRA	(TS)
Echium plantagineum	PURPLE BUGLOSS	(H)
Echium vulgare	BLUE WEED	(A)
Echium vulgare	VIPER'S BUGLOSS	(H)
Ectocarpus spp	MAIDEN HAIR	(SW)
Edgeworthia	PAPER BUSH	(S)
Eichhornia crassipes	WATER HYACINTH	(WP)
Elaeagnus angustifolia	OLEASTER	(ST)
Elaeagnus angustifolia	RUSSIAN OLIVE	(ST)
Elaeagnus commutata	SILVER BERRY	(S)
Elaeagnus multiflora	CHERRY ELAEAGNUS	(S)
Elaeagnus umbellata	AUTUMN OLIVE	(S)
Elaeis guineensis	OIL PALM	(P)
Elaeocarpus reticulatus	BLUEBERRY ASH	(S)
Elaeocarpus serratus	CEYLON OLIVE	(TT)
Elatine hexandra	WATERWORT	(WP)
Eleocharis	SPIKE RUSH	(G)
Eleocharis acicularis	NEEDLE SPIKE-RUSH	(G)
Eleocharis effusum	SAW GRASS	(G)
Eleocharis palustris	COMMON SPIKE-RUSH	(G)
Eleocharis tuberosa	CHINESE WATER CHESTNUT	(G)
Eleocharis uniglumis	SLENDER SPIKE-RUSH	(G)
Eleusine sp.	MILLET	(V)G.
Eleutherococcus senticosus	SIBERIAN GINSENG	(S)
Elletaria cardamomum	CARDAMON	(HP)
Elodea	DITCHMOSS	(WP)
Elodea callitrichoides	GREATER WATER-THYME	(WP)
Elodea canadensis	CANADIAN PONDWEED	(WP)
Elodea nuttallii	NUTTALL'S WATER-THYME	(WP)
Elsholtzia stauntonii	MINT BUSH	(S)

Know Your Common Plant Names

Botanical	Common	Type
Elymus	WILD RYE	(G)
Elymus arenarius	LYME GRASS	(G)
Elymus caninus	BEARDED COUCH	(G)
Elymus farctus	SAND COUCH	(G)
Elymus pycnanthus	SEA COUCH	(G)
Elymus repens	COMMON COUCH	(G)
Elymus repens	COUCH GRASS	(G)
Elymus repens	CREEPING TWITCH	(G)
Elymus repens	DOG-GRASS	(G)
Elymus repens	TWITCH	(G)
Elymus repens	WITCH-GRASS	(G)
Embelia ribes	EMBELIA	(H)
Embothrium	CHILEAN FIRE BUSH	(T)
Emilia javanica	TASSEL FLOWER	(H)
Emilia sagittata	TASSEL FLOWER	(H)
Emmenanthe	CALIFORNIA GOLDEN BELLS	(A)
Emmenanthe penduliflora	CALIFORNIAN WHISPERING BELLS	(H)
Empetrum nigrum	CROWBERRY	(H)
Empetrum rubrum	SOUTH AMERICAN CROWBERRY	(S)
Encephalartos altensteinii	BREAD TREE	(FN)
Enchylaena tomentosa	RUBY SALTBUSH	(TS)
Endymion hispanicus	SPANISH BLUEBELL	(BB)
Enseta ventricosa	ABYSSINIAN BANANA	(F)
Entada scandens	SWORD BEAN	(H)
Entandophragma	SAPELE	(TT)
Entandrophragma cylindricum	SAPELE	(TT)
Entermorpha	STONE HAIR	(SW)
Eomecon chionanthe	SNOW POPPY	(H)
Epacris impressa	AUSTRALIAN HEATH	(S)
Eperua falcata	WALLABA	(TT)
Ephedera spp	DESERT TEA	(S)
Ephedera vulgaris	MA HUANG	(S)
Ephedra distachya	EUROPEAN SHRUBBY HORSETAIL	(S)
Ephedra distachya	JOINT PINE	(H)
Ephedra nevadensis	MORMON TEA	(H)
Epigaea repens	GROUND LAUREL	(S)
Epigaea repens	MAYFLOWER	(S)
Epigaea repens	TRAILING ARBUTUS	(S)
Epilobium	WILLOW HERB	(HA)
Epilobium alsinifolium	CHICKWEED WILLOWHERB	(H)
Epilobium angustifolium	FIREWEED	(A.H)
Epilobium angustifolium	ROSEBAY WILLOW-HERB	(A)
Epilobium brunnescens	NEW ZEALAND WILLOW HERB	(H)
Epilobium ciliatum	AMERICAN WILLOWHERB	(H)
Epilobium hirsutum	CODLINS AND CREAM	(H)
Epilobium hirsutum	GREAT WILLOWHERB	(H)
Epilobium lanceolatum	SPEAR-LEAVED WILLOWHERB	(H)

Know Your Common Plant Names

Botanical	Common	Type
Epilobium montanum	BROAD-LEAVED WILLOW HERB	(H)
Epilobium obcordatum	ROCK FRINGE	(H)
Epilobium obcordatum	ROCK-FRINGE	(H)
Epilobium palustra	MARSH WILLOWHERB	(H)
Epilobium parviflorum	HAIRY WILLOW HERB	(H)
Epilobium parviflorum	HOARY WILLOWHERB	(H)
Epilobium roseum	PALE WILLOWHERB	(H)
Epilobium tetragonum	SQUARE-STALKED WILLOW HERB	(H)
Epimedium	BARRENWORT	(H)
Epimedium	BISHOP'S HAT	(H)
Epipactis atrorubans	DARK RED HELLEBORINE	(O)
Epipactis dunensis	DUNE HELLEBORINE	(O)
Epipactis helleborine	BROAD-LEAVED HELLEBORINE	(O)
Epipactis leptochila	NARROW-LIPPED ORCHID	(O)
Epipactis palustris	MARSH HELLEBORINE	(O)
Epipactis phyllanthes	GREEN-FLOWERED HELLEBORINE	(O)
Epipactis purpurata	VIOLET HELLEBORINE	(O)
Epiphyllum	ORCHID CACTUS	(CS)
Epiphyllum	STRAP CACTUS	(CS)
Epiphyllum anguliger	FISHBONE CACTUS	(CS)
Epipremnum aureum	GOLDEN HUNTERS ROBE	(HP)
Epipremnum aureum	POTHOS VINE	(HP)
Epipremnum aureum	SOLOMON ISLAND'S IVY	(HP)
Epipremnum aureus	DEVIL'S IVY	(HP)
Epipremnum pictum 'Argyraeus'	SILVER VINE	(CL)
Episcia cupreata	FLAME VIOLET	(HP)
Episcia dianthiflora	LACE FLOWER	(H)
Episcia dianthiflora	LACE FLOWER VINE	(H)
Epithelontha bokei	BUTTON CACTUS	(CS)
Equisetum	HORSE TAIL	(H)
Equisetum arvense	FIELD HORSETAIL	(H)
Equisetum arvense	SHAVE GRASS	(H)
Equisetum fluviatile	WATER HORSETAIL	(H)
Equisetum hyemale	DUTCH RUSH	(G)
Equisetum sylvaticum	WOOD HORSETAIL	(H)
Equisetum telmateia	GREAT HORSETAIL	(H)
Eragrostis	LOVE GRASS	(G)
Eragrostis amabilis	JAPANESE LOVE GRASS	(G)
Eragrostis elegans	LOVE GRASS	(G)
Eranthemum	BLUE SAGE	(HP)
Eranthis hyemalis	WINTER ACONITE	(BB)
Erechtites hieracifolia	FIREWEED	(H)
Erechtites hieracifolia	PILEWORT	(A)
Eremocitrus	AUSTRALIAN DESERT KUMQUAT	(TS)
Eremophila	EMU BUSH	(TS)
Eremophila maculata	SPOTTED EMU BUSH	(S)
Eremostachys	DESERT ROD	(TS)

Know Your Common Plant Names

Botanical	Common	Type
Eremurus	DESERT CANDLE	(BB)
Eremurus	FOXTAIL LILY	(B)
Erianthus	PLUME-GRASS	(G)
Erianthus ravennnae	PLUME GRASS	(G)
Erica arborea	BRIAR	(S)
Erica arborea	TREE HEATH	(S)
Erica australis	SPANISH HEATH	(S)
Erica, Calluna	HEATH	(S)
Erica carnea	WINTER HEATH	(S)
Erica ciliaris	CILIATE HEATH	(S)
Erica ciliaris	DORSET HEATH	(S)
Erica cinerea	BELL HEATHER	(S)
Erica cinerea	BELLFLOWER HEATHER	(S)
Erica cinerea	GREY HEATH	(S)
Erica cinerea	PURPLE HEATHER	(S)
Erica erigena	IRISH HEATH	(S)
Erica herbacea	SNOW HEATH	(S)
Erica herbacea	SPRING HEATH	(S)
Erica Hyemalis	CAPE HEATH	(HP)
Erica hyemalis	FRENCH HEATHER	(HP)
Erica lusitanica	PORTUGAL HEATH	(S)
Erica mackaiana	MACKAYS HEATH	(S)
Erica mammosa	RED SIGNAL HEATH	(S)
Erica scoparia	BESOM HEATH	(S)
Erica terminalis	CORSICAN HEATH	(S)
Erica tetralix	BOG HEATHER	(S)
Erica tetralix	CROSS-LEAVED HEATH	(S)
Erica vagans	CORNISH HEATH	(S)
Erigeron acre	BLUE FLEABANE	(H)
Erigeron annuus	SWEET SCABIOUS	(A)
Erigeron aurantiacus	ORANGE DAISY	(H)
Erigeron borealis	ALPINE FLEABANE	(H)
Erigeron karkinskianus	MEXICAN FLEABANE	(H)
Erigeron karvinskianum	AUSTRALIAN FLEABANE	(H)
Erigeron karvinskianus	WALL DAISY	(H)
Erinacea	HEDGEHOGBROOM	(S)
Erinacea anthyllis	BLUE BROOM	(S)
Erinus alpinus	FAIRY FOXGLOVE	(R)
Erinus alpinus	SUMMER STARWORT	(H)
Eriobotrya japonica	JAPANESE LOQUAT	(S)
Eriobotrya japonica	LOQUAT	(S)
Eriocaulon aquaticum	PIPEWORT	(WP)
Eriodictyon glutinosum	HOLY HEAD	(H)
Eriodictyon glutinosum	YERBA SANTA	(TS)
Eriogonum	WILD BUCKWHEAT	(H)
Eriogonum fasciculatum	CALIFORNIA BUCKWHEAT	(S)
Eriogonum fasciculatum	CALIFORNIA BUCKWHEAT	(H)

Botanical	Common	Type
Eriogonum giganteum	ST. CATHERINE'S LACE	(S)
Eriophorum	COTTON GRASS	(G)
Eriophorum angustifolium	COMMON COTTON-GRASS	(G)
Eriophorum vaginatum	HARESTAIL COTTON-GRASS	(G)
Eriostemon gardneri	PEPPER AND SALT	(H)
Eritrichium	FAIRY FORGET-ME-NOT	(R)
Eritrichium nanum	HERALD OF HEAVEN	(R)
Eritrichium nanum	KING OF THE ALPS	(R)
Erodium	HERON'S BILL	(H)
Erodium cicutarium	COMMON STORK'S-BILL	(R)
Erodium maritimum	SEA STORK'S BILL	(R)
Erophila verna	WHITLOW GRASS	(G)
Eruca sativa	ROCKET	(H)
Eruca sativa	SALAD ROCKET	(HB)
Erucastrum gallicum	HAIRY ROCKET	(H)
Eryngium	ERYNGO	(H)
Eryngium campestre	FIELD ERYNGO	(H)
Eryngium giganteum	GIANT SEA HOLLY	(H)
Eryngium giganteum	MISS WILLMOTT'S GHOST	(H)
Eryngium maritimum	COMMON SEA HOLLY	(H)
Eryngium maritimum	SEA HOLLY	(H)
Erysimum	BLISTERCRESS	(H)
Erysimum alpinum	ALPINE WALLFLOWER	(R)
Erysimum cheiranthoides	TREACLE MUSTARD	(A)
Erythea armata	BLUE FAN PALM	(P)
Erythea armata	BLUE PALM	(P)
Erythrina corallodendron	COMMON CORAL BEAN	(TT)
Erythrina corallodendron	CORAL TREE	(S/T)
Erythrina crista-galli	COCK'S COMB	(S)
Erythrina crista-galli	COCKSPUR CORAL TREE	(S)
Erythrina crista-galli	CORAL TREE	(S)
Erythrina lysistemon	LUCKY BEAN TREE	(S/T)
Erythrina zeyheri	PLOUGH BREAKER	(TS)
Erythrina zeyheri	PRICKLY CARDINAL	(TS)
Erythronium	ADDER'S TONGUE	(BB)
Erythronium americanum	ADDER'S TONGUE	(BB)
Erythronium americanum	SERPENTS TONGUE	(BB)
Erythronium americanum	YELLOW SNOWDROP	(BB)
Erythronium dens-canis	DOG'S TOOTH VIOLET	(BB)
Erythronium montanum	AVALANCHE LILY	(BB)
Erythronium montanum	AVALANCHE TREE	(BB)
Erythronium revolutum	AMERICAN TROUT LILY	(BB)
Erythronium revolutum	TROUT LILY	(BB)
Erythrophloeum guineense	SASSY BARK	(TT)
Erythroxylon coca	COCA	(T)
Erythroxylum coca	COCAINE	(TT)
Escallonia	ESCALLONIA	(S)

Know Your Common Plant Names

Botanical	Common	Type
Eschsocholtzia	CALIFORNIAN POPPY	(H)
Escobaria tuberculosa	COB CACTUS	(CS)
Espostoa lanata	COTTON BALL CACTUS	(CS)
Eucalyptus	GUM TREE	(T)
Eucalyptus	IRONBARK	(T)
Eucalyptus acacae formis	WATTLE-LEAVED PEPPERMINT	(T)
Eucalyptus aggregata	BLACK GUM	(T)
Eucalyptus archeri	ALPINE GUM	(T)
Eucalyptus bakeri	MALEE BOX	(T)
Eucalyptus baxteri	BROWN STRINGY BARK	(T)
Eucalyptus caesia	GUNGURRU	(T)
Eucalyptus camaldulensis	MURRAY RED GUM	(T)
Eucalyptus camaldulensis	RED RIVER GUM	(T)
Eucalyptus cinerea	ARGYLE APPLE	(T)
Eucalyptus citriodora	LEMON-SCENTED GUM	(T)
Eucalyptus cladocalyx	SUGAR GUM	(T)
Eucalyptus coccifera	MOUNT WELLINGTON PEPPERMINT	(T)
Eucalyptus coccifera	TASMANIAN SNOW GUM	(T)
Eucalyptus cordata	HEART-LEAVED SILVER GUM	(T)
Eucalyptus cornuta	YATE	(T)
Eucalyptus dalrympleana	BROAD-LEAVED KINDLING BARK	(T)
Eucalyptus delegatensis	ALPINE ASH	(T)
Eucalyptus delegatensis	GUM-TOP STRINGY BARK	(T)
Eucalyptus diversicolor	KARRI	(T)
Eucalyptus erythro	ILLYARRI	(T)
Eucalyptus erythronema	RED-FLOWERED MALLEE	(T)
Eucalyptus ficifolia	RED-FLOWERING GUM	(T)
Eucalyptus forrestiana	FUCHSIA GUM	(T)
Eucalyptus glaucescens	TINGIRINGI GUM	(T)
Eucalyptus globulus	BLUE GUM	(T)
Eucalyptus globulus	STRINGY BARK TREE	(T)
Eucalyptus globulus	TASMANIAN BLUE GUM	(T)
Eucalyptus goniocalyx	SPOTTED MOUNTAIN GUM	(T)
Eucalyptus grandis	FLOODED GUM	(T)
Eucalyptus grandis	ROSE GUM	(T)
Eucalyptus gumnifera	RED BLOODWOOD	(T)
Eucalyptus gunnii	CIDER GUM	(T)
Eucalyptus johnstonii	TASMANIAN BROWN GUM	(T)
Eucalyptus johnstonii	YELLOW GUM	(T)
Eucalyptus leucoxylon	WHITE IRONBARK	(T)
Eucalyptus macarthurii	PADDY RIVER BOX	(T)
Eucalyptus macrocarpa	BLUE BUSH	(T)
Eucalyptus maculata	SPOTTED GUM	(T)
Eucalyptus mannifera	RED SPOTTED GUM	(T)
Eucalyptus marginata	JARRAH	(T)
Eucalyptus marginata	WEST AUSTRALIAN MAHOGANY	(T)
Eucalyptus melliodora	YELLOW BOX	(T)

Know Your Common Plant Names

Botanical	Common	Type
Eucalyptus microcorys	TALLOW WOOD	(T)
Eucalyptus microtheca	COOLABAH	(T)
Eucalyptus microtheca	JINBUL	(T)
Eucalyptus microtheca	MOOLAR	(T)
Eucalyptus mitchelliana	WEEPING SALLY	(T)
Eucalyptus muelleriana	YELLOW STRINGY-BARK	(T)
Eucalyptus niphophila	SNOW GUM	(T)
Eucalyptus nitens	SILVER TOP	(T)
Eucalyptus obliqua	MESSMATE	(T)
Eucalyptus ovata	SWAMP GUM	(T)
Eucalyptus paniculata	GREY IRON BARK	(T)
Eucalyptus papuana	GHOST GUM	(T)
Eucalyptus parvifolia	SMALL-LEAVED GUM	(T)
Eucalyptus pauciflora	CABBAGE GUM	(T)
Eucalyptus pauciflora	WHITE SALLY	(T)
Eucalyptus perriniana	SPINNING GUM	(T)
Eucalyptus pilularis	BLACK BUTT	(T)
Eucalyptus pilularis	BLACKBUTT	(T)
Eucalyptus polyanthemos	AUSTRALIAN BEECH	(TT)
Eucalyptus polyanthemos	SILVER DOLLAR GUM	(T)
Eucalyptus polybractea	SILVER MALEE SCRUB	(T)
Eucalyptus propinqua	SMALL-FRUITED GREY GUM	(T)
Eucalyptus radiata	GREY PEPPERMINT	(T)
Eucalyptus radiata	NARROW-LEAVED PEPPERMINT	(T)
Eucalyptus radiata	WHITE TOP PEPPERMINT	(T)
Eucalyptus regnans	GIANT GUM	(T)
Eucalyptus regnans	MOUNTAIN ASH	(T)
Eucalyptus resinifera	RED MAHOGANY	(T)
Eucalyptus robusta	SWAMP MAHOGANY	(T)
Eucalyptus rossii	WHITE GUM	(T)
Eucalyptus rubida	CANDLE-BARK GUM	(T)
Eucalyptus rudis	DESERT GUM	(T)
Eucalyptus saligna	SYDNEY BLUE GUM	(T)
Eucalyptus salmonophloia	SALMON GUM	(T)
Eucalyptus sideroxylon	MUGGA	(T)
Eucalyptus sideroxylon	RED IRONBARK	(T)
Eucalyptus smithii	GULLY ASH	(T)
Eucalyptus spp.	MALLEE	(T)
Eucalyptus staigeriana	LEMON-SCENTED IRON BARK	(T)
Eucalyptus stellulata	BLACK SALLY	(T)
Eucalyptus tereticornis	FOREST RED GUM	(T)
Eucalyptus tereticornis	GREY GUM	(T)
Eucalyptus tetradonta	DARWIN STRINGY BARK	(T)
Eucalyptus tetragona	WHITE-LEAVED MARLOCK	(T)
Eucalyptus tetraptera	FOUR-WINGED MALLEE	(T)
Eucalyptus torquata	CORAL GUM	(T)
Eucalyptus urnigera	URN-FRUITED GUM	(T)

Know Your Common Plant Names

Botanical	Common	Type
Eucalyptus vernicosa	VARNISH-LEAVED GUM	(T)
Eucalyptus viminalis	MANNA GUM	(T)
Eucalyptus viminalis	RIBBON GUM	(T)
Eucharis	AMAZON LILY	(BB)
Eucharis grandiflora	AMAZON LILY	(BB)
Euclea crispa	BUSH GWARRI	(H)
Eucnide	ROCK NETTLE	(TS)
Eucomis	PINEAPPLE FLOWER	(BB)
Eucomis pallidiflora	GIANT PINEAPPLE FLOWER	(BB)
Eucommia ulmoides	GUTTA-PERCHA TREE	(T)
Eucryphia	BRUSH BUSH	(S)
Eucryphia cordifolia	ULMO	(S)
Eucryphia lucida	LEATHERWOOD	(S)
Eucryphia moorai	PLUMWOOD	(S)
Eugenia	FRUITING MYRTLE	(S)
Eugenia	ROSE APPLE	(S)
Eugenia aquea	ROSE APPLE	(TF)
Eugenia caryophyllus	CLOVE TREE	(F)
Eugenia cheken	CHEKEN	(T)
Eugenia jambolana	JAMBOLAN	(TT)
Eugenia jambolana	JAMBUL	(TS)
Eugenia jambolana	JAVA PLUM	(TS)
Eugenia malaccensis	MALAY APPLE	(TF)
Eugenia myrtifolia	AUSTRALIAN BRUSH CHERRY	(S)
Eugenia smithii	LILLY-PILLY	(S)
Eugenia uniflora	SURINAM CHERRY	(TT)
Euonymus alatus	WINGED SPINDLE	(S)
Euonymus americanus	STRAWBERRY BUSH	(S)
Euonymus atropurpureus	BURNING BUSH	(S)
Euonymus atropurpureus	WAHOO	(S)
Euonymus europaeus	COMMON SPINDLE	(S)
Euonymus europaeus	SKEWERWOOD	(S)
Euonymus europeaus	SPINDLE TREE	(BB)
Euonymus fortunei	EVERGREEN BITTERSWEET	(CL)
Euonymus japonicus	JAPANESE EUONYMUS	(S)
Euonymus latifolius	BROAD-LEAVED SPINDLE	(S)
Eupatorium	AGUE WEED	(H)
Eupatorium	THOROUGH-WORT	(H)
Eupatorium cannabinum	DUTCH AGRIMONY	(H)
Eupatorium cannabinum	HEMP AGRIMONY	(H)
Eupatorium cannabinum	HOLY ROPE	(H)
Eupatorium cannabinum	ST. JOHN'S HERB	(H)
Eupatorium coelestinum	MIST FLOWER	(H)
Eupatorium maculatum	JOE-PYE WEED	(H)
Eupatorium perfoliatum	BONESET	(H)
Eupatorium perfoliatum	THOROUGHWORT	(H)
Eupatorium prupureum	JOE-PYE WEED	(H)

Botanical	Common	Type
Eupatorium purpureum	GRAVEL WEED	(H)
Eupatorium purpureum	GRAVELROOT	(HB)
Eupatorium purpureum	PURPLE BONESET	(H)
Eupatorium purpureum	QUEEN OF THE MEADOW	(H)
Eupatorium rugosum	HARDY AGE	(H)
Eupatorium rugosum	MIST FLOWER	(H)
Eupatorium rugosum	WHITE SNAKE-ROOT	(H)
Eupatorium teucrifolium	WILD HORSEHOUND	(H)
Euphorbia	SPURGE	(S)
Euphorbia	WOLF'S MILK	(H)
Euphorbia angydaloides	WOOD SPURGE	(H)
Euphorbia antisyphilitica	CANDELILLA	(CS)
Euphorbia antisyphilitica	WAX PLANT	(CS)
Euphorbia arctica	GREATER EYEBRIGHT	(H)
Euphorbia candelabrum	CANDELABRA TREE	(TT)
Euphorbia caput-medusae	MEDUSA'S HEAD	(H)
Euphorbia corollata	FLOWERING SPURGE	(H)
Euphorbia corollata	WHITE PURSLANE	(H)
Euphorbia cyparissias	CYPRESS SPURGE	(H)
Euphorbia dulcis	SWEET SPURGE	(H)
Euphorbia epithymoides	CUSHION SPURGE	(H)
Euphorbia esula	LEAFY SPURGE	(H)
Euphorbia exigua	DWARF SPURGE	(H)
Euphorbia fulgens	SCARLET PLUME	(TH)
Euphorbia gorgonis	DRAGON'S HEAD	(CS)
Euphorbia gorgonis	GORGON'S HEAD	(CS)
Euphorbia helioscopia	SUN SPURGE	(A)
Euphorbia heterophylla	FIRE ON THE MOUNTAIN	(H)
Euphorbia hirta	ASTHMA WEED	(H)
Euphorbia hirta	PILL-BEARING SPURGE	(H)
Euphorbia hyberna	IRISH SPURGE	(H)
Euphorbia lathyris	MOLE PLANT	(H)
Euphorbia lathyrus	CAPER SPURGE	(H)
Euphorbia maculata	MILK PURSLANE	(A)
Euphorbia mammillaris	CORNCOB CACTUS	(CS)
Euphorbia marginata	MOUNTAIN SNOW	(H)
Euphorbia marginata	SNOW ON THE MOUNTAIN	(H)
Euphorbia milii	CROWN OF THORNS	(CS)
Euphorbia myrsinites	BLUE SPURGE	(H)
Euphorbia obesa	BASEBALL CACTUS	(CS)
Euphorbia paralias	SEA SPURGE	(H)
Euphorbia peplis	PURPLE SPURGE	(H)
Euphorbia peplus	PETTY SPURGE	(H)
Euphorbia pilulifera	CATS HAIR	(H)
Euphorbia platyphyllos	BROAD-LEAVED SPURGE	(H)
Euphorbia pulcherrima	CHRISTMAS STAR	(HP)
Euphorbia pulcherrima	FIRE PLANT	(A)

Know Your Common Plant Names

Botanical	Common	Type
Euphorbia pulcherrima	LOBSTER PLANT	(HP)
Euphorbia pulcherrima	POINSETTIA	(A)
Euphorbia resinifera	OFFICINAL SPURGE	(H)
Euphorbia resinifera	POISONOUS GUM-THISTLE	(H)
Euphorbia robbiae	ROBB'S BONNET	(H)
Euphorbia stricta	UPRIGHT SPURGE	(H)
Euphorbia villosa	HAIRY SPURGE	(H)
Euphrasia memorosa	EYEBRIGHT	(H)
Euphrasia nemorosa	COMMON EYEBRIGHT	(H)
Euphrasia nemorosa	WIND EYEBRIGHT	(H)
Euphrasia tetraquetra	BROAD-LEAVED EYEBRIGHT	(H)
Eurphorbia pulcherrima	PAINTED LEAF	(A)
Eurycles	BRISBANE LILY	(BB)
Euryops tenuissimus	RESIN BUSH	(H)
Eustoma	PRAIRIE-GENTIAN	(H)
Eutrema wasabi	JAPANESE HORSERADISH	(V)
Exacum affine	ARABIAN VIOLET	(HP)
Exacum affine	GERMAN VIOLET	(HP)
Exacum affine	PERSIAN VIOLET	(A)
Exocarpus cupressiformis	AUSTRALIAN CHERRY	(S)
Exochorda	PEARL BUSH	(S)
Fabiana	FALSE HEATH	(S)
Fabiana imbricata	PICHI	(S)
Fagara Flava	SATINWOOD	(T)
Fagopyrum esculentum	BUCKWHEAT	(H)
Fagopyrum tataricum	TATARY BUCKWHEAT	(H)
Fagus	BEECH	(T)
Fagus englerana	CHINESE BEECH	(T)
Fagus grandifolia	AMERICAN BEECH	(T)
Fagus japonica	JAPANESE BEECH	(T)
Fagus orientalis	ORIENTAL BEECH	(T)
Fagus syl. heterophylla	CUT-LEAF BEECH	(T)
Fagus syl 'Rohanii'	CUT-LEAF PURPLE BEECH	(T)
Fagus sylvatica	COMMON BEECH	(T)
Fagus sylvatica 'Cristata'	COCK'S COMB BEECH	(T)
Fagus sylvatica 'Dawyck'	DAWYCK BEECH	(T)
Fagus sylvatica heterophylla	FERN-LEAF BEECH	(T)
Fagus sylvatica 'Pendula'	WEEPING BEECH	(T)
Fagus sylvatica purpurea	COPPER BEECH	(ST)
Fagus sylvatica Purpurea	PURPLE BEECH	(S.T)
Fagus sylvatica 'Purpurea Pendula'	PURPLE-LEAVED WEEPING BEECH	(T)
Fagus sylvatica 'Purpurea Pendula'	WEEPING PURPLE BEECH	(T)
Fagus sylvatica 'Rohanii'	PURPLE FERN-LEAVED BEECH	(T)
Fagus sylvatica 'Zlatia'	GOLDEN BEECH	(T)
Falcaria vulgaris	LONGLEAF	(H)
Fallopia baldschuanicum	FLEECE VINE	(CL)
Fallopia baldschuanicum	MILE-A-MINUTE VINE	(CL)

Know Your Common Plant Names

Botanical	Common	Type
Fallopia baldschuanicum	RUSSIAN VINE	(CL)
Fallopia baldschuanicum	SILVER LACE VINE	(CL)
Fallopia convolvulus	BLACK BINDWEED	(H)
Fallopia japonica	JAPANESE KNOTWEED	(H)
Fallopia japonica	JAPANESE POLYGONUM	(H)
Fallopia sachalinensis	GIANT KNOTWEED	(H)
Fallugia paradoxa	APACHE PLUME	(S)
Fatsia	JAPANESE FIGLEAF PALM	(S)
Fatsia japonica	CASTOR OIL PLANT	(H)
Fatsia japonica	FALSE CASTOR OIL PLANT	(S)
Faucaria	TIGER'S CHAPS	(CS)
Faucaria	WOLFCHOP	(CS)
Faucaria tigrina	TIGER JAW	(C)
Fedia	AFRICAN VALERIAN	(TS)
Fedia cornucopiae	HORN OF PLENTY	(H)
Felicia	BLUE DAISY	(H)
Felicia amelloides	BLUE MARGUERITE	(H)
Felicia bergeriona	KINGFISHER DAISY	(H)
Fenestraria aurantiaca	BABY'S TOES	(CS)
Ferocactus	FISHHOOK CACTI	(CS)
Ferocactus latispinus	DEVIL'S TONGUE	(CS)
Ferocactus viridescens	SMALL BARREL CACTUS	(CS)
Feronia limonia	ELEPHANT'S APPLE	(S)
Feronia limonia	WOOD APPLE	(S)
Feronia limonia	WOOD-APPLE	(H)
Ferraria	BLACK IRIS	(BB)
Ferula communis	GIANT FENNEL	(HB)
Ferula foetida	ASAFETIDA	(HB)
Ferula foetida	DEVILS DUNG	(H)
Ferula foetida	FOOD OF THE GODS	(H)
Ferula gabaniflua	GALBANUM	(HB)
Ferula suaveolens	SAMBAL	(HB)
Ferula sumbul	SUMBUL	(HB)
Festuca	FESCUE	(G)
Festuca altissima	WILD FESCUE	(G)
Festuca altissima	WOOD FESCUE	(G)
Festuca amethystina	AMETHYST FESCUE	(G)
Festuca amethystina	TUFTED FESCUE	(G)
Festuca arundinacea	TALL FESCUE	(G)
Festuca gigantea	GIANT FESCUE	(G)
Festuca glauca	BLUE FESCUE	(G)
Festuca glauca	GREY FESCUE	(G)
Festuca longifolia	HARD FESCUE	(G)
Festuca ovina	SHEEP'S FESCUE	(G)
Festuca pratensis	MEADOW FESCUE	(G)
Festuca rubra	CREEPING FESCUE	(G)
Festuca rubra	RED FESCUE	(G)

Know Your Common Plant Names

Botanical	Common	Type
Ficus auriculata	ROXBURGH FIG	(HP)
Ficus benghalensis	BANYAN	(T)
Ficus benjamina	TROPIC LAUREL	(HP)
Ficus benjamina	WEEPING FIG	(HP)
Ficus carica	FIG	(F)
Ficus caricca	COMMON FIG	(F)
Ficus deltoidea	MISTLETOE FIG	(HP)
Ficus elastica	INDIA-RUBBER PLANT	(HP)
Ficus elastica	RUBBER PLANT	(HP)
Ficus lyrata	FIDDLE LEAF FIG	(HP)
Ficus macrophylla	AUSTRALIAN BANYAN	(HP)
Ficus macrophylla	MORETON BAY FIG	(HP)
Ficus pretoriae	WONDERBOOM	(HP)
Ficus pumila	CREEPING FIG	(HP)
Ficus racemosa	CLUSTER FIG	(HP)
Ficus radicans	TRAILING FIG	(HP)
Ficus religios	BO-TREE	(TT)
Ficus religiosa	BO TREE	(HP)
Ficus religiosa	PEEPUL TREE	(T)
Ficus rubiginosa	RUSTY FIG	(HP)
Ficus sycamorus	SYCAMORE FIG	(TT)
Ficus sycomorus	MULBERRY FIG	(HP)
Ficus sycomorus	PHAROAHS FIG	(HP)
Ficus tinctoria	DYE FIG	(HP)
Ficus tinctoria	HUMPED FIG	(HP)
Filago lutescens	PLANTAIN LEOPARD'S BANE	(H)
Filago lutescens	RED-TIPPED CUDWEED	(H)
Filago vulgaris	CUDWEED	(H)
Filipendula rubra	QUEEN OF THE PRAIRIE	(H)
Filipendula ulmaria	MEADOW SWEET	(H)
Filipendula ulmaria	QUEEN OF THE MEADOW	(H)
Filipendula vulgaris	DROPWORT	(H)
Firmiana simplex	CHINESE PARASOL TREE	(T)
Fistulina hepatica	BEEFSTEAK FUNGUS	(FU)
Fittonia argyroneura	MOSAIC PLANT	(HP)
Fittonia argyroneura	SILVER NET LEAF	(HP)
Fitzroya	ALERCE CYPRESS	(C)
Fitzroya	PATAGONIAN CYPRESS	(C)
Flammulina velutipes	VELVET SHANK	(FU)
Flourensia cernua	TAR BRUSH	(S)
Foeniculum vulgare	FENNEL	(HB)
Foeniculum vulgare dulce	FINOCCHIO	(HB)
Foeniculum vulgare dulce	FLORENCE FENNEL	(V)
Foeniculum vulgare purpureum	BRONZE FENNEL	(H)
Foeniculum vulgare purpureum	PURPLE-LEAF FENNEL	(HB)
Foninalis antipyretica	WILLOW MOSS	(WP)
Fontinalis	WATER MOSS	(WP)

Know Your Common Plant Names

Botanical	Common	Type
Fontinalis	WILLOW MOSS	(WP)
Foresteria acuminata	SWAMP PRIVET	(S)
Forsythia	GOLDEN BELL	(S)
Forsythia ovata	KOREAN FORSYTHIA	(S)
Forsythia suspensa	WEEPING FORSYTHIA	(S)
Fortunella	KUMQUAT	(F)
Fortunella japonica	ROUND KUMQUAT	(F)
Fothergilla	AMERICAN WYCH HAZEL	(S)
Fothergilla	DWARF ALDER	(S)
Fouquiera	CANDLEWOOD	(TS)
Fouquiera splendens	JACOB'S STAFF	(H)
Fouquieria splendens	OCOTILLO	(CS)
Fragaria	STRAWBERRY	(F)
Fragaria moschata	HAUTBOIS STRAWBERRY	(F)
Fragaria vesca	ALPINE STRAWBERRY	(R)
Fragaria vesca	WILD STRAWBERRY	(H)
Fragaria x ananassa	GARDEN STRAWBERRY	(F)
Francoa ramosa	MAIDEN'S WREATH	(R)
Francoa sonchifolia	BRIDAL WREATH	(R)
Frankenia laevis	SEA HEATH	(R)
Frasera carolinensis	AMERICAN COLOMBO	(TS)
Fraxinus	ASH	(T)
Fraxinus americana	AMERICAN ASH	(T)
Fraxinus americana	WHITE ASH	(T)
Fraxinus angustifolia	NARROW-LEAVED ASH	(T)
Fraxinus anomala	UTAH ASH	(T)
Fraxinus caroliniana	WATER ASH	(T)
Fraxinus chinensis	CHINESE ASH	(T)
Fraxinus exc. 'Diversifolia'	ONE-LEAFED ASH	(T)
Fraxinus exc. 'Diversifolia'	SINGLE-LEAFED ASH	(T)
Fraxinus excelsior	COMMON ASH	(T)
Fraxinus excelsior 'Aurea Pendula'	GOLDEN WEEPING ASH	(T)
Fraxinus excelsior 'Jaspidea'	GOLDEN-BARKED ASH	(T)
Fraxinus excelsior 'Jaspidea'	YELLOW-BARK ASH	(T)
Fraxinus excelsior 'Pendula'	WEEPING ASH	(T)
Fraxinus latifolia	OREGON ASH	(T)
Fraxinus mariesii	CHINESE FLOWERING ASH	(T)
Fraxinus nigra	BLACK ASH	(T)
Fraxinus nigra	BLAK ASH	(T)
Fraxinus ornus	FLOWERING ASH	(T)
Fraxinus ornus	MANNA ASH	(T)
Fraxinus oxycarpa 'Raywood'	CLARET ASH	(T)
Fraxinus pennsylvanica	RED ASH	(T)
Fraxinus pennsylvanica lanceolata	GREEN ASH	(T)
Fraxinus quadrangulata	BLUE ASH	(T)
Fraxinus tomentosa	PUMPKIN ASH	(T)
Fraxinus velutina	ARIZONA ASH	(T)

Botanical	Common	Type
Fraxinus velutina	VELVET ASH	(T)
Fraxinus xanthoxyloides	AFGHAN ASH	(T)
Fraxinus xanthoxyloides	VARNISH-LEAVED GUM	(T)
Fraxinus xanthoxyloides dimorpha	ALGERIAN ASH	(T)
Freesia hybrida	OUTDOOR FREESIA	(BB)
Fremontodendron	FLANNEL BUSH	(S)
Fremontodendron	FREMONTIA	(S)
Fritillaria	FRITILLARY	(BB)
Fritillaria biflora	MISSION BELLS	(BB)
Fritillaria camschatcensis	BLACK SARANA	(BB)
Fritillaria camschatensis	BLACK FRITILLARY	(BB)
Fritillaria camschatensis	BLACK LILY	(BB)
Fritillaria imperialis	CROWN IMPERIAL	(BB)
Fritillaria meleagris	CHEQUERED LILY	(BB)
Fritillaria meleagris	SNAKE'S HEAD FRITILLARY	(BB)
Fritillaria pudica	YELLOW FRITILLARY	(BB)
Fritillaria uva-vulpis	FOX'S GRAPE	(BB)
Fritillaris meleagris	CHEQUERED DAFFODIL	(BB)
Fucas serratus	BITTER WRACK	(SW)
Fucas vesicosus	POP WEED	(SW)
Fuchsia	LADY'S EARDROPS	(S)
Fuchsia procumbens	CREEPING FUCHSIA	(S)
Fucus serratus	SERRATED WRACK	(SW)
Fucus serratus	TOOTHED WRACK	(SW)
Fucus vesiculosus	BLADDERWRACK	(SW)
Fumaria capreolata	RAMPING FUMITORY	(H)
Fumaria capreolata	WHITE FUMITORY	(H)
Fumaria indica	AMERICAN FUMITORY	(H)
Fumaria muralis	COMMON RAMPING FUMITORY	(H)
Fumaria officinalis	COMMON FUMITORY	(A)
Fumaria officinalis	EARTH SMOKE	(H)
Fumaria officinalis	FUMITORY	(H/A)
Fumitoria vesicaria	BLADDERED FUMITORY	(A)
Fusanus acuminatus	QUANDONG	(TS)
Gagea bohemica	BOHEMIAN GAGEA	(H)
Gagea lutea	YELLOW STAR OF BETHLEHEM	(BB)
Gagea minima	LEAST GAGEA	(H)
Gagea pratensis	MEADOW GAGEA	(H)
Gagea spathacea	BELGIAN GAGEA	(H)
Gagea sylvatica	YELLOW STAR OF BETHLEHEM	(H)
Gaillardia	BLANKET FLOWER	(H)
Gaillardia	JAM TARTS	(H)
Gaillardia pulchella	ANNUAL GAILLARDIA	(A)
Galanthus	SNOWDROP	(BB)
Galanthus elwesii	GIANT SNOWDROP	(BB)
Galanthus nivalis	COMMON SNOWDROP	(BB)
Galanthus nivalis	FAIR MAIDS OF FEBRUARY	(BB)

Know Your Common Plant Names

Botanical	Common	Type
Galanthus reginae-olgae	AUTUMN SNOWDROP	(BB)
Galax aphylla	CARPENTER'S LEAF	(H)
Galax aphylla	WAND PLANT	(H)
Galega officinalis	FRENCH LILAC	(H)'
Galega officinalis	GOAT'S RUE	(H)
Galeopsis	HEMP NETTLE	(H)
Galeopsis angustifolia	RED HEMP NETTLE	(A)
Galeopsis segetum	DOWNY HEMP-NETTLE	(H)
Galeopsis speciosa	LARGE FLOWERED HEMP-NETTLE	(H)
Galeopsis tetrahit	COMMON HEMP-NETTLE	(H)
Galinsoga	GALLANT SOLDIER	(H)
Galinsoga ciliata	SHAGGY SOLDIER	(A)
Galium	BEDSTRAW	(AH)
Galium album	HEDGE BEDSTRAW	(H)
Galium aparine	CLEAVERS	(H)
Galium aparine	GOOSEGRASS	(HA)
Galium aparine	HEDGEBURS	(H)
Galium aparine	STICKY-WILLIE	(H)
Galium aparine	SWEETHEARTS	(A)
Galium palustre	MARSH BEDSTRAW	(H)
Galium parisiense	WALL BEDSTRAW	(H)
Galium pumilum	SLENDER BEDSTRAW	(H)
Galium saxatile	HEATH BEDSTRAW	(H)
Galium sylvaticum	WOOD BEDSTRAW	(H)
Galium uliginosum	FEN BEDSTRAW	(H)
Galium vernum	LADY'S BEDSTRAW	(AH)
Gallium cruciata	CROSSWORT	(H)
Galpinia transvaalica	WILD PRIDE OF INDIA	(TT)
Galtonia candicans	GIANT SUMMER HYACINTH	(BB)
Galtonia candicans	SPIRE LILY	(BB)
Galtonia candicans	SUMMER HYACINTH	(BB)
Garcinia cambogia	GAMBOGE	(F)
Garcinia mangostana	MANGOSTEEN	(TT)
Gardenia	CAPE JASMINE	(HP)
Gardenia jasminoides	CAPE JASMINE	(HP)
Garrya	SILK TASSEL BUSH	(S)
Garrya	TASSEL BUSH	(S)
Garrya elliptica	QUININE BUSH	(S)
Garrya fremontii	FEVER BUSH	(S)
Gasteria	DUTCH WINGS	(HP)
Gasteria	LAWYER'S TONGUE	(HP)
Gastridium ventricosum	NIT GRASS	(G)
Gaultheria	BOX BERRY	(S)
Gaultheria	CANADA TED	(S)
Gaultheria	MOUNTAIN TEA	(S)
Gaultheria hispida	SNOW-BERRY	(S)
Gaultheria hispida	TASMANIAN WAXBERRY	(S)

Know Your Common Plant Names

Botanical	Common	Type
Gaultheria mucronata	PRICKLY HEATH	(S)
Gaultheria procumbens	BOX BERRY	(S)
Gaultheria procumbens	BOXBERRY	(S)
Gaultheria procumbens	CHECKER BERRY	(S)
Gaultheria procumbens	CREEPING WINTERGREEN	(S)
Gaultheria procumbens	PARTRIDGE BERRY	(S)
Gaultheria procumbens	TEA-BERRY	(S)
Gaultheria procumbens	WINTERGREEN	(S)
Gaultheria shallon	SALAL	(S)
Gaylussacia	HUCKLEBERRY	(F)
Gaylussacia baccata	BLACK HUCKLEBERRY	(S)
Gaylussacia brachycera	BOX HUCKLEBERRY	(S)
Gaylussacia dumosa	DWARF HUCKLEBERRY	(S)
Gaylussacia frondosa	DANGLEBERRY	(S)
Gaylussacia ursina	BEAR HUCKLEBERRY	(S)
Gazania	TREASURE FLOWER	(A)
Gazania pavonia	CAPE TREASURE FLOWER	(A)
Geastrum	EARTH STAR	(FU)
Gelidium amansii	AGAR-AGAR	(SW)
Gelidium amansii	JAPANESE ISINGLASS	(SW)
Gelidium spp	JELLY PLANT	(SW)
Gelsemium	FALSE JASMINE	(CL)
Gelsemium sempervirens	CAROLINA JESSAMINE	(CL)
Gelsemium sempervirens	YELLOW JASMINE	(CL)
Gelsemium sempervirens	YELLOW JESSAMINE	(CL)
Genipa americana	GENIPAP	(S)
Genipa americana	GENIPAP FRUIT	(F)
Genipa americana	MARMALADE BOX	(TF)
Genista aetnensis	MOUNT ETNA BROOM	(S)
Genista anglica	NEEDLE FURZE	(S)
Genista anglica	PETTY WHIN	(S)
Genista canariensis	FLORIST'S GENISTA	(S)
Genista germanica	GERMAN GREENWEED	(S)
Genista hispanica	SPANISH GORSE	(S)
Genista januensis	GENOA BROOM	(S)
Genista nyssana	NISH BROOM	(S)
Genista pilosa	HAIRY GREENWOOD	(S)
Genista raetam	JUNIPER RUSH	(S)
Genista raetam	WHITE BROOM	(S)
Genista sagittalis	ARROW BROOM	(S)
Genista sylvestris	DALMATIAN BROOM	(S)
Genista tenera 'Golden Shower'	ASHY WOADWAXEN	(S)
Genista tinctoria	DYER'S BROOM	(S)
Genista tinctoria	DYER'S GREENWEED	(S)
Genista tinctoria	GREENWEED	(S)
Genista tinctoria	WOAD WAXEN	(S)
Genista virgata	MADEIRA BROOM	(S)

Know Your Common Plant Names

Botanical	Common	Type
Gentiana	GENTIAN	(RH)
Gentiana acaulis	TRUMPET GENTIAN	(R)
Gentiana asclepiadea	WILLOW GENTIAN	(R)
Gentiana brachyphylla	SHORT-LEAVED GENTIAN	(H)
Gentiana cruciata	CROSS GENTIAN	(H)
Gentiana kochiana	TRUMPET GENTIAN	(H)
Gentiana lutea	YELLOW GENTIAN	(H)
Gentiana pneumonanthe	CALATHIAN VIOLET	(H)
Gentiana pneumonanthe	MARSH GENTIAN	(H)
Gentiana punctata	SPOTTED GENTIAN	(H)
Gentiana scabrae	JAPANESE GENTIAN	(H)
Gentiana septemfida	CRESTED GENTIAN	(H)
Gentiana tergestina	KARST GENTIAN	(H)
Gentiana terglouensis	TRIGLAV GENTIAN	(H)
Gentiana utriculosa	BLADDER GENTIAN	(H)
Gentiana verna	SPRING GENTIAN	(R)
Gentiana verna	VERNAL GENTIAN	(R)
Gentianella amarella	AUTUMN FELWORT	(H)
Gentianella campestris	FIELD FELWORT	(H)
Gentianella campestris	FIELD GENTIAN	(H)
Gentianella uliginosa	DUNE FELWORT	(H)
Geoffraea	BASTARD CABBAGE TREE	(TT)
Geogenanthus undatus	SEERSUCKER PLANT	(HP)
Geranium columbinum	DOVE'S FOOT CRANESBILL	(H)
Geranium columbinum	LONG-STALKED CRANE'S BILL	(H)
Geranium dissectum	CUT-LEAVED CRANESBILL	(H)
Geranium endressii	FRENCH CRANE'S BILL	(H)
Geranium ibericum	IBERIAN CRANE'S BILL	(H)
Geranium lucidum	SHINING CRANESBILL	(H)
Geranium macrorrhizum	BALKAN CRANE'S BILL	(H)
Geranium macrorrhizum	ROCK CRANESBILL	(H)
Geranium maculatum	AMERICAN CRANESBILL	(H)
Geranium maculatum	WILD CRANSBILL	(H)
Geranium maculatum	WILD GERANIUM	(H)
Geranium molle	SOFT CRANESBILL	(H)
Geranium phaeum	DUSKY CRANESBILL	(H)
Geranium phaeum	MOURNING WIDOW	(H)
Geranium pratense	MEADOW CRANESBILL	(H)
Geranium pratense	MEADOW GERANIUM	(H)
Geranium purpureum	LESSER HERB ROBERT	(H)
Geranium pyrenaicum	HEDGEROW CRANE'S BILL	(H)
Geranium pyrenaicum	MOUNTAIN CRANESBILL	(H)
Geranium robertianum	HERB ROBERT	(H)
Geranium sanguineum	BLOOD-RED GERANIUM	(H)
Geranium sanguineum	BLOODY CRANE'S BILL	(H)
Geranium sylvaticum	CROW FLOWER	(H)
Geranium sylvaticum	WOOD CRANESBILL	(H)

Botanical	Common	Type
Gerbera	TRANSVAAL DAISY	(A)
Gerbera jamesonii	BARBERTON DAISY	(H)
Gerbera jamesonii	TRANSVAAL DAISY	(H)
Geum montanum	ALPINE AVENS	(H)
Geum reptans	CREEPING AVENS	(H)
Geum rivale	NODDING AVENS	(WP)
Geum rivale	WATER AVENS	(WP)
Geum urbanum	AVENS	(H)
Geum urbanum	CLOVE ROOT	(H)
Geum urbanum	COLEWORT	(H)
Geum urbanum	HERB BENNET	(H)
Geum urbanum	INDIAN CHOCOLATE	(H)
Geum urbanum	WATER FLOWER	(H)
Geum urbanum	WOOD AVENS	(H)
Gevuina avellana	CHILEAN HAZEL	(S)
Gevuina avellana	CHILEAN NUT	(S)
Gilia californica	PRICKLY PHLOX	(H)
Gilia capitata	QUEEN ANNE'S THIMBLES	(H)
Gilia tricolor	BIRD'S EYES	(H)
Gillenia	INDIAN PHYSIC	(H)
Gillenia trifoliata	BOWMAN'S ROOT	(S)
Gillenia trifoliata	INDIAN HIPPO	(H)
Gingko biloba	MAIDENHAIR TREE	(C)
Gladiolus	SWORD LILY	(BB)
Gladiolus callianthus	ACIDANTHERA	(BB)
Gladiolus primulinus	MAID OF THE MIST	(BB)
Gladiolus tristis	YELLOW MARSH AFRIKANDER	(BB)
Glaucium	SEA POPPY	(H)
Glaucium flavum	HORNED POPPY	(H)
Glaucum flavum	YELLOW HORNED-POPPY	(H)
Glaux maritima	SEA MILKWORT	(R)
Glechoma hederacca	GILL-OVER-THE-GROUND	(H)
Glechoma hederacea	ALEHOOF	(H)
Glechoma hederacea	GROUND IVY	(H)
Gleditsia aquatica	WATER LOCUST	(T)
Gleditsia sinensis	CHINESE HONEY LOCUST	(T)
Gleditsia triacanthos	HONEY LOCUST	(T)
Gleichenia	NETFERN	(FN)
Globularia	GLOBE FLOWER	(H)
Globuria	GLOBE DAISY	(R)
Gloriosa	CLIMBING LILY	(BB)
Gloriosa	GLORY LILY	(BB)
Glyceria	MANNA GRASS	(G)
Glyceria	SWEET GRASS	(G)
Glyceria fluitans	FLOATING SWEET GRASS	(G)
Glyceria maxima	REED SWEET GRASS	(G)
Glycine max	SOYA BEAN	(V)

Botanical	Common	Type
Glycyrrhiza glabra	LIQUORICE	(HB)
Glycyrrhiza glandulifera	PERSIAN LIQUORICE	(H)
Glycyrrhiza glandulifera	RUSSIAN LIQUORICE	(H)
Glycyrrhiza lepidota	AMERICAN LIQUORICE	(H)
Glycyrrhiza uralensis	ASIATIC LIQUORICE	(H)
Gnaphalium luteoalbum	JERSEY CUDWEED	(H)
Gnaphalium polycephalum	INDIAN POSY	(H)
Gnaphalium polycephalum	WHITE BALSAM	(H)
Gnaphalium uliginosum	MARSH CUDWEED	(H)
Godetia	FAREWELL TO SPRING	(A)
Godetia grandiflora	GODETIA	(A)
Gompholobium	WEDGE-PEA	(S)
Gompholobium latifolium	BROAD WEDGE-PEA	(H)
Gomphrena globosa	GLOBE AMARANTH	(A)
Gonystylus bancanus	RAMIN	(TT)
Goodyera	RATTLESNAKE PLANTAIN	(O)
Goodyera oblongifolia	RATTLESNAKE PLANTAIN	(O)
Goodyera pubescens	ADDERS VIOLET	(H)
Goodyera repens	CREEPING LADY'S TRESSES	(O)
Gordonia lasianthus	LOBLOLLY BAY	(S)
Gossypiospermum praecox	WEST INDIAN BOXWOOD	(TT)
Gossypium	COTTON	(F)
Gossypium arboreum	TREE COTTON	(H)
Gossypium bardadense	EGYPTIAN COTTON	(S)
Gossypium herbaceum	LEVANT COTTON	(H)
Gossypium hirsutum	UPLAND COTTON	(H)
Gossypium indicum	INDIAN COTTON	(H)
Gossypium mexicanum	MEXICAN COTTON	(H)
Graptopetalum paraguayense	GHOST PLANT	(H)
Graptopetalum paraguayense	MOTHER OF PEARL PLANT	(H)
Graptopetalum paraguayense	MOTHER-OF-PEARL PLANT	(CS)
Graptophyllum pictum	CARICATURE PLANT	(CS)
Grataegus	THORN	(T)
Gratiola officinalis	HEDGE HYSSOP	(HB)
Grevillea robusta	SILK OAK	(HP)
Grindelia	GUMPLANT	(S)
Grindelia camporum	TABWEED	(H)
Grindelia robusta	GUM PLANT	(S)
Griselinia littoralis	BROADLEAF	(S)
Groenlandia densa	OPPOSITE-LEAVED PONDWEED	(WP)
Guaiacum officinale	LIGNUM VITAE	(TT)
Guaicum officinale	TREE OF LIFE	(TT)
Guazuma ulmifolia	BASTARD CEDAR	(TT)
Guizotia abyssinica	NIGER SEED	(TS)
Gulielma gassipaes	PEACH PALM	(TT)
Gunnera	GIANT PRICKLY RHUBARB	(H)
Gunnera	PRICKLY RHUBARB	(H)

Know Your Common Plant Names

Botanical	Common	Type
Gunnera manicata	CHILE RHUBARB	(H)
Gustavia augusta	STINKWOOD	(TT)
Gymnadenia conopsea	FRAGRANT ORCHID	(O)
Gymnocalycium denudatum	SPIDER CACTUS	(CS)
Gymnocalycium mihanouichii	PLAID CACTUS	(O)
Gymnocalycium quehlianum	CHIN CACTUS	(CS)
Gymnocalycium quehlianum	ROSE-PLAID CACTUS	(CS)
Gymnocarpium dryopteris	OAK FERN	(FN)
Gymnocladus dioica	KENTUCKY COFFEE TREE	(T)
Gymnocladus dioica	KNICKER TREE	(T)
Gynerium sagittatum	MOA GRASS	(G)
Gynura sarmentosa	PURPLE VELVET PLANT	(HP)
Gynura sarmentosa	ROYAL VELVET PLANT	(HP)
Gypsophila	BABYS BREATH	(A/H)
Gypsophila muralis	ANNUAL GYPSOPHILA	(H)
Gypsophila paniculata	CHALK PLANT	(H)
Gypsophila repens	ALPINE GYPSOPHILA	(H)
Habenaria	FRINGED ORCHIS	(O)
Haemanthus	BLOOD LILY	(BB)
Haemanthus	RED CAPE TULIP	(HP)
Haemanthus coccineus	OX-TONGUE LILY	(HP)
Haemanthus magnificus	ROYAL PAINT BRUSH	(HP)
Haematoxylon campeachianum	PEACHWOOD	(TT)
Haematoxylum campeachianum	LOGWOOD	(T)
Haematoxylum campechianum	BLOODWOOD TREE	(TT)
Haematoxylum campechianum	CAMPEACHY WOOD	(TT)
Haematoxylum campechianum	COMPEACHY-WOOD	(TT)
Hagenia abyssinica	KOUSSO	(TT)
Hakea bucculenta	RED POKERS	(S)
Hakea laurina	SEA URCHIN	(S)
Hakea victoriae	ROYAL HAKEA	(S)
Halesia	SNOWDROP TREE	(ST)
Halesia carolina	CAROLINA SILVERBELL	(T/S)
Halesia monticola	MOUNTAIN SILVERBELL	(T)
Halesia monticola	MOUNTAIN SNOWDROP TREE	(T)
Halimione portulacoides	SEA PURSLANE	(HS)
Halimodendron	SALT TREE	(ST)
Halleria lucida	AFRICAN HONEYSUCKLE	(TS)
Hamamelis	WINTERBLOOM	(S)
Hamamelis	WITCH HAZEL	(S)
Hamamelis japonica	JAPANESE WITCH HAZEL	(S)
Hamamelis mollis	CHINESE WITCH HAZEL	(S)
Hamamelis vernalis	OZARK WITCH HAZEL	(S)
Hamamelis virginiana	COMMON WITCHHAZEL	(S)
Hamatocactus hamatacanthus	TURK'S HEAD	(CS)
Hamatocactus setispinus	STRAWBERRY CACTUS	(CS)
Hamatocactus uncinatus	CAT CLAW CACTUS	(CS)

Know Your Common Plant Names

Botanical	Common	Type
Hardenbergia monophylla	AUSTRALIAN LILAC	(S)
Hardenbergia violacea	AUSTRALIAN SARSAPARILLA	(S)
Hardenbergia violacea	CORAL PEA	(CL)
Hardenbergia violacea	VINE LILAC	(CL)
Harpagophytum procumbens	GRAPPLE PLANT	(H)
Harpephyllum caffrum	KAFFIR PLUM	(S)
Harpogophytum procumbens	DEVIL'S CLAW	(H)
Hatiora salicornioides	BOTTLE PLANT	(CS)
Hatiora salicornioides	DRUNKARD'S DREAM	(CS)
Haworthia margaritiflora	PEARL PLANT	(CS)
Haworthia tessellata	WART PLANT	(HP)
Hebe	SHRUBBY VERONICA	(S)
Hebe	VERONICA (SHRUB)	(S)
Hebe cupressoides	CYPRESS HEBE	(S)
Hebe hulkeana	NEW ZEALAND LILAC	(S)
Hebeloma crustuliniforma	POISON PIE	(FU)
Hebeloma crustuliniforme	FAIRY CAKE FUNGUS	(FU)
Hechtia scariosa	FAIRY AGAVE	(CS)
Hedera	IVY	(CL)
Hedera canariensis	CANARY ISLAND IVY	(CL)
Hedera colchica	PERSIAN IVY	(CL)
Hedera helix	COMMON IVY	(CL)
Hedera helix 'Hibernica'	IRISH IVY	(CL)
Hedera helix poetica	ITALIAN IVY	(CL)
Hedera nepalensis	HIMALAYAN IVY	(CL)
Hedera rhombea	JAPANESE IVY	(CL)
Hedychium	GINGER LILY	(BB)
Hedychium coccineum	SCARLET GINGER LILY	(BB)
Hedychium coronarium	BUTTERFLY GINGER	(TH)
Hedychium coronarium	BUTTERFLY LILY	(BB)
Hedychium coronarium	GARLAND FLOWER	(TH)
Hedychium gardnerianum	KAHLI GINGER	(BB)
Hedyotis caerulea	BLUETS	(H)
Hedyotis caerulea	INNOCENCE	(H)
Hedysarum coronarium	FRENCH HONEYSUCKLE	(S)
Hedysarum obscurum	ALPINE SAINFOIN	(R)
Heimia salicifolia	SINICUICHI	(S)
Helenium autumnale	SNEEZEWEED	(H)
Helesia carolina	SILVER BELL	(ST)
Helianthemum	ROCK ROSE	(R)
Helianthemum	SUNROSE	(S)
Helianthemum canadense	FROSTWEED	(S)
Helianthemum canadense	FROSTWORT	(S)
Helianthemum nummularium	COMMON ROCKROSE	(R)
Helianthus	SUN FLOWER	(H)
Helianthus annuus	ANNUAL SUNFLOWER	(A)
Helianthus annuus	MARIGOLD OF PERU	(A)

Botanical	Common	Type
Helianthus tuberosus	GIRASOLE	(V)
Helianthus tuberosus	JERUSALEM ARTICHOKE	(V)
Helichrysum	STRAW DAISY	(A/H)
Helichrysum	STRAW FLOWER	(H/A)
Helichrysum, Anaphalis, Limonium	EVERLASTING FLOWER	(H)
Helichrysum bellidiodes	EVERLASTING DAISY	(R)
Helichrysum bracteatum	STRAW FLOWER	(A)
Helichrysum seotinum	CURRY PLANT	(S)
Helichrysum stoechas	GOLDILOCKS	(S)
Helichrysum thyrsoideum	SNOW-IN-SUMMER	(H)
Helichrysum; Xeranthemum; Erythina	IMMORTELLES	(A)
Helicodiceros muscivorus	DRAGON'S MOUTH	(H)
Helicodiceros muscivorus	TWIST-ARUM	(H)
Heliconia	FALSE PLANTAIN	(H)
Heliconia	LOBSTER CLAW	(TS)
Heliconia	LOBSTER CLAWS	(TS)
Heliconia	WILD BANANA	(TS)
Heliconia bihai	BALISIER	(H)
Heliconia psittacorum	PARROT'S PLANTAIN	(TH)
Heliconia rostrata	BEAKED HELICONIA	(TH)
Heliconia wagneriana	WILD PLANTAIN	(TH)
Helictotrichon pubescens	DOWNY OAT	(G)
Helictotrichon sempervirens	OAT GRASS	(G)
Heliocarpus americanus	SUN FRUIT	(TT)
Heliocereus speciosus	SUN CACTUS	(CS)
Heliophila	CAPE STOCK	(H)
Heliopsis	FALSE SUNFLOWER	(H)
Heliopsis	ORANGE SUNFLOWER	(H)
Heliotropium	CHERRY-PIE	(A)
Heliotropium	HELIOTROPE	(A)
Heliotropium	TURNSOLE	(A)
Helipterum	AUSTRALIAN EVERLASTING FLOWER	(H)
Helipterum	PAPER DAISY	(H)
Helipterum	SUNRAY	(H)
Helleborus	HELLEBORE	(H)
Helleborus foetidus	SETTERWORT	(H)
Helleborus foetidus	STINKING HELLEBORE	(H)
Helleborus niger	BLACK HELLEBORE	(H)
Helleborus niger	CHRISTMAS ROSE	(H)
Helleborus orientalis	LENTEN ROSE	(H)
Helleborus viridis	GREEN HELLEBORE	(H)
Helonias bullata	STUD FLOWER	(H)
Helonias bullata	SWAMP PINK	(H)
Helychrysum bracteatum	STRAWFLOWER	(A)
Hemerocallis	DAY LILY	(H)
Hemerocallis flava	YELLOW DAY LILY	(H)
Hemidesmus indica	INDIAN SARSAPARILLA	(TS)

Know Your Common Plant Names

Botanical	Common	Type
Hemigraphis alternata	RED IVY	(HP)
Hepatica	LIVERWORT	(R)
Heptacodium jasminoides	SEVEN SON FLOWER OF ZHEJIANG	(S)
Heracleum mantegazzianum	CARTWHEEL FLOWER	(H)
Heracleum mantegazzianum	GIANT HOGWEED	(H)
Heracleum sphondylium	COW PARSLEY	(H)
Heracleum sphondylium	HOGWEED	(H)
Hericium erinaceum	HEDGEHOG	(FU)
Heritiera macrophylla	LOOKING GLASS TREE	(TT)
Hermadoctylus turberosus	SNAKE'S HEAD IRIS	(H)
Herminiera elaphroxylon	AMBASH	(TT)
Herminiera elaphroxylon	PITH-TREE	(TT)
Herminium monorchis	MUSK ORCHID	(O)
Herminium monorchis	MUSK ORCHIS	(O)
Hermodactylus tuberosus	SNAKES HEAD	(H)
Hermodactylus tuberosus	WIDOW IRIS	(H)
Herniaria	BURSTWORT	(H)
Herniaria	RUPTUREWORT	(H)
Herniaria ghabra	GREEN CARPET	(H)
Herniaria glabra	GLABROUS RUPTUREWORT	(R)
Herperis matronalis	DAMASK VIOLET	(H)
Hesperaloe parviflora	RED-FLOWERED YUCCA	(H)
Hesperantha	EVENING FLOWER	(H)
Hesperis matrionalis	SWEET ROCKET	(H)
Hesperis matronalis	DAME'S VIOLET	(H)
Hesperis matronalis	ROCKET	(H)
Hesperus	EVENING FLOWER	(H)
Heteranthera graminea	WATER STAR GRASS	(G)
Heteromeles arbutifolia	CALIFORNIAN MAYBUSH	(S)
Heteromeles arbutifolia	CHRISTMAS BERRY	(S)
Heteromeles arbutifolia	TOLLON	(S)
Heteromeles arbutifolia	TOYON	(T)
Heteropyxis natalensis	LAVENDER TREE	(TS)
Heuchera	ALUMROOT	(H)
Heuchera	CORAL BELLS	(H)
Heuchera	CORAL FLOWER	(H)
Heuchera hispida	SATIN-LEAF	(H)
Hevea brasiliensis	PARA RUBBER	(TT)
Hevea brasiliensis	RUBBER TREE	(T)
Hibbertia scandens	GUINEA FLOWER	(H)
Hibbertia scandens	GUINEA GOLD VINE	(CL)
Hibbertia scandens	SNAKE VINE	(CL)
Hibiscus cannabinus	KENAF	(TS)
Hibiscus diversifolius	CAPE HIBISCUS	(S)
Hibiscus diversifolius	WILD COTTON	(S)
Hibiscus elatus	CUBAN BAST	(TT)
Hibiscus elatus	MAHOE	(TS)

295

Know Your Common Plant Names

Botanical	Common	Type
Hibiscus elatus	MOUNTAIN MAHOE	(TT)
Hibiscus elatus	TREE HIBISCUS	(TT)
Hibiscus huegelii	SATIN HIBISCUS	(S)
Hibiscus moscheutos	ROSE-MALLOW	(HP)
Hibiscus moscheutos	SWAMP ROSE-MALLOW	(S)
Hibiscus mutabilis	CONFEDERATE ROSE	(S)
Hibiscus mutabilis	COTTON ROSE	(S)
Hibiscus rosa-sinensis	CHINESE HIBISCUS	(S)
Hibiscus rosa-sinensis	ROSE OF CHINA	(HP)
Hibiscus sabdarifa	ROSELLE	(TS)
Hibiscus sabdariffa	JAMAICA SORREL	(TS)
Hibiscus schizopetalus	CORAL HIBISCUS	(TS)
Hibiscus schizopetalus	FRINGED HIBISCUS	(TS)
Hibiscus syriacus	ROSE OF SHARON	(S)
Hibiscus syriacus	TREE HOLLYHOCK	(S)
Hibiscus trionum	BLADDER KETMIA	(S)
Hibiscus trionum	FLOWER OF AN HOUR	(A)
Hidalgoa	CLIMBING DAHLIA	(CL)
Hieraceum aurantiacum	DEVIL'S PAINTBRUSH	(H)
Hieraceum pilosella	MOUSE-EAR HAWKWEED	(AH)
Hieracium	HAWKWEED	(H)
Hieracium aurantiacum	GRIM THE COLLIER	(H)
Hieracium aurantiacum	ORANGE HAWKWEED	(H)
Hieracium brunneocroceum	ORANGE HAWKWEED	(H)
Hieracium lanatum	WOOLLY HAWKWEED	(H)
Hieracium umbellatum	LEAFY HAWKWEED	(H)
Hieracium villosum	SHAGGY HAWKWEED	(H)
Hieracium vulgatum	COMMON HAWKWEED	(H)
Hierochloe odorata	HOLY GRASS	(G)
Hierochloe odorata	VANILLA GRASS	(G)
Himantoglossum hircinun	LIZARD ORCHID	(O)
Hippeastrum	AMARYLLIS	(BB)
Hippeastrum	KNIGHT'S STAR	(BB)
Hippeastrum edule	BARBADOS LILY	(BB)
Hippeastrum equestre	BARBADOS LILY	(BB)
Hippeastrum reginae	MEXICAN LILY	(BB)
Hippocrepis comosa	HORSESHOE VETCH	(H)
Hippomane mancinella	MANCHINEEL	(S)
Hippothae rhamnoides	SALLOW THORN	(S)
Hippothae rhamnoides	SEA BUCKTHORN	(S)
Hippuris vulgaris	MARE'S TAIL	(H)
Hirschfeldia incana	HOARY MUSTARD	(H)
Histiopteris incisa	BAT'S WING FERN	(FN)
Hodgsonia heteroclita	LARD FRUIT	(TS)
Hoheria lyallii	LACE BARK	(S)
Hoheria lyallii	RIBBONWOOD	(S)
Holcus lanatus	VELVET GRASS	(G)

Know Your Common Plant Names

Botanical	Common	Type
Holcus lanatus	YORKSHIRE FOG	(G)
Holcus mollis	CREEPING SOFT GRASS	(G)
Holcus mollis	SOFT GRASS	(G)
Holcus virgatus	TUNIS GRASS	(G)
Holeus sorghum	SORGHUM GRASS	(G)
Holmskioldia sanguinea	CHINESE HAT PLANT	(TS)
Holodiscus discolor	OCEAN SPRAY	(S)
Holodiscus discolor	SPRAY BUSH	(S)
Homoglossum merianella	FLAMES	(BB)
Homogyne alpina	ALPINE COLTSFOOT	(H)
Honkenya peploides	SEA PURSLANE	(HS)
Honkenya peploides	SEA SANDWORT	(H)
Hordelymus europaeus	WOOD BARLEY	(G)
Hordeum	BARLEY	(V)
Hordeum	SQUIRREL-TAIL GRASS	(G)
Hordeum distichon	PEARL BARLEY	(G)
Hordeum jubatum	FOXTAIL BARLEY	(G)
Hordeum murinum	WALL BARLEY	(G)
Hordeum murinum	WILD BARLEY	(G)
Hordeum secalinum	MEADOW BARLEY	(G)
Hordeum vulgare	SIX-ROWED BARLEY	(G)
Horminum pyranaicum	DRAGON MOUTH	(H)
Horminum pyrenaicum	DRAGON'S MOUTH	(R)
Hosta	FUNKIA	(H)
Hosta	PLANTAIN LILY	(H)
Hosta decorata	BLUNT PLANTAIN LILY	(H)
Hosta lancifolia	NARROW-LEAVED PLANTAIN LILY	(CH)
Hosta plantaginea	FRAGRANT PLAINTAIN LILY	(H)
Hosta undulata	WAVY-LEAVED PLANTAIN LILY	(H)
Hottonia palustris	FEATHERFOIL	(H)
Hottonia palustris	WATER VIOLET	(WP)
Houmiria floribunda	BASTARD BULLET TREE	(TT)
Houstonia; Hedyotis	QUAKER LADIES	(H)
Hovenia dulcis	JAPANESE RAISIN TREE	(T)
Howea belmoreana	CURLY PALM	(P)
Howea belmoreana	CURLY SENTRY PALM	(P)
Howea forsteriana	KENTIA PALM	(P)
Howea forsteriana	PARADISE PALM	(P)
Howeia forsteriana	SENTRY PALM	(P)
Hoya carnosa	HONEY PLANT	(HP)
Hoya carnosa	WAX FLOWER	(HP)
Hoya carnosa	WAX PLANT	(HP)
Hudsonia ericoides	FALSE HEATHER	(S)
Hudsonia tomentosa	BEACH HEATHER	(S)
Humata tyermannii	BEAR'S FOOT FERN	(FN)
Humea elegans	AMARANTH FEATHERS	(S)
Humea elegans	INCENSE PLANT	(A)

Know Your Common Plant Names

Botanical	Common	Type
Humulus japonicus	JAPANESE HOP	(CL)
Humulus lupulus	HOP	(CL)
Humulus lupulus 'Aureus'	GOLDEN HOP	(CL)
Hunnemannia fumariifolia	MEXICAN TULIP POPPY	(A)
Hura crepitans	SANDBOX TREE	(TT)
Hutchinsia alpina	CHAMOIS GRASS	(G)
Hyacinthoides hispanica	GIANT BLUEBELL	(BB)
Hyacinthoides non-scripta	BLUEBELL	(BB)
Hyacinthoides non-scripta	CULVERKEYS	(BB)
Hyacinthoides non-scripta	RING O' BELLS	(BB)
Hyacinthoides non-scripta	WILD HYACINTH	(BB)
Hyacinthoides non-scripta	WOOD BELLS	(BB)
Hyacinthoides non-scripta	WOOD HYACINTH	(BB)
Hyacinthus orientalis	COMMON HYACINTH	(BB)
Hyacinthus orientalis	HYACINTH	(BB)
Hyacinthus orientalis albulus	ROMAN HYACINTH	(BB)
Hybanthus floribundus	SHRUB VIOLET	(S)
Hydrangea arborescens	SEVEN BARKS	(S)
Hydrangea aspera	ROUGH-LEAVED HYDRANGEA	(S)
Hydrangea 'hortensia'	MOP-HEAD HYDRANGEA	(S)
Hydrangea macrophylla	LACE-CAP HYDRANGEA	(S)
Hydrangea petiolaris	CLIMBING HYDRANGEA	(CL)
Hydrangea quercifolia	OAK-LEAFED HYDRANGEA	(S)
Hydrastis canadensis	GOLDEN SEAL	(H)
Hydrastis canadensis	GROUND RASPBERRY	(H)
Hydrastis canadensis	INDIAN PAINT	(H)
Hydrastis canadensis	INDIAN TURMERIC	(TS)
Hydrastis canadensis	ORANGE ROOT	(H)
Hydrastis canadensis	YELLOW PUCCOON	(H)
Hydrocera angustifolia	WATER BALSAM	(WP)
Hydrocharis morsus ranae	FROG-BIT	(W.P.)
Hydrocleys nymphoides	WATER POPPY	(WP)
Hydrocotyle	WATER-PENNYWORT	(HP)
Hydrocotyle asiatica	GUTA KOLA	(TS)
Hydrocotyle asiatica	INDIAN PENNYWORT	(H)
Hydrocotyle vulgaris	MARSH PENNYWORT	(H)
Hydrophyllum	WATER LEAF	(WP)
Hygraphila difformis	WATER WISTERIA	(WP)
Hygrocybe psittacina	PARROT FUNGUS	(FU)
Hylocereus undatus	NIGHT-BLOOMING CEREUS	(CS)
Hylocereus undatus	QUEEN-OF-THE-NIGHT	(CS)
Hymenaea courbaril	ANIME RESIN	(T)
Hymenaea courbaril	LOCUST TREE	(T)
Hymenocallis	SPIDER LILY	(BB)
Hymenocallis narcissiflora	PERUVIAN DAFFODIL	(BB)
Hymenophyllum	FILMY FERN	(FN)
Hymenosporum flavum	NATIVE FRANGIPANI	(TS)

Botanical	Common	Type
Hyolepis punctata	BRAMBLE FERN	(FN)
Hyophorbe	PIGNUT PALM	(P)
Hyophorbe verschaffeltii	SPINDLE PALM	(P)
Hyoscyamus albus	WHITE HENBABE	(H)
Hyoscyamus niger	HENBANE	(H)
Hyoscyamus niger	HOGBEAN	(B)
Hypericum	ST. JOHN'S WORT	(S)
Hypericum	ST. PETER'S WORT	(S)
Hypericum androsaemum	BIBLE LEAF	(S)
Hypericum androsaemum	TUTSAN	(S)
Hypericum ascyron	ST. PETER'S WORT	(H)
Hypericum calycinum	AARON'S BEARD	(S)
Hypericum calycinum	ROSE OF SHARON	(S)
Hypericum coris	YELLOW CORIS	(R)
Hypericum elodes	MARSH ST. JOHN'S WORT	(WP)
Hypericum hircinum	STINKING TUTSAN	(S)
Hypericum hirsutum	HAIRY ST. JOHN'S WORT	(H)
Hypericum humifusum	CREEPING ST. JOHN'S WORT	(H)
Hypericum lanuginosum	DOWNY ST. JOHN'S WORT	(H)
Hypericum linarifolium	FLAX-LEAVED ST. JOHN'S WORT	(H)
Hypericum montanum	MOUNTAIN ST. JOHN'S WORT	(S)
Hypericum perforatum	PERFORATE ST. JOHN'S WORT	(A)
Hypericum tetrapterum	SQUARE-STEMMED ST. JOHN'S WORT	(H)
Hypericum undulatum	WAVY ST. JOHN'S WORT	(S)
Hypericum x inodorum	TALL TUTSAN	(S)
Hyphaene thebaica	DOUM PALM	(P)
Hypholoma fasciculare	SULPHUR TUFT	(FU)
Hypochoeris glabra	SMOOTH CAT'S EAR	(H)
Hypochoeris maculata	SPOTTED CAT'S EAR	(H)
Hypochoeris radicata	CAT'S EAR	(H)
Hypochoeris radicata	COMMON CAT'S EAR	(H)
Hypoestes	FRECKLE FACE	(HP)
Hypoestes	POLKA-DOT PLANT	(HP)
Hypoestes phyllostachya	BABYS TEARS	(HP)
Hypolepis	NEW ZEALAND BRACKEN	(FN)
Hypoxis	STAR GRASS	(BB)
Hyssopus officinalis	HYSSOP	(HB)
Iberis	CANDYTUFT	(AH)
Iberis amara	WILD CANDYTUFT	(R)
Iberis amora	CANDYTUFT	(R)
Iberis umbellata	ANNUAL CANDYTUFT	(A)
Iberis umbellata	COMMON CANDYTUFT	(R)
Idesia	LIGIRI TREE	(T)
Idesia polycarpa	IGIRI TREE	(T)
Ilex	HOLLY	(ST)
Ilex aquifilium 'Argenteomarginata Pendula'	PERRY'S SILVER WEEPING HOLLY	(ST)
Ilex aquifilium 'Bacciflava'	YELLOW-FRUITED HOLLY	(ST)

Know Your Common Plant Names

Botanical	Common	Type
Ilex aquifolium	COMMON HOLLY	(ST)
Ilex aquifolium	ENGLISH HOLLY	(ST)
Ilex aquifolium	HULVER BUSH	(S/T)
Ilex aquifolium "argenteomarginata"	BROAD-LEAVED SILVER HOLLY	(S.T.)
Ilex aquifolium 'Argenteomarginata Pendula'	WEEPING SILVER HOLLY	(T)
Ilex aquifolium 'Bacciflava'	YELLOW-BERRIED HOLLY	(ST)
Ilex aquifolium 'Ferox'	HEDGEHOG HOLLY	(S.T)
Ilex aquifolium 'Ferox Argentea'	SILVER HEDGEHOG HOLLY	(ST)
Ilex aquifolium 'Ferox Aurea'	GOLD HEDGEHOG HOLLY	(S)
Ilex aquifolium 'Flavescens'	MOONLIGHT HOLLY	(S)
Ilex aquifolium 'Pendula'	WEEPING HOLLY	(T)
Ilex cassine	DAHOON HOLLY	(S)
Ilex cornuta	CHINESE HOLLY	(S)
Ilex cornuta	HORNED HOLLY	(S/T)
Ilex crenata	JAPANESE HOLLY	(S)
Ilex decidua	POSSUMHAW HOLLY	(S)
Ilex dipyrena	HIMALAYAN HOLLY	(S)
Ilex glabra	INKBERRY	(S)
Ilex latifolia	TARAJO HOLLY	(T)
Ilex opaca	AMERICAN HOLLY	(S)
Ilex paraguensis	MATE	(TT)
Ilex paraguensis	PARAGUAY TEA	(ST)
Ilex paraguensis	YERBA MATE	(VT)
Ilex perado	AZOREAN HOLLY	(T)
Ilex perado	MADEIRA HOLLY	(T)
Ilex pernyi	PERNY'S HOLLY	(T)
Ilex platyphylla	CANARY ISLAND HOLLY	(S)
Ilex verticilliata	BLACK ALDER	(S/T)
Ilex verticilliata	WINTERBERRY	(ST)
Ilex vomitoria	CASSINE	(T)
Ilex vomitoria	YAUPON	(S)
Ilex x altaclarensis	HIGHCLERE HOLLY	(S)
Ilex x attenuata	TOPAL HOLLY	(S)
Ilex x meservae	BLUE HOLLY	(S)
Iliamna rivularis	MOUNTAIN HOLLYHOCK	(A)
Illecebrum verticilliatum	CORAL NECKLACE	(H)
Illecebrum verticilliatum	KNOT-GRASS	(H)
Illicium anisatum	ANISEED TREE	(T)
Illicium anisatum	STAR ANISE	(S)
Illicium floridanum	PURPLE ANISE	(S)
Illicium parviflorum	YELLOW STAR ANISE	(T)
Illicium vernum	CHINESE STAR ANISE	(T)
Illicium verum	STAR ANISE	(S)
Impatiens	JEWEL WEED	(H)
Impatiens	SNAPWEED	(A/H)
Impatiens aurea	BALSAM-WEED	(H)
Impatiens aurea	JEWELWEED	(H)

Botanical	Common	Type
Impatiens balsamina	BALSAM	(A)
Impatiens capensis	ORANGE BALSAM	(A)
Impatiens glandulifera	HIMALAYAN BALSAM	(A)
Impatiens glandulifera	INDIAN BALSAM	(A)
Impatiens glandulifera	JUMPING JACK	(HP)
Impatiens glandulifera	POLICEMAN'S HELMET	(A)
Impatiens noli-tangere	TOUCH-ME-NOT	(A)
Impatiens noli-tangere	WILD BALSAM	(A)
Impatiens parviflora	SMALL BALSAM	(A)
Impatiens sultanii	BUSY LIZZIE	(A)
Incarvillea	HARDY GLOXINIA	(H)
Incarvillea	TRUMPET FLOWER	(H)
Incarvillea delavayi	CHINESE TRUMPET FLOWER	(H)
Indigofera tinctoria	INDIGO	(S)
Inocarpus edulis	OTAHEITE CHESTNUT	(TT)
Inula conyza	PLOUGHMAN'S SPIKENARD	(H)
Inula crithmoides	GOLDEN SAMPHIRE	(H)
Inula ensifolia	NARROW-LEAVED INULA	(H)
Inula helenium	ELECAMPANE	(H)
Inula helenium	SCABWORT	(H)
Inula helenium	WILD SUNFLOWER	(H)
Inula magnifica	GIANT INULA	(H)
Ionidium capense	CAPE VIOLET	(TS)
Ionidium ipecacuanha	WHITE IPECACUANHA	(TS)
Ionopsidium acaule	CARPET PLANT	(A)
Ionopsidium acaule	DIAMOND FLOWER	(H)
Ionopsidium acaule	VIOLET CRESS	(A)
Ipheion	FLOWER OF THE INCAS	(BB)
Ipheion	SPRING STARFLOWER	(BB)
Ipomloea pennata	CYPRESS VINE	(CL)
Ipomoea	MORNING GLORY	(A.CL)
Ipomoea alba	MOONFLOWER	(H)
Ipomoea alba	MOONFLOWER	(CL)
Ipomoea aquatica	WATER CONVOLVULUS	(WP)
Ipomoea arborescens	MORNING GLORY TREE	(TT)
Ipomoea batatas	SWEET POTATO	(V)
Ipomoea coccinea	RED MORNING GLORY	(CL)
Ipomoea coccinea	STAR IPOMOEA	(CL)
Ipomoea dissecta	ALAMO VINE	(CL)
Ipomoea fastigiata	WILD POTATO	(CL)
Ipomoea fistulosa	MORNING GLORY BUSH	(TS)
Ipomoea learii	BLUE DAWN FLOWER	(CL)
Ipomoea noctiflora	QUEEN OF THE NIGHT	(A)
Ipomoea pandurata	MAN OF THE EARTH	(CL)
Ipomoea pandurata	WILD JALOP	(H)
Ipomoea pandurata	WILD POTATO VINE	(CL)
Ipomoea pes-caprae	BEACH MORNING GLORY	(TH)

Know Your Common Plant Names

Botanical	Common	Type
Ipomoea purga	JALAP	(TS)
Ipomoea purpurea	COMMON MORNING GLORY	(CL)
Ipomoea quamoclit	CARDINAL CLIMBER	(TCL)
Ipomoea quamoclit	CYPRESS VINE	(CL)
Ipomoea setosa	BRAZILIAN MORNING GLORY	(CL)
Ipomoea turpethum	INDIAN JALAP	(TS)
Ipomoea turpethum	TURPETH	(TS)
Ipomopsis rubra	STANDING CYPRESS	(H)
Iponioea coccinea	STAR GLORY	(CL)
Ipsea speciosa	DAFFODIL ORCHID	(O)
Iresine herbstii	BEEFSTEAK PLANT	(HP)
Iresine herbstii	BLOOD-LEAF	(HP)
Iris aurea	GOLDEN FLAG	(H)
Iris florentina	FLEUR-DE-LYS	(H)
Iris florentina	ORRIS ROOT	(H)
Iris foetidissima	GLADDON	(H)
Iris foetidissima	GLADWYN	(H)
Iris foetidissima	ROAST-BEEF PLANT	(H)
Iris foetidissima	STINKING IRIS	(H)
Iris fulva	RED IRIS	(H)
Iris germanica	BEARDED IRIS	(H)
Iris germanica	COMMON IRIS	(H)
Iris germanica	GERMAN IRIS	(H)
Iris kaempferi	JAPANESE FLAG IRIS	(H)
Iris kaempferi	JAPANESE IRIS	(H)
Iris latifolia	ENGLISH IRIS	(BB)
Iris pallida	GREAT PURPLE FLAG	(H)
Iris pseudacorus	FLAG IRIS	(W.P)
Iris pseudacorus	YELLOW FLAG IRIS	(WP)
Iris pseudocorus	WATER FLAG	(WP)
Iris pumila	DWARF FLAG	(H)
Iris reticulata	NETTED IRIS	(BB)
Iris sibirica	SIBERIAN FLAG	(H)
Iris spuria	BUTTERFLY IRIS	(H)
Iris susiana	MOURNING IRIS	(BB)
Iris tectorum	ROOF IRIS	(R)
Iris tenax	OREGON IRIS	(H)
Iris unguicularis	ALGERIAN IRIS	(H)
Iris versicolor	BLUE FLAG	(H)
Iris versicolor	POISON FLAG	(H)
Iris versicular	FLAC LILY	(H)
Iris xiphium	SPANISH IRIS	(BB)
Iris xiphium (hybrids)	DUTCH IRIS	(BB)
Isatis tinctoria	COMMON DYER'S WEED	(H)
Isatis tinctoria	WOAD	(HB)
Isoetes	QUILLWORT	(H)
Isomeris arborea	BLADDERPOD	(H)

Know Your Common Plant Names

Botanical	Common	Type
Isopogon anemonifolius	TALL CONE-BUSH	(S)
Itea illicifolia	HOLLY-LEAF SWEETSPIRE	(S)
Itea japonica	JAPANESE SWEETSPIRE	(S)
Itea virginica	VIRGINIA SWEETSPIRE	(S)
Itea virginica	VIRGINIAN WILLOW	(S)
Ixia	AFRICAN CORN LILY	(BB)
Ixia	CORN LILY	(BB)
Ixia viridiflora	GREEN IXIA	(BB)
Ixora coccinea	FLAME OF THE WOOD	(HP)
Ixora coccinea	JUNGLE FLAME	(HP)
Jacaranda acutifolia	FEARN TREE	(TT)
Jacaranda procera	CAROB TREE	(TT)
Jacobinia carnea	BRAZILIAN PLUME	(HP)
Jacobinia carnea	KING'S CROWN	(HP)
Jacobinia carnea	PINK ACANTHUS	(H)
Jacquinia armillaris	BRACELET WOOD	(TT)
Jasione montana	SHEEP'S BIT SCABIOUS	(R)
Jasminium nudiflorum	WINTER JASMINE	(S)
Jasminum	JASMINE	(CL)
Jasminum	JESSAMINE	(CL)
Jasminum grandiflorum	ROYAL JASMINE	(CL)
Jasminum grandiflorum	SPANISH JASMINE	(CL)
Jasminum humile	HIMALAYAN JASMINE	(S)
Jasminum humile	ITALIAN JASMINE	(S)
Jasminum mesnyi	PRIMROSE JASMINE	(CL)
Jasminum odoratissimum	YELLOW JASMINE	(CL)
Jasminum officinale	COMMON WHITE JASMINE	(CL)
Jasminum sambac	ARABIAN JASMINE	(CL)
Jasminum sambac	ZAMBAK	(CL)
Jateorhiza calumba	CALUMBA	(TT)
Jatropha curcas	BARBADOS NUT	(TS)
Jatropha curcas	FRENCH PHYSIC NUT	(TS)
Jatropha curcas	PHYSIC NUT	(T)
Jatropha curcas	PURGING NUT	(TS)
Jatropha integerrima	PEREGRINA	(TS)
Jatropha podagrica	GUATEMALAN RHUBARB	(TS)
Jeffersonia diphylla	GROUND SQUIRREL TEA	(H)
Jeffersonia diphylla	RHEUMATISM ROOT	(H)
Jeffersonia diphylla	TWIN-LEAF	(H)
Johnsonia lupulina	HOODED LILY	(HP)
Jovibarba sobolifera	HEN AND CHICKENS HOUSELEEK	(R)
Jubaea chilensis	WINE PALM	(P)
Juglans	JUPITER'S NUTS	(T)
Juglans	WALNUT	(T)
Juglans ailantifolia	HEARTNUT	(T)
Juglans ailantifolia	JAPANESE WALNUT	(T)
Juglans cathayensis	CHINESE WALNUT	(T)

Know Your Common Plant Names

Botanical	Common	Type
Juglans cinerea	BUTTER-NUT	(T)
Juglans cinerea	WHITE WALNUT	(T)
Juglans hindsii	CALIFORNIAN BLACK WALNUT	(T)
Juglans microcarpa	TEXAS WALNUT	(T)
Juglans nigra	BLACK WALNUT	(T)
Juglans regia	COMMON WALNUT	(T)
Juglans regia	ENGLISH WALNUT	(T)
Juglans regia	NUX REGIA	(T)
Juglans regia	PERSIAN WALNUT	(T)
Juglans regia 'Laciniata'	CUT-LEAVED WALNUT	(T)
Juglans rupestris	TEXAN WALNUT	(T)
Juncus	RUSH	(G)
Juncus acutus	SHARP RUSH	(G)
Juncus articulatus	JOINTED RUSH	(G)
Juncus bufonius	TOAD RUSH	(G)
Juncus capitatus	DWARF RUSH	(G)
Juncus castaneus	CHESTNUT RUSH	(G)
Juncus communis	COMMON RUSH	(G)
Juncus effusus	SOFT RUSH	(G)
Juncus effusus 'Spiralis'	CORKSCREW RUSH	(WP)
Juncus effusus 'Spiralis'	SPIRAL RUSH	(WP)
Juncus inflexus	HARD RUSH	(G)
Juncus inflexus	HARD RUSH	(G)
Juncus maritimus	SEA RUSH	(G)
Juncus squarrosus	HEATH RUSH	(G)
Juncus subuliflorus	COMMON RUSH	((G)
Juncus tenuis	SLENDER RUSH	(G)
Juniperus	JUNIPER	(C)
Juniperus ashei	MOUNTAIN CEDAR	(C)
Juniperus bermudiana	BERMUDA JUNIPER	(C)
Juniperus chinensis	CHINESE JUNIPER	(C)
Juniperus chinensis 'Kaizuka'	HOLLYWOOD JUNIPER	(C)
Juniperus communis	COMMON JUNIPER	(C)
Juniperus communis 'Compressa"	NOAH'S ARK JUNIPER	(C)
Juniperus communis 'Depressa'	CANADIAN JUNIPER	(C)
Juniperus communis 'Hibernica'	IRISH JUNIPER	(C)
Juniperus communis 'Suecica'	SWEDISH JUNIPER	(C)
Juniperus conferta	SHORE JUNIPER	(C)
Juniperus deppeana	ALLIGATOR JUNIPER	(C)
Juniperus drupacea	SYRIAN JUNIPER	(C)
Juniperus excelsa	GRECIAN JUNIPER	(C)
Juniperus excelsa	GREEK JUNIPER	(C)
Juniperus flaccida	MEXICAN JUNIPER	(C)
Juniperus horizontalis	CREEPING JUNIPER	(C)
Juniperus horizontalis "Douglasii"	WAUKEGAN JUNIPER	(C)
Juniperus monosperma	CHERRYSTONE JUNIPER	(C)
Juniperus occidentalis	WESTERN JUNIPER	(C)

Botanical	Common	Type
Juniperus oxycedrus	CADE	(C)
Juniperus oxycedrus	PRICKLY JUNIPER	(C)
Juniperus oxycedrus	SHARP CEDAR	(C)
Juniperus pachyphlaea	ALLIGATOR JUNIPER	(C)
Juniperus procera	AFRICAN JUNIPER	(C)
Juniperus procera	APRICAN JUNIPER	(C)
Juniperus procera	EAST AFRICAN JUNIPER	(C)
Juniperus procumbens	CREEPING JUNIPER	(C)
Juniperus recurva	DROOPING JUNIPER	(C)
Juniperus recurva 'Coxii'	COFFIN JUNIPER	(C)
Juniperus rigida	NEEDLE JUNIPER	(C)
Juniperus rigida	STIFF-LEAVED JUNIPER	(C)
Juniperus rigida	TEMPLE JUNIPER	(C)
Juniperus sabina	SAVIN	(C)
Juniperus sabina tamariscifolia	SPANISH SAVIN JUNIPER	(C)
Juniperus scopulorum	ROCKY MOUNTAIN JUNIPER	(C)
Juniperus squamata	SCALY-LEAVED NEPAL JUNIPER	(C)
Juniperus thurifera	INCENSE JUNIPER	(C)
Juniperus thurifera	SPANISH JUNIPER	(C)
Juniperus virginiana	EASTERN RED CEDAR	(C)
Juniperus virginiana	PENCIL JUNIPER	(C)
Juniperus virginiana	RED CEDAR	(C)
Juniperus wallichiana	BLACK JUNIPER	(C)
Juniperus x media 'Pfitzerana'	PFITZER JUNIPER	(C)
Juniperus x media 'Pfitzerana Aurea'	GOLDEN PFITZER JUNIPER	(C)
Justicia americana	WATER WILLOW	(WP)
Justicia brandegeana	SHRIMP PLANT	(HP)
Kaempferia galanga	MARABA	(H)
Kalanchoe	FLAMING KATY	(HP)
Kalanchoe beharensis	FELT BUSH	(HP)
Kalanchoe beharensis	VELVET LEAF	(HP)
Kalanchoe daigremontanum	DEVIL'S BACKBONE	(HP)
Kalanchoe daigremontianum	GOOD LUCK PLANT	(HP)
Kalanchoe marmorata	PEN WIPER	(HP)
Kalanchoe pinnatum	AIR PLANT	(HP)
Kalanchoe tomentosa	PANDA PLANT	(HP)
Kalanchoe tomentosa	PUSSY EARS	(HP)
Kalanchoe tubiflora	CHANDELIER PLANT	(HP)
Kalistroemeria grand flora	ARIZONA POPPY	(A)
Kallstroemia platyptera	CORK HOPBUSH	(TS)
Kalmia angustifolia	LAMB KILL	(S)
Kalmia angustifolia	SHEEP LAUREL	(S)
Kalmia glauca	AMERICAN SWAMP-LAUREL	(S)
Kalmia glauca	SWAMP LAUREL	(S)
Kalmia latifolia	AMERICAN LAUREL	(S)
Kalmia latifolia	CALICO BUSH	(S)
Kalmia latifolia	MOUNTAIN LAUREL	(S)

Botanical	Common	Type
Kalmia latifolia	SPOONWOOD	(S)
Kalopanax	PRICKLY CASTOR OIL TREE	(T)
Kennedia nigricans	BLACK BEAN	(CL)
Kennedia rubicunda	DUSKY CORAL PEA	(CL)
Kennedya	AUSTRALIAN BEAN FLOWER	(HP)
Kennedya prostrata	RUNNING POSTMAN	(HP)
Kernera saxatilis	KERNERA	(H)
Kerria japonica	JEW'S MALLOW	(S)
Kerria japonica	JEWS MALLOW	(S)
Kerria japonica 'Plena'	BACHELORS BUTTONS	(S)
Khaya	AFRICAN MAHOGANY	(TT)
Khaya spp.	AFRICAN MAHOGANY	(TT)
Kickxia	FLUELLEN	(H)
Kickxia eletine	SHARP-LEAVED FLUELLEN	(H)
Kickxia spuria	ROUND-LEAVED FLUELLEN	(H)
Kigelia africana	SAUSAGE TREE	(TT)
Kiggelaria africana	WILD PEACH	(TT)
Kirka acuminata	WHITE SERINGA	(HP)
Kleinia articulata	CANDLE PLANT	(HP)
Kleinia articulata	HOTDOG PLANT	(HP)
Knautia arvensis	FIELD SCABIOUS	(H)
Knightia Excelsa	NEW ZEALAND HONEYSUCKLE	(T)
Knightia excelsa	REWA REWA	(T)
Kniphofia	CLUB LILY	(H)
Kniphofia	POKER PLANT	(H)
Kniphofia	RED-HOT POKER	(H)
Kniphofia	TORCH FLOWER	(H)
Kniphofia	TORCH LILY	(H)
Kniphofia	TRITOMA	(H)
Kobresia simpliciuscula	FALSE SEDGE	(G)
Kochia	BLUE BUSH	(A)
Kochia scoparia	BURNING BUSH	(A)
Kochia scoparia	SUMMER CYPRESS	(A)
Kochia scoparia trichophylla	BELVEDERE	(A)
Kochia scoparia trichophylla	BROOM CYPRESS	(A)
Kochia scoparia trichophylla	BURNING BUSH	(A)
Kochia scoparia trichophylla	FIRE-BUSH	(A)
Kochia scoparia trichophylla	MOCK CYPRESS	(A)
Kochia scoparia trichophylla	SUMMER CYPRESS	(A)
Koeleria macrantha	CRESTED HAIR-GRASS	(G)
Koelreuteria	CHINA TREE	(T)
Koelreuteria	GOLDEN RAIN	(T)
Koelreuteria	PRIDE OF INDIA	(T)
Kokoona zeylanica	KOKOON TREE	(TT)
Kola vera	KOLA NUTS	(T)
Kolkwitzia amabilis	AMERICAN BEAUTY BUSH	(S)
Kolkwitzia amabilis	BEAUTY BUSH	(S)

Know Your Common Plant Names

Botanical	Common	Type
Krameria triandra	RHATANY	(H)
Krigia	DWARF DANDELION	(H)
Lablab purpurea	BONAVIST	(S)
Lablab purpureus	AUSTRALIAN PEA	(CL)
Lablab purpureus	HYACINTH BEAN	(H)
Lablab purpureus	LABLAB	(H)
+ Laburnocytisus adamii	ADAM'S LABURNUM	(T)
Laburnum	GOLDEN CHAIN	(T)
Laburnum	GOLDEN RAIN	(T)
Laburnum	LABURNUM	(T)
Laburnum alpinum	ALPINE LABURNUM	(T)
Laburnum alpinum	SCOTCH LABURNUM	(T)
Laburnum alpinum 'Pendulum'	WEEPING SCOTCH LABURNUM	(T)
Laburnum anagyroides	COMMON LABURNUM	(T)
Laburnum anagyroides 'Aureum'	GOLDEN-LEAVED LABURNUM	(T)
Laburnum anagyroides 'Pendulum'	WEEPING LABURNUM	(T)
Laburnum x watereri 'Vossii'	VOSS'S LABURNUM	(T)
Laccaria amethystea	AMETHYST DECEIVER	(FU)
Laccaria laccata	DECEIVER	(FU)
Laccaria laccata	THE DECEIVER	(FU)
Lachenalia	CAPE COWSLIP	(HP)
Lachenalia contaminata	WILD HYACINTH	(BB)
Lachnanthes tinctoria	PAINROOT	(H)
Lachnanthes tinctoria	REDROOT	(H)
Lachnostachys eriobotrya	LAMBSWOOL	(H)
Lacrymaria velutina	WEEPING WIDOW	(FU)
Lactarius	MILK CUP	(FU)
Lactarius sp.	MILK CAPS	(FU)
Lactuca aplina	BLUE SOW-THISTLE	(H)
Lactuca saligna	LEAST LETTUCE	(H)
Lactuca sativa	LETTUCE	(AV)
Lactuca sativa angustana	CELTUCE	(V)
Lactuca sativa capitata	CABBAGE LETTUCE	(V)
Lactuca sativa longifolia	COS LETTUCE	(V)
Lactuca serriola	PRICKLY LETTUCE	(H)
Lactuca tatarica	RUSSIAN LETTUCE	(H)
Lactuca virosa	GREAT LETTUCE	(H)
Lagarostrobus franklinii	HUON PINE	(C)
Lagenaria siceraria	BOTTLE GOURD	(V)
Lagenaria siceraria	BOTTLE GOURD	(F)
Lagenaria siceraria	CALABASH GOURD	(F)
Lagenaria siceraria	CUCUZZI	(F)
Lagerosiphon major	CURLY WATER-THYME	(WP)
Lagerstroemia speciosa	PRIDE OF INDIA	(TT)
Lagerstromia indica	CRANESBILL	(T)
Lagochilus inebrians	INTOXICATING MINT	(H)
Lagunaria patersonii	COW ITCH TREE	(T)

Know Your Common Plant Names

Botanical	Common	Type
Lagunaria patersonii	NORFOLK ISLAND HIBISCUS	(S)
Lagunaria patersonii	PRIMROSE TREE	(T)
Lagunaria patersonii	QUEENSLAND PYRAMIDAL TREE	(TT)
Lagurus ovatus	HARE'S TAIL	(G)
Lagurus ovatus	HARE'S-TAIL GRASS	(G)
Lagurus ovatus	HARES TAIL GRASS	(G)
Lagurus ovatus	HARESTAIL GRASS	(G)
Lamarckia	GOLDEN TOP	(S)
Laminaria longicruris	OAR WEED	(SW)
Laminaria saccharina	SUGAR KELP	(SW)
Laminaria sp.	KELP	(SW)
Lamium	WEASEL'S SNOUT	(H)
Lamium album	ARCHANGEL	(H)
Lamium album	BEE NETTLE	(H)
Lamium album	BLIND NETTLE	(H)
Lamium album	WHITE DEAD-NETTLE	(H)
Lamium amplexicaule	HENBIT	(H)
Lamium amplexicaule	HENBIT DEADNETTLE	(H)
Lamium galeobdolon	WEAZEL SNOUT	(H)
Lamium galeobdolon	YELLOW ARCHANGEL	(H)
Lamium maculatum	DEAD NETTLE	(H)
Lamium maculatum	SPOTTED DEAD-NETTLE	(H)
Lamium orvala	GIANT DEAD NETTLE	(H)
Lamium purpureum	PURPLE ARCHANGEL	(H)
Lamium purpureum	PURPLE DEAD-NETTLE	(H)
Lamium purpureum	RED DEAD-NETTLE	(H)
Landolphia kirkii	RUBBER PINE	(C)
Lansium domesticum	LANGSAT	(TF)
Lantana camara	YELLOW SAGE	(HP)
Lapageria	CHILEAN BELL-FLOWER	(CL)(CA)
Lapageria rosea	CHILE BELLFLOWER	(CL)
Lapageria rosea	COPIHUE	(CL)
Lappula squarrosa	BUR FORGET-NE-NOT	(H)
Lapsana communis	NIPPLEWORT	(H)
Larix	LARCH	(C)
Larix decidua	COMMON LARCH	(C)
Larix decidua	EUROPEAN LARCH	(C)
Larix decidua 'Pendula'	WEEPING EUROPEAN LARCH	(C)
Larix gmelini principis-rupprechtii	PRINCE RUPPRECHT LARCH	(C)
Larix gmelinii	DAHURIAN LARCH	(C)
Larix griffithiana	HIMALAYAN LARCH	(C)
Larix griffithiana	SIKKIM LARCH	(C)
Larix kaempferi	JAPANESE LARCH	(C)
Larix kaempferi 'Pendula'	WEEPING JAPANESE LARCH	(C)
Larix laricina	AMERICAN LARCH	(C)
Larix laricina	BLACK LARCH	(C)
Larix laricina	EASTERN LARCH	(C)

Botanical	Common	Type
Larix laricina	TAMARACK	(C)
Larix lyallii	ALPINE LARCH	(C)
Larix occidentalis	WESTERN LARCH	(C)
Larix potaninii	CHINESE LARCH	(C)
Larix russica	SIBERIAN LARCH	(C)
Larix sibirica	SIBERIAN LARCH	(C)
Larix x eurolepis	DUNKELD LARCH	(C)
Larix x pendula	WEEPING LARCH	(C)
Larrea divaricata	CREOSOTE BUSH	(S)
Larrea tridentata	CREOSOTE BUSH	(S)
Laser trilobum	LASER	(H)
Laserpitium latifolium	BROAD-LEAVED SERMOUNTAIN	(H)
Latania	BOURBON PALM	(P)
Lathraea squamaria	TOOTHWORT	(H)
Lathyrus	PULSE	(H)
Lathyrus aphaca	YELLOW VETCHLING	(A)
Lathyrus hirsutus	HAIRY VETCHLING	(H)
Lathyrus japonicus	SEA PEA	(H)
Lathyrus latifolius	EVERLASTING PEA	(H)
Lathyrus latifolius	PERENNIAL SWEET PEA	(H)
Lathyrus littoralis	BEACH PEA	(H)
Lathyrus maritimus	BEACH PEA	(H)
Lathyrus maritimus	SEA PEA	(H)
Lathyrus montanus	BITTER VETCH	(H)
Lathyrus nervosus	LORD ANSON'S PEA	(H)
Lathyrus niger	BLACK PEA	(V)
Lathyrus nissolia	GRASS VETCHLING	(H)
Lathyrus odoratus	SWEET PEA	(A)
Lathyrus palustris	MARSH PEA	(H)
Lathyrus pratensis	MEADOW VETCHLING	(CL)
Lathyrus rotundifolium	PERSIAN EVERLASTING PEA	(H)
Lathyrus sativus	CHICKLING PEA	(H)
Lathyrus sativus	GRASS PEA	(H)
Lathyrus splendens	PRIDE OF CALIFORNIA	(H)
Lathyrus sylvestris	WILD PEA	(H)
Lathyrus tingitanus	TANGIER PEA	(V)
Lathyrus tingitanus	TANGIER SCARLET PEA	(H)
Lathyrus tuberosus	TUBEROUS PEA	(H)
Lathyrus vernuus	SPRING VETCH	(H)
Lathyrus vernuus	SPRING VETCHLING	(H)
Laurelia serrata	CHILEAN LAUREL	(B)
Laurus	BAY-TREE	(S/T)
Laurus azorica	CANARY ISLAND LAUREL	(S)
Laurus canariensis	CANARY ISLAND LAUREL	(S/T)
Laurus nobilis	BAY	(S)
Laurus nobilis	BAY LAUREL	(S)
Laurus nobilis	POET'S LAUREL	(HB)

Know Your Common Plant Names

Botanical	Common	Type
Laurus nobilis	ROMAN LAUREL	(S/T)
Laurus nobilis	ROYAL BAY	(S)
Laurus nobilis	SWEET BAY	(HB/S)
Laurus nobilis	TRUE LAUREL	(S/T)
Laurus nobilis angustifolia	WILLOW-LEAF BAY	(S)
Laurus nobilis aureus	GOLDEN BAY	(HB)
Lavandula	LAVENDER	(S)
Lavandula ang. 'Vera'	DUTCH LAVENDER	(S)
Lavandula angustifolia	COMMON LAVENDER	(S)
Lavandula dentata	FRINGED LAVENDER	(S)
Lavandula stoechas	BUTTERFLY LAVENDER	(S)
Lavandula stoechas	FRENCH LAVENDER	(S)
Lavatera arborea	TREE MALLOW	(S)
Lavatera olba	SHRUBBY MALLOW	(S)
Lavatera olbia	BUSH MALLOW	(S)
Lavatera olbia	TREE MALLOW	(S)
Lavatera trimestris	ANNUAL MALLOW	(A)
Lavatera trimestris	ROSE MALLOW	(A)
Lavendula angustifolia	OLD ENGLISH LAVENDER	(S)
Lawsonia inermis	EGYPTIAN PRIVET	(S)
Lawsonia inermis	HENNA	(S)
Lawsonia inermis	MIGNONETTE TREE	(S)
Layia elegans	TIDY TIPS	(HP)
Layia platyglossa	TIDY TIPS	(H)
Lecythis grandiflora	WADADURA	(TS)
Lecythis usitata	MONKEY POT TREE	(TF)
Lecythis zabucajo	PARADISE NUT	(TT)
Ledebouria socialis	SILVER SQUILL	(HP)
Ledum groenlandicum	LABRADOR TEA	(S)
Ledum groenlandicum	ST.JAME'S TEA	(S)
Ledum palustre	MARSH ROSEMARY	(S)
Ledum palustre	MARSH TEA	(S)
Ledum palustre	WILD ROSEMARY	(S)
Legousia hybrida	VENUS LOOKING GLASS	(H)
Legousia speculum-veneris	VENUS'S LOOKING GLASS	(H)
Leichhardtia australis	AUSTRALIAN DOUBAH	(S)
Leiophyllum buxifolium	SAND MYRTLE	(S)
Leitneria floridana	CORKWOOD	(T)
Leitneria floridana	FLORIDA CORKWOOD	(T)
Lemaireocereus marginatus	ORGAN-PIPE CACTUS	(CS)
Lemairocereus thurbori	ORGAN-PIPE CACTUS	(CS)
Lembotropis nigricans	BLACK BROOM	(S)
Lemna	DUCKWEED	(WP)
Lemna gibba	FAT DUCKWEED	(WP)
Lemna miniscula	LESSER DUCKWEED	(WP)
Lemna minor	COMMON DUCKWEED	(WP)
Lemna trisulca	IVY DUCKWEED	(WP)

Botanical	Common	Type
Lemna trisulca	IVY-LEAVED DUCKWEED	(WP)
Lens culinaris	LENTIL	(V)
Lens esculenta	LENTIL	(V)
Leonotis leonurus	LION'S EAR	(S)
Leontodon	HAWKBIT	(H)
Leontodon autumnalis	AUTUMN HAWKBIT	(H)
Leontodon hispidus	ROUGH HAWKBIT	(H)
Leontondon taraxacoides	LESSER HAWKBIT	(H)
Leontopodium alpinum	EDELWEISS	(R)
Leontopodium alpinum	LION'S FOOT	(R)
Leonurus	LION'S TAIL	(S)
Leonurus cardiaca	MOTHERWORT	(HB)
Leopoldinia piassaba	PIASSABA	(P)
Lepidium	PEPPER-GRASS	(H)
Lepidium campestre	FIELD PEPPERWORT	(H)
Lepidium heterophyllum	SMITH'S CRESS	(H)
Lepidium latifolium	DITTANDER	(H)
Lepidium ruderale	NARROW-LEAVED PEPPERWORT	(H)
Lepidium sativum	CRESS	(V)
Lepidium sativum	GARDEN CRESS	(V)
Lepidium sativum	PEPPERGRASS	(H)
Lepidium sativum	PEPPERWORT	(H)
Lepiota procera	PARASOL MUSHROOM	(FU)
Lepiota rhacodes	SHAGGY PARASOL	(FU)
Lepista nuda	WOOD BLEWIT	(FU)
Lepista saeva	BLEWIT	(FU)
Leptandra virginica	BLACK ROOT	(H)
Leptopteris superba	PRINCE OF WALES FEATHERS	(FN)
Leptospermum	NEW ZEALAND TEA TREE	(S)
Leptospermum scoparium	MANUKA	(S)
Leptospermum scoparium	TEA TREE	(S)
Lespedeza	BUSH CLOVER	(S)
Leucadendron	SILVER TREE	(T)
Leucanthemella serotina	HUNGARIAN DAISY	(H)
Leucanthemella serotina	MOON DAISY	(H)
Leucanthemopsis alpina	ALPINE MOON-DAISY	(H)
Leucanthemum vulgare	DOG DAISY	(H)
Leucanthemum vulgare	DUN DAISY	(H)
Leucanthemum vulgare	FIELD DAISY	(H)
Leucanthemum vulgare	HORSE DAISY	(H)
Leucanthemum vulgare	MARGUERITE	(H)
Leucanthemum vulgare/	OX-EYE DAISY	(H)
Leucanthemum vulgare	WHITE WEED	(H)
Leucanthemum x superbum	SHASTA DAISY	(H)
Leucocoryna ixioides	GLORY-OF-THE-SUN	(BB)
Leucocoryne ixioides	GLORY OF THE SUN	(BB)
Leucocrinum	SAND LILY	(BB)

Botanical	Common	Type
Leucogenes	NEW ZEALAND EDELWEISS	(H)
Leucojum	SNOWFLAKE	(BB)
Leucojum aestivum	LODDON LILY	(BB)
Leucojum aestivum	SUMMER SNOWFLAKE	(BB)
Leucojum vernum	SPRING SNOWFLAKE	(BB)
Leuconthemum vulgare	MOON DAISY	(H)
Leucopogon	AUSTRALIAN CURRANT	(S)
Leucothoe	SIERRA LAUREL	(S)
Leucothoe catesbaei	DOG HOBBLE	(S)
Leucothoe fontanesiana	FETTERBUSH	(S)
Leucothoe racemosa	SWAMP SWEETBELLS	(S)
Levisticum officinale	LOVAGE	(HB)
Lewisia	BITTERWORT	(R)
Lewisia rediviva	BITTER ROOT	(R)
Leycesteria formosa	FLOWERING NUTMEG	(S)
Leycesteria formosa	HIMALAYAN HONEYSUCKLE	(S)
Leycesteria formosa	PHEASANT BERRY	(S)
Leycoperdon species	PUFFBALL	(FU)
Liatris	BLAZING STAR	(H)
Liatris	GAYFEATHER	(H)
Liatris	KANSAS GAYFEATHER	(H)
Liatris	PRAIRIE BUTTON	(H)
Liatris odoratissima	DEER'S TONGUE	(H)
Liatris odoratissimum	VANILLA LEAF	(H)
Liatris odoratissimum	WILD VANILLA	(H)
Liatris pycnostachya	PRAIRIE BLAZING STAR	(H)
Liatris spicata	BUTTON SNAKEROOT	(H)
Liatris squarrosa	RATTLESNAKE MASTER	(H)
Libertia grandiflora	NEW ZEALAND SATIN FLOWER	(H)
Libocedrus bidwillii	PAHAUTEA	(C)
Libocedrus plumosa	KAWAKA	(C)
Licula grandis	RUFFLED FAN PALM	(P)
Ligusticum scoticum	SCOTCH LOVAGE	(H)
Ligustrum	PRIVET	(S.T)
Ligustrum amurense	AMUR PRIVET	(S)
Ligustrum japonicum	JAPANESE PRIVET	(S)
Ligustrum lucidum	GLOSSY PRIVET	(ST)
Ligustrum lucidum	SHINING PRIVET	(ST)
Ligustrum lucidum	WAX-LEAF PRIVET	(S)
Ligustrum ovalifolium	OVAL-LEAF PRIVET	(S)
Ligustrum ovalifolium 'Argenteum'	SILVER PRIVET	(S)
Ligustrum ovalifolium 'Aureum'	GOLDEN PRIVET	(S)
Ligustrum sinense	CHINESE PRIVET	(S)
Ligustrum vulgare	COMMON PRIVET	(S)
Lilium	LILY	(BB)
Lilium auratum	GOLDEN BANDED LILY	(BB)
Lilium auratum	GOLDEN-RAYED LILY	(BB)

Know Your Common Plant Names

Botanical	Common	Type
Lilium bulbiferum	FIRE LILY	(BB)
Lilium bulbiferum	ORANGE LILY	(BB)
Lilium canadense	CANADA LILY	(BB)
Lilium canadense	MEADOW LILY	(BB)
Lilium candidum	MADONNA LILY	(BB)
Lilium chalcedonicum	SCARLET MARTAGON LILY	(BB)
Lilium lancifolium	TIGER LILY	(BB)
Lilium longiflorum	BERMUDA LILY	(BB)
Lilium longiflorum	EASTER LILY	(BB)
Lilium martagon	MARTAGON LILY	(BB)
Lilium martagon	TURK'S CAP LILY	(BB)
Lilium pardalinum	LEOPARD LILY	(BB)
Lilium pardalinum	PANTHER LILY	(BB)
Lilium pardalinum giganteum	SUNSET LILY	(BB)
Lilium pumilum	CORAL LILY	(BB)
Lilium rubescens	CHAPARRAL LILY	(BB)
Lilium rubescens	REDWOOD LILY	(BB)
Lilium superbum	SWAMP LILY	(BB)
Lilium testaceum	NANKEEN LILY	(BB)
Limmanthes douglasii	MEADOW FOAM	(A)
Limnanthes	MARSH FLOWER	(A)
Limnanthes douglasii	POACHED EGG PLANT	(A)
Limodorum abortiva	VIOLET BIRD'S NEST ORCHID	(O)
Limonium	MARSH ROSEMARY	(H)
Limonium	SEA LAVENDER	(H)
Limonium bellidifolium	MATTED SEA-LAVENDER	(H)
Limonium binervosum	ROCK SEA LAVENDER	(H)
Limonium caroliniana	AMERICAN SEA-LAVENDER	(H)
Limonium sinuatum	STATICE	(H)
Limonium suworowi	PINK POKERS	(H)
Limosella aquatica	MUDWORT	(H)
Linanthus grandiflorus	MOUNTAIN PHLOX	(H)
Linaria	TOADFLAX	(H)
Linaria arenaria	SAND TOADFLAX	(H)
Linaria purpurea	PURPLE TOADFLAX	(H)
Linaria repens	PALE TOADFLAX	(H)
Linaria vulgaris	BRIDEWEED	(H)
Linaria vulgaris	BUTTER AND EGGS	(H)
Linaria vulgaris	CALVE'S SNOUT	(H)
Linaria vulgaris	COMMON TOADFLAX	(H)
Linaria vulgaris	EGGS AND BACON	(H)
Linaria vulgaris	FLAXWEED	(H)
Linaria vulgaris	PEDLAR'S BASKET	(H)
Linaria vulgaris	YELLOW TOADFLAX	(H)
Lindera	FEVERBUSH	(S)
Lindera benzoin	BENJAMIN BUSH	(S)
Lindera benzoin	BENZOIN	(S)

Know Your Common Plant Names

Botanical	Common	Type
Lindera bnenzoin	SPICE BUSH	(S)
Lindheimera texana	STAR DAISY	(A)
Linnaea borealis	TWIN-FLOWER	(S)
Linospadix monostachyus	WALKING-STICK PALM	(P)
Linum arboreum	TREE FLAX	(S)
Linum bienne	PALE FLAX	(B)
Linum catharticum	FAIRY FLAX	(H)
Linum catharticum	WHITE FLAX	(H)
Linum flavum	GOLDEN FLAX	(H)
Linum flavum	YELLOW FLAX	(R)
Linum grandiflorum	RED FLAX	(H)
Linum grandiflorum 'Rubrum'	SCARLET FLAX	(H)
Linum lewisii	PRAIRIE FLAX	(H)
Linum monogynum	NEW ZEALAND FLAX	(H)
Linum perenne	BLUE FLAX	(H)
Linum usitatissimum	COMMON FLAX	(H)
Linum usitatissimum	FLAX	(H)
Linum usitatissimum	LINSEED	(A)
Liparia	TWAYBLADE	(H)
Liparis loeselii	FEN ORCHID	(O)
Lippia dulcis	YERBA DULCE	(TS)
Liquidambar	SWEET GUM	(T)
Liquidambar orientalis	STORAX	(T)
Liquidambar styraciflua	RED GUM	(T)
Liquidambar styraciflua	SATINWOOD	(T)
Liriodendron	TULIP TREE	(T)
Liriodendron tulipfera	WHITEWOOD	(T)
Liriodendron tulipifera	YELLOW POPLAR	(T)
Liriope	LILY TURF	(H)
Liriope muscari	BIG BLUE LILY-TURF	(H)
Listera	TWAYBLADE	(O)
Listera cordata	LESSER TWAYBLADE	(O)
Listera ovata	COMMON TWAYBLADE	(O)
Litchi chinensis	LICHEE	(F)
Litchi chinensis	LITCHI	(F)
Litchi chinensis	LYCHEE	(F)
Lithocarpus densiflorus	TANBARK OAK	(T)
Lithops	LIVING STONES	(R)
Lithops	PEBBLE PLANTS	(R)
Lithospermum carolinense	PUCCOON	(H)
Lithospermum officinale	COMMON GROMWELL	(R)
Lithospermum officinale	GROMWELL	(H)
Littonia modesta	CLIMBING LILY	(BB)
Littorella uniflora	SHORE-WEED	(H)
Livistona australis	AUSTRALIAN CABBAGE PALM	(P)
Livistona australis	AUSTRALIAN FAN PALM	(P)
Livistona australis	CABBAGE PALM	(P)

Botanical	Common	Type
Livistona australis	GIPPSLAND FOUNTAIN PALM	(P)
Livistona chinensis	CHINESE FAN PALM	(P)
Lloydia serotina	MOUNTAIN SPIDERWORT	(BB)
Lobelia cardinalis	CARDINAL FLOWER	(H)
Lobelia cardinalis	SCARLET LOBELIA	(H)
Lobelia dortmannia	WATER LOBELIA	(H)
Lobelia erinus	BEDDING LOBELIA	(A)
Lobelia erinus	EDGING LOBELIA	(A)
Lobelia erinus pendula	HANGING BASKET LOBELIA	(A)
Lobelia erinus pendula	TRAILING LOBELIA	(A)
Lobelia inflata	ASTHMA WEED	(H)
Lobelia inflata	INDIAN TOBACCO	(H)
Lobelia siphililea	GREAT LOBELIA	(H)
Lobelia siphilitica	BLUE LOBELIA	(H)
Lobelia urens	BLUE LOBELIA	(H)
Lobelia urens	HEATH LOBELIA	(H)
Lobivia hertrichiana	COB CACTUS	(C)
Lobostemon fruticosus	EIGHTY-DAY-HEALING BUSH	(S)
Lobularia maritima	SEA ALYSSUM	(R)
Lobularia maritima	SWEET ALISON	(R)
Lobularia maritima	SWEET ALYSSUM	(R)
Locophillum	TEXAS RANGER	(H)
Lodoicea maldarica	COCO-DE-MER	(P)
Lodoicea maldivica	COCODEMER	(P)
Lodoicea maldivica	DOUBLE COCONUT	(P)
Logfia minima	SMALL CUDWEED	(A)
Loiseleuria procumbens	ALPINE AZALEA	(S)
Loiseleuria procumbens	MOUNTAIN AZALEA	(C)
Loiseleuria procumbens	TRAILING AZALEA	(S)
Lolium multiflorum	ITALIAN RYEGRASS	(G)
Lolium perenne	PERENNIAL RYEGRASS	(G)
Lolium perenne	RYE GRASS	(G)
Lolium temulentum	DARNEL	(G)
Lomatium nudicaule	PESTLE PARSNIP	(H)
Lonicera	HONEYSUCKLE	(S.CL)
Lonicera alpigena	ALPINE HONEYSUCKLE	(S)
Lonicera brownii 'Fuchsoides'	SCARLET TRUMPET HONEYSUCKLE	(CL)
Lonicera caerulea	BLUE-BERRIED HONEYSUCKLE	(S)
Lonicera caprifolium	EARLY CREAM HONEYSUCKLE	(CL)
Lonicera caprifolium	GOAT HONEYSUCKLE	(CL)
Lonicera caprifolium	ITALIAN HONEYSUCKLE	(CL)
Lonicera caprifolium	PERFOLIATE HONEYSUCKLE	(CL)
Lonicera ciliosa	ORANGE TRUMPET HONEYSUCKLE	(CL)
Lonicera ciliosa	WESTERN TRUMPET HONEYSUCKLE	(CL)
Lonicera fragrantissima	WINTER HONEYSUCKLE	(S)
Lonicera hildebrandtiana	GIANT HONEYSUCKLE	(CL)
Lonicera implexa	MINORCA HONEYSUCKLE	(CL)

Know Your Common Plant Names

Botanical	Common	Type
Lonicera involucrata	TWIN BERRY	(S)
Lonicera involucrata	TWIN BERRY	(S)
Lonicera japonica	JAPANESE HONEYSUCKLE	(CL)
Lonicera nitida	POOR MAN'S BOX	(S)
Lonicera periclymenum	ENGLISH WILD HONEYSUCKLE	(CL)
Lonicera periclymenum	WOODBINE	(CL)
Lonicera periclymenum 'Belgica'	DUTCH WOODBINE	(CL)
Lonicera periclymenum 'Belgica'	EARLY DUTCH HONEYSUCKLE	(CL)
Lonicera periclymenum 'Serotina'	LATE DUTCH HONEYSUCKLE	(CL)
Lonicera sempervirens	TRUMPET HONEYSUCKLE	(CL)
Lonicera standishii	WINTER HONEYSUCKLE	(S)
Lonicera tatarica	TATARIAN HONEYSUCKLE	(S)
Lonicera tragophylla	CHINESE WOODBINE	(CL)
Lonicera x purpusii	WINTER BEAUTY	(S)
Lonicera x purpusii	WINTER HONEYSUCKLE	(S)
Lonicera xylosteum	FLY HONEYSUCKLE	(S)
Lophira alata	AFRICAN OAK	(TT)
Lophira lanceolata	AFRICAN OAK	(TT)
Lophocereus schottii	SENITA CEREUS	(CS)
Lophophora williamasii	DRY WHISKY	(CS)
Lophophora williamsii	DUMPLING CACTUS	(CS)
Lophophora williamsii	MESCAL BUTTONS	(CS)
Lophophora williamsii	PEYOTE	(CS)
Lotus	TREFOIL	(H)
Lotus corniculatus	BACON AND EGGS	(H)
Lotus corniculatus	BIRD'S FOOT TREFOIL	(H)
Lotus pedunculatus	MARSH BIRD'S FOOT TREFOIL	(H)
Lotus scoparius	DEER WEED	(H)
Lotus scoparius	DEERWEED	(H)
Lotus tetragonolobus	ASPARAGUS PEA	(V)
Ludwigia	PRIMROSE WILLOW	(S)
Ludwigia palustris	HAMPSHIRE PURSLANE	(H)
Luffa	RAG GOURD	(H)
Luffa	VEGETABLE SPONGE	(H)
Luffa acutangula	STRAINER VINE	(TS)
Luffa cylindrica	DISHCLOTH GOURD	(V)
Luffa cylindrica	LOOFAH	(V)
Luffa cylindrica	LOOFAH GOURD	(V)
Luma apiculata	ORANGE-BARK MYRTLE	(T)
Luma chequen	CHEKEN	(T)
Lunaria	MONEY FLOWER	(A/H)
Lunaria	MOONWORT	(B)
Lunaria	SATIN FLOWER	(A)
Lunaria	SATIN-FLOWER	(H)
Lunaria annua	HONESTY	(B)
Lunaria rediviva	PERENNIAL HONESTY	(H)
Lupinus	LUPIN	(H)

Botanical	Common	Type
Lupinus albus	WHITE LUPIN	(H)
Lupinus arboreus	TREE LUPIN	(S)
Lupinus arboreus	YELLOW TREE LUPIN	(S)
Lupinus lepidus	PRAIRIE LUPIN	(H)
Lupinus luteus	YELLOW LUPIN	(A)
Lupinus perennis	BLUE BEAN	(H)
Lupinus polyphyllus	GARDEN LUPIN	(H)
Lupinus polyphyllus 'Russell Hybrids'	RUSSELL LUPINS	(H)
Lupinus subcarnosus	TEXAS BLUEBONNET	(H)
Lupinus vallicola	VALLEY LUPIN	(A)
Luronium natans	FLOATING WATER PLANTAIN	(WP)
Luzula	WOODRUSH	(G)
Luzula campestris	FIELD WOOD-RUSH	(G)
Luzula multiflora	HEATH WOOD-RUSH	(G)
luzula nivea	SNOWY WOODRUSH	(G)
Luzula pilosa	HAIRY WOOD-RUSH	(G)
Luzula spicata	SPIKED WOOD-RUSH	(G)
Luzula sylvatica	GREAT WOOD-RUSH	(G)
Lychnis	CAMPION	(A/H)
Lychnis	EVENING CAMPION	(H)
Lychnis alpina	ALPINE CAMPION	(R)
Lychnis chalcedonica	JERUSALEM CROSS	(H)
Lychnis chalcedonica	MALTESE CROSS	(H)
Lychnis coronaria	ROSE CAMPION	(H)
Lychnis flos-cuculi	RAGGED ROBIN	(H)
Lychnis flos-jovis	FLOWER OF JOVE	(H)
Lychnis silene	CATCHFLY	(H)
Lychnis viscaria	RED CATCHFLY	(H)
Lychnis viscaria	STICKY CATCHFLY	(H)
Lycium	BOX THORN	(S)
Lycium afrum	KAFFIR-THORN	(TS)
Lycium balbarum	MATRIMONY VINE	(S)
Lycium barbarum	CHINESE BOX THORN	(S)
Lycium chinense	CHINA TEA PLANT	(S)
Lycium chinense	DUKE OF ARGYLE'S TEA TREE	(S)
Lycopersicon esculentum	TOMATO	(F)
Lycopersicon esculentum cerasiforme	CHERRY TOMATO	(F)
Lycopersicon esulentum	LOVE APPLE	(F)
Lycopersicon piminellifolium	CURRANT TOMATO	(H)
Lycopodium	GROUND PINE	(H)
Lycopodium selaginella	CLUB-MOSS	(R)
Lycopsis arvensis	LESSER BUGLOSS	(H)
Lycopus europaeus	GIPSYWORT	(H)
Lycopus virginicus	BUGLEWEED	(H)
Lycopus virginicus	GIPSYWEED	(H)
Lycopus virginicus	SWEET BUGLE	(H)
Lycopus virginicus	WATER BUGLE	(H)

Botanical	Common	Type
Lycoris africana	GOLDEN SPIDER LILY	(BB)
Lycoris aurea	GOLDEN LILY	(BB)
Lycoris aurea	GOLDEN SPIDER-LILY	(BB)
Lycoris radiata	RED SPIDER LILY	(BB)
Lycoris squamigera	MAGIC LILY	(BB)
Lycoris squamigera	RESURRECTION LILY	(BB)
Lygodium	CLIMBING FERN	(FN)
Lygodium japonicum	JAPANESE CLIMBING FERN	(FN)
Lyonia lucida	FETTER-BUSH	(S)
Lyonia mariana	STAGGER BUSH	(S)
Lyonothamnus floribundus	CATALINA IRONWOOD	(T)
Lysichiton americanum	BOGA ARUM	(WP)
Lysichiton americanum	SKUNK CABBAGE	(WP)
Lysimachia	LOOSESTRIFE	(H)
Lysimachia clethroides	CHINESE LOOSESTRIFE	(H)
Lysimachia clethroides	SHEPHERD'S CROOK	(H)
Lysimachia nemorum	WOOD PIMPERNEL	(H)
Lysimachia nemorum	YELLOW PIMPERNEL	(H)
Lysimachia nummularia	CREEPING JENNY	(H)
Lysimachia nummularia	MONEYWORT	(H)
Lysimachia nummularia	STRING OF SOVEREIGNS	(H)
Lysimachia nummularia	WANDERING JENNY	(H)
Lysimachia punctata	CIRCLE FLOWER	(H)
Lysimachia punctata	DOTTED LOOSESTRIFE	(H)
Lysimachia thyrsiflora	TUFTED LOOSESTRIFE	(H)
Lysimachia vulgaris	WOOD PIMPERNEL	(H)
Lysimachia vulgaris	YELLOW LOOSESTRIFE	(H)
Lysimachia vulgaris	YELLOW WILLOW HERB	(H)
Lythrum hyssopifolia	GRASS-POLY	(H)
Lythrum portula	WATER PURSLANE	(H)
Lythrum salicaria	PURPLE LOOSESTRIFE	(H)
Lythrum salicaria	PURPLE WILLOW HERB	(H)
Lythrum salicaria	SPIKED LOOSESTRIFE	(H)
Lythrum verticillatum	SWAMP WILLOW HERB	(H)
Macadamia ternifolia	QUEENSLAND NUT	(TT)
Macleaya	PLUME POPPY	(H)
Maclura pomifera	OSAGE ORANGE	(ST)
Macrocystis	GIANT KELP	(SW)
Macrolepiota procera	PARASOL MUSHROOM	(FU)
Macrozania	AUSTRALIAN CYCAD	(TS)
Madia	TAR WEED	(H)
Madia	TARWEED	(H)
Madia sativa	CHILEAN OIL PLANT	(H)
Magnolia	MAGNOLIA	(ST)
Magnolia acuminata	BLUE MAGNOLIA	(T)
Magnolia acuminata	CUCUMBER TREE	(T)
Magnolia campbellii	PINK TULIP TREE	(T)

Botanical	Common	Type
Magnolia cordata	YELLOW CUCUMBER TREE	(T)
Magnolia denudata	LILY TREE	(S)
Magnolia denudata	YULAN	(ST)
Magnolia (erroneus)	TULIP TREE	(ST)
Magnolia grandiflora	BULLBAY	(S)
Magnolia grandiflora	EVERGREEN MAGNOLIA	(ST)
Magnolia grandiflora	LAUREL MAGNOLIA	(ST)
Magnolia grandiflora	LOBLOLLY MAGNOLIA	(ST)
Magnolia grandiflora	SOUTHERN MAGNOLIA	(ST)
Magnolia grandiflora 'Exmouth'	EXMOUTH MAGNOLIA	(ST)
Magnolia hypoleuca	JAPANESE BIG-LEAVED MAGNOLIA	(ST)
Magnolia kobus	NORTHERN JAPANESE MAGNOLIA	(S)
Magnolia salicifolia	WILLOW-LEAFED MAGNOLIA	(ST)
Magnolia stellata	STARRY MAGNOLIA	(S)
Magnolia tripetalia	UMBRELLA TREE	(T)
Magnolia virginiana	SWAMP BAY	(S)
Magnolia virginiana	SWEET BAY	(S)
Magnolia virginiana	WHITE BAY	(S/T)
Magnolia virginiana	WHITE LAUREL	(ST)
Mahernia verticilliata	HONEY-BELL	(S)
Mahonia aquifolium	HOLLY-LEAVED BARBERRY	(S)
Mahonia aquifolium	MOUNTAIN GRAPE	(S)
Mahonia aquifolium	OREGON GRAPE	(S)
Mahonia nervosa	WATER HOLLY	(S)
Mahonia repens	CREEPING BARBERRY	(S)
Maianthemum bifolium	MAY LILY	(H)
Malaviscus arboreus	PEPPER HIBISCUS	(TS)
Malaviscus arboreus	SLEEPY MALLOW	(TS)
Malaviscus arboreus	TURK'S CAP	(TS)
Malcolmia maritima	VIRGINIA STOCK	(A)
Mallotus	KAMILA TREE	(T)
Mallotus philippinensis	KAMALA	(T)
Malope trifolia	MALLOW-WORT	(A)
Malpighia glabra	BARBADOS CHERRY	(TT)
Malpighia urens	COW-ITCH CHERRY	(H)
Malus	CRAB APPLE	(T)
Malus angustifolia	SOUTHERN CRAB	(T)
Malus baccata cvs	SIBERIAN CRAB	(T)
Malus coronaria	GARLAND CRAB	(T)
Malus coronaria	SWEET CRAB APPLE	(T)
Malus domestica	CULTIVATED APPLE	(F)
Malus domestica	ORCHARD APPLE	(T)
Malus 'Echtermeyer'	WEEPING CRAB	(T)
Malus florentina	HAWTHORN-LEAVED CRAB APPLE	(T)
Malus floribunda	JAPANESE CRAB	(T)
Malus fusca	OREGON CRAB	(T)
Malus huphensis	HUPEH CRAB	(T)

Know Your Common Plant Names

Botanical	Common	Type
Malus ioensis	PRAIRIE CRAB	(T)
Malus ioensis 'Plena'	DECHTEL CRAB	(T)
Malus 'Magdeburgensis'	MAGDEBURG CRAB	(T)
Malus 'Red Jade'	WEEPING CRAB	(T)
Malus sieboldii	TORINGO CRAB	(T)
Malus spectabilis	CHINESE CRAB	(T)
Malus spectabilis	HAI-TUNG CRAB	(T)
Malus sylvestris	COMMON APPLE	(T)
Malus sylvestris	COMMON CRAB APPLE	(T)
Malus sylvestris	WILD CRAB	(T)
Malus tschonoskii	PILLAR APPLE	(T)
Malus x purpurea	PURPLE CRAB	(T)
Malus x robusta cvs	SIBERIAN CRAB	(T)
Malus xhalliana	HALL'S APPLE	(T)
Malva	MALLOW	(AH)
Malva alcea	CUT-LEAVED MALLOW	(H)
Malva crispa	CURLED MALLOW	(H)
Malva moschata	MUSK MALLOW	(H)
Malva neglecta	DWARF MALLOW	(H)
Malva pusilla	SMALL MALLOW	(H)
Malva sylvestris	COMMON MALLOW	(A)
Malvastrum	FALSE MALLOW	(H)
Malvaviscus arboreu	SLEEPING HIBISCUS	(TS)
Malvaviscus arboreus	WAX MALLOW	(TS)
Mammea americana	MAMMEE-APPLE	(F)
Mammillaria bocasana	POWDER-PUFF CACTUS	(CS)
Mammillaria bocasana	POWDERPUFF	(CS)
Mammillaria bocasana	SNOWBALL CACTUS	(CS)
Mammillaria elongata	GOLD LACE CACTUS	(CS)
Mammillaria elongata	LACE CACTUS	(CS)
Mammillaria hahniana	OLD LADY	(CS)
Mammillaria heyderi	CORAL CACTUS	(CS)
Mammillaria heyderi	CREAM CACTUS	(CS)
Mammillaria plumosa	FEATHER CACTUS	(CS)
Mammillaria prolifera	LITTLE CANDLES	(CS)
Mammillaria prolifera	SILVER CLUSTER CACTUS	(CS)
Mammillaria zeilmanniana	ROSE PINCUSHION	(CS)
Manattia inflata	FIRECRACKER VINE	(HP)
Mandevilla suaveolens	CHILEAN JASMINE	(CL)
Mandragora officinarum	DEVIL'S APPLE	(HB)
Mandragora officinarum	MANDRAKE	(H)
Mandragora officinarum	SATAN'S APPLE	(HB)
Mangifera indica	MANGO	(F)
Manihot esculenta	CASSAVA	(V)
Manihot esculenta	MANDIOCA	(TT)
Manihot esculenta	MANIOC	(F)
Manihot esculenta	TAPIOCA	(F)

Botanical	Common	Type
Manihot glaziovii	CEARA RUBBER	(TT)
Manihot utilissima	BITTER CASSAVA	(F)
Manilkara zapota	MARMALADE PLUM	(TT)
Manilkara zapota	NASEBERRY	(F)
Manilkara zapota	SAPODILLA	(H)
Manilkara zapota	SAPODILLA PLUM	(TT)
Maranta	PRAYER PLANT	(HP)
Maranta arundinacea	ARROWROOT	(HB)
Maranta arundinacea	WEST INDIAN ARROWROOT	(TS)
Maranta leuconeura Kerchoviana	RABBIT TRACKS	(HP)
Maranta tricolor	HERRINGBONE PLANT	(HP)
Marasmius androsaccus	HORSEHAIR FUNGUS	(FU)
Marasmius oreades	FAIRY RING CHAMPIGNON	(FU)
Marasmius oreades	FAIRY RING MUSHROOM	(FU)
Margyricarpus pinnatus	PEARL BERRY	(S)
Margyricarpus pinnatus	PEARL FRUIT	(S)
Marrubim vulgare	WHITE HOREHOUND	(H)
Marrubium	HOARHOUND	(H)
Marrubium	HOREHOUND	(H)
Martynia annua	UNICORN PLANT	(A)
Mathiola	STOCK	(HA)
Mathiola incana	HOARY STOCK	(H)
Mathiola sinuata	SEA STOCK	(H)
Matricaria	MAYWEED	(H)
Matricaria maritima	SEA MAYWEED	(H)
Matricaria perforata	SCENTLESS CHAMOMILE	(AH)
Matricaria perforata	SCENTLESS MAYWEED	(A)
Matricaria recutita	GERMAN CHAMOMILE	(H)
Matricaria recutita	SCENTED MAYWEED	(H)
Matricaria recutita	WILD CHAMOMILE	(A)
Matteucia struthiopteris	OSTRICH FERN	(FN)
Matthiola bicornis	NIGHT-SCENTED STOCK	(A)
Matthiola incana	BROMPTON STOCK	(B)
Matthiola incana annua	TEN WEEK STOCK	(A)
Maurovenia capensis	HOTTENTOT CHERRY	(A)
Maytenus boaria	MAITEN	(S)
Meconopsis betonicifolia	BLUE POPPY	(H)
Meconopsis betonifolia	HIMALAYAN BLUE POPPY	(H)
Meconopsis cambrica	WELSH POPPY	(H)
Meconopsis integrifolia	LAMPSHADE POPPY	(H)
Meconopsis napaulensis	SATIN POPPY	(H)
Meconopsis quintuplinervia	HAREBELL POPPY	(H)
Medicago	MEDICK	(H)
Medicago arabica	SPOTTED MEDICK	(H)
Medicago arborea	MOON TREFOIL	(S)
Medicago echinus	CALVARY CLOVER	(H)
Medicago falcata	YELLOW MEDICK	(H)

Botanical	Common	Type
Medicago lupulina	BLACK MEDICK	(H)
Medicago lupulina	NONSUCH	(H)
Medicago lupulina	SHAMROCK	(H)
Medicago minima	BUR MEDICK	(H)
Medicago sativa	ALFALFA	(V)
Medicago Sativa	BUFFALO HERB	(HB)
Medicago sativa	LUCERNE	(H)
Melaleuca	PAPER BARK	(T)
Melaleuca armillaris	BRACELET HONEY MYRTLE	(S/T)
Melaleuca elliptica	GRANITE BOTTLEBRUSH	(S)
Melaleuca leucadendron	CAJUPUT	(S)
Melaleuca leucadendron	WHITE TEA TREE	(T)
Melaleuca nematophylla	WIRY HONEYMYRTLE	(S)
Melaleuca nesophylla	WESTERN TEA-MYRTLE	(S)
Melaleuca quinquenervia	PAPER-BARK TREE	(T)
Melaleuca squarrosa	SCENTED PAPER-BARK	(S)
Melampyrum	COW WHEAT	(H)
Melampyrum arvense	FIELD COW-WHEAT	(H)
Melampyrum pratense	COMMON COW-WHEAT	(H)
Melampyrum pratense	YELLOW COW-WHEAT	(H)
Melanthium	BUNCH FLOWER	(H)
Melia azadirachta	AZADIRACHTA	(T)
Melia azedarach	BEAD TREE	(T)
Melia azedarach	CHINA BERRY	(T)
Melia azedarach	INDIAN LILAC	(T)
Melia azedarach	PRIDE OF CHINA	(T)
Melia azedarach	PRIDE OF INDIA	(T)
Melia dubium	CEYLON MAHOGANY	(TT)
Melia dubium	WHITE CEDAR	(TT)
Melianthus major	HONEY BUSH	(S)
Melica	MELIC GRASS	(G)
Melica ciliata	EYELASH PEARL GRASS	(G)
Melica nutans	MOUNTAIN MELICK	(G)
Melica uniflora	WOOD MELICK	(G)
Melicocca bijuga	GENIP TREE	(S)
Melicocca bijuga	HONEY-BERRY	(S)
Melicocca bijuga	MALMONCILLO	(TT)
Melicocca bijuja	GENIP	(S)
Melicytus ramiflorus	MAHOE	(S)
Melicytus ramiflorus	WHITEYWOOD	(S)
Melilotus alba	WHITE MELILOT	(H)
Melilotus altissima	YELLOW MELILOT	(H)
Melilotus officinalis	KING'S CLOVER	(H)
Melilotus officinalis	MELILOT	(H)
Melilotus officinalis	RIBBED MELILOT	(H)
Melilotus officinalis	SWEET CLOVER	(H)
Melissa officinalis	BALM	(HB)

Know Your Common Plant Names

Botanical	Common	Type
Melissa officinalis	LEMON BALM	(HB)
Melissa officinalis aurea	GOLDEN BALM	(HB)
Melissa officinalis Variegata	VARIEGATED LEMON BALM	(HB)
Melittis melissophyllum	BASTARD BALM	(HB)
Melocactus communis	MELON CACTUS	(CS)
Menispermum canadense	CANADA MOONSEED	(CL)
Menispermum canadense	CANADIAN MOONSEED	(CL)
Menispermum canadense	MOONSEED	(CL)
Menisperum canadense	YELLOW PARILLA	(CL)
Mentha aquatica	WATER MINT	(WP)
Mentha arvensis	CORN MINT	(H)
Mentha arvensis piperascens	JAPANESE MINT	(HB)
Mentha citrata	LEMON MINT	(HB)
Mentha longifolia	HORSE MINT	(HB)
Mentha piperita	PEPPERMINT	(HB)
Mentha Pulegium	PENNYROYAL	(HB)
Mentha pulegium	PUDDING GRASS	(HB)
Mentha requienii	CORSICAN MINT	(HB)
Mentha species	MINT	(HB)
Mentha spicata	GARDEN MINT	(H)
Mentha spicata	LAMB MINT	(HB)
Mentha spicata	SAGE OF BETHLEHEM	(HB)
Mentha spicata	SPEARMINT	(HB)
Mentha spicata 'Crispa'	CURLY MINT	(HB)
Mentha suaveolens	APPLE MINT	(HB)
Mentha suaveolens	PINEAPPLE MINT	(HB)
Mentha x gentilis	BUSHY MINT	(HB)
Mentha x gentilis	GINGER MINT	(HB)
Mentha x piperita citrata	BERGAMOT MINT	(HB)
Mentha x piperita citrata	EAU-DE-COLOGNE MINT	(HB)
Mentha x verticilliata	WHORLED MINT	(H)
Mentha x verticilliata	WILD MINT	(HB)
Mentzelia	PRAIRIE LILY	(H)
Mentzelia lindleyi	BLAZING STAR	(S)
Menyanthes	BOG BEAN	(H)
Menyanthes	BUCK-BEAN	(H)
Menyanthes trifoliata	BROOK BEAN	(WP)
Menyanthes trifoliata	MARSH CLOVER	(WP)
Menyanthes trifoliata	MARSH TREFOIL	(WP)
Menyanthes trifoliata	WATER SHAMROCK	(H)
Mercurialis	HERB-MERCURY	(H)
Mercurialis	MERCURY	(H)
Mercurialis annua	ANNUAL MERCURY	(A)
Mercurialis perennis	DOG'S MERCURY	(H)
Meremia tuberosa	WOOD ROSE	(S)
Merendera	PYRENEAN MEADOW SAFFRON	(H)
Merremia tuberosa	YELLOW MORNING GLORY	(CL)

Know Your Common Plant Names

Botanical	Common	Type
Mertensia maritima	NORTHERN SHORE-WORT	(H)
Mertensia maritima	OYSTER PLANT	(H)
Mertensia pulmonarioides	VIRGINIAN COWSLIP	(H)
Mesembryanthemum	FIG MARIGOLD	(A)
Mesembryanthemum crystallinum	ICE PLANT	(A)
Mespilus germanica	MEDLAR	(T)
Mesurea ferrea	IRONWOOD	(TT)
Metasequoia	DAWN REDWOOD	(C)
Metasequoia	WATER FIR	(C)
Metasequoia glyptostroboides	SHUI-HSA	(C)
Methysticodendron amnesianum	TREE DATURA	(S)
Metrosideros	IRON TREE	(T)
Metrosideros robusta	RATA	(TS)
Metrosideros tomentosa	NEW ZEALAND CHRISTMAS TREE	(T)
Metroxylon sagu	SAGO PALM	(P)(F)
Meum athamanticum	SPIGNEL	(H)
Meum atramanticum	BALD MONEY	(H)
Michelia champaca	ORANGE CHEMPACA	(S/T)
Microcitrus	FINGER-LIME	(S)
Microcoelum weddellianum	WEDDEL PALM	(P)
Micromeria	PEPPER NETTLE	(H)
Micromeria thymifolia	MOUNTAIN MINT	(H)
Microsorium pteropus	JAVA MOSS	(FN)
Mikania	CLIMBING HEMPWEED	(CL/S)
Milium	MILLET GRASS	(G)
Milium effusum	WOOD MILLET	(G)
Milium effusum 'Aureum'	BOWLE'S GOLDEN GRASS	(G)
Miltonia	PANSY ORCHID	(O)
Mimosa pudica	HUMBLEPLANT	(HP)
Mimosa pudica	SENSITIVE PLANT	(HP)
Mimosa pudica	TOUCH-ME-NOT	(HP)
Mimulus	MONKEY FLOWER	(RH)
Mimulus aurantiacus	SHRUBBY MUSK	(S)
Mimulus cardinalis	SCARLET MONKEY FLOWER	(H)
Mimulus luteus	MONKEY MUSK	(H)
Mimulus moschatus	MUSK	(HA)
Mimusops balata	BEEFWOOD	(S)
Minuartia hybrida	FINE-LEAVED SANDWORT	(R)
Minuartia rubella	MOUNTAIN SANDWORT	(H)
Minuartia sedoides	CYPHEL	(H)
Minuartia sedoides	MOSSY CYPHEL	(H)
Minuartia verna	SPRING SANDWORT	(H)
Minuartia verna	VERNAL SANDWORT	(R)
Minuartia viscosa	STICKY SANDWORT	(H)
Mirabilis jalapa	FOUR O'CLOCK PLANT	(H)
Mirabilis jalapa	FOUR-O'-CLOCK	(S)
Mirabilis jalapa	JALAP	(H)

Know Your Common Plant Names

Botanical	Common	Type
Mirabilis jalapa	MARVEL OF PERU	(H)
Miscanthus floridulus	SILVER GRASS	(G)
Miscanthus sacchariflorus	AMUR SILVER GRASS	(G)
Miscanthus sin. 'zebrina'	ZEBRA GRASS	(G)
Miscanthus sinensis	CHINESE SILVER GRASS	(G)
Miscanthus sinensis 'Zebrinus'	TIGER GRASS	(G)
Mitchella repens	CHECKERBERRY	(S)
Mitchella repens	PARTRIDGE BERRY	(S)
Mitchella repens	SQUAW VINE	(S)
Mitchella repens	SQUAW-BERRY	(S)
Mitella	BISHOP'S CAP	(R)
Mitella	MITREWORT	(H)
Mitraria coccinea	MITRE FLOWER	(S)
Mochringia muscosa	MOSSY SANDWORT	(H)
Moehringia	SANDWORT	(R)
Moehringia trinervia	THREE-VEINED SANDWORT	(H)
Moenchia erecta	UPRIGHT CHICKWEED	(H)
Molina caerulea	PURPLE MOOR-GRASS	(G)
Molinia coerulea	BLUE BENT GRASS	(G)
Molospermum peloponnesiacum	STRIPED HEMLOCK	(H)
Molucella	SHELL FLOWER	(H)
Molucella laevis	BELLS OF IRELAND	(A)
Molucella laevis	MOLUCCA BALM	(H)
Molucella laevis	SHELL-FLOWER	(H)
Momordica balsmina	BALSAM APPLE	(H)
Momordica charantia	BALSAM APPLE	(F)
Momordica charantia	BALSAM PEAR	(H)
Monarda citriodora	LEMON BERGAMOT	(H)
Monarda didyma	BEE BALM	(H)
Monarda didyma	BERGAMOT	(H)
Monarda didyma	OSWEGO TEA	(H)
Monarda didyma	SWEET BERGAMOT	(H)
Monarda fistulosa	WILD BERGAMOT	(HB)
Monarda punctata	AMERICAN HORSEMINT	(H)
Monarda punctata	HORSE MINT	(H)
Moneses uniflora	ONE-FLOWERED PYROLA	(H)
Monodora myristica	CALABASH NUTMEG	(S)
Monopsis lutea	YELLOW LOBELIA	(A)
Monotropa hypophega	YELLOW BIRD'S NEST	(H)
Monotropa hypopitys	YELLOW-BIRD'S NEST	(H)
Monotropa uniflora	GHOST FLOWER	(H)
Monotropa uniflora	GHOSTFLOWER	(S)
Monotropa uniflora	INDIAN PIPE	(H)
Monstera acuminata	SHINGLE PLANT	(HP)
Monstera deliciosa	CERIMAN	(H/P)
Monstera deliciosa	SHINGLE PLANT	(HP)
Monstera deliciosa	SWISS CHEESE PLANT	(HP)

Know Your Common Plant Names

Botanical	Common	Type
Montia fontana	BLINKS	(H)
Montia fontana	WATER BLINKS	(WP)
Montia perfoliata	SPRING BEAUTY	(H)
Montia sibirica	PINK PURSLANE	(A)
Moquila utilis	POTTERY TREE	(TT)
Moraea	PEACOCK IRIS	(BB)
Moraea: Iris ochroleuca	BUTTERFLY IRIS	(BB)
Morchella esculenta	COMMON MOREL	(H)
Morina	WHORL-FLOWER	(H)
Morina longifolia	WHORL FLOWER	(H)
Morinda	INDIAN MULBERRY	(S)
Moringa	HORSE RADISH TREE	(TT)
Moringa oleifera	BEN OIL	(TT)
Moringa oleifera	HORSERADISH TREE	(TT)
Morus	MULBERRY	(T)
Morus alba	SILKWORM MULBERRY	(T)
Morus alba	WHITE MULBERRY	(T)
Morus alba 'Pendula'	WEEPING MULBERRY	(T)
Morus nigra	BLACK MULBERRY	(T)
Morus nigra	COMMON MULBERRY	(T)
Morus rubra	RED MULBERRY	(T)
Mucuna pruriens	COWHAGE	(H)
Muehlenbeckia adpressa	AUSTRALIAN IVY	(CL)
Muehlenbeckia complexa	WIRE-PLANT	(CL)
Mundulea sericea	SILVER BUSH	(S)
Murraya	SATINWOOD TREE	(T)
Murraya exotica	ORANGE JESSAMINE	(S)
Murraya koenigii	CURRY LEAF	(S)
Murraya koenigii	KARAPINCHA	(S)
Murraya paniculata	CURRY-LEAF	(S)
Musa basjoo	JAPANESE BANANA	(F)
Musa cavendishii	CANARY ISLANDS BANANA	(F)
Musa coccinea	SCARLET BANANA	(F)
Musa ornata	FLOWERING BANANA	(H)
Musa paradisiaca	PLANTAIN BANANA	(F)
Musa sapientum	BANANA	(F)
Musa textilis	ABACA	(F)
Musa textilis	MANILA HEMP	(CF)
Musanga cecropioides	UMBRELLA TREE	(TT)
Muscari	GRAPE HYACINTH	(BB)
Muscari botryoides	SMALL GRAPE HYACINTH	(BB)
Muscari comosum	FEATHER HYACINTH	(BB)
Muscari comosum	TASSEL HYACINTH	(BB)
Muscari moschatum	MUSK HYACINTH	(BB)
Muscari muscarini	MUSK HYACINTH	(BB)
Muscari neglectum	COMMON GRAPE HYACINTH	(BB)
Mussaenda erythrophylla	RED FLAG BUSH	(TS)

Know Your Common Plant Names

Botanical	Common	Type
Myagrum perfoliatum	MITRE CRESS	(H)
Mycelis muralis	WALL LETTUCE	(H)
Mycena ribula	LITTLE NAIL FUNGUS	(FU)
Myoporum laetum	NGAIO	(S)
Myosotidium	ANTARCTIC FORGET-ME-NOT	(H)
Myosotidium hortensia	CHATHAM ISLAND LILY	(H)
Myosotis	FORGET-ME-NOT	(H)
Myosotis	SCORPION GRASS	(B)
Myosotis alpestris	ALPINE FORGET-ME-NOT	(R)
Myosotis aquaticum	WATER CHICKWEED	(WP)
Myosotis arvensis	FIELD FORGET-ME-NOT	(H)
Myosotis discolor	YELLOW FORGET-ME-NOT	(H)
Myosotis scopioides	WATER FORGET-ME-NOT	(WP)
Myosotis scorpioides	WATER-FORGET-ME-NOT	(WP)
Myosotis secunda	MARSH FORGET-ME-NOT	(H)
Myosotis sylvatica	WOOD FORGET-ME-NOT	(H)
Myosurus minimus	MOUSE TAIL	(H)
Myosurus minimus	MOUSE-TAIL	(H)
Myosurus minimus	MOUSETAIL	(H)
Myrica californica	CALIFORNIAN BAYBERRY	(S)
Myrica cerifera	CANDLEBERRY	(S)
Myrica cerifera	TALLOW SHRUB	(S)
Myrica cerifera	WAX MYRTLE	(S)
Myrica gale	BOG MYRTLE	(S)
Myrica gale	GALE	(S)
Myrica gale	SWEET GALE	(S)
Myrica pennsylvanica	NORTHERN BAYBERRY	(S)
Myrica pensylvanica	BAYBERRY	(S)
Myricaria	FALSE TAMARISK	(S)
Myriocephalus stuartii	POACHED EGGS	(H)
Myriophyllum	WATER-MILFOIL	(WP)
Myriophyllum aquaticum	PARROTS FEATHER	(WP)
Myriophyllum spicatum	SPIKED WATER MILFOIL	(WP)
Myriophyllum verticilliatum	WHORLED WATER MILFOIL	(WP)
Myristica flagrans	NUTMEG	(HB)
Myristica fragrans	MACE	(HB)
Myroxylon balsamum	TOLU TREE	(P)
Myroxylon pereirae	BALSAM OF PERU	(TS)
Myroxylon pereirae	TOLU BALSAM	(TT)
Myrrhis odorata	BRITISH MYRRH	(HB)
Myrrhis odorata	MYRRH	(HB)
Myrrhis odorata	SWEET BRACKEN	(HB)
Myrrhis odorata	SWEET CHERVIL	(HB)
Myrrhis odorata	SWEET CICELY	(HB)
Myrsina africana	AFRICAN BOXWEED	(T)
Myrsine africana	CAPE MYRTLE	(S)
Myrtillocactus geometrizans	BLUE CANDLE	(CS)

327

Know Your Common Plant Names

Botanical	Common	Type
Myrtus	MYRTLE	(S)
Myrtus communis	COMMON MYRTLE	(S)
Mysporum parvifolium	CREEPING BOOBIALLA	(TS)
Myssa sylvatica	TUPELO	(T)
Naegelia zebrina	TEMPLE BELLS	(HP)
Najas flexilis	FLEXIBLE NAIAD	(WP)
Najas marina	GREATER NAIAD	(WP)
Nandina	CHINESE SACRED BAMBOO	(S)
Nandina	HEAVENLY BAMBOO	(S)
Nandina	NANTEN	(S)
Nandina	SACRED BAMBOO	(S)
Napoleona heudottii	NAPOLEAN'S BUTTON	(TT)
Narcissus	DAFFODIL	(BB)
Narcissus	DAFFY-DOWN-DILLY	(BB)
Narcissus 'Actaea' (false)	PHEASANT-EYE NARCISSUS	(BB)
Narcissus bulbocodium	HOOP-PETTICOAT	(BB)
Narcissus jonquilla	JONQUIL	(BB)
Narcissus jonquilla	WILD JONQUIL	(WP)
Narcissus poeticus	POET'S NARCISSUS	(BB)
Narcissus poeticus recurvus	PHEASANT-EYE NARCISSUS	(BB)
Narcissus pseudonarcissus	LENT LILY	(BB)
Narcissus pseudonarcissus	WILD DAFFODIL	(BB)
Narcissus pseudonarcissus obvallaris	TENBY DAFFODIL	(BB)
Narcissus tazetta	BUNCH-FLOWERED NARCISSUS	(WP)
Narcissus tazetta orientalis	CHINESE SACRED LILY	(BB)
Narcissus tazetta papyraceus	PAPERWHITES	(BB)
Narcissus triandus albus	ANGELS TEARS	(BB)
Narcissus x medioluteus	PRIMROSE PEERLESS	(BB)
Nardostachys jatamansi	SPIKENARD	(TS)
Nardus stricta	MAT GRASS	(G)
Nardus stricta	MOOR MAT GRASS	(G)
Narthecium ossifragum	BOG ASPHODEL	(H)
Nasturtium officinale	WATER CRESS	(CV)
Nauclea latifolia	AFRICAN PEACH	(TT)
Nectandra rodiaei	GREENHEART	(TT)
Nelumbo	SACRED BEAN	(H)
Nelumbo	SACRED LOTUS	(WP)
Nelumbo	YELLOW SACRED BEAN	(WP)
Nelumbo nucifera	LOTUS	(WP)
Nelumbo nucifera	SACRED INDIAN LOTUS	(WP)
Nemalion helminthoidesn	SEA NOODLE	(SW)
Nemesia strumosa	NEMESIA	(A)
Nemopanthus	MOUNTAIN HOLLY	(S)
Nemophila maculata	FIVE-SPOT BABY	(A)
Nemophila menziesii	BABY BLUE EYES	(A)
Nemophila phacelia	CALIFORNIAN BLUEBELL	(A)
Nemophile maculata	FIVE SPOT	(A)

Know Your Common Plant Names

Botanical	Common	Type
Neobessya similis	NIPPLE CACTUS	(CS)
Neoregelia carolinae	BLUSHING BROMELIAD	(HP)
Neoregelia carolinae tricolor	BLUSHING BROMELIAD	(HP)
Neoregelia spectabilis	FINGERNAIL PLANT	(HP)
Neotinea maculata	DENSE-FLOWERED ORCHID	(O)
Neottia nidus-avis	BIRD'S NEST ORCHID	(O)
Nepeta cataria	CATMINT	(H)
Nepeta cataria	CATNEP	(H)
Nepeta cataria	CATNIP	(H)
Nephelium lappaceum	PULASAN	(TT)
Nephelium lappaceum	RAMBUTAN	(TF)
Nephelium malaiense	MATA KUCHING	(TT)
Nephelium mutabile	PULASAN	(TF)
Nephrolepis	SWORD FERN	(FN)
Nephrolepis cordifolia	ERECT SWORD FERN	(FN)
Nephrolepis exaltata	BOSTON FERN	(FN)
Nephrolepis exaltata bostoniensis	BOSTON FERN	(FN)
Nerine Sarniensis	GUERNSEY LILY	(BB)
Nerium oleader	OLEANDER	(S)
Nerium oleander	ROSEBAY	(S)
Nertera depressa	BEAD PLANT	(HP)
Neslia paniculata	BALL MUSTARD	(H)
Neviusa alabamensis	ALABAMA SNOW WREATH	(S)
Nicandra physaloides	APPLE OF PERU	(A)
Nicandra physaloides	SHOO-FLY PLANT	(A)
Nicodemia diversifolia	INDOOR OAK	(HP)
Nicotiana alata	TOBACCO PLANT	(A)
Nicotiana glauca	YELLOW TREE TOBACCO	(H)
Nicotiana rustica	TURKISH TOBACCO	(H)
Nicotiana sylvestris	FLOWERING TOBACCO	(H)
Nicotiana tabacum	COMMON TOBACCO	(H)
Nicotiana tabacum	TOBACCO	(A)
Nidularium fulgens	BLUSHING BROMELIAD	(HP)
Nierembergia	CUP FLOWER	(H)
Nierembergia rivularis	CUP FLOWER	(R)
Nigella	FENNEL-FLOWER	(A/H)
Nigella damascena	LOVE-IN-A-MIST	(A)
Nigella sativa	BLACK CUMIN	(A)
Nigella sativa	FENNEL FLOWER	(A)
Nigella sativa	NUTMEG FLOWER	(A)
Nigella sativa	ROMAN CORIANDER	(A)
Nigritella nigra	BLACK VANILLA ORCHID	(O)
Nolana	CHILEAN BELLFLOWER	(S)
Noltea africana	SOAP BUSH	(S)
Nonea pulla	NONEA	(H)
Nopalxochia ackermannii	ORCHID CACTUS	(CS)
Nopalxochia ackermannii	RED ORCHID CACTUS	(CS)

Know Your Common Plant Names

Botanical	Common	Type
Nothofagus	SOUTHERN BEECH	(T)
Nothofagus antarctica	ANTARCTIC BEECH	(T)
Nothofagus antarctica	GUINDO	(T)
Nothofagus antarctica	NIRE	(T)
Nothofagus antartica	NIRRE	(T)
Nothofagus betuloides	COIGUE DE MAGELLANES	(T)
Nothofagus cliffortioides	MOUNTAIN BEECH	(T)
Nothofagus cunninghamii	MYRTLE BEECH	(T)
Nothofagus dombeyi	COIGUE	(T)
Nothofagus fusca	RED BEECH	(T)
Nothofagus glauca	HUALO	(T)
Nothofagus glauca	ROBLE DE MAULE	(T)
Nothofagus menziesii	SILVER BEECH	(T)
Nothofagus obliqua	COYAN	(T)
Nothofagus obliqua	HUALLE	(T)
Nothofagus obliqua	ROBLE BEECH	(T)
Nothofagus obliqua	ROBLE PELLIN	(T)
Nothofagus procera	RAOUL	(T)
Nothofagus procera	RAULI	(T)
Nothofagus pumilio	LENGA	(T)
Nothofagus pumilio	ROBLE BLANCO	(T)
Nothofagus solandri	BLACK BEECH	(T)
Nothofagus truncata	HARD BEECH	(T)
Nothogagus gunnii	TANGLEFOOT BEECH	(T)
Notholaena	CLOAK FERN	(FN)
Notocactus haselbergii	SCARLET BALL CACTUS	(CS)
Notocactus leninghausii	GOLDEN BALL CACTUS	(CS)
Notocactus scopa	SILVER BALL CACTUS	(CS)
Notospartium carmicheliae	PINK BROOM	(S)
Notothlaspi rosulatum	PENWIPER PLANT	(H)
Nuphar	WATER LILY	(WP)
Nuphar advena	AMERICAN SPATTER DOCK	(WP)
Nuphar advena	SPATTER-DOCK	(WP)
Nuphar advena	YELLOW POND LILY	(WP)
Nuphar lutea	BRANDY BOTTLE	(WP)
Nuphar lutea	YELLOW WATER LILY	(WP)
Nutisia	CLIMBING GAZANIA	(CL)
Nuytsia floribunda	CHRISTMAS TREE	(TT)
Nuytsia floribunda	FIRE TREE	(TT)
Nyctanthes arbor-tristis	TREE OF SADNESS	(T)
Nyctanthes arbortristis	INDIAN NIGHT JASMINE	(CL)
Nymphaea	INDIA LOTUS	(WP)
Nymphaea	WATER LILY	(WP)
Nymphaea alba	WHITE WATER LILY	(WP)
Nymphaea caerulea	BLUE EGYPTIAN LOTUS	(WP)
Nymphaea capensis	BLUE WATER LILY	(WP)
Nymphaea capensis	CAPE BLUE WATER LILY	(WP)

Botanical	Common	Type
Nymphaea lotus	EGYPTIAN LOTUS	(WP)
Nymphaea lotus	WHITE EGYPTIAN LOTUS	(WP)
Nymphaea odorata	SWEET WATER LILY	(WP)
Nymphaea stellata	BLUE LOTUS OF INDIA	(WP)
Nymphaea stellata	BLUE LOTUS OF THE NILE	(WP)
Nyssa	SOUR GUM	(T)
Nyssa aquatica	COTTON GUM	(T)
Nyssa aquatica	WATER TUPELO	(T)
Nyssa candicans	OGECHEE LIME	(T)
Nyssa sylvatica	BLACK GUM	(T)
Nyssa sylvatica	PEPPERIDGE	(T)
Ochna serrulata	MICKEY-MOUSE PLANT	(S)
Ochroma lagopus	BALSA	(TT)
Ochroma pyramidale	BALSA	(TT)
Ocimum basilicum	BASIL	(HB)
Ocimum basilicum	SWEET BASIL	(HB)
Ocimum basilicum minimum	BUSH BASIL	(HB)
Ocimum basilicum 'Purpurascens'	DARK OPAL BASIL	(HB)
Ocotea	GREEN HEART	(TT)
Ocotea bullata	BLACK STINKWOOD	(TT)
Ocotea radiaei	GREENHEART	(TT)
Odontites verna	RED BARTSIA	(H)
Odontoglossum crispum	LACE ORCHID	(O)
Odontoglossum grande	TIGER ORCHID	(O)
Odontoglossum pulchellum	LILY OF THE VALLEY ORCHID	(O)
Odontoglossum pulchellum	LILY-OF-THE-VALLEY ORCHID	(O)
Oemleria cerasiformis	INDIAN PLUM	(S)
Oemleria cerasiformis	OSOBERRY	(S)
Oenanthe aquatica	FINE-LEAVED WATER DROPWORT	(H)
Oenanthe aquatica	WATER FENNEL	(H)
Oenanthe crocata	HEMLOCK WATER DROPWORT	(H)
Oenanthe crocata	HORSEBANE	(H)
Oenanthe crocata	WATER LOVAGE	(H)
Oenanthe fistulosa	COMMON WATER DROPWORT	(H)
Oenanthe fistulosa	WATER DROPWORT	(WP)
Oenanthe fistulosa	WATER LOVAGE	(H)
Oenanthe fluviatilis	RIVER WATER DROPWORT	(H)
Oenanthe lachenalis	PARSLEY WATER DROPWORT	(WP)
Oenocarpus batava	PATANA PALM	(P)
Oenothera biennis	EVENING PRIMROSE	(H)
Oenothera biennis	FIELD PRIMROSE	(H)
Oenothera fruticosa	SUNDROPS	(H)
Oenothera glazioviana	LARGE-LEAVED EVENING PRIMROSE	(H)
Oenothera missouriensis	PRAIRIE EVENING PRIMROSE	(H)
Oenothera perennis	SUN DROPS	(H)
Oenothera rosea	PINK EVENING PRIMROSE	(H)
Oenothera stricta	FRAGRANT EVENING PRIMROSE	(H)

Know Your Common Plant Names

Botanical	Common	Type
Oenothera tetragona	SUN DROPS	(H)
Olea africana	WILD OLIVE	(TT)
Olea europaea	OLIVE	(ST)
Olea ferruninea	INDIAN OLIVE	(T)
Olea laurifolia	BLACK IRON WOOD	(S)
Olearia	DAISY BUSH	(S)
Olearia	NEW ZEALAND DAISY BUSH	(S)
Olearia	TREE ASTER	(S)
Olearia	TREE DAISY	(S)
Olearia argophylla	MUSKWOOD	(S)
Olearia illicifolia	MAORI HOLLY	(S)
Olearia illicifolia	MOUNTAIN HOLLY	(S)
Olearia macrodonta	NEW ZEALAND HOLLY	(S)
Olearia phlogopappa	TASMANIAN DAISY BUSH	(S)
Olinia emarginata	TRANSVAAL HARD PEAR	(TT)
Olmadioperebea sclerophylla	INDIAN SNUFF	(H)
Omalotheca norvegica	HIGHLAND CUDWEED	(H)
Omalotheca sylvatica	HEATH CUDWEED	(H)
Omalotheca sylvatica	WOOD CUDWEED	(H)
Omphalodes linifolia	VENUS'S NAVELWORT	(H)
Omphalodes; Umbilicus	NAVELWORT	(H)
Omphalodes Verna	BLUE-EYED MARY	(H)
Omphalodes verna	CREEPING FORGET-ME-NOT	(H)
Oncidium	DANCING LADY ORCHID	(O)
Oncidium cheirophorum	COLOMBIA BUTTERCUP	(O)
Oncidium flexuosum	DANCING DOLL ORCHID	(O)
Oncidium papilio	BUTTERFLY ORCHID	(O)
Oncoba spinosa	SNUFFBOX TREE	(TT)
Onobrychis viciifolia	SAINFOIN	(H)
Onoclea sensibilis	SENSITIVE FERN	(FN)
Ononis arvensis	GROUND FURZE	(S)
Ononis natrix	GOAT-ROOT	(S)
Ononis natrix	LARGE YELLOW REST-HARROW	(H)
Ononis repens	REST HARROW	(H)
Ononis spinosa	SPINY RESTHARROW	(S)
Onopordon	THISTLE	(H)
Onopordon acanthium	COTTON THISTLE	(H)
Onopordon acanthium	DOWN THISTLE	(H)
Onopordon acanthium	SCOTCH THISTLE	(H)
Onopordon acanthium	SCOTTISH THISTLE	(B)
Onopordon acanthium	WOOLLY THISTLE	(B)
Onopordon arabicum	ARABIAN THISTLE	(B)
Onopordon arabicum	HERALDIC THISTLE	(H)
Onopordon arabicum	SILVER THISTLE	(B)
Onosma	DONKEY PLANT	(H)
Onosma pyramidale	HIMALAYAN COMFREY	(H)
Ophioglossum	SNAKE'S TONGUE	(H)

Know Your Common Plant Names

Botanical	Common	Type
Ophioglossum vulgatum	ADDER'S TONGUE FERN	(FN)
Ophiopogon	SNAKE'S BEARD	(H)
Ophiopogon jaburan	WHITE LILY TURF	(H)
Ophiopogon japonicus	MONDO GRASS	(H)
Ophrys apifera	BEE ORCHID	(O)
Ophrys holoserica	LATE SPIDER ORCHID	(O)
Ophrys insectifera	FLY ORCHID	(O)
Ophrys sphegodes	EARLY SPIDER ORCHID	(O)
Oplismenus hirtellus	BASKET GRASS	(HP)
Oplismenus hirtellus	RIBBON GRASS	(HP)
Oplopanax horridus	DEVIL'S CLUB	(T)
Optunia leptocaulis	DESERT CHRISTMAS CACTUS	(CS)
Opunta arbuscula	PENCIL CHOLLA	(CS)
Opuntia	CHOLLA	(CS)
Opuntia	INDIAN FIG	(CS)
Opuntia bigclorii	TEDDY BEAR CHOLLA	(CS)
Opuntia cylindrica	CANE CACTUS	(CS)
Opuntia ficus-indica	FIG OF INDIA	(CS)
Opuntia ficus-indica	INDIAN FIG CACTUS	(CS)
Opuntia imbricata	CHAIN-LINK CACTUS	(CS)
Opuntia leptocaulis	TASAJILLO	(CS)
Opuntia megacantha	NOPAL	(CS)
Opuntia microdasys	BUNNYEARS	(CS)
Opuntia microdasys	PRICKLY PEAR	(CS)
Opuntia microdasys rufida	CINNAMON CACTUS	(CS)
Opuntia rufida	CINNAMON CACTUS	(CS)
Opuntia rufida	RED BUNNY EARS	(CS)
Opuntia santa-rita	PURPLE PRICKLY PEAR	(CS)
Opuntia schottii	DEVIL CACTUS	(CS)
Opuntia schottii	DOG CHOLLA	(CS)
Opuntia subulata	EVE'S PIN CACTUS	(CS)
Opuntia versiculor	STAGHORN CHOLLA	(CS)
Opuntia vestita	COTTON-POLE CACTUS	(CS)
Opuntia vestita	COTTONPOLE CACTUS	(CS)
Opuntia vestita	OLD MAN OPUNTIA	(CS)
Orbignya speciosa	BABASSU	(P)
Orbignya speciosa	BABASSU PALM	(P)
Orchis coriophora	BUG ORCHID	(O)
Orchis laxiflora	JERSEY ORCHID	(O)
Orchis mascula	DEAD MAN'S FINGERS	(O)
Orchis mascula	EARLY PURPLE ORCHID	(O)
Orchis militaris	SOLDIER ORCHID	(O)
Orchis morio	GREEN-WINGED ORCHID	(O)
Orchis moro	GANDERGOOSE	(O)
Orchis purpurea	LADY ORCHID	(O)
Orchis simia	MONKEY ORCHID	(O)
Orchis tridentata	TOOTHED ORCHID	(O)

Botanical	Common	Type
Orchis ustulata	BURNT-TIP ORCHID	(O)
Orchis ustulata	DWARF ORCHID	(O)
Oreocereus trollii	OLD MAN OF THE ANDES	(CO)
Oreopteris limbosperma	LEMON-SCENTED FERN	(FN)
Origanum	MARJORY	(HB)
Origanum dictamnus	CRETAN DITTANY	(H)
Origanum majorana	SWEET MARJORAM	(HB)
Origanum onites	POT MARJORAM	(HB)
Origanum vulgare	OREGANO	(HB)
Origanum vulgare	WILD MARJORAM	(HB)
Origanum vulgare 'Aureum'	GOLDEN MARJORY	(HB)
Orlaya grandiflora	ORLAYA	(H)
Ornithogallum nutans	DROOPING STAR OF BETHLEHEM	(BB)
Ornithogalum pyrenaicum	BATH ASPARAGUS	(BB)
Ornithogalum pyrenaicum	FRENCH ASPARAGUS	(BB)
Ornithogalum thyrsoides	CHINCHERINCHEE	(BB)
Ornithogalum umbellatum	STAR OF BETHLEHEM	(BB)
Ornithopus perpusillus	BIRD'S FOOT	(H)
Ornithopus perpusillus	BIRDS FOOT	(H)
Ornithopus sativus	CULTIVATED BIRD'S FOOT	(H)
Orobanche	BROOMRAPE	(H)
Orobanche alba	RED BROOMRAPE	(PE/H)
Orobanche alba	THYME BROOMRAPE	(PE/H)
Orobanche gracilis	SLENDER BROOMRAPE	(PE/H)
Orobanche hederae	IVY BROOMRAPE	(PE/H)
Orobanche maritima	CARROT BROOMRAPE	(PE/H)
Orobanche minor	COMMON BROOMRAPE	(PE/H)
Orobanche purpurea	YARROW BROOMRAPE	(PE/H)
Orobanche ramosa	HEMP BROOMRAPE	(PE/H)
Orobanche rapum-genistre	GREATER BROOMRAPE	(PE/H)
Orontium	GOLDEN CLUB	(H)
Oryza sativa	RICE	(G)
Osmanthus	SWEET OLIVE	(S)
Osmanthus americanus	DEVILWOOD	(S)
Osmanthus fragrans	FRAGRANT OLIVE	(S)
Osmanthus heterophyllus	FALSE HOLLY	(S)
Osmunda	FLOWERING FERN	(FN)
Osmunda cinnamomea	CINNAMON FERN	(FN)
Osmunda regalis	ROYAL FERN	(FN)
Osteospermum	AFRICAN DAISY	(H)
Ostrowskia magnifica	GIANT BELLFLOWER	(BB)
Ostrya carpinfolia	HOP HORNBEAM	(T)
Ostrya carpinifolia	EUROPEAN HOP HORNBEAM	(T)
Ostrya japonica	JAPANESE HOP HORNBEAM	(T)
Ostrya virginiana	EASTERN HOP HORNBEAM	(T)
Ostrya virginiana	LEVER-WOOD	(T)
Ostryavirginiana	IRONWOOD	(T)

Know Your Common Plant Names

Botanical	Common	Type
Othonna	AFRICAN RAGWORT	(H)
Oudemansiella mucida	POACHED EGG FUNGUS	(FU)
Oudemansiella radicata	LONGROOT	(FU)
Ourisia macrophylla	MOUNTAIN FOXGLOVE	(H)
Oxalis Acetosella	SHAMROCK	(H)
Oxalis acetosella	WOOD-SORREL	(H)
Oxalis articulata	PINK OXALIS	(H)
Oxalis caprina	GOATS FOOT	(H)
Oxalis corniculata	YELLOW SORREL	(H)
Oxalis pes-caprae	BERMUDA BUTTERCUP	(BB)
Oxandra lanceolata	LANCEWOOD	(TT)
Oxydendrum	SORREL TREE	(ST)
Oxydendrum arboreum	SOUR WOOD	(ST)
Oxyria digyna	MOUNTAIN SORREL	(H)
Oxytropis	LOCOWEED	(H)
Oxytropis campestris	YELLOW OXYTROPIS	(H)
Oxytropis halleri	PURPLE OXYTROPIS	(H)
Oxytropis pilosa	WOOLLY MILK-VETCH	(H)
Pachycereus pecten-aboriginum	NATIVE'S COMB	(CS)
Pachyphytum	BLUE HAZE	(H)
Pachyphytum glutinicaule	STICKY MOONSTONES	(CS)
Pachyphytum oviferum	MOONSTONES	(CS)
Pachyphytum oviferum	SUGARED-ALMOND PLUM	(CS)
Pachyrhizus erosus	YAM BEAM	(V)
Pachyrhizus tuberosus	JICAMA	(H)
Pachysandra	MOUNTAIN SPURGE	(S)
Pachysandra procumbens	ALLEGHENY SPURGE	(S)
Pachysandra terminalis	JAPANESE SPURGE	(S)
Pachystachys coccinea	CARDINAL'S GUARD	(HP)
Pachystachys lutea	LOLLIPOP PLANT	(HP)
Paeonia	PAEONY	(H/S)
Paeonia	PEONY	(HS
Paeonia delavayi	TREE PEONY	(S)
Paeonia lactiflora	CHINESE PEONY	(H)
Paeonia lutea 'ludlowii'	TREE PEONY	(S)
Paeonia suffruticosa	MOUTAN	(S)
Paeonia suffruticosa cvs	TREE PEONY	(S)
Palaquium gutta	GUTTA PERCHA	(TT)
Paliurus spina-christi	CHRIST'S THORN	(S)
Paliurus spina-christi	CROWN OF THORNS	(S)
Paliurus spina-christi	JERUSALEM THORN	(S)
Panax ginseng	GINSENG	(HB)
Panax ginseng	ORIENTAL GINSENG	(TS)
Panax pseudoginseng	SANQI GINSENG	(S)
Panax quinquifolium	AMERICAN GINSENG	(S)
Pancratium maritimum	MEDITERRANEAN LILY	(BB)
Pancratium maritimum	SEA DAFFODIL	(BB)

Botanical	Common	Type
Pancratium maritimum	SEA LILY	(BB)
Pandanus	SCREW PINE	(C)
Pandanus leram	NICOBAR BREADFRUIT	(TS)
Pandorea jasminioides	BOWER PLANT OF AUSTRALIA	(TS)
Pandorea jasminoides	BOWER PLANT	(S)
Pandorea pandorana	WONGA WONGA VINE	(CHP)
Panicum capillare	OLD-WITCH GRASS	(G)
Panicum capillare	WITCH GRASS	(G)
Panicum miliaceum	COMMON MILLET	(G)
Panicum miliaceum	PROSO	(G)
Panicum millaceum	BROOMCORN MILLET	(G)
Panicum sp.	MILLET	(V)G.
Panicum texanum	COLORADO GRASS	(G)
Panicum virgatum	SWITCH GRASS	(G)
Papaver	POPPY	(AH)
Papaver alpinum	ALPINE POPPY	(R)
Papaver commutatum	LADYBIRD POPPY	(A)
Papaver dubium	LONG-HEADED POPPY	(A)
Papaver glaucum	TULIP POPPY	(H)
Papaver nudicaule	ISLAND POPPY	(A)
Papaver orientale	ORIENTAL POPPY	(H)
Papaver pavoninum	PEACOCK POPPY	(A)
Papaver radicatum	ARCTIC POPPY	(H)
Papaver rhoeas	COMMON POPPY	(A)
Papaver rhoeas	COMMON RED POPPY	(H)
Papaver rhoeas	CORN POPPY	(A)
Papaver rhoeas	FIELD POPPY	(A)
Papaver rhoeas strains	SHIRLEY POPPY	(A)
Papaver rupifragum	SPANISH POPPY	(H)
Papaver somniferum	OPIUM POPPY	(A)
Papaver somniferum	WHITE POPPY	(A)
Paphiopedilum	SLIPPER ORCHID	(O)
Parachorea sp.	PHILLIPINE MAHOGANY	(TT)
Paradisea liliastrum	ST. BRUNO'S LILY	(H)
Parapholis strigosa	HARD GRASS	(G)
Parentucellia viscosa	YELLOW BARTSIA	(H)
Parietaria diffusa	WALL PELLITORY	(R)
Parietaria judaica	PELLITORY-OF-THE-WALL	(R)
Parietaria officinalis	PARIETARIA	(H)
Parinari curatellifolia	MOBALA PLUM	(TT)
Parinari excelsa	GUINEA PLUM	(TT)
Parinari macrophylla	GINGERBREAD PLUM	(TT)
Parinarium macrophyllum	GINGERBREAD TREE	(T)
Paris quadrifolia	HERB PARIS	(H)
Parkia speciosa	PETAI	(TT)
Parkinsonia aculeata	JERUSALEM THORN	(TT)
Parmentiera cercifera	PANAMA CANDLE TREE	(TT)

Botanical	Common	Type
Parmentiera cereifera	CANDLE TREE	(TT)
Parnassia palustris	GRASS OF PARNASSUS	(H)
Parochetus	BLUE OXALIS	(H)
Parochetus	SHAMROCK PEA	(H)
Parodia aureispina	GOLDEN TOM THUMB	(CS)
Paronychia	NAILWORT	(R)
Parrotia	PERSIAN IRONWOOD	(T)
Parrotia persica	IRONTREE	(T)
Parrotia persica	IRONWOOD	(T)
Parrya nudicaulis	PARRYA	(H)
Parthenocissus henryana	CHINESE VIRGINIA CREEPER	(CL)
Parthenocissus inserta	COMMON VIRGINIA CREEPER	(CL)
Parthenocissus quingefolia	AMERICAN IVY	(CL)
Parthenocissus quinquefolia	VIRGINIA CREEPER	(CL)
Parthenocissus tricuspidata	JAPANESE CREEPER	(CL)
Parthenocissus veitchii	BOSTON IVY	(CL)
Paspalum sp.	MILLET	(V)G.
Passerina	SPARROW-WORT	(H)
Passerina stelleri	GROUND JASMINE	(S)
Passiflora coerulea	BLUE PASSION FLOWER	(CL)
Passiflora edulis	GRANADILLA	(F)
Passiflora edulis	PASSION FRUIT	(F)
Passiflora edulis	PURPLE GRANADILLA	(CL)
Passiflora edulis flaviocarpa	YELLOW PASSION FRUIT	(F)
Passiflora incarnata	MAY APPLE	(CL)
Passiflora incarnata	MAYPOP	(CL)
Passiflora incarnata	PASSION FLOWER	(CL)
Passiflora laurifolia	JAMAICA HONEYSUCKLE	(CL)
Passiflora laurifolia	WATER MELON	(CL)
Passiflora maliformis	APPLE-FRUITED PASSION FLOWER	(CL)
Passiflora maliformis	SWEET CALABASH	(CL)
Passiflora quadrangularis	GIANT GRANADILLA	(CL)
Passiflora quandrangularis	GRANADILLA	(F)
Passiflora racemosa	RED PASSION FLOWER	(CL)
Passiflora suberosa	MELONCILLO	(TS)
Pastinaca sativa	PARSNIP	(V)
Pastinaca sativa	WILD PARSNIP	(H)
Paullinia	SUPPLE-JACK	(TS)
Paullinia cupana	GUARANA	(TF)
Paulownia	EMPRESS TREE	(T)
Paulownia	FOX-GLOVE TREE	(T)
Paulownia tomentosa	PRINCESS TREE	(T)
Pedicularis	WOOD-BETONY	(H)
Pedicularis palustris	MARSH LOUSEWORT	(A)
Pedicularis palustris	RED RATTLE	(A)
Pedicularis sceptrum-carolinum	MOOR-KING	(H)
Pedicularis sylvatica	LOUSEWORT	(H)

Botanical	Common	Type
Pedilanthus	JACOBS LADDER	(H)
Pedilanthus tithymaloides	JEW BUSH	(S)
Pedilanthus tithymaloides	REDBIRD FLOWER	(CS)
Pedilanthus tithymaloides	RIBBON CACTUS	(CS)
Pedilanthus tithymaloides	SLIPPER FLOWER	(CS)
Pediocactus simpsonii	PLAINS CACTUS	(CS)
Peganum harmala	SYRIAN RUE	(H)
Pelargonium	GERANIUM	(A)
Pelargonium	PELARGONIUM	(A)
Pelargonium capitatum	ROSE-SCENTED GERANIUM	(A)
Pelargonium citriodorum	LEMON-SCENTED GERANIUM	(A)
Pelargonium crispum	LEMON-SCENTED GERANIUM	(A)
Pelargonium erodium	STORK'S BILL	(HP)
Pelargonium filicifolium	BALSAM-SCENTED GERANIUM	(A)
Pelargonium glutinosum	PHEASANT FOOT	(A)
Pelargonium graveolens	ROSE-SCENTED GERANIUM	(A)
Pelargonium grossularioides	GOOSEBERRY GERANIUM	(A)
Pelargonium odoratissimum	APPLE SCENTED GERANIUM	(A)
Pelargonium peltatum	IVY LEAVED GERANIUM	(A)
Pelargonium peltatum	IVY-LEAVED GERANIUM	(A)
Pelargonium 'Prince of Orange'	ORANGE-SCENTED GERANIUM	(A)
Pelargonium quercifolium	OAK LEAVED GERANIUM	(HP)
Pelargonium radula	BALSAM-SCENTED GERANIUM	(A)
Pelargonium tomentosum	PEPPERMINT-SCENTED GERANIUM	(A)
Pelargonium x domesticum	REGAL PELARGONIUM	(A)
Pelargonium x fragrans	NUTMEG-SCENTED GERANIUM	(A)
Pelargonium x fragrans	PINE-SCENTED GERANIUM	(A)
Pelargonium x hortorum	BEDDING GERANIUM	(A)
Pelargonium x hortorum	ZONAL PELARGONIUM	(HP)
Pellaea	CLIFF BREAK FERN	(FN)
Pellaea	CLIFFBRAKE FERN	(FN)
Pellaea atropurpurea	PURPLE CLIFF BRAKE	(FN)
Pellaea rotundifolia	BUTTON FERN	(FN)
Pellaea viridis	GREEN CLIFF BRAKE	(FN)
Pellaea viridis	GREEN CLIFFBRAKE	(FN)
Pellionia dareavana	TRAILING WATERMELON BEGONIA	(HP)
Pellionia pulchra	RAINBOW VINE	(HP)
Pellionia pulchra	SATIN PELLIONIA	(HP)
Peltandra	ARROW-ARUM	(H)
Peltandra undulata	GREEN ARROW ARUM	(H)
Peltaria	SHIELD WORT	(H)
Peltophorum pterocarpum	COPPER-POD	(TS)
Peltophorum pterocarpum	YELLOW FLAME	(TT)
Pelvetia canaliculata	CHANNELLED WRACK	(SW)
Pelvetia canaliculata	COW TANG	(SW)
Pennisetum alopecuroides	CHINESE FOUNTAIN GRASS	(G)
Pennisetum glaucum	CUSCUS	(G)

Know Your Common Plant Names

Botanical	Common	Type
Pennisetum glaucum	PEARL MILLET	(G)
Pennisetum purpureum	NAPIER GRASS	(G)
Pennisetum setaceum	AFRICAN FOUNTAIN GRASS	(G)
Pennisetum setaceum	FOUNTAIN GRASS	(G)
Pennisetum villosum	ABYSSINIAN FEATHERTOP	(G)
Penstemon	BEARD TONGUE	(H)
Penstemon newberryi	MOUNTAIN PRIDE	(R)
Pentaglottis sempervirens	ALKANET	(H)
Pentaglottis sempervirens	GREEN ALKANET	(H)
Pentas lanceolata	EGYPTIAN STAR CLUSTER	(HP)
Penthorum sedoides	VIRGINIAN STONECROP	(H)
Peperomia	PEPPER ELDER	(HP)
Peperomia argyreia	RUGBY FOOTBALL PLANT	(HP)
Peperomia argyreia	WATER-MELON PEPEROMIA	(HP)
Peperomia caperata	EMERALD RIPPLE	(HP)
Peperomia fraseri	MIGNONETTE PEPEROMIA	(HP)
Peperomia glabella	WAX PRIVET	(HP)
Peperomia griseoargentea	IVY LEAF PEPEROMIA	(HP)
Peperomia griseoargentea	IVY PEPEROMIA	(HP)
Peperomia griseorgentea	SILVERLEAF PEPEROMIA	(HP)
Peperomia magnoliifolia	DESERT PRIVET	(HP)
Peperomia obtusifolia	BABY RUBBER PLANT	(HP)
Pereskia aculeata	BARBADOS GOOSEBERRY	(TT)
Pereskia aculeata	LEMON VINE	(CL)
Perilla frutescens	BEEFSTEAK PLANT	(HP)
Periploca graeca	SILK VINE	(CL)
Periploca sepium	CHINESE SILK VINE	(CL)
Peristeria	DOVE ORCHID	(O)
Peristeria elata	HOLY GHOST FLOWER	(H)
Perovskia	RUSSIAN SAGE	(S)
Persea americana	ALLIGATOR PEAR	(F)
Persea americana	AVOCADO	(F)
Persea borbonia	RED BAY	(T)
Persea indica	INDIAN LAUREL	(TS)
Persicaria bistorta	ADDERWORT	(H)
Persicaria bistorta	BISTORT	(H)
Persicaria bistorta	RED LEGS	(H)
Persicaria bistorta	SNAKEWEED	(H)
Persicaria polystachyum	HIMALAYAN KNOTGRASS	(H)
Petalonia fasciata	PETAL WEED	(SW)
Petalostemon purpureum	PRAIRIE CLOVER	(H)
Petasites albus	WHITE BUTTERBUR	(H)
Petasites fragrans	SWEET COLTSFOOT	(H)
Petasites fragrans	WINTER HELIOTROPE	(H)
Petasites hybridus	BUTTERBURR	(H)
Petasites hybridus	UMBRELLA PLANT	(H)
Petasites japonicus	GIANT BUTTERBUR	(H)

Know Your Common Plant Names

Botanical	Common	Type
Petasites vulgaris	BOG RHUBARB	(H)
Petasites vulgaris	BUTTER-DOCK	(H)
Petrea volubilis	BLUE PETREA	(TCL)
Petrea volubilis	BLUEBIRD VINE	(TCL)
Petrea volubilis	PURPLE WREATH	(H)
Petrea volubilis	QUEEN'S WREATH	(H)
Petrocallis pyrenaica	ROCK BEAUTY	(R)
Petrophila sessilis	PRICKLY CONESTICKS	(R)
Petrorhagia prolifera	PROLIFEROUS PINK	(H)
Petrorhagia saxifraga	TUNIC FLOWER	(H)
Petroselinum crispum	PARSLEY	(HB)
Petroselinum segetum	CORN PARSLEY	(H)
Petteria ramentacea	DALMATIAN LABURNUM	(S)
Peucedanum officinale	HOG'S FENNEL	(H)
Peucedanum officinale	SULPHUR-WEED	(H)
Peucedanum officinale	SULPHURWORT	(H)
Peucedanum ostruthium	MASTERWORT	(H)
Peucedanum palustre	MILK-PARSLEY	(H)
Peumus boldus	BOLDO	(T)
Peumus boldus	CHILEAN BOLDO TREE	(T)
Phacelia	BLUE BELL	(A)
Phacelia campanularia	PHACELIA	(A)
Phacelia whitlavia	CALIFORNIA BLUEBELL	(A)
Phaedranassa	QUEEN LILY	(BB)
Phalaenopsis	MOTH ORCHID	(O)
Phalaris arundinacea	REED CANARY-GRASS	(G)
Phalaris arundinacea	RIBBON GRASS	(G)
Phalaris arundinacea 'Picta'	GARDENER'S GARTERS	(G)
Phalaris canariensis	CANARY GRASS	(G)
Phallus impudicus	STINKHORN	(FU)
Phanerophlebia falcata	HOUSE HOLLY FERN	(FN)
Phanerophlebia falcata	JAPANESE HOLLY FERN	(FN)
Phanerophlebia falcatum	HOLLY FERN	(FN)
Phaseolus angularis	ADZUKIBEAN	(V)
Phaseolus aureus	GREEN GRAM	(V)
Phaseolus aureus	MUNG BEAN	(V)
Phaseolus calcaratus	RICE BEAN	(V)
Phaseolus caracalla	SNAIL FLOWER	(H)
Phaseolus coccineus	RUNNER BEAN	(V)
Phaseolus coccineus	SCARLET RUNNER	(V)
Phaseolus limensis	LIMA BEAN	(V)
Phaseolus lunatus	LIMA BEAN	(V)
Phaseolus vulgaris	BUTTERBEAN	(V)
Phaseolus vulgaris	FLAGEOLET BEAN	(V)
Phaseolus vulgaris	FRENCH BEAN	(V)
Phaseolus vulgaris	HARICOT BEAN	(V)
Phaseolus vulgaris	KIDNEY BEAN	(V)

Botanical	Common	Type
Phaseolus vulgaris	PINTO BEAN	(V)
Phegopteris connectilis	BEECH FERN	(FN)
Phellodendron	CORK TREE	(T)
Phellodendron amurense	AMUR CORK TREE	(T)
Phellodendron japonicum	JAPANESE CORK TREE	(T)
Philadelphus	MOCK ORANGE	(S)
Philadelphus	SYRINGA	(S)
Phillyrea	JASMINE BOX	(S)
Philodendron erubescens	BLUSHING PHILODENDRON	(HP)
Philodendron erubescens	REDLEAF PHILODENDRON	(HP)
Philodendron melanochrysum	BLACK-GOLD PHILODENDRON	(HP)
Philodendron scandens	HEARTLEAF PHILODENDRON	(HP)
Phleum	CAT TAIL	(G)
Phleum arenarium	SAND CAT'S TAIL	(G)
Phleum bertulonii	LESSER CAT'S TAIL	(G)
Phleum phleoides	PURPLE-STEM CAT'S TAIL	(G)
Phleum pratense	CAT'S TAIL	(G)
Phleum pratense	TIMOTHY GRASS	(G)
Phlomis fruticosa	JERUSALEM SAGE	(S)
Phlox douglasii	ALPINE PHLOX	(R)
Phlox drummondii	ANNUAL PHLOX	(A)
Phlox subulata	MOSS PHLOX	(R)
Phoenix canariensis	CANARY DATE PALM	(P)
Phoenix canariensis	CANARY ISLAND DATE PALM	(P)
Phoenix dactylifera	DATE PALM	(P)
Phoenix paludosa	MANGROVE DATE PALM	(P)
Phoenix roebelenii	MINIATURE DATE PALM	(P)
Phoenix sp.	DATE PALM	(P)
Pholidota	RATTLESNAKE ORCHID	(O)
Phoradendron flavescens	AMERICAN MISTLETOE	(PE)
Phormium	FLAX-LILY	(S)
Phormium	NEW ZEALAND FLAX	(S)
Phormium colensoi	MOUNTAIN FLAX	(S)
Phormium cookianum	MOUNTAIN FLAX	(S)
Photinia serrulata	CHINESE HAWTHORN	(T)
Phragmites australis	COMMON REED	(G)
Phragmites communis	REED	(G)
Phygelius capensis	CAPE FIGWORT	(H)
Phygelius capensis	CAPE FUCHSIA	(H)
Phygelius capensis	RIVER BELLS	(S)
Phyllanthus	OTAHEITE GOOSEBERRY	(S)
Phyllanthus acidus	INDIAN GOOSEBERRY	(TS)
Phyllitis scolopendrium	HART'S TONGUE FERN	(FN)
Phyllocladus alpinus	CELERY PINE	(C)
Phyllocladus aspleniifolius	ADVENTURE BAY PINE	(C)
Phyllocladus aspleniifolius	CELERY-TOP PINE	(C)
Phyllocladus aspleniifolius	CELERY-TOPPED PINE	(C)

Know Your Common Plant Names

Botanical	Common	Type
Phyllocladus glaucus	TOATOA	(C)
Phyllocladus trichomanoides	TANEKAHA	(C)
Phyllodoce caerulea	BLUE HEATH	(H)
Phyllodoce caerulea	MOUNTAIN HEATH	(H)
Phyllostachys	BAMBOO	(G)
Phyllostachys aurea	FISHPOLE BAMBOO	(G)
Phyllostachys aurea	GOLDEN BAMBOO	(G)
Phyllostachys aureosulcata	GOLDEN-GROOVE BAMBOO	(G)
Phyllostachys bambosoides	MADAKE	(C)
Phyllostachys flexuosa	ZIGZAG BAMBOO	(G)
Phyllostachys nigra	BLACK BAMBOO	(G)
Phyllostachys pubescens	MOSO-CHIKU	(C)
Physalis	BLADDER CHERRY	(H)
Physalis	BLADDER HERB	(H)
Physalis	CHERRY-BLADDER	(H)
Physalis	CHINESE LANTERN	(H)
Physalis alkekengi	WINTER CHERRY	(H)
Physalis ixocarpa	TOMATILLO	(TS)
Physalis peruviana	CAPE GOOSEBERRY	(H)
Physalis peruviana	STRAWBERRY TOMATO	(H)
Physalis philadelphica	TOMATILLO	(H)
Physocarpus opulifolius	NINE BARK	(S)
Physoplexis comosa	DEVIL'S CLAW	(HP)
Physospermum cornubiense	BLADDERSEED	(H)
Physostegia	FALSE DRAGONHEAD	(H)
Physostegia	OBEDIENT PLANT	(H)
Physostigma venenosum	CALABAR BEAN	(V)
Physostigma venenosum	ORDEAL BEAN	(TS)
Phytelephas macrocarpa	IVORY-NUT PALM	(P)
Phyteuma	RAMPION	(H)
Phyteuma nigrum	BLACK RAMPION	(H)
Phyteuma scheuchzeri	HORNED RAMPION	(H)
Phyteuma spicatum	SPIKED RAMPION	(H)
Phytolacca americana	PIGEON BERRY	(H)
Phytolacca americana	POKE ROOT	(H)
Phytolacca americana	POKEBERRY	(H)
Phytolacca americana	POKEWEED	(H)
Phytolacca americana	RED INK PLANT	(H)
Phytolacca americana	VIRGINIAN POKE	(H)
Phytolacca americana	VIRGINIAN POKE WEED	(H)
Phytolacca dioica	ELEPHANT TREE	(H)
Phytolacca dioica	OMBU	(H)
Phytolacea	GARGET	(H)
Picea	SPRUCE	(C)
Picea abies	CHRISTMAS TREE	(C)
Picea abies	COMMON SPRUCE	(C)
Picea abies	NORWAY SPRUCE	(C)

Botanical	Common	Type
Picea abies carpathica	CARPATHIAN SPRUCE	(C)
Picea abies 'Maxwellii'	MAXWELL SPRUCE	(C)
Picea abies 'Nidiformis'	NEST SPRUCE	(C)
Picea asperata	CHINESE SPRUCE	(C)
Picea asperata	DRAGON SPRUCE	(C)
Picea bicolor	ALCOCK SPRUCE	(C)
Picea brewerana	BREWERS WEEPING SPRUCE	(C)
Picea brewerana	SISKIYOU SPRUCE	(C)
Picea brewerana	WEEPING SPRUCE	(C)
Picea engelmannii	ENGELMANN SPRUCE	(C)
Picea glauca	WHITE SPRUCE	(C)
Picea glauca albertiana	ALBERTA WHITE SPRUCE	(C)
Picea glauca albertiana 'Glauca'	DWARF ALBERTA SPRUCE	(C)
Picea glehnii	SAKHALIN SPRUCE	(C)
Picea jezoensis	YEZO SPRUCE	(C)
Picea jezoensis hondoensis	HONDO SPRUCE	(C)
Picea koyamai	KOYAMA SPRUCE	(C)
Picea likiangensis purpurea	PURPLE SPRUCE	(C)
Picea mariana	BLACK SPRUCE	(C)
Picea montigena	CANDALABRA SPRUCE	(C)
Picea morrisonicola	MOUNT MORRISON SPRUCE	(C)
Picea morrisonicola	TAIWAN SPRUCE	(C)
Picea obovata	SIBERIAN SPRUCE	(C)
Picea omorika	SERBIAN SPRUCE	(C)
Picea orientalis	ORIENTAL SPRUCE	(C)
Picea polita	JAPANESE SPRUCE	(C)
Picea polita	TIGER TAIL SPRUCE	(C)
Picea polita	TIGER-TAIL SPRUCE	(C)
Picea pungens	COLORADA SPRUCE	(C)
Picea pungens 'Glauca' cvs	BLUE SPRUCE	(C)
Picea rubens	AMERICAN RED SPRUCE	(C)
Picea rubens	RED SPRUCE	(C)
Picea sitchensis	SITKA SPRUCE	(C)
Picea smithiana	HIMALAYAN SPRUCE	(C)
Picea smithiana	INDIAN SPRUCE	(C)
Picea smithiana	MORINDA SPRUCE	(C)
Picea smithiana	WEST HIMALAYAN SPRUCE	(C)
Picea spinulosa	EAST HIMALAYAN SPRUCE	(C)
Picea spinulosa	SIKKIM SPRUCE	(C)
Picraena excelsa	BITTER ASH	(T)
Picraena excelsa	JAMAICA QUASSIA	(TT)
Picramnia antidesma	CASCARA	(TS)
Picramnia pentandra	BITTERBUSH	(S)
Picreana excelsa	QUASSIA	(T)
Picris echioides	BRISTLY OX-TONGUE	(H)
Picris hieracioides	HAWKWEED OX-TONGUE	(H)
Pieris	LILY-OF-THE-VALLEY SHRUB	(S)

Know Your Common Plant Names

Botanical	Common	Type
Pieris floribunda	MOUNTAIN ANDROMEDA	(S)
Pieris phillyreifolia	CLIMBING HEATH	(S)
Pilea cadieri	ALUMINIUM PLANT	(HP)
Pilea involucrata	PAN-AMERICAN FRIENDSHIP PLANT	(HP)
Pilea involucrata	PANAMIGO	(HP)
Pilea microphylla	ARTILLERY PLANT	(HP)
Pilea nummulariifolia	CREEPING CHARLIE	(HP)
Pileantus peduncularis	COPPERCUPS	(HP)
Pilocarpus jaborandi	JABORAND	(T)
Pilocarpus jaborandi	JABORANDI	(TS)
Pimelea	RICE FLOWER	(S)
Pimelia	RICE-FLOWER	(S)
Pimelia physodes	QUALUP BELL	(S)
Pimenta	PIMENTO	(HB)
Pimenta officinalis	JAMAICA PEPPER	(S)(T)
Pimenta officinialis	ALLSPICE TREE	(T)
Pimpinella anisum	ANISE, ANISEED	(HB)
Pimpinella anisum	SWEET ALICE	(H)
Pimpinella major	GREATER BURNET SAXIFRAGE	(HB)
Pimpinella saxifraga	BURNETT SAXIFRAGE	(HB)
Pimpinella saxifraga	LESSER BURNET SAXIFRAGE	(HB)
Pinckneya pubens	BITTER-BARK	(TS)
Pinguicula	BUTTERWORT	(H)
Pinguicula grandiflora	GREATER BUTTERWORT	(R)
Pinguicula grandiflora	LARGE-FLOWERED BUTTERWORT	(R)
Pinguicula vulgaris	COMMON BUTTERWORT	(R)
Pinus	PINE	(C)
Pinus albicaulis	WHITE BARK PINE	(C)
Pinus aristata	BRISTLE-CONE PINE	(C)
Pinus armandii	DAVID'S PINE	(C)
Pinus attenuata	KNOBCONE PINE	(C)
Pinus ayacahuite	MEXICAN WHITE PINE	(C)
Pinus balfouriana	FOXTAIL PINE	(C)
Pinus banksiana	JACK PINE	(C)
Pinus bungeana	LACE-BARK PINE	(C)
Pinus bungeana	LACEBARK PINE	(C)
Pinus canariensis	CANARY ISLAND PINE	(C)
Pinus caribaea	CARIBBEAN PINE	(C)
Pinus cembra	AROLLA PINE	(C)
Pinus cembroides	MEXICAN NUT PINE	(C)
Pinus cembroides	MEXICAN STONE PINE	(C)
Pinus cembroides	NUT PINE	(C)
Pinus cembroides	NUTPINE	(C)
Pinus cembroides	PINYON PINE	(C)
Pinus cenbra	SWISS STONE PINE	(C)
Pinus clausa	SAND PINE	(C)
Pinus contorta	BEACH PINE	(C)

Botanical	Common	Type
Pinus contorta	SHORE PINE	(C)
Pinus contorta latifolia	LODGEPOLE PINE	(C)
Pinus coulteri	BIG CONE PINE	(C)
Pinus densiflora	JAPANESE RED PINE	(C)
Pinus echinata	SHORT-LEAF PINE	(C)
Pinus elliottii	SLASH PINE	(C)
Pinus engelmannii	APACHE PINE	(C)
Pinus flexilis	LIMBER PINE	(C)
Pinus gerardiana	CHILGHOZA PINE	(C)
Pinus halepensis	ALEPPO PINE	(C)
Pinus halepensis	JERUSALEM PINE	(C)
Pinus jeffreyi	JEFFREY'S PINE	(C)
Pinus khasya	KHASYA PINE	(C)
Pinus koraiensis	KOREAN PINE	(C)
Pinus lambertiana	SUGAR PINE	(C)
Pinus leucodermis	BOSNIAN PINE	(C)
Pinus luchuensis	LUCHU PINE	(C)
Pinus luchuensis	OKINAWA PINE	(C)
Pinus montezumae	MONTEZUMA PINE	(C)
Pinus montezumae	ROUGH-BARKED MEXICAN PINE	(C)
Pinus monticola	CALIFORNIAN MOUNTAIN PINE	(C)
Pinus monticola	MOUNTAIN WHITE PINE	(C)
Pinus monticola	WESTERN WHITE PINE	(C)
Pinus mugo	DWARF MOUNTAIN PINE	(C)
Pinus mugo	MOUNTAIN PINE	(C)
Pinus mugo pumilio	EUROPEAN SCRUB PINE	(C)
Pinus muricata	BISHOP PINE	(C)
Pinus Nigra	AUSTRIAN PINE	(C)
Pinus nigra caramanica	CRIMEAN PINE	(C)
Pinus nigra cebennensis	CEVENNES PINE	(C)
Pinus nigra cebennensis	PYRENEAN PINE	(C)
Pinus nigra maritina	CORSICAN PINE	(C)
Pinus occidentalis	CUBAN PINE	(C)
Pinus palustris	LONGLEAF PINE	(C)
Pinus palustris	PITCH PINE	(C)
Pinus palustris	SOUTHERN PINE	(C)
Pinus palustris	SOUTHERN PITCH PINE	(C)
Pinus parviflora	JAPANESE WHITE PINE	(C)
Pinus patula	JELECOTE PINE	(C)
Pinus patula	MEXICAN WEEPING-PINE	(C)
Pinus patula	SPREAD-LEAVED PINE	(C)
Pinus patula	SPREADING-LEAVED PINE	(C)
Pinus peuce	MACEDONIAN PINE	(C)
Pinus pinaster	BOURNEMOUTH PINE	(C)
Pinus pinaster	CLUSTER PINE	(C)
Pinus pinaster	MARITIME PINE	(C)
Pinus pinea	ITALIAN STONE PINE	(C)

Botanical	Common	Type
Pinus pinea	STONE PINE	(C)
Pinus pinea	UMBRELLA PINE	(C)
Pinus ponderosa	PONDEROSA PINE	(C)
Pinus ponderosa	WESTERN YELLOW PINE	(C)
Pinus pumila	DWARF SIBERIAN PINE	(C)
Pinus pumila	JAPANESE STONE PINE	(C)
Pinus pungens	HICKORY PINE	(C)
Pinus pungens	PRICKLY PINE	(C)
Pinus pungens	TABLE MOUNTAIN PINE	(C)
Pinus radiata	MONTEREY PINE	(C)
Pinus resinosa	AMERICAN RED PINE	(C)
Pinus resinosa	CANADIAN RED PINE	(C)
Pinus resinosa	RED PINE	(C)
Pinus rigida	NORTHERN PITCH PINE	(C)
Pinus roxhurgii	LONG-LEAVED INDIAN PINE	(C)
Pinus sabiniana	DIGGER PINE	(C)
Pinus strobus	DEAL PINE	(C)
Pinus strobus	EASTERN WHITE PINE	(C)
Pinus strobus	WEYMOUTH PINE	(C)
Pinus strobus	WHITE PINE	(C)
Pinus sylvestris	SCOTS PINE	(C)
Pinus sylvestris rubra	HIGHLAND PINE	(C)
Pinus tabulaeformis	CHINESE PINE	(C)
Pinus taeda	LOBLOLLY PINE	(C)
Pinus teocote	TWISTED-LEAVED PINE	(C)
Pinus thunbergii	BLACK PINE	(C)
Pinus thunbergii	JAPANESE BLACK PINE	(C)
Pinus Toeda	FRANKINCENSE PINE	(C)
Pinus torreyana	SOLEDAD PINE	(C)
Pinus uncinata	MOUNTAIN PINE	(C)
Pinus virginiana	SCRUB PINE	(C)
Pinus wallichiana	BHUTAN PINE	(C)
Pinus wallichianum	HIMALAYAN PINE	(C)
Pinus x holfordiana	HOLFORD'S PINE	(C)
Piper album	WHITE PEPPER	(F)
Piper angustifolium	MATICO	(S)
Piper betel	BETEL	(T)
Piper betle	BETEL PEPPER	(TF)
Piper cubeba	CUBEBS	(H)
Piper methysticum	KAVA KAVA	(F)
Piper nigrum	BLACK PEPPER	(F)
Piper nigrum	PEPPER	(F)
Piptanthus	EVERGREEN LABURNUM	(S)
Piptanthus	NEPAL LABURNUM	(S)
Piptoporus betulinus	BIRCH BRACKET	(FU)
Piscidia erythrina	FISH-POISON TREE	(TS)
Piscidia erythrina	JAMAICA DOGWOOD	(TS)

Know Your Common Plant Names

Botanical	Common	Type
Piscidia erythrina	JAMAICAN DOGWOOD	(TS)
Pisonia alba	LETTUCE TREE	(TS)
Pisonia grandis	BROWN CABBAGE TREE	(TS)
Pisonia umbellifera	BIRD-CATCHER TREE	(HP)
Pisonia umbellifera	PARA PARA	(HP)
Pistacia chinensis	CHINESE PISTACHIO	(T)
Pistacia lentiscus	MASTIC	(T)
Pistacia terabinthus	TURPENTINE TREE	(T)
Pistacia terebinthus	CHIAN TURPENTINE TREE	(T)
Pistacia terebinthus	TEREBINTH	(T)
Pistacia vera	PISTACHIO	(T)
Pistia	WATER LETTUCE	(WP)
Pistia stratiotes	WATER LETTUCE	(WP)
Pisum sativum	PEA	(V)
Pisum sativum saccharata	MANGE TOUT	(V)
Pisum sativum saccharatum	SUGAR PEA	(V)
Pittosporum	PARCHMENT-BARK	(S/T)
Pittosporum crassifolium	KARO	(S)
Pittosporum eugenioides	TARATA	(S)
Pittosporum tenuifolium	KOHUHU	(S)
Pittosporum tobira	AUSTRALIAN LAUREL	(ST)
Pittosporum tobira	TOBIRA	(S)
Pittosporum undulatum	VICTORIA BOX	(S)
Pittosporum undulatum	VICTORIAN BOX	(V)
Pityrogramma	GOLD FERN	(FN)
Pityrogramma calomelanos	SILVER FERN	(FN)
Plagianthus	RIBBONWOOD	(T)
Planera aquatica	WATER ELM	(T)
Plantago	PLANTAIN	(H)
Plantago coronopus	BUCK'S HORN PLANTAIN	(H)
Plantago indica	PSYLLIUM SEEDS	(H)
Plantago lanceolata	RIBWORT	(H)
Plantago lanceolata	RIBWORT PLANTAIN	(H)
Plantago major	GREAT PLANTAIN	(H)
Plantago major	WAYBREAD	(H)
Plantago maritima	SEA PLANTAIN	(H)
Plantago media	HOARY PLANTAIN	(H)
Plantago ovata	ISPAGHUL PLAINTAIN	(H)
Platanthera bifolia	LESSER BUTTERFLY ORCHID	(O)
Platanthera chlorantha	BUTTERFLY ORCHID	(O)
Platanthera chloranthe	GREATER BUTTERFLY ORCHID	(O)
Platanus	PLANE	(T)
Platanus occidentalis	AMERICAN PLANE	(T)
Platanus occidentalis	AMERICAN SYCAMORE	(T)
Platanus occidentalis	BUTTONWOOD	(T)
Platanus occidentalis	WESTERN PLANE	(T)
Platanus orientalis	CHENNAR TREE	(T)

Botanical	Common	Type
Platanus orientalis	ORIENTAL PLANE	(T)
Platanus x hispanica	LONDON PLANE	(T)
Platycerium bifurcatum	STAG'S HORN FERN	(FN)
Platycodon	BALLOON FLOWER	(H)
Platycodon	CHINESE BALLOON FLOWER	(H)
Platycodon	CHINESE BELLFLOWER	(H)
Platycodon	JAPANESE BALLOON FLOWER	(H)
Platycodon	JAPANESE BELLFLOWER	(H)
Platylobium	FLAT PEA	(F)
Platystemon californicus	CREAM CUPS	(A)
Plectranthus australis	SWEDISH IVY	(HP)
Plectranthus oertendahlii	CANDLE PLANT	(HP)
Pleione	INDIAN CROCUS	(O)
Pleiospilos bolusii	LIVING ROCK	(CS)
Pleiospilos bolusii	MIMICRY PLANT	(CS)
Pleomele reflexa 'Variegata'	SONG OF INDIA	(HP)
Pleomeles reflexa	SONG OF INDIA	(HP)
Pleurotus ostreatus	OYSTER FUNGUS	(FU)
Pluchea	STINKWEED	(H)
Plueria rubra	PAGODA TREE	(TT)
Plumbaga auriculata	SOUTH AFRICAN LEADWORT	(TS)
Plumbago	LEADWORT	(HP)
Plumbago auriculata	CAPE LEADWORT	(TS)
Plumera rubra	RED JASMINE	(TT)
Plumeria rubra	FRANGIPANI	(TT)
Plumeria rubra	TEMPLE TREE	(TT)
Plumeria rubra	WEST INDIAN JASMINE	(TT)
Poa alpina	ALPINE MEADOW GRASS	(G)
Poa annua	ANNUAL MEADOW GRASS	(A)
Poa bulbosa	BULBOUS MEADOW GRASS	(G)
Poa nemoralis	WOOD MEADOW GRASS	(G)
Poa palustris	MARSH MEADOW GRASS	(G)
Poa pratensis	KENTUCKY BLUE GRASS	(G)
Poa pratensis	MEADOW GRASS	(G)
Poa pratensis	SMOOTH MEADOW-GRASS	(G)
Poa trivialis	ROUGH MEADOW-GRASS	(G)
Podalyria calyptrata	WATER BLOSSOM PEA	(TS)
Podocarpus	ALPINE TOTARA	(C)
Podocarpus andinus	CHILEAN YEW	(C)
Podocarpus andinus	PLUM-FRUITED YEW	(C)
Podocarpus elatus	SHE PINE	(C)
Podocarpus elatus	WHITE PINE	(C)
Podocarpus elongatus	AFRICAN YELLOW WOOD	(C)
Podocarpus falcatus	OTENIQUA YELLOW WOOD	(C)
Podocarpus gracilior	AFRICAN FERN PINE	(C)
Podocarpus macrophyllus	BUDDHIST PINE	(C)
Podocarpus macrophyllus	KUSAMAKI	(C)

Botanical	Common	Type
Podocarpus spicatus	MATAI	(C)
Podocarpus totara	TOTARA	(C)
Podophyllum pelatum	MAY APPLE	(H)
Podophyllum peltatum	AMERICAN MANDRAKE	(H)
Podophyllum peltatum	RACOON BERRY	(H)
Podophyllum peltatum	WILD LEMON	(H)
Podophyllum pertatum	DUCKSFOOT	(H)
Podranea ricasoliana	PINK TRUMPET VINE	(TCL)
Pogonia	ADDER'S MOUTH	(O)
Pogonia	SNAKE'S MOUTH ORCHID	(O)
Pogostemon patchouli	PATCHOULI	(TS)
Polemonium coeruleum	GREEK VALERIAN	(H)
Polemonium coeruleum	JACOB'S LADDER	(H)
Polemonium reptans	ABCESS ROOT	(HB)
Polemonium reptans	AMERICAN GREEK VALERIAN	(H)
Polemonium reptans	BLUE BELLS	(H)
Polemonium reptans	SWEATROOT	(H)
Polianthes tuberosa	TUBEROSE	(H)
Polycarpon diphyllum	TWO-LEAVED ALLSEED	(H)
Polycarpon tetraphyllum	FOUR-LEAVED ALLSEED	(H)
Polycnemum majus	POLYCNEMUM	(H)
Polygala	MILKWORT	(SH)
Polygala	ROGATION FLOWER	(H/S)
Polygala calcarea	CHALK MILKWORT	(H)
Polygala chamaebuxus	GROUND BOX	(S)
Polygala chamaebuxus	SHRUBBY MILKWORT	(S)
Polygala senega	RATTLESNAKE ROOT	(H)
Polygala senega	SENEGA	(H)
Polygala senega	SNAKEROOT	(H)
Polygala serpyllifolia	HEATH MILKWORT	(H)
Polygala vulgaris	COMMON MILKWORT	(H)
Polyganatum x hybridum	DAVID'S HARP	(H)
Polygonatum commutatum	GIANT SOLOMON'S SEAL	(H)
Polygonatum multiflorum	LADY'S SEAL	(H)
Polygonatum x hybridum	SOLOMON'S SEAL	(H)
Polygonum	KNOTWEED	(H)
Polygonum amplexicaule	MOUNTAIN FLEECE	(H)
Polygonum ariculare	ARMSTRONG	(A)
Polygonum aviculare	BIRD'S TONGUE	(H)
Polygonum aviculare	COMMON KNOTGRASS	(H)
Polygonum aviculare	KNOTGRASS	(H)
Polygonum aviculare	NINE-JOINTS	(A)
Polygonum erectum	RUSSIAN KNOTGRASS	(H)
Polygonum hydropiper	BITING PERSICARIA	(H)
Polygonum hydropiper	RED KNEES	(H)
Polygonum hydropiper	SMARTWEED	(A)
Polygonum hydropiper	WATER PEPPER	(WP)

Know Your Common Plant Names

Botanical	Common	Type
Polygonum lapathifolium	PALE PERSICARIA	(H)
Polygonum maritimum	SEA KNOTGRASS	(H)
Polygonum nodosum	SPOTTED PERSICARIA	(H)
Polygonum oxyspermum	RAY'S KNOTGRASS	(H)
Polygonum persicaria	COMMON PERSICARIA	(H)
Polygonum persicaria	RED SHANK	(A)
Polygonum persicaria	REDLEGS	(H)
Polygonum persicaria	REDSHANK	(H)
Polygonum viviporum	ALPINE BISTORT	(H)
Polymnia uvedalia	BEARSFOOT	(H)
Polypodium	WALL FERN	(FN)
Polypodium aureum	HARE'S FOOT FERN	(FN)
Polypodium glycyrrhiza	LIQUORICE FERN	(FN)
Polypodium interjectum	WESTERN POLYPODY	(FN)
Polypodium vulgare	COMMON POLYPODY	(FN)
Polypodium vulgare	POLYPODY	(FN)
Polypogon monspeliensis	ANNUAL BEARD-GRASS	(G)
Polypogon viridis	WATER BENT	(G)
Polyporus squamosus	DRYAD'S SADDLE	(FU)
Polyscias balfouriana	BALFOUR ARALIS	(HP)
Polyscias balfouriana	DINNER PLATE ARALIA	(HP)
Polyscias guilfoylei	WILD COFFEE	(TS)
Polystichum	SHIELD FERN	(FN)
Polystichum acrostichoides	CHRISTMAS FERN	(FN)
Polystichum aculeatum	HARD SHIELD FERN	(FN)
Polystichum lonchitis	HOLLY FERN	(FN)
Polystichum munitum	SWORD FERN	(FN)
Polystichum munitum	WESTERN SWORD FERN	(FN)
Polystichum setiferum	SOFT SHIELD FERN	(FN)
Poncirus	JAPANESE BITTER ORANGE	(S)
Poncirus trifoliata	HARDY ORANGE	(S)
Pontaderia cordata	PICKEREL-WEED	(WP)
Populus	POPLAR	(T)
Populus alba	ABELE	(T)
Populus alba	WHITE POPLAR	(T)
Populus angustifolia	WILLOW-LEAVED POPLAR	(T)
Populus balsamifera	BALSAM POPLAR	(T)
Populus balsamifera	TACAMAHAC	(T)
Populus candicans	BALM OF GILEAD	(T)
Populus candicans	ONTARIO POPLAR	(T)
Populus canescens	GREY POPLAR	(T)
Populus deltoides	COTTONWOOD	(T)
Populus deltoides	EASTERN COTTONWOOD	(T)
Populus deltoides	NECKLACE POPLAR	(T)
Populus eugenei	CAROLINA POPLAR	(T)
Populus grandidentata	BIG-TOOTHED ASPEN	(T)
Populus heterophylla	SWAMP COTTONWOOD	(T)

Botanical	Common	Type
Populus lasiocarpa	CHINESE NECKLACE POPLAR	(T)
Populus nigra	BLACK POPLAR	(T)
Populus nigra 'Betulifolia'	DOWNY BLACK POPLAR	(T)
Populus nigra 'Betulifolia'	MANCHESTER POPLAR	(T)
Populus nigra 'Italica'	ITALIAN POPLAR	(T)
Populus nigra 'Italica'	LOMBARDY POPLAR	(T)
Populus 'Regenerata'	RAILWAY POPLAR	(T)
Populus 'robusta'	FALSE LOMBARDY POPLAR	(T)
Populus sargentii	GREAT PLAINS COTTONWOOD	(T)
Populus serotina	BLACK ITALIAN POPLAR	(T)
Populus 'Serotina Aurea'	GOLDEN POPLAR	(T)
Populus sieboldii	JAPANESE ASPEN	(T)
Populus temula	TREMBLING ASPEN	(T)
Populus tremula	ASPEN	(T)
Populus tremula	EUROPEAN ASPEN	(T)
Populus tremula 'Pendula'	WEEPING ASPEN	(T)
Populus tremuloides	AMERICAN ASPEN	(T)
Populus tremuloides	QUAKING ASPEN	(T)
Populus tremuloides 'pendula'	PARASOL DE ST.JULIEN	(T)
Populus trichocarpa	BLACK COTTONWOOD	(T)
Populus trichocarpa	WESTERN BALSAM POPLAR	(T)
Populus x berolinensis	BERLIN POPLAR	(T)
Populus x canadensis	HYBRID BLACK POPLAR	(T)
Porana paniculata	BRIDAL BOUQUET	(CL)
Porana paniculata	SNOW CREEPER	(CL)
Porphyra umbilicalis	LAVER	(SW)
Portulaca oleracea	PURSLANE	(A)
Portulaca oleracea sativa	GOLDEN PURSLANE	(H)
Portulacaria afra	ELEPHANT BUSH	(S)
Portulacca grandiflora	SUN PLANT	(A)
Potamogeton	POND WEED	(WP)
Potamogeton alpinus	REDDISH PONDWEED	(WP)
Potamogeton coloratus	FEN PONDWEED	(WP)
Potamogeton compressus	GRASS-WRACK PONDWEED	(WP)
Potamogeton crispus	CURLED PONDWEED	(WP)
Potamogeton epihydrus	AMERICAN PONDWEED	(WP)
Potamogeton filiformis	SLENDER-LEAVED PONDWEED	(WP)
Potamogeton friesii	FLAT-STALKED PONDWEED	(WP)
Potamogeton gramineus	VARIOUS-LEAVED PONDWEED	(WP)
Potamogeton lucens	SHINING PONDWEED	(WP)
Potamogeton natans	FLOATING PONDWEED	(WP)
Potamogeton nodosus	LODDON PONDWEED	(WP)
Potamogeton obtusifolius	GRASSY PONDWEED	(WP)
Potamogeton pectinatus	FENNEL PONDWEED	(WP)
Potamogeton perfoliatus	PERFOLIATE PONDWEED	(WP)
Potamogeton polygonifolius	BOG PONDWEED	(WP)
Potamogeton pusillus	SMALL PONDWEED	(WP)

Know Your Common Plant Names

Botanical	Common	Type
Potamogeton trichoides	HAIR-LIKE PONDWEED	(WP)
Potentilla	BUTTERCUP SHRUB	(S)
Potentilla	CINQUEFOIL	(HS)
Potentilla	FIVE FINGER	(H.S)
Potentilla alba	WHITE CINQUEFOIL	(H)
Potentilla anglica	PROCUMBENT CINQUEFOIL	(H)
Potentilla anserina	SILVERWEED	(H)
Potentilla anserina	SILVERY CINQUEFOIL	(H)
Potentilla argentea	HOARY CINQUEFOIL	(H)
Potentilla cinerea	GREY CINQUEFOIL	(H)
Potentilla crantzii	ALPINE CINQUEFOIL	(H)
Potentilla erecta	BLOODROOT	(H)
Potentilla erecta	EWE DAISY	(H)
Potentilla erecta	RED ROOT	(H)
Potentilla erecta	TORMENTIL	(H)
Potentilla fruiticosa	SHRUBBY CINQUEFOIL	(S)
Potentilla palustris	MARSH CINQUEFOIL	(H)
Potentilla recta	SULPHUR CINQUEFOIL	(H)
Potentilla recta	UPRIGHT CINQUEFOIL	(H)
Potentilla reptans	CREEPING CINQUEFOIL	(H)
Potentilla reptans	FIVE FINGERS	(H)
Potentilla reptans	FIVE-LEAF GRASS	(H)
Potentilla ruprestris	ROCK CINQUEFOIL	(R)
Potentilla sterilis	BARREN STRAWBERRY	(H)
Potentilla tabernaemontani	SPRING CINQUEFOIL	(H)
Potentilla tormentilla	SHEPHERD'S KNOT	(H)
Pouteria sapota	SAPOTE	(TS)
Prenanthes alba	LION'S FOOT	(H)
Prenanthes purpurea	PURPLE LETTUCE	(H)
Primula auricula	AURICULA	(R)
Primula auricula	BEAR'S EAR	(R)
Primula auricula	DUSTY MILLER	(R)
Primula denticulata	DRUMSTICK PRIMROSE	(H)
Primula elatior	OXLIP	(H)
Primula elatior	PAIGLE	(H)
Primula elatior	PAIGLES	(H)
Primula farinosa	BIRD'S EYE PRIMROSE	(H)
Primula florindae	GIANT YELLOW COWSLIP	(H)
Primula florindae	HIMALAYAN COWSLIP	(H)
Primula helodoxa	GLORY-OF-THE-MARSH	(H)
Primula malacoides	FAIRY PRIMROSE	(HP)
Primula obconica	GERMAN PRIMROSE	(H/P)
Primula polyantha	POLYANTHUS	(H)
Primula varis	FAIRY CUPS	(H)
Primula veris	COWSLIP	(H)
Primula veris	HERB PETER	(H)
Primula veris	KEYFLOWER	(H)

Know Your Common Plant Names

Botanical	Common	Type
Primula veris	PALSYWORT	(H)
Primula veris	ST. PETER'S WORT	(H)
Primula vulgaris	PRIMROSE	(H)
Proboscidea	UNICORN PLANT	(H)
Prosopis juliflora	MESQUITE	(S)
Prostranthera	AUSTRALIAN MINT BUSH	(S)
Prostranthera lasianthos	CHRISTMAS BUSH	(S)
Prostranthera nivea	SNOWY MINT-BUSH	(S)
Prostranthera rotundifolia	MINT BUSH	(S)
Protea aurea	WATERLILY PROTEA	(TS)
Protea barbigera	GIANT WOOLLY PROTEA	(TS)
Protea cynaroides	GIANT PROTEA	(TS)
Protea cynaroides	KING PROTEA	(TS)
Protea repens	SUGAR BUSH	(S)
Prumnopitys ferruginea	MIRO	(C)
Prumnopitys taxifolia	BLACK PINE OF NEW ZEALAND	(C)
Prumnopitys taxifolia	MATAI	(C)
Prunella	BRUNELLA	(H)
Prunella grandiflora	LARGE SELF-HEAL	(H)
Prunella vulgaris	HEAL-ALL	(H)
Prunella vulgaris	SELF-HEAL	(H)
Prunus	CHERRRY	(S.T.)
Prunus	FLOWERING CHERRY	(T)
Prunus alleghaniensis	AMERICAN SLOE	(S)
Prunus alleghaniensis	AMERICAN SOLE	(T)
Prunus 'Amanogawa'	LOMBARDY POPLAR CHERRY	(T)
Prunus americana	AMERICAN RED PLUM	(T)
Prunus angustifolia	CHICKASAW PLUM	(S)
Prunus armenaica	APRICOT	(F)
Prunus armeniaea	COMMON APRICOT	(S)
Prunus avium	GEAN	(T)
Prunus avium	MAZZARD	(T)
Prunus avium	WILD CHERRY	(ST)
Prunus avium 'Plena'	DOUBLE GEAN	(T)
Prunus besseyi	ROCKY MOUNTAIN CHERRY	(S)
Prunus besseyi	SAND CHERRY	(S)
Prunus brigantina	BRIANCON APRICOT	(T)
Prunus campanulata	BELL-FLOWERED CHERRY	(T)
Prunus campanulata	FORMOSAN CHERRY	(T)
Prunus canescens	GREYLEAF CHERRY	(S)
Prunus capuli	MEXICAN CHERRY	(TS)
Prunus cerasifera	CHERRY PLUM	(ST)
Prunus cerasifera	FLOWERING PLUM	(T)
Prunus cerasifera	"GREENGLOW"	(S.T)
Prunus cerasifera	MYROBALAN PLUM	(ST)
Prunus cerasifera nigra	BLACK-LEAVED PLUM	(S.T)
Prunus cerasifera 'Nigra'	BLAZE	(TS)

Know Your Common Plant Names

Botanical	Common	Type
Prunus cerasifera "Pissardii"	"PURPLE FLASH"	(S)
Prunus cerasifera 'Pissardii'	PURPLE-LEAVED PLUM	(S.T)
Prunus cerasus	SOUR CHERRY	(T)
Prunus cerasus "Semperflorens"	ALLSAINTS CHERRY	(T)
Prunus 'Cistena'	CRIMSON DWARF	(S)
Prunus 'Cistena'	PURPLE-LEAF SAND CHERRY	(S)
Prunus cornuta	HIMALAYAN BIRD CHERRY	(S)
Prunus dascycarpa	BLACK APRICOT	(S)
Prunus davidiana	CHINESE PEACH	(TS)
Prunus domestica	PLUM	(F)
Prunus domestica	PRUNE	(F)
Prunus domestica	WILD PLUM	(T)
Prunus domestica insititia	BULLACE	(F)
Prunus domestica insititia	DAMSON	(F)
Prunus domestica italica	GREENGAGE	(F)
Prunus dulcis	ALMOND	(T)
Prunus dulcis	COMMON ALMOND	(T)
Prunus dulcis	SWEET ALMOND	(T)
Prunus dulcis amara	BITTER ALMOND	(T)
Prunus emarginata	BITTER CHERRY	(T)
Prunus fruticosa	GROUND CHERRY	(S)
Prunus glandulosa	CHINESE BUSH BERRY	(S)
Prunus 'Hilling's Weeping'	WEEPING CHERRY	(T)
Prunus illicifolia	HOLLY-LEAVED CHERRY	(T)
Prunus incana	WILLOW CHERRY	(S)
Prunus incisa	FUJI CHERRY	(S.T)
Prunus 'Ivensii'	WEEPING CHERRY	(T)
Prunus jacquemontii	AFGHAN CHERRY	(S)
Prunus 'Kiku Shidare Sakura'	WEEPING CHERRY	(T)
Prunus 'Kiku-Shidare Sakura'	WEEPING CHERRY	(T)
Prunus laurocerasus	CHERRY LAUREL	(S)
Prunus laurocerasus	COMMON LAUREL	(S)
Prunus laurocerasus	LAUREL	(S)
Prunus litigiosa	TASSEL CHERRY	(T)
Prunus lusitanica	PORTUGAL LAUREL	(S)
Prunus maackii	MANCHURIAN CHERRY	(T)
Prunus mahaleb	ST. LUCIE CHERRY	(T)
Prunus maritima	BEACH PLUM	(T)
Prunus mume	JAPANESE APRICOT	(ST)
Prunus nipponica	JAPANESE ALPINE CHERRY	(T)
Prunus padus	BIRD CHERRY	(T)
Prunus padus	EUROPEAN BIRD CHERRY	(T)
Prunus padus 'Colorata'	PURPLE-LEAF BIRD CHERRY	(T)
Prunus pennsylvanica	WILD RED CHERRY	(T)
Prunus pensylvanica	PIN CHERRY	(T)
Prunus persica	COMMON PEACH	(F)
Prunus persica	PEACH	(F)

Know Your Common Plant Names

Botanical	Common	Type
Prunus persica nectarina	NECTARINE	(F)
Prunus prostrata	MOUNTAIN CHERRY	(S)
Prunus prostrata	ROCK CHERRY	(S)
Prunus pumila	DWARF AMERICAN CHERRY	(S)
Prunus pumila	SAND CHERRY	(S)
Prunus rufa	HIMALAYAN CHERRY	(T)
Prunus salicifolia	CAPULIN CHERRY	(T)
Prunus salicina	JAPANESE PLUM	(S)
Prunus sargentii	SARGENT'S CHERRY	(T)
Prunus serotina	AMERICAN BIRD CHERRY	(T)
Prunus serotina	BLACKCHERRY	(T)
Prunus serotina	RUM CHERRY	(T)
Prunus serrula	BIRCH-BARK CHERRY	(T)
Prunus serrula	PAPERBARK CHERRY	(T)
Prunus serrula	TIBETAN CHERRY	(T)
Prunus serrulata huphensis	CHINESE HILL CHERRY	(T)
Prunus serrulata huphensis	HUPEH CHERRY	(T)
Prunus serrulata 'Pubescens'	KOREAN HILL CHERRY	(T)
Prunus serrulata spontanea	HILL CHERRY	(T)
Prunus 'Shidare Yoshino'	WEEPING CHERRY	(T)
Prunus sibirica	SIBERIAN APRICOT	(S)
Prunus simonii	APRICOT PLUM	(T)
Prunus speciosa	OSHIMA CHERRY	(T)
Prunus spinosa	BLACKTHORN	(ST)
Prunus spinosa	SLOE	(ST)
Prunus sub.'Pendula'	WEEPING CHERRY	(T)
Prunus sub. 'pendula'	WEEPING SPRING CHERRY	(T)
Prunus subcordata	OREGON PLUM	(S)
Prunus subhirtalla 'Autumnalis'	WINTER CHERRY	(S/T)
Prunus subhirtella	SPRING CHERRY	(T)
Prunus subhirtella 'Ascendens'	ROSE BUD CHERRY	(T)
Prunus subhirtella 'Autumnalis'	AUTUMN CHERRY	(T)
Prunus subhirtella 'Autumnalis'	HIGAN CHERRY	(T)
Prunus subhirtella 'Autumnalis'	WINTER-FLOWERING CHERRY	(T)
Prunus 'tai-haku'	GREAT WHITE CHERRY	(T)
Prunus tenella	DWARF RUSSIAN ALMOND	(S)
Prunus tenella	RUSSIAN ALMOND	(S)
Prunus tomentosa	DOWNY CHERRY	(S)
Prunus tomentosa	NANKING CHERRY	(S)
Prunus virginiana	CHOKE CHERRY	(T)
Prunus virginiana	VIRGINIAN BIRD CHERRY	(T)
Prunus x dawyckensis	DAWYCK CHERRY	(T)
Prunus x gondounii	DUKE CHERRY	(T)
Prunus x yedoensis	YOSHINO CHERRY	(T)
Prunus yedoensis 'Shidare Yoshino'	WEEPING YOSHINO CHERRY	(T)
Prunus 'Amanogawa'	APPLE BLOSSOM CHERRY	(T)
Psalliota silvicola	WOOD MUSHROOM	(FU)

Know Your Common Plant Names

Botanical	Common	Type
Pseudocydonia sinensis	CHINESE QUINCE	(T)
Pseudolarix amabilis	GOLDEN LARCH	(C)
Pseudopanax arboreus	FIVE FINGERS	(S)
Pseudopanax crassifolius	LANCEWOOD	(S)
Pseudosasa japonica	ARROW BAMBOO	(G)
Pseudotsuga	DOUGLAS FIR	(C)
Pseudotsuga japonica	JAPANESE DOUGLAS FIR	(C)
Pseudotsuga macrocarpa	BIGCONE SPRUCE	(C)
Pseudotsuga macrocarpa	LARGE-CONED DOUGLAS FIR	(C)
Pseudotsuga menziesii	OREGON DOUGLAS FIR	(C)
Pseudotsuga menziesii glauca	BLUE DOUGLAS FIR	(C)
Pseudotsuga sinensis	CHINESE DOUGLAS FIR	(C)
Pseudowintera axillaris	HEROPITO	(S)
Pseudowintera colorata	PEPPER TREE	(S/T)
Pseuolmedia	BASTARD BREADNUT	(TT)
Psidium cattleianum	STRAWBERRY GUAVA	(F)
Psidium guajava	GUAVA	(F)
Psidium montanum	MOUNTAIN GUAVA	(F)
Psidium montanum	SPICE GUAVA	(F)
Psilocybe; Conocybe	MAGIC MUSHROOMS	(FU)
Psilocybe semilanceata	LIBERTY CAP	(FU)
Psilostrophe cooperi	PAPER FLOWER	(A)
Psoralea	PRAIRIE POTATO	(H)
Psoralea	SCURFY PEA	(V)
Psoralea pinnata	BLUE BROOM	(TS)
Ptelea trifoliata	HOP TREE	(ST)
Ptelea trifoliata	SHRUBBY TREFOIL	(S/T)
Ptelea trifoliata	STINKING ASH	(S)
Ptelea trifoliata	SWAMP DOGWOOD	(S/T)
Ptelea trifoliata	WAFER ASH	(ST)
Ptelea trifoliata	WINGSEED	(S/T)
Pteridium aquilinum	BRACKEN	(FN)
Pteridium aquilinum	BRAKE FERN	(FN)
Pteris	TABLE FERN	(FN)
Pteris cretica	CRETAN BRAKE	(FN)
Pteris cretica	CRETAN FERN	(FN)
Pteris cretica	RIBBON FERN	(FN)
Pteris ensiformis	SNOW BRAKE	(FN)
Pteris ensiformis	SWORD BRAKE	(FN)
Pteris multifida	SPIDER FERN	(FN)
Pteris tremula	AUSTRALIAN BRAKE	(FN)
Pteris tremula	TREMBLING BRAKE	(H)
Pteris tremula	TREMBLING FERN	(FN)
Pterocarpus angolensis	TRANSVAAL TEAK	(TT)
Pterocarpus angolensis	WEST AFRICAN BARWOOD	(TT)
Pterocarpus marsupium	BASTARD TEAK	(TT)
Pterocarpus marsupium	KINOS	(TT)

Know Your Common Plant Names

Botanical	Common	Type
Pterocarpus santalinus	RED SAUNDERS	(TT)
Pterocarya	WING NUT	(T)
Pterocarya fraxinifolia	CAUCASIAN WING NUT	(T)
Pterocarya rhoifolia	JAPANESE WING NUT	(T)
Pterocarya stenoptera	CHINESE WING-NUT	(T)
Pterocarya x rehderana	HYBRID WINGNUT	(T)
Pterostyrax hispida	ASGARA	(T)
Pterostyrax hispida	EPAULETTE TREE	(T)
Ptychotis saxifraga	PTYCHOTIS	(H)
Puccinella maritima	COMMON SALTMARSH GRASS	(G)
Puccinellia	SALTMARSH GRASS	(G)
Pueraria lobata	KUDZU	(CL)
Pueraria thunbergiana	KUDZU VINE	(CL)
Pulicaria dysenterica	COMMON FLEABANE	(H)
Pulicaria dysenterica; Erigeron	FLEABANE	(H)
Pulmonaria	JERUSALEM COWSLIP	(H)
Pulmonaria	LUNGWORT	(H)
Pulmonaria angustifolia	BLUE COWSLIP	(H)
Pulmonaria longifolia	NARROW-LEAVED LUNGWORT	(H)
Pulmonaria officinalis	SOLDIERS AND SAILORS	(H)
Pulmonaria officinalis	SPOTTED DOG	(H)
Pulmonaria saccharata	BETHLEHEM SAGE	(H)
Pulsatilla alba	WHITE PASQUE FLOWER	(R)
Pulsatilla vulgaris	MEADOW ANEMONE	(R)
Pulsatilla vulgaris	PASQUE FLOWER	(R)
Pultenaea	BUSH-PEA	(S)
Punica granatum	POMEGRANATE	(F)
Punica granatum 'Nana'	DWARF POMEGRANATE	(S)
Purshia tridentata	ANTELOPE BITTERBRUSH	(S)
Purshia tridentata	QUININE BRUSH	(S)
Puschkinia scilloides	SPRIPED SQUILL	(BB)
Pycnanthemum	MOUNTAIN MINT	(H)
Pycnanthemum virginianum	VIRGINIA THYME	(H)
Pycnanthemum virginianum	WILD HYSSOP	(H)
Pyracantha	FIRETHORN	(S)
Pyracantha atalantoides	GIBB'S FIRETHORN	(S)
Pyracantha coccinea	BUISSON ARDENT	(S)
Pyracantha crenulata	NEPALESE WHITE THORN	(S)
Pyrola	SHINLEAF	(S)
Pyrola minor	COMMON WINTERGREEN	(H)
Pyrola minor	WINTERGREEN	(H)
Pyrola rotundifolia	LARGE WINTERGREEN	(H)
Pyrola rotundifolia	ROUND-LEAVED WINTERGREEN	(H)
Pyrola rotundifolia	WILD LILY-OF-THE-VALLEY	(H)
Pyrola secunda	SERRATED WINTERGREEN	(H)
Pyrola secunda	WHITE SHINLEAF	(H)
Pyrolirion	FLAME-LILY	(HP)

Know Your Common Plant Names

Botanical	Common	Type
Pyrostegia venusta	FLAME FLOWER	(CL)
Pyrostegia venusta	FLAME VINE	(TCL)
Pyrostegia venusta	GOLDEN SHOWER	(CL)
Pyrostegia venusta	ORANGE TRUMPET VINE	(TCL)
Pyrus	PEAR	(F)
Pyrus amygdaliformis	ALMOND LEAVED PEAR	(T)
Pyrus communis	COMMON PEAR	(T)
Pyrus nivalis	SNOW PEAR	(T)
Pyrus pyraster	WILD PEAR	(T)
Pyrus pyrifolia	KUMOI	(F)
Pyrus pyrifolia	NASHI	(F)
Pyrus salicifolia	WILLOW-LEAFED PEAR	(T)
Pyrus salicifolia 'Pendula'	WEEPING PEAR	(T)
Pyrus salicifolius	SILVER PEAR	(T)
Quassia amara	BITTERWOOD	(TT)
Quercus	OAK	(T)
Quercus acuta	JAPANESE EVERGREEN OAK	(T)
Quercus acutissima	JAPANESE CHESTNUT OAK	(T)
Quercus acutissima	SAWTOOTH OAK	(T)
Quercus agrifolia	CALIFORNIAN LIVE OAK	(T)
Quercus agrifolia	ENCINA	(T)
Quercus alba	WHITE OAK	(T)
Quercus alnifolia	GOLDEN OAK OF CYPRUS	(T)
Quercus bicolor	SWAMP WHITE OAK	(T)
Quercus calliprinos	PALESTINE OAK	(T)
Quercus canariensis	ALGERIAN OAK	(T)
Quercus canariensis	MIRBECK'S OAK	(T)
Quercus castanaefolia	CHESTNUT-LEAFED OAK	(T)
Quercus cerris	BITTER OAK	(T)
Quercus cerris	TURKEY OAK	(T)
Quercus chrysolepis	CALIFORNIAN LIVE OAK	(T)
Quercus chrysolepis	CANYON LIVE OAK	(T)
Quercus chrysolepis	GOLDEN-CUP OAK	(T)
Quercus chrysolepis	MAUL OAK	(ST)
Quercus coccifera	KERMES OAK	(T)
Quercus coccinea cvs	SCARLET OAK	(T)
Quercus dentata	DAIMIO OAK	(T)
Quercus douglasii	BLUE OAK	(T)
Quercus dumosa	CALIFORNIAN SCRUB OAK	(T)
Quercus dumosa	SCRUB OAK	(T)
Quercus faginea	PORTUGUESE OAK	(T)
Quercus falcata	SPANISH OAK	(T)
Quercus frainetto	HUNGARIAN OAK	(T)
Quercus gambelii	SHIN OAK	(T)
Quercus garryana	OREGON OAK	(T)
Quercus ilex	EVERGREEN OAK	(T)
Quercus ilex	HOLLY OAK	(T)

Know Your Common Plant Names

Botanical	Common	Type
Quercus ilex	HOLM OAK	(T)
Quercus illicifolia	BEAR OAK	(T)
Quercus illicifolia	SCRUB OAK	(T)
Quercus imbricaria	SHINGLE OAK	(T)
Quercus kelloggii	CALIFORNIAN BLACK OAK	(T)
Quercus laurifolia	LAUREL OAK	(T)
Quercus libani	LEBANON OAK	(T)
Quercus lobata	VALLEY OAK	(T)
Quercus lyrata	OVERCUP OAK	(T)
Quercus macranthera	CAUCASIAN OAK	(T)
Quercus macrocarpa	BURR OAK	(T)
Quercus macrocarpa	MOSSY-CUP OAK	(T)
Quercus macrolepis	VALONIA OAK	(T)
Quercus marilandica	BLACKJACK OAK	(T)
Quercus muhlenbergii	YELLOW CHESTNUT OAK	(T)
Quercus nigra	WATER OAK	(T)
Quercus palustris	PIN OAK	(T)
Quercus petraea	DURMAST OAK	(T)
Quercus petraea	SESSILE OAK	(T)
Quercus phellos	WILLOW OAK	(T)
Quercus pontica	ARMENIAN OAK	(T)
Quercus pontica	PONTINE OAK	(T)
Quercus prinoides	CHINQUAPIN OAK	(T)
Quercus prinus	BAMBOO-LEAVED OAK	(T)
Quercus prinus	BASKET OAK	(T)
Quercus prinus	CHESTNUT OAK	(T)
Quercus pubescens	DOWNY OAK	(T)
Quercus pyrenaica	PYRENEAN OAK	(T)
Quercus robur	COMMON OAK	(T)
Quercus robur	ENGLISH OAK	(T)
Quercus robur	PEDUNCULATE OAK	(T)
Quercus robur 'Concordia'	GOLDEN OAK	(T)
Quercus robur 'Fastigiata'	CYPRESS OAK	(T)
Quercus robur 'Filicifolia'	CUT-LEAF OAK	(T)
Quercus robur 'Pendula'	WEEPING OAK	(T)
Quercus robur 'Purpurascens'	PURPLE ENGLISH OAK	(T)
Quercus rubra	RED OAK	(T)
Quercus sadleriana	DEER OAK	(T)
Quercus shumardii	SHUMARD'S OAK	(T)
Quercus stellata	POST OAK	(T)
Quercus suber	CORK OAK	(T)
Quercus trojana	MACEDONIAN OAK	(T)
Quercus vacciniifolia	HUCKLEBERRY OAK	(T)
Quercus variabilis	ORIENTAL CORKOAK	(T)
Quercus velutina	BLACK OAK	(T)
Quercus velutina	QUERCITRON OAK	(T)
Quercus velutina	YELLOW-BARK OAK	(T)

Know Your Common Plant Names

Botanical	Common	Type
Quercus velutina 'Rubrifolia'	CHAMPION'S OAK	(T)
Quercus virginiana	LIVE OAK	(T)
Quercus warburgii	CAMBRIDGE OAK	(T)
Quercus x heterophylla	BARTRAM'S OAK	(T)
Quercus x hispanica 'Fulhamensis'	FULHAM OAK	(T)
Quercus x hispanica 'Lucombeana'	LUCOMBE OAK	(T)
Quercus x ludoviciana	LUDWIG'S OAK	(T)
Quercus x rosacea 'Filicifolia'	FERN-LEAVED OAK	((T)
Quercus x turneri	TURNER'S OAK	(T)
Quillaja saponaria	SOAP BARK	(TT)
Quillaja saponaria	SOAP TREE	(TT)
Quillaja saponaria	SOAP-BARK TREE	(T)
Quisqualis indica	RANGOON CREEPER	(CL)
Radiola linoides	ALLSEED	(H)
Rafflesia arnoldii	MONSTER PLANT	(TS)
Ranunculus	BACHELORS BUTTONS	(BB/H)
Ranunculus	BUTTERCUP	(H)
Ranunculus	CROWFOOT	(H)
Ranunculus aconitifolius	ACONITE-LEAVED BUTTERCUP	(H)
Ranunculus aconitifolius	FAIR MAIDS OF KENT	(H)
Ranunculus aconitifolius	SUPPLE JACK	(S)
Ranunculus aconitifolius	WHITE BATCHELORS BUTTONS	(H)
Ranunculus acris	BACHELOR'S BUTTONS	(H)
Ranunculus acris	GOLD CUP	(H)
Ranunculus acris	MEADOW BLOOM	(H)
Ranunculus acris	MEADOW BUTTERCUP	(A)
Ranunculus acris "Flora Pleno"	YELLOW BACHELORS BUTTONS	(H)
Ranunculus alpestris	ALPINE BUTTERCUP	(R)
Ranunculus amplexicaulis	WHITE BUTTERCUP	(H)
Ranunculus aquatalis	COMMON WATER CROWFOOT	(H)
Ranunculus aquatilis	WATER BUTTERCUP	(WP)
Ranunculus aquatilis	WATER CROWFOOT	(WP)
Ranunculus arvensis	CORN BUTTERCUP	(H)
Ranunculus arvensis	CORN CROWFOOT	(H)
Ranunculus asiaticus	PERSIAN BUTTERCUP	(BB)
Ranunculus asiaticus	TURBAN BUTTERCUP	(BB)
Ranunculus auricumus	GOLDILOCKS	(H)
Ranunculus bulbosus	BULBOUS BUTTERCUP	(H)
Ranunculus ficaria	LESSER CELANDINE	(H)
Ranunculus ficaria	PILEWORT	(H)
Ranunculus fluitans	RIVER CROWFOOT	(WP)
Ranunculus fluitans	RIVER WATER-CROWFOOT	(WP)
Ranunculus hederaceus	IVY-LEAVED CROWFOOT	(H)
Ranunculus lingua	GREAT SPEARWORT	(H)
Ranunculus lingua	GREATER SPEARWORT	(H)
Ranunculus lyalli	ROCKWOOD LILY	(H)
Ranunculus peltatus	POND WATER CROWFOOT	(H)

Know Your Common Plant Names

Botanical	Common	Type
Ranunculus repens	CREEPING BUTTERCUP	(H)
Ranunculus sceleratus	CELERY-LEAVED CROWFOOT	(H)
Ranunuculus flammula	LESSER SPEARWORT	(H)
Raoulia eximia	VEGETABLE SHEEP	(R)
Raphanus caudatus	JAVA RADISH	(V)
Raphanus caudatus	RAT'S TAIL RADISH	(V)
Raphanus raphanistrum	WILD RADISH	(V)
Raphanus raphanistrum maritimus	SEA RADISH	(H)
Raphanus sativus	DAIKON	(V)
Raphanus sativus	RADISH	(V)
Raphia	RAFFIA	(T.T)
Raphiolepis	INDIA HAWTHORN	(S)
Raphiolepis umbellata	INDIAN HAWTHORN	(S)
Rapistrum rugosum	BASTARD CABBAGE	(H)
Ratibida columnifera	PRAIRIE CONEFLOWER	(S)
Ratibida pinnata	GREYHEAD CONEFLOWER	(S)
Ravenala madagascariensis	TRAVELLER'S TREE	(TT)
Ravenala madagascariensis	TRAVELLERS PALM	(TT)
Ravensara aromatica	MADAGASCAR NUTMEG	(TS)
Rebutia	CROWN CACTUS	(CS)
Rebutia minuscula	RED CROWN	(CS)
Rebutia minuscula	RED CROWN CACTUS	(CS)
Rebutia senilis	FIRE CROWN	(CS)
Rebutia senilis	FIRE CROWN CACTUS	(CS)
Rehmannia angulata	CHINESE FOXGLOVE	(H)
Reinwardtia indica	YELLOW FLAX	(S)
Reseda alba	WHITE MIGNONETTE	(H)
Reseda lutea	WILD MIGNONETTE	(H)
Reseda luteola	DYER'S ROCKET	(H)
Reseda luteola	WELD	(H)
Reseda odorata	MIGNONETTE	(A)
Reseda phyteuma	CORN MIGNONETTE	(H)
Rhamnus	BUCKTHORN	(S.T.)
Rhamnus caroliana	INDIAN CHERRY	(S)
Rhamnus cathartica	COMMON BUCKTHORN	(S)
Rhamnus cathartica	RAMSTHORN	(S/T)
Rhamnus frangula	BLACK DOGWOOD	(S/T)
Rhamnus infectoria	AVIGNON BERRY	(S)
Rhamnus purshiana	CALIFONIAN BUCKTHORN	(S)
Rhamnus purshiana	CASCARA SAGRADA	(T)
Rhamnus saxitilis	ROCK BUCKTHORN	(R)
Rhamnusfrangula	ALDER BUCKTHORN	(ST)
Rhamus californica	COFFEE-BERRY	(S)
Rhapidophyllum	BLUE PALMETTO	(TS)
Rhapis	GROUND RATTAN	(P)
Rhapis	LADY PALM	(P)
Rhapis excelsa	BAMBOO PALM	(P)

Botanical	Common	Type
Rhapis excelsa	CHINA CANE	(P)
Rhapis excelsa	GROUND RATTAN CANE	(P)
Rhapis excelsa	LITTLE LADY PALM	(P)
Rhapis excelsa	PARTRIDGE CANE	(P)
Rhapis humilis	REED RHAPIS	(P)
Rhapis humilis	SLENDER LADY PALM	(P)
Rheum	ORNAMENTAL RHUBARB	(H)
Rheum officinale	CHINESE RHUBARB	(H)
Rheum palmatum	TURKEY RHUBARB	(H)
Rheum rhaponticum	COMMON RHUBARB	(F)
Rheum rhaponticum	RHUBARB	(V)
Rheum x cultorum	RHUBARB	(V)
Rhexia	DEER-GRASS	(G)
Rhexia	MEADOW BEAUTY	(S)
Rhexia	MEADOW-BEAUTY	(H)
Rhinanthus	RATTLES	(H)
Rhinanthus minor	COCKSCOMB	(A)
Rhinanthus minor	HAY-RATTLE	(H)
Rhinanthus minor	HAYRATTLE	(A)
Rhinanthus minor	YELLOW RATTLE	(A)
Rhinanthus serotinus	GREATER HAYRATTLE	(H)
Rhipogonum scandens	SUPPLE JACK	(S)
Rhipsalidopsis gaertneri	EASTER CACTUS	(HP)
Rhipsalis baceifera	MISTLETOE CACTUS	(CS)
Rhipsalis houlletiana	SNOWDROP CACTUS	(CS)
Rhipsalis paradoxa	CHAIN CACTUS	(CS)
Rhizophora	MANGROVE	(TT)
Rhizophora mangle	RED MANGROVE	(TT)
Rhodiola rosea	MIDSUMMER MEN	(H)
Rhodiola rosea	ROSEROOT	(R)
Rhodochiton atrosonguineum	PURPLE BELL VINE	(CL)
Rhodochiton volubile	PURPLE BELL VINE	(CL)
Rhododendron	AZALEA	(S)
Rhododendron	ROSE BAY	(S)
Rhododendron catawbiense	MOUNTAIN ROSE BAY	(S)
Rhododendron ferrugineum	ALPENROSE	(S)
Rhododendron hirsutum	HAIRY ALPEN ROSE	(S)
Rhododendron luteum	COMMON YELLOW AZALEA	(S)
Rhododendron maximum	GREAT LAUREL	(S)
Rhododendron maximum	ROSE BAY	(S)
Rhododendron maximum	ROSEBAY	(S)
Rhododendron oldhamii	FORMOSAN AZALEA	(S)
Rhododendron simsii	INDIAN AZALEA	(HP)
Rhododendron viscosum	SWAMP HONEYSUCKLE	(S)
Rhodosphaera rhodanthema	YELLOW-WOOD	(TT)
Rhodothamnus chamaecistus	GROUND CISTUS	(S)
Rhodotypos scandens	BLACK JETBEAD	(S)

Botanical	Common	Type
Rhodotypos scandens	WHITE JEW'S MALLOW	(S)
Rhodymania palmata	DULSE	(SW)
Rhodymenia palmata	RED KALE	(SW)
Rhoicissus capensis	MONKEY ROPE	(CL)
Rhombophyllum nelii	ELK'S HORNS	(HP)
Rhus	SUMACH	(ST)
Rhus aromatica	FRAGRANT SUMACH	(S)
Rhus aromatica	SWEET SUMACH	(S)
Rhus copallina	DWARF SUMACH	(S)
Rhus copallina	SHINING SUMACH	(S)
Rhus coriaria	TANNER'S SUMACH	(S)
Rhus glabra	SMOOTH SUMACH	(S)
Rhus glabra	UPLAND SUMACH	(S)
Rhus hirta	STAG'S HORN SUMACH	(ST)
Rhus integrifolia	LEMONADE BERRY	(S)
Rhus radicans	COW-ITCH	(S)
Rhus succedanka	WAX TREE	(T)
Rhus toxicodendron	POISON IVY	(S)
Rhus toxicodendron	POISON OAK	(CL)
Rhus trilobata	SKUNK BUSH	(S)
Rhus vernicifera	JAPAN VARNISH TREE	(T)
Rhus vernicifera	LACQUER TREE	(S)
Rhus verniciflua	VARNISH TREE	(S)
Rhus vernix	POISON SUMACH	(S)
Rhynchelytrum repens	NATAL GRASS	(G)
Rhynchelytrum repens	RUBY GRASS	(G)
Rhynchosinapis cheiranthos	WALLFLOWER CABBAGE	(H)
Rhynchosinapis wrightii	LUNDY CABBAGE	(H)
Ribes	CURRANT	(S)
Ribes alpinum	ALPINE CURRANT	(S)
Ribes alpinum	MOUNTAIN CURRANT	(S)
Ribes americanum	AMERICAN BLACKCURRANT	(S)
Ribes bracteosum	CALIFORNIAN BLACK CURRANT	(S)
Ribes nigrum	BLACKCURRANT	(F)
Ribes odoratum	BUFFALO CURRANT	(S)
Ribes odoratum	GOLDEN CURRANT	(S)
Ribes sanguineum	FLOWERING CURRANT	(S)
Ribes speciosum	FUCHSIA-FLOWERED GOOSEBERRY	(S)
Ribes uva-crispa	GOOSEGOG	(F)
Ribes uva-crispi	COMMON GOOSEBERRY	(S)
Ribes uva-crispi	GOOSEBERRY	(F)
Ribes viburnumifolium	EVERGREEN CURRANT	(S)
Riccia	CRYSTAL WORT	(H)
Richordia scabra	MEXICAN CLOVER	(TS)
Ricinus	PALMA CHRISTI	(P)
Ricinus communis	CASTOR BEAN	(A)
Ricinus communis	CASTOR OIL PLANT	(A)

Know Your Common Plant Names

Botanical	Common	Type
Ricinus communis	PALMA CHRISTI	(A)
Rivina	BLOOD BERRY	(H)
Rivina	ROUGE BERRY	(R)
Rivina humilis	ROUGE PLANT	(HP)
Robinia	FALSE ACACIA	(ST)
Robinia hispida	BRISTLY LOCUST	(T)
Robinia hispida	ROSE ACACIA	(S.T)
Robinia pseud. 'Frisia'	GOLDEN LOCUST	(T)
Robinia pseudo acacia 'Frisia'	GOLDEN ACACIA	(ST)
Robinia pseudoacacia	BLACK LOCUST	(T)
Robinia pseudoacacia	COMMON ACACIA	(T)
Robinia pseudoacacia	LOCUST	(T)
Robinia pseudoacacia	YELLOW LOCUST	(T)
Robinia pseudoacacia 'Appalachia'	SHIPMAST ACACIA	(T)
Robinia pseudoacacia 'Umbraculifera'	MOP-HEAD ACACIA	(T)
Robinia viscosa	CLAMMY LOCUST	(T)
Roella	SOUTH AFRICAN HAREBELL	(S)
Roella ciliata	AFRICAN HAREBELL	(H)
Rohdea japonica	LILY OF CHINA	(HP)
Romneya	CALIFORNIAN TREE POPPY	(S)
Romneya	WHITE BUSH POPPY	(S)
Romneya coulteri	MATILIJA POPPY	(H/S)
Romneya cvs	TREE POPPY	(S)
Romulea columnae	SAND CROCUS	(BB)
Rorippa	YELLOWCRESS	(H)
Rorippa amphibia	GREAT YELLOWCRESS	(H)
Rorippa islandica	MARSH YELLOW CRESS	(H)
Rorippa sylvestris	CREEPING YELLOWCRESS	(H)
Rosa	ROSE	(T)
Rosa acicularis	NEEDLE ROSE	(S)
Rosa agrestis	FIELD BRIAR	(S)
Rosa alpina (pendulina)	ALPINE ROSE	(S)
Rosa arvensis	AYRSHIRE ROSE	(S)
Rosa arvensis	FIELD ROSE	(S)
Rosa arvensis	TRAILING ROSE	(S)
Rosa banksiae	BANKSIAN ROSE	(S)
Rosa banksiae 'lutea'	YELLOW BANKSIAN ROSE	(S)
Rosa blanda	MEADOW ROSE	(S)
Rosa blanda	SMOOTH ROSE	(S)
Rosa bracteata	MACARTNEY ROSE	(S)
Rosa brunonii	HIMALAYAN MUSK ROSE	(S)
Rosa canina	BRIAR ROSE	(S)
Rosa canina	COMMON BRIAR	(S)
Rosa canina	DOGROSE	(S)
Rosa centifolia	CABBAGE ROSE	(S)
Rosa centifolia	PROVENCE ROSE	(S)
Rosa centifolia cristata	CRESTED MOSS ROSE	(S)

Botanical	Common	Type
Rosa centifolia muscosa	MOSS ROSE	(S)
Rosa chinensis	CHINA ROSE	(S)
Rosa chinensis	MONTHLY ROSE	(S)
Rosa chinensis 'Viridiflora'	GREEN ROSE	(S)
Rosa damasceana	DAMASK ROSE	(S)
Rosa damasceana 'Versicolor'	YORK AND LANCASTER ROSE	(S)
Rosa damascena "Trigintipetala"	KAZANLIK ROSE	(S)
Rosa elegantula 'Persetosa'	THREEPENNY-BIT ROSE	(S)
Rosa filipes 'Kiftsgate'	KIFTSGATE ROSE	(CL)
Rosa foetida	AUSTRIAN BRIAR	(S)
Rosa foetida 'Bicolor'	AUSTRIAN COPPER ROSE	(ST)
Rosa foetida 'Persiana'	PERSIAN YELLOW ROSE	(S)
Rosa gallica	FRENCH ROSE	(S)
Rosa gallica	PROVINS ROSE	(S)
Rosa gallica	RED ROSE	(S)
Rosa gallica 'Officinalis'	APOTHECARY'S ROSE	(S)
Rosa gallica 'Officinalis'	RED ROSE OF LANCASTER	(S)
Rosa gallica 'Versicolor'	ROSA MUNDI	(S)
Rosa gymnocarpa	BALDHIP ROSE	(S)
Rosa gymnocarpa	REDWOOD ROSE	(S)
Rosa hemisphaerica	SULPHUR ROSE	(S)
Rosa laevigata	CHEROKEE ROSE	(CL.S)
Rosa majalis	CINNAMON ROSE	(S)
Rosa majalis	MAY ROSE	(S)
Rosa moschata	MUSK ROSE	(S)
Rosa multiflora 'grevillei'	SEVEN SISTERS ROSE	(S)
Rosa odorata	TEA ROSE	(S)
Rosa pimpinellifolia	BURNET ROSE	(S)
Rosa pimpinellifolia	SCOTCH BRIAR	(S)
Rosa pimpinellifolia	SCOTCH ROSE	(S)
Rosa primula	INCENSE ROSE	(S)
Rosa roxburghii	BURR ROSE	(S)
Rosa roxburghii	CHESTNUT ROSE	(S)
Rosa rubiginosa	EGLANTINE	(S)
Rosa rubiginosa	SWEET BRIAR	(S)
Rosa rugosa	HEDGEHOG ROSE	(R)
Rosa rugosa	JAPANESE ROSE	(S)
Rosa rugosa	RAMANAS ROSE	(S)
Rosa sericea	MOUNT OMEI ROSE	(S)
Rosa setigera	PRAIRIE ROSE	(S)
Rosa sherardii	NORTHERN DOWNY ROSE	(S)
Rosa stellata mirifica	SACRAMENTO ROSE	(S)
Rosa tomentosa	DOWNY ROSE	(S)
Rosa villosa	APPLE ROSE	(S)
Rosa villosa	SOFT-LEAVED ROSE	(S)
Rosa villosa 'Duplex'	WOLLEY-DODS ROSE	(S)
Rosa wichuraiana	MEMORIAL ROSE	(R)

Botanical	Common	Type
Rosa x alba	WHITE ROSE OF YORK	(S)
Rosa x alba 'Maxima'	JACOBITE ROSE	(S)
Rose 'Rose d'amour'	ST. MARK'S ROSE	(S)
Rosmarinus	ROSEMARY	(HB)
Rothmannia capensis	SCENTED CUPS	(H)
Roystonea	ROYAL PALMS	(P)
Roystonea oleracea	CABBAGE PALM	(P)
Roystonea oleracea	SOUTH AMERICAN ROYAL PALM	(P)
Roystonea regia	CUBAN ROYAL PALM	(P)
Roystonea regia	ROYAL PALM	(P)
Rubia peregrina	MADDER	(H)
Rubia peregrina	WILD MADDER	(H)
Rubia tinctoria	MADDER	(H)
Rubus	BRAMBLE	(F)
Rubus	ORNAMENTAL BRAMBLE	(S)
Rubus caesius	DEWBERRY	(F)
Rubus carpinifolius	BLACKBERRY	(F)
Rubus chamaemorus	CLOUDBERRY	(S)
Rubus cissoides	BUSH LAUREL	(S)
Rubus deliciosus	ROCKY MOUNTAIN RASPBERRY	(S)
Rubus fruticosus	BLACKBERRY	(F)
Rubus idaeus	BRAMBLE OF MOUNT IDA	(F)
Rubus idaeus	RASPBERRY	(F)
Rubus idaeus	WILD RASPBERRY	(S)
Rubus illecebrosus	STRAWBERRY-RASPBERRY	(S)
Rubus lacinatus	PARSLEY- LEAVED BRAMBLE	(F)
Rubus laciniatus	CUT-LEAVED BRAMBLE	(S)
Rubus leucodermis	BLACKCAP	(S)
Rubus loganobaccus	BOYSEN BERRY	(F)
Rubus loganobaccus	LOGANBERRY	(F)
Rubus loganobaccus	PHENOMENAL BERRY	(F)
Rubus occidentalis	BLACK CAP	(S)
Rubus occidentalis	BLACK RASPBERRY	(S)
Rubus odoratus	AMERICAN BRAMBLE	(S)
Rubus odoratus	FLOWERING RASPBERRY	(S)
Rubus 'Oregon Thornless'	PARSLEY- LEAVED BRAMBLE	(F)
Rubus phoenicolasius	WINEBERRY	(CL)
Rubus porviflorus	THIMBLE-BERRY	(S)
Rubus procerus	HIMALAYA BERRY	(S)
Rubus radula	BLACKBERRY	(F)
Rubus saxatilis	ROCK BRAMBLE	(S)
Rubus saxatilis	ROEBUCK BERRY	(S)
Rubus saxatilis	STONE BRAMBLE	(H)
Rubus silvaticus	BLACKBERRY	(F)
Rubus spectabilis	SALMON BERRY	(S)
Rubus strigosus	WILD RED RASPBERRY	(S)
Rubus 'Sunberry'	SUNBERRY	(F)

Botanical	Common	Type
Rubus ulmifolius	BLACKBERRY	(F)
Rubus vestitus	BLACKBERRY	(F)
Rudbeckia	CONE FLOWER	(H)
Rudbeckia hirta	ANNUAL RUDBECKIA	(A)
Rudbeckia hirta	BLACK-EYED SUSAN	(H)
Rudbeckia hirta	YELLOW DAISY	(H)
Rudbeckia triloba	BROWN-EYED SUSAN	(H)
Ruellia ciliosa	WILD PETUNIA	(H)
Ruellia macrantha	CHRISTMAS PRIDE	(HP)
Ruellia makoyana	TRAILING VELVET PLANT	(HP)
Rumax scutatus	BUCKLER LEAF SORREL	(HB)
Rumex	DOCK	(H)
Rumex acetosa	GARDEN SORREL	(HB)
Rumex acetosa	GREEN SAUCE	(HB)
Rumex acetosa	SORREL	(HB)
Rumex acetosella	SHEEP'S SORREL	(H)
Rumex alpinus	MONK'S RHUBARB	(H)
Rumex conglomeratus	SHARP DOCK	(H)
Rumex crispus	CURLED DOCK	(H)
Rumex crispus	YELLOW DOCK	(H)
Rumex hydrolapathan	GREAT WATER DOCK	(WP)
Rumex hydrolapathum	WATER DOCK	(WP)
Rumex maritimus	GOLDEN DOCK	(H)
Rumex obtusifolius	BROAD-LEAVED DOCK	(H)
Rumex palustris	MARSH DOCK	(H)
Rumex patientia	HERB PATIENCE	(H)
Rumex patientia	PATIENCE	(H)
Rumex patientia	SPINACH DOCK	(H)
Rumex pulcher	FIDDLE DOCK	(H)
Rumex rupestris	SHORE DOCK	(H)
Rumex sanguineus	BLOODWORT	(H)
Rumex sanguineus	WOOD DOCK	(H)
Rumex sanguineus sanguineus	BLOODY DOCK	(H)
Rumex sanguineus viridis	RED-VEINED DOCK	(H)
Rumex scutatus	FRENCH SORREL	(HB)
Ruppia cirrhosa	SPIDER TASSEL PONDWEED	(WP)
Ruppia maritima	BEAKED TASSEL PONDWEED	(WP)
Ruscus aculeatus	BOX HOLLY	(S)
Ruscus aculeatus	BUTCHER'S BROOM	(S)
Ruscus aculeatus	JEW'S MYRTLE	(S)
Ruscus aculeatus	KNEE HOLY	(S)
Russelia equisetiformis	CORAL PLANT	(TS)
Russelia equisetiformis	FOUNTAIN BUSH	(TS)
Russelia juncea	CORAL PLANT	(TS)
Russelia juncea	FIRECRACKER	(TS)
Russelia juncea	FOUNTAIN PLANT	(TS)
Ruta	RUE	(HB)

Know Your Common Plant Names

Botanical	Common	Type
Ruta graveolens	HERB OF GRACE	(HB)
Sabal mauritiiformis	TRINIDAD PALM	(P)
Sabal minor	DWARF PALMETTO	(P)
Sabal palmetto	PALMETTO	(T)
Sabatia angularis	AMERICAN CENTAURY	(HB)
Sabatia angularis	BITTER BROOM	(HB)
Sabatia angularis	BITTER CLOVER	(HB)
Sabatia angularis	WILD SUCCORY	(HB)
Sabbatia angularis	ROSE PINK	(TS)
Saccharum officinarum	SUGAR CANE	(G)
Sagina	PEARLWORT	(R)
Sagina maritima	SEA PEARLWORT	(R)
Sagina nodosa	KNOTTED PEARLWORT	(H)
Sagina procumbens	COMMON PEARLWORT	(H)
Sagina subulata	HEATH PEARLWORT	(R)
Sagittaria latifolia	DUCK POTATO	(WP)
Sagittaria sagittifolia	ARROWHEAD	(WP)
Sagittaria sagittifolia	COMMON ARROWHEAD	(WP)
Sagittaria sagittifolia	WATER ARCHER	(WP)
Sagittaria sagittifolia leucopetala	JAPANESE ARROWHEAD	(WP)
Saintpaulia	AFRICAN VIOLET	(HP)
Salacea edulis	SALAC	(P)
Salicornia	GLASSWORT	(H)
Salicornia ramosissima	PROSTRATE GLASSWORT	(H)
Salix	WILLOW	(ST)
Salix acutifolia	CASPIAN WILLOW	(S)
Salix aegyptiaca	CALAF OF PERSIA WILLOW	(S/T)
Salix aegyptiaca	MUSK WILLOW	(ST)
Salix alba	WHITE WILLOW	(ST)
Salix alba 'Caerulea'	BLUE WILLOW	(T)
Salix alba 'Caerulea'	CRICKET BAT WILLOW	(T)
Salix alba 'Chermesina'	CORAL-BARK WILLOW	(ST)
Salix alba 'Chermesina'	SCARLET WILLOW	(ST)
Salix alba 'Sericea'	SILVER WILLOW	(T)
Salix alba 'vitellina'	GOLDEN WILLOW	(ST)
Salix alba 'Vitellina'	YOLK-OF-EGG WILLOW	(S/T)
Salix andersoniana	GREEN MOUNTAIN SALLOW	(S)
Salix aquatica	WATER SALLOW	(S)
Salix arbuscula	LITTLE TREE WILLOW	(S)
Salix arbuscula	MOUNTAIN WILLOW	(S)
Salix arenaria	SAND WILLOW	(S)
Salix artica	ARCTIC WILLOW	(S)
Salix aurita	EARED WILLOW	(S)
Salix aurita	TRAILING SALLOW	(S)
Salix avrita	ROUND-EARED WILLOW	(S)
Salix babylonica	WEEPING WILLOW	(T)
Salix babylonica pekinensis	PEKING WILLOW	(T)

Know Your Common Plant Names

Botanical	Common	Type
Salix babylonica pekinensis 'Pendula'	WEEPING WILLOW	(T)
Salix babylonica Pekinensis 'Tortuosa'	CONTORTED WILLOW	(ST)
Salix babylonica pekinensis 'Tortuosa'	CORKSCREW WILLOW	(ST)
Salix babylonica pekinensis 'Tortuosa'	DRAGON'S CLAW WILLOW	(T)
Salix babylonica pikinensis "Tortuosa Aurea"	GOLDEN CURLS	
(T)		
Salix 'Basfordiana'	BASFORD WILLOW	(S)
Salix bebbiana	BEAK WILLOW	(S)
Salix blanda	WISCONSIN WEEPING WILLOW	(T)
Salix caesia	BLUE WILLOW	(S)
Salix candida	SAGE WILLOW	(S)
Salix capra	GOAT WILLOW	(ST)
Salix caprea	GREAT SALLOW	(ST)
Salix caprea	PALM WILLOW	(ST)
Salix caprea	PUSSY WILLOW	(ST)
Salix caprea	SALLOW	(ST)
Salix caprea 'Pendula'	WEEPING WILLOW	(T)
Salix caprea 'Pendula' (female)	KILMARNOCK WILLOW	(T)
Salix caprea 'Pendula' (female)	WEEPING SALLY	(S)
Salix cinerea	COMMON SALLOW	(S)
Salix cinerea	GREY SALLOW	(ST)
Salix cinerea	GREY WILLOW	(ST)
Salix cinerea oleifolia	COMMON SALLOW	(S)
Salix cordata	FURRY WILLOW	(S)
Salix cordata	HEART-LEAVED WILLOW	(S)
Salix crassifolia	THICK-LEAVED SALLLOW	(S)
Salix daphnoides	VIOLET WILLOW	(ST)
Salix daphnoides	'VIOLETS'	(S)
Salix eleagnos	HOARY WILLOW	(S)
Salix exigua	COYOTE WILLOW	(S)
Salix fragilis	CRACK WILLOW	(T)
Salix gracilistyla	JAPANESE PUSSY WILLOW	(S)
Salix hastata	HALBERD-LEAVED WILLOW	(S)
Salix helvetica	SWISS SALLOW	(S)
Salix herbacea	DWARF WILLOW	(S)
Salix herbacea	LEAST WILLOW	(S)
Salix humilis	PRAIRIE WILLOW	(S)
Salix interior	SANDBAR WILLOW	(S)
Salix laevigata	RED WILLOW	(S)
Salix lanata	WOOLLY WILLOW	(S)
Salix lapponum	DOWNY WILLOW	(S)
Salix lapponum	LAPLAND WILLOW	(S)
Salix lasiandra	PACIFIC WILLOW	(S)
Salix lucida	SHINING WILLOW	(S)
Salix magnifica	MAGNOLIA-LEAFED WILLOW	(ST)
Salix melanostachys	BLACK PUSSY WILLOW	(S)
Salix myrsinites	WHORTLE WILLOW	(S)

Botanical	Common	Type
Salix myrsinites	WHORTLE-LEAVED WILLOW	(S)
Salix nigra	BLACK WILLOW	(T)
Salix nigricans	DARK LEAVED WILLOW	(S)
Salix nigricans	DARK-LEAVED WILLOW	(S)
Salix pellita	SATINY WILLOW	(S)
Salix pentandra	BAY WILLOW	(S)
Salix pentandra	LAUREL WILLOW	(S)
Salix petraea	ROCK SALLOW	(S)
Salix phylicifolia	TEA-LEAF WILLOW	(S)
Salix purpurea	PURPLE OSIER	(S)
Salix purpurea 'pendula'	WEEPING PURPLE OSIER	(T)
Salix purpurea 'Pendula'	WEEPING WILLOW	(T)
Salix pyrifolia	BALSAM WILLOW	(S)
Salix reiculata	NETTED WILLOW	(S)
Salix repens	CREEPING WILLOW	(S)
Salix reticulata	NET-LEAVED WILLOW	(S)
Salix 'Russeliana'	DUKE OF BEDFORD'S WILLOW	(S)
Salix salviaefolia	SAGE-LEAVED WILLOW	(S)
Salix triandra	ALMOND LEAVED WILLOW	(ST)
Salix triandra	FRENCH WILLOW	(S/T)
Salix uva-ursi	BEARBERRY WILLOW	(S)
Salix vimanalis	BASKET WILLOW	(S)
Salix viminalis	COMMON OSIER	(T)
Salix viminalis	OSIER	(ST)
Salix x elegantissima	THURLOW WEEPING WILLOW	(T)
Salix x sepulcralis chrysocoma	GOLDEN WEEPING WILLOW	(T)
Salix x sepulcralis chrysocoma	WEEPING WILLOW	(T)
Salix xerythroflexuosa	GOLDEN CURLS	(ST)
Salpichroa origanifolia	SALPICHROA	(H)
Salpiglossis	PAINTED TONGUE	(A)
Salpiglossis sinuata	VELVET TRUMPET FLOWER	(A)
Salsola	RUSSIAN THISTLE	(H)
Salsola kaki	SALTWORT	(H)
Salvadora persica	TOOTHBRUSH TREE	(TT)
Salvia argentea	SILVER SAGE	(H)
Salvia azurea	BLUE SAGE	(H)
Salvia fulgens	CARDINAL SAGE	(S)
Salvia fulgens	CARDINAL SALVIA	(A)
Salvia fulgens	MEXICAN RED SAGE	(S)
Salvia glutinosa	JUPITERS DISTAFF	(H)
Salvia glutinosa	STICKY SAGE	(H)
Salvia horminoides	WILD SAGE	(H)
Salvia horminum	ANNUAL CLARY	(H)
Salvia horminum	BLUEBEARD	(H)
Salvia leucantha	MEXICAN BUSH SAGE	(S)
Salvia nemorosa	WILD SAGE	(H)
Salvia officinalis	COMMON SAGE	(HB)

Botanical	Common	Type
Salvia officinalis	SAGE	(HB)
Salvia officinalis 'Purpurascens'	PURPLE SAGE	(S)
Salvia patens	BLUE SAGE	(H)
Salvia patens	GENTIAN SAGE	(A)
Salvia pratensis	MEADOW CLARY	(H)
Salvia rutilans	PINEAPPLE SAGE	(HB)
Salvia sclarea	CLARY	(HB)
Salvia sclarea	CLEAR EYE	(HB)
Salvia splendens	SCARLET SAGE	(A)
Salvia superba	PERENNIAL SAGE	(H)
Salvia verbenacea	WILD CLARY	(H)
Salvinia auriculata	FLOATING FERN	(WP)
Samanea saman	MONKEY-POD TREE	(TT)
Samanea saman	RAIN-TREE	(TT)
Sambucus	ELDER	(HS)
Sambucus caerulea	BLUE ELDER BERRY	(S)
Sambucus canadensis	AMERICAN ELDER	(C)
Sambucus canadensis 'Aurea'	GOLDEN AMERICAN ELDER	(S)
Sambucus ebulus	DANEWORT	(H)
Sambucus ebulus	DWARF ELDER	(H)
Sambucus nigra	BLACK ELDER	(S/T)
Sambucus nigra	BOURTREE	(S)
Sambucus nigra	COMMON ELDER	(S)
Sambucus nigra	PIPE TREE	(T)
Sambucus nigra 'Aurea'	GOLDEN ELDER	(S)
Sambucus nigra 'Guincho Purple'	PURPLE-LEAVED ELDER	(S)
Sambucus nigra 'Laciniata'	CUT-LEAVED ELDER	(S)
Sambucus nigra 'Laciniata'	FERN-LEAVED ELDER	(S)
Sambucus nigra 'laciniata'	PARSLEY-LEAVED ELDER	(S)
Sambucus racemosa	RED-BERRIED ELDER	(S)
Samolus	WATER PIMPERNEL	(WP)
Samolus valerandi	BROOKWEED	(H)
Samuela	DATE YUCCA	(F)
Sandersonia aurantiaca	CHINESE LANTERNS	(HP)
Sandersonia aurantiaca	CHINESE-LANTERN LILY	(BB)
Sandoricum indicum	SANDAL TREE	(TT)
Sandoricum koetjapa	SENTOL	(TT)
Sanguinaria	BLOODROOT	(H)
Sanguinaria	BLOODWORT	(H)
Sanguinaria	PUCCOON	(H)
Sanguinaria canadensis	COONROOT	(H)
Sanguinaria canadensis	INDIAN PAINT	(H)
Sanguinaria canadensis	RED PUCOON	(H)
Sanguisorba minor	SALAD BURNET	(HB)
Sanguisorba officinalis	BURNET	(HB)
Sanguisorba officinalis	GREAT BURNET	(HB)
Sanicula europaea	SANICLE	(H)

Know Your Common Plant Names

Botanical	Common	Type
Sanicula marilandica	AMERICAN SANICLE	(H)
Sansevieria	ANGOLA HEMP	(HP)
Sansevieria	DEVIL'S TONGUE	(HP)
Sansevieria	GOOD LUCK PLANT	(HP)
Sansevieria	LUCKY PLANT	(HP)
Sansevieria	SNAKE PLANT	(HP)
Sansevieria hahnii	BOWSTRING HEMP	(HP)
Sansevieria trifasciata	MOTHER-IN-LAW'S-TONGUE	(HP)
Santalum album	SANDALWOOD	(TT)
Santalum rubrum	RED SANDALWOOD	(TT)
Santolina	COTTON LAVENDER	(S)
Santolina chamaecyparisus	LAVENDER COTTON	(S)
Santolina rosmarinifolia	HOLY FLAX	(S)
Sanvitalia procumbens	CREEPING ZINNIA	(HP)
Sapindus drummondii	SOAP BERRY	(T)
Sapindus drummondii	WILD CHINA TREE	(T)
Sapium hippomane	MILK TREE	(T)
Sapium salicifolium	TALLOW TREE	(T)
Sapium sebiferum	CHINESE TALLOW TREE	(T)
Saponaria ocymoides	ROCK SOAPWORT	(R)
Saponaria ocymoides	TUMBLING TED	(R)
Saponaria officinalis	BOUNCING BETT	(H)
Saponaria officinalis	SOAPWORT	(RH)
Saraca indica	ASOKA TREE	(TT)
Sarcobatus vermiculatus	GREASEWOOD	(H)
Sarcocephalus esculentus	GUINEA PEACH	(TS)
Sarcococca	CHRISTMAS BOX	(S)
Sarcococca	SWEET BOX	(S)
Sarcostemma acidum	SOMA	(H)
sargassum muticum	JAP WEED	(SW)
Sarmienta repens	CHILE PITCHER-FLOWER	(S)
Sarracenia	HUNTSMAN'S HORN	(HP)
Sarracenia	SIDE-SADDLE FLOWER	(HP)
Sarracenia leucophylla	FIDDLER'S TRUMPETS	(HP)
Sarracenia leucophylla	LACE TRUMPETS	(HP)
Sarracenia purpurea	HUNTSMAN'S CUP	(H)
Sarracenia purpurea	PITCHER PLANT	(HP)
Sasa	BAMBOO	(G)
Sassafras albidum	AGUE TREE	(T)
Satureia	SAVOURY	(HB)
Satureia hortensis	SUMMER SAVOURY	(HB)
Satureia montana	WINTER SAVOURY	(HB)
Satureja douglasii	YERBA BUENA	(S)
Sauromatum guttatum	MONARCH OF THE EAST	(H)
Sauromatum venosum	MONARCH OF THE EAST	(H)
Sauromatum venosum	VOODOO LILY	(BB)
Saururus	LIZARD'S TAIL	(H)

Know Your Common Plant Names

Botanical	Common	Type
Saururus cernuus	AMERICAN SWAMP LILY	(BB)
Saururus cernuus	SWAMP LILY	(WP)
Saururus cernuus	WATER DRAGON	(WP)
Sauvagesia erecta	IRON SHRUB	(S)
Saxegothea conspicua	PRINCE ALBERT'S YEW	(C)
Saxifraga	ROCKFOIL	(R)
Saxifraga	SAXIFRAGE	(R)
Saxifraga aizoides	YELLOW MOUNTAIN SAXIFRAGE	(R)
Saxifraga caesia	BLUE SAXIFRAGE	(R)
Saxifraga cespitosa	TUFTED SAXIFRAGE	(H)
Saxifraga cotyledon	PYRAMIDAL SAXIFRAGE	(R)
Saxifraga granulata	FAIR MAIDS OF FRANCE	(R)
Saxifraga granulata	MEADOW SAXIFRAGE	(R)
Saxifraga hieracifolia	HAWKWEED SAXIFRAGE	(R)
Saxifraga hirsuta	KIDNEY SAXIFRAGE	(R)
Saxifraga hypnoides	DOVEDALE MOSS	(R)
Saxifraga hypnoides	MOSSY ROCKFOIL	(R)
Saxifraga hyproides	MOSSY SAXIFRAGE	(R)
Saxifraga moschata	MUSKY SAXIFRAGE	(R)
Saxifraga oppositifolia	PURPLE SAXIFRAGE	(R)
Saxifraga rosacea	IRISH SAXIFRAGE	(R)
Saxifraga stellaris	STARRY SAXIFRAGE	(H)
Saxifraga stellata	STARRY SAXIFRAGE	(R)
Saxifraga stolonifera	MOTHER OF THOUSANDS	(HP)
Saxifraga tridactylotes	RUE-LEAVED SAXIFRAGE	(H)
Saxifraga umbrosa	NANCY-PRETTY	(CR)
Saxifraga urbium	LONDON PRIDE	(R)
Saxifraga urbium	NANCY-PRETTY	(R)
Saxifraga urbium	NONE-SO-PRETTY	(R)
Saxifraga 'urbium'	ST. PATRICK'S CABBAGE	(R)
Scabiosa	MOURNING BRIDE	(H)
Scabiosa	PINCUSHION FLOWER	(HR)
Scabiosa	SCABIOUS	(H/R)
Scabiosa atropurpurea	MOURNFUL WIDOW	(H)
Scabiosa atropurpurea	SWEET SCABIOUS	(H)
Scabiosa columbaria	SMALL SCABIOUS	(H)
Scabiosa columbaria ochraleuca	YELLOW SCABIOUS	(H)
Scabiosa lucida	SHINING SCABIOUS	(H)
Scadoxus multiflorus katherinae	BLOOD FLOWER	(HP)
Scadoxus puniceus	ROYAL PAINTBRUSH	(BB)
Scandix pecten-veneris	SHEPHERD'S NEEDLE	(H)
Scandix pecten-veneris	VENUS'S COMB	(H)
Schefflera	UMBRELLA TREE	(HP)
Schefflera actinophylla	QUEENSLAND UMBRELLA TREE	(HP)
Schefflera arboricola	HEPTAPLEURUM	(HP)
Schefflera arboricola	PARASOL PLANT	(HP)
Scheuchzeria palustris	RANNOCH RUSH	(H)

Botanical	Common	Type
Schinopsis balansae	QUEBRACHO	(TS)
Schinopsis lorentzii	QUEBRACHO	(TS)
Schinus molle	AMERICAN MASTIC TREE	(T)
Schinus molle	PEPPER TREE	(T)
Schinus molle	PERUVIAN MASTIC TREE	(TT)
Schinus terebinthifolius	BRAZILIAN PEPPER TREE	(TT)
Schinzanthus	FRINGE FLOWER	(H/P)
Schizaea	COMB FERN	(FN)
Schizaea	RUSH FERN	(FN)
Schizanthus	BUTTERFLY FLOWER	(A)
Schizanthus	POOR MAN'S ORCHID	(A)
Schizocentron elegans	SPANISH SHAWL	(HP)
Schizophragma hydrangeoides	JAPANESE HYDRANGEA VINE	(CL)
Schizostylis	KAFFIR LILY	(H)
Schizostylis coccinea	CRIMSON FLAG	(H)
Schlumbergera 'Bridgesii'	CHRISTMAS CACTUS	(CS)
Schlumbergera truncata	CLAW CACTUS	(CS)
Schlumbergera truncata	CRAB CACTUS	(CS)
Schlumbergera truncata	THANKSGIVING CACTUS	(CS)
Schoenus	BOG-RUSH	(G)
Schotia latifolia	ELEPHANT HEDGE BEAN TREE	(TT)
Sciadophyllum brownii	GALAPEE TREE	(TT)
Sciadopitys	UMBRELLA PINE	(C)
Sciadopitys verticilliata	JAPANESE UMBRELLA PINE	(C)
Sciadopitys verticilliata	PARASOL PINE	(C)
Scilla	SQUILL	(BB)
Scilla autumnalis	AUTUMN SQUILL	(BB)
Scilla autumnalis	AUTUMN-FLOWERING SQUILL	(BB)
Scilla bifolia	ALPINE SQUILL	(BB)
Scilla peruviana	CUBAN LILY	(BB)
Scilla verna	SPRING SQUILL	(BB)
Scillia sibirica	SIBERIAN SQUILL	(BB)
Scindapsusn	IVY ARUM	(HP)
Scirpus	BULRUSH	(G)
Scirpus	CLUB-RUSH	(G)
Scirpus cespitosus	DEER GRASS	(G)
Scirpus cespitosus	DEERGRASS	(G)
Scirpus setaceus	BRISTLE CLUB-RUSH	(G)
Scirpus sylvaticus	WOOD CLUB-RUSH	(G)
Scirpus tabernaemontani 'Zebrinus'	ZEBRA RUSH	(H)
Scleranthus	KNAWEL	(A)
Scleranthus perennis	PERENNIAL KNAWEL	(H)
Scolochloa festucacea	SWAMP GRASS	(G)
Scolymus hispanicus	GOLDEN THISTLE	(H)
Scolymus hispanicus	SPANISH OYSTER PLANT	(H)
Scoparia dulcis	SWEET BROOM	(S)
Scopola carniolica	SCOPOLIA	(S)

Botanical	Common	Type
Scorzonera	BLACK SALSIFY	(B)
Scorzonera	SCORZONERA	(V)
Scorzonera	VIPERS GRASS	(V)
Scrophularia	FIGWORT	(H)
Scrophularia auriculata	WATER BETONY	(H)
Scrophularia aurieulata	WATER FIGWORT	(H)
Scrophularia nodosa	CARPENTER'S SQUARE	(H)
Scrophularia nodosa	KNOTTED FIGWORT	(H)
Scrophularia scorodonia	BALM-LEAVED FIGWORT	(H)
Scrophularia umbrosa	GREEN FIGWORT	(H)
Scrophularia vernalis	YELLOW FIGWORT	(H)
Scutellaria	HELMET FLOWER	(H)
Scutellaria	SKULLCAP	(H)
Scutellaria lateriflora	MAD-DOG SCULLCAP	(H)
Scutellaria lateriflora	MADWEED	(H)
Scutellaria lateriflora	VIRGINIAN SKULLCAP	(H)
Scutellaria minor	LESSER SKULL-CAP	(H)
Scytosiphon lomentaria	SUGARA	(SW)
Scytosiphon lonentaria	BEENWEED	(SW)
Sebastiana pringlei	JUMPING BEAN	(TS)
Sebastiana pringlei	JUMPING BEAN PLANT	(TS)
Secale cereale	RYE	(V)
Sechium edule	CHAYOTE	(TS)
Securinega durissima	OTAHEITE MYRTLE	(TS)
Sedum	STONECROP	(RH)
Sedum acre	BITING STONECROP	(R)
Sedum acre	GOLDEN MOSS	(H)
Sedum acre	WALL PEPPER	(A)
Sedum adolphi	GOLDEN SEDUM	(HP)
Sedum album	WHITE STONECROP	(H)
Sedum anglicum	ENGLISH STONECROP	(H)
Sedum dasyphyllum	THICK-LEAVED STONECROP	(H)
Sedum forsteranum	ROCK STONECROP	(H)
Sedum morganianum	BEAVER TAIL	(H)
Sedum morganianum	BURRO'S TAIL	(H)
Sedum morganianum	DONKEY'S TAIL	(HP)
Sedum morganianum	HORSE'S TAIL	(HP)
Sedum morganianum	LAMB'S TAIL	(HP)
Sedum reflexum	REFLEXED STONECROP	(H)
Sedum rubrotinctum	CHRISTMAS CHEER	(HP)
Sedum spectabile	ICE PLANT	(H)
Sedum telephium	LIVE FOR EVER	(HR)
Sedum telephium	LIVELONG	(H)
Sedum telephium	MIDSUMMER MEN	(H)
Sedum telephium	ORPINE	(H)
Sedum villosum	HAIRY STONECROP	(H)
Sedum x rubrotinctum	PORK AND BEANS	(H)

Botanical	Common	Type
Selaginella	SPIKE MOSS	(MS)
Selaginella lepidophylla	RESURRECTION PLANT	(H)
Selaginella lepidophylla	ROSE OF JERICHO	(H)
Selago thunbergii	BLUE HAZE	(H)
Selenicereus grandiflorus	NIGHT-BLOOMING CEREUS	(CS)
Selenicereus grandiflorus	QUEEN OF THE NIGHT	(CS)
Selenicereus grandiflorus	QUEEN-OF-THE-NIGHT	(CS)
Selenicereus pteronthus	PRINCESS OF THE NIGHT	(CS)
Selinum carvifolia	CAMBRIDGE MILK-PARSLEY	(H)
Selinum tenuifolium	HIMALAYAN PARSLEY	(HB)
Semecarpus anacardium	DHOBI'S NUT	(TS)
Semecarpus anacardium	MARKING-NUT TREE	(TT)
Semele androgyna	CLIMBING BUTCHER'S BROOM	(CL)
Semiarundinaria fastuosa	NARIHIRA BAMBOO	(G)
Semperrivum tectorum	BULLOCK'S EYE	(R)
Sempervivum	HOUSE LEEK	(R)
Sempervivum	THUNDER-PLANT	(R/H)
Sempervivum arachnoideum	COBWEB HOUSE-LEEK	(R)
Sempervivum tectorum	COMMON HOUSELEEK	(H)
Sempervivum tectorum	JUPITER'S EYE	(H)
Senecia vulgaris	GROUNDSEL	(A)
Senecio aquaticus	MARSH RAGWORT	(B)
Senecio aureus	GOLDEN GROUNDSEL	(H)
Senecio bicolor cineraria	SILVER RAGWORT	(H/S)
Senecio confusus	MEXICAN FLAME VINE	(CL)
Senecio cruentus	CINERARIA	(HP)
Senecio erucifolius	HOARY RAGWORT	(H)
Senecio fluviatilis	BROAD-LEAVED RAGWORT	(H)
Senecio integrifolius	FIELD FLEAWORT	(H)
Senecio jacobaca	ST. JAME'S WORT	(H)
Senecio jacobaea	JACOBEA	(H)
Senecio jacobaea	RAGWORT	(H)
Senecio jacobaea	STAGGERWORT	(H)
Senecio macroflossus	CAPE IVY	(HP)
Senecio macroglossus	WAX VINE	(HP)
Senecio mikanioides	GERMAN IVY	(HP)
Senecio mikanioides	PARLOUR IVY	(HP)
Senecio mikanioides	WATER IVY	(HP)
Senecio nemorensis	WOOD RAGWORT	(H)
Senecio palustris	MARSH FLEAWORT	(H)
Senecio petasites	VELVET GROUNDSEL	(H)
Senecio rowleyanus	STRING OF BEADS	(HP)
Senecio squalidus	OXFORD RAGWORT	(A)
Senecio sylvaticus	WOOD GROUNDSEL	(H)
Senecio viscosus	STICKY GROUNDSEL	(H)
Sequoia sempervirens	CALIFORNIAN REDWOOD	(C)
Sequoia sempervirens	COAST REDWOOD	(C)

Botanical	Common	Type
Sequoia sempervivens	REDWOOD	(C)
Sequoiadendron	BIG TREE	(C)
Sequoiadendron	WELLINGTONIA	(C)
Sequoiadendron giganteum	CALIFORNIA BIG TREE	(C)
Sequoiadendron giganteum	MAMMOTH TREE	(C)
Sequoiadendron giganteum	SIERRA REDWOOD	(C)
Serenoa repens	SABAL	(P)
Serenoa repens	SAW-PALMETTO	(P)
Sericocarpus conyzoides	SILK FRUIT	(TT)
Serratula tinctoria	SAW-WORT	(H)
Serruria florida	BLUSHING BRIDE	(H)
Sesame indicum	GINGILLY	(F)
Sesamoides canescens	SESAMOIDES	(H)
Sesamum indicum	SESAME	(S)
Sesbania formosa	WHITE DRAGON TREE	(TT)
Sesbania tripetii	WISTERIA TREE	(TT)
Seseli libanotis	MOON CARROT	(H)
Sesleria albicans	BLUE MOOR GRASS	(G)
Sesleria heufleriana	BALKAN BLUE GRASS	(G)
Setaria	BRISTLE-GRASS	(G)
Setaria	FOXTAIL GRASSES	(G)
Setaria italica	FOXTAIL BRISTLE-GRASS	(G)
Setaria italica	FOXTAIL MILLET	(G)
Setaria italica	ITALIAN MILLET	(G)
Setcreasea purpurea	PURPLE HEART	(HP)
Shepherdia argentea	BUFFALO BERRY	(S)
Sherardia arvensis	FIELD MADDER	(H)
Shibataea	BAMBOO	(G)
Shorea robusta	SAL	(TT)
Shortia galacifolia	OCONEE BELLS	(R)
Sibthorpia europaea	CORNISH MONEYWORT	(H)
Sicana odorifera	CASSA-BANANA	(TS)
Sicyos angulatus	BUR CUCUMBER	(S)
Sicyos angulatus	BUR-CUCUMBER	(F)
Sida petrophila	ROCKSIDA	(H)
Sidalcea	FALSE MALLOW	(H)
Sidalcea	GREEK MALLOW	(H)
Sidalcea	PRAIRIE MALLOW	(H)
Sideritis	IRONWORT	(S)
Silaum silaus	PEPPER SAXIFRAGE	(H)
Silaum silaus	PEPPER-SAXIFRAGE	(H)
Silene	CAMPION	(A/H)
Silene acaulis	MOSS CAMPION	(H)
Silene alba	WHITE CAMPION	(H)
Silene armeria	SWEET WILLIAM CATCHFLY	(H)
Silene armeria	SWEET-WILLIAM CATCHFLY	(H)
Silene conica	SAND CATCHFLY	(H)

Botanical	Common	Type
Silene conica	STRIATED CATCHFLY	(H)
Silene dichotoma	FORKED CATCHFLY	(H)
Silene dioica	RED CAMPION	(H)
Silene gallica	SMALL CATCHFLY	(H)
Silene italica	ITALIAN CATCHFLY	(H)
Silene latifolia	WHITE CAMPION	(H)
Silene maritima	SEA CAMPION	(R)
Silene noctiflora	NIGHT-FLOWERING CATCHFLY	(H)
Silene nutans	NOTTINGHAM CATCHFLY	(H)
Silene otites	SPANISH CATCHFLY	(H)
Silene rupestris	ROCK CAMPION	(R)
Silene vulgaris	BLADDER CAMPION	(H)
Siliphium terebinthaceum	TURPENTINE	(T)
Silphium	ROSIN PLANT	(H)
Silphium	ROSINWEED	(H)
Silphium laciniatum	COMPASS PLANT	(H)
Silphium laciniatum	PILOT WEED	(H)
Silphium laciniatum	POLAR PLANT	(H)
Silphium pacinatum	ROSIN-WEED	(H)
Silphium perfiliatum	CUP PLANT	(H)
Silphium perfoliatum	INDIAN CUP-PLANT	(H)
Silphium perfoliatum	RAGGED CUP	(H)
Silphium terebinthinaceum	PRAIRIE DOCK	(H)
Silybum marianum	HOLY THISTLE	(H)
Silybum marianum	LADY'S THISTLE	(H)
Silybum marianum	MILK THISTLE	(H)
Silybum marianum	OUR LADY'S THISTLE	(H)
Silybum marianum	ST. MARY'S THISTLE	(H)
Simaba cedron	CEDRON	(TS)
Simaruba amara	BITTER DAMSON	(TT)
Simaruba amara	DYSENTERY BARK	(TT)
Simaruba amara	SIMARUBA	(H)
Simethis planifolia	KERRY LILY	(BB)
Simmondsia chinensis	JOJOBA	(S)
Sinapis alba	MUSTARD	(V)
Sinapis alba	WHITE MUSTARD	(V)
Sinapis alba	YELLOW MUSTARD	(V)
Sinapis arvensis	CHARLOCK	(H)
Sinapis arvensis	FIELD MUSTARD	(H)
Sinapis arvensis	WILD MUSTARD	(H)
Sinningia cardinalis	CARDINAL FLOWER	(HP)
Sinningia cardinalis	HELMET FLOWER	(HP)
Sinningia leucotricha	BRAZILIAN EDELWEISS	(HP)
Sinningia regina	CINDERELLA SLIPPERS	(HP)
Sinningia speciosa	BRAZILIAN GLOXINIA	(HP)
Sinningia speciosa	FLORIST'S GLOXINIA	(HP)
Sinningia speciosa	GLOXINIA	(HP)

Know Your Common Plant Names

Botanical	Common	Type
Sinomenium acutum	CHINESE MOONSEED	(CL)
Sison amomum	HEDGE STONEWORT	(H)
Sison amomum	STONE PARSLEY	(H)
Sisymbrium altissimum	TALL ROCKET	(H)
Sisymbrium irio	LONDON ROCKET	(H)
Sisymbrium loeselii	FALSE LONDON ROCKET	(H)
Sisymbrium officinale	HEDGE MUSTARD	(H)
Sisymbrium orientale	EASTERN ROCKET	(H)
Sisyrinchium	PIGROOT	(H)
Sisyrinchium	RUSH LILY	(RH)
Sisyrinchium	SATIN FLOWER	(H)
Sisyrinchium	SATIN-FLOWER	(H)
Sisyrinchium angustifolium	BLUE-EYED GRASS	(H)
Sisyrinchium douglasii	GRASS WIDOW	(H)
Sisyrinchium douglasii	SPRING BELL	(H)
Sium latifolium	WATER PARSNIP	(H)
Sium sisarum	SKIRRET	(H)
Sloanea woolii	GREY CARABEEN	(MS)
Sloanea woolsii	YELLOW CARABEEN	(MS)
Smilacina	FALSE SOLOMON'S SEAL	(H)
Smilacina racemosa	FALSE SPIKENARD	(H)
Smilacina stellata	STAR-FLOWERED FALSE SOLOMONS SEAL	(H)
Smilacina stellata	STAR-FLOWERED LILY OF THE VALLEY	(H)
Smilax	CAT BRIER	(CL)
Smilax	GREEN BRIAR	(CL)
Smilax aspera	ROUGH BINDWEED	(S)
Smilax china	CHINA ROOT	(CL)
Smilax glauca	SAW BRIER	(S)
Smilax hispida	HAG BRIER	(S)
Smilax officinalis	SARSAPARILLA	(CL)
Smilax ornata	JAMAICA SARSAPARILLA	(TS)
Smilax rotundifolia	GREEN BRIER	(CL)
Smilax rotundifolia	HORSE BRIAR	(CL)
Smilax rotundifolia	HORSE BRIER	(S)
Smithiantha zebrina	TEMPLE BELLS	(HP)
Smyrnium olusatrum	ALEXANDERS	(H)
Smyrnium olusatrum	BLACK LOVAGE	(H)
Socratea exorhiza	ZANONA PALM	(P)
Sohenotoma gracilis	PAPER-HEATH	(S)
Solandra maxima	CAPA DE ORO	(CL)
Solandra maxima	GOLDEN-CHALICE VINE	(CL)
Solandra nitida	CHALICE VINE	(TCL)
Solandra nitida	CUP-OF-GOLD	(TCL)
Solandra nitida	GOLDEN CHALICE	(TCL)
Solanum, Atropa	NIGHT SHADE	(AH)
Solanum aviculare	KANGAROO APPLE	(S)
Solanum capsicastrum	FALSE JERUSALEM CHERRY	(HP)

Botanical	Common	Type
Solanum capsicastrum	WINTER CHERRY	(HP)
Solanum caralinense	POISON POTATO	(H)
Solanum carolinense	APPLE OF SODOM	(H)
Solanum carolinense	BULL NETTLE	(H)
Solanum carolinense	HORSENETTLE	(H)
Solanum crispum	CHILEAN POTATO TREE	(CL)
Solanum dulcamara	BITTER-SWEET	(H)
Solanum dulcamara	WOODY NIGHTSHADE	(H)
Solanum jasminoides	JASMINE NIGHTSHADE	(CL)
Solanum laciniatum	KANGAROO APPLE	(CL)
Solanum laciniatum	POROPORO	(H)
Solanum melongena	AUBERGINE	(V)
Solanum melongena	BRINJAL	(V)
Solanum melongena	EGGPLANT	(V)
Solanum melongena	JEW'S APPLE	(H)
Solanum muricatum	MELON PEAR	(S)
Solanum muricatum	PEPINO	(V)
Solanum nigrum	BLACK NIGHTSHADE	(A)
Solanum pseudocapsicum	JERUSALEM CHERRY	(HP)
Solanum quitoense	NARANJILLA	(TS)
Solanum seaforthianum	POTATO CREEPER	(CL)
Solanum sosomeum	APPLE OF SODOM	(H)
Solanum topiro	COCONA	(TS)
Solanum tuberosum	POTATO	(V)
Solanum wendlandii	COSTA RICAN NIGHTSHADE	(CL)
Soldanella	MOONWORT	(R)
Soldanella	SNOWBELL	(R)
Soldanella alpina	ALPINE SNOWBELL	(R)
Soldanella montana	MOUNTAIN TASSEL	(R)
Soleanea berteriana	MOTILLO	(TT)
Soleirolia	BABYS TEARS	(R)
Soleirolia	MIND YOUR OWN BUSINESS	(HP)
Solidago canadensis	CANADIAN GOLDEN-ROD	(H)
Solidago odora	SWEET GOLDENROD	(H)
Solidago virgaurea	GOLDENROD	(H)
Solidago virgaurea	WOUNDWORT	(H)
Sollya fusiformis	AUSTRALIAN BLUE-BELL CREEPER	(CL)
Sollya heterphylla	BLUEBELL CREEPER	(CL)
Sonchus arvensis	CORN SOWTHISTLE	(H)
Sonchus asper	PRICKLY SOW THISTLE	(H)
Sonchus oleraceus	COMMON SOW THISTLE	(H)
Sonchus oleraceus	MILK THISTLE	(H)
Sonchus oleraceus	SMOOTH SOW-THISTLE	(H)
Sonchus palustris	MARSH SOW-THISTLE	(H)
Sonchus species	SOWTHISTLE	(AH)
Sophora japonica	JAPANESE PAGODA TREE	(T)
Sophora japonica	PAGODA TREE	(T)

Know Your Common Plant Names

Botanical	Common	Type
Sophora japonica	SCHOLAR'S TREE	(T)
Sophora secundiflora	MESCAL BEAN	(T)
Sophora secundiflora	TEXAS MOUNTAIN LAUREL	(S)
Sophora tetraptera	KOWHAI	(S)
Sophora tetraptera	NEW ZEALAND LABURNUM	(S)
Sorbaria	FALSE SPIRAEA	(S)
Sorbus	ROWAN	(T)
Sorbus americana	AMERICAN MOUNTAIN ASH	(T)
Sorbus americana	DOGBERRY	(T)
Sorbus americana	MISSEY-MOOSEY	(T)
Sorbus anglica	CHEDDAR WHITEBEAM	(T)
Sorbus aria	WHITEBEAM	(T)
Sorbus aucuparia	COMMON MOUNTAIN ASH	(T)
Sorbus aucuparia	COMMON ROWAN	(T)
Sorbus aucuparia	EUROPEAN MOUNTAIN ASH	(T)
Sorbus aucuparia	MOUNTAIN ASH	(T)
Sorbus aucuparia	QUICKEN TREE	(T)
Sorbus aucuparia	RANTRY	(T)
Sorbus aucuparia 'Aspenifolia'	CUT-LEAVED MOUNTAIN ASH	(T)
Sorbus aucuparia 'Pendula'	WEEPING MOUNTAIN ASH	(T)
sorbus aucuparia 'Rossica Major'	RUSSIAN MOUNTAIN ASH	(T)
Sorbus aucuparia 'Xanthocarpa'	YELLOW-BERRIED MOUNTAIN ASH	(T)
Sorbus cashmeriana	KASHMIR ROWAN	(T)
Sorbus chamaemespilus	ALPINE WHITEBEAM	(S)
Sorbus chamaemespilus	FALSE MEDLAR	(S)
Sorbus commixta	JAPANESE ROWAN	(T)
Sorbus commixta 'Embley'	CHINESE SCARLET ROWAN	(T)
Sorbus cuspidata	HIMALAYAN WHITEBEAM	(T)
Sorbus devoniensis	FRENCH HALES	(T)
Sorbus domestica	SERVICE TREE	(T)
Sorbus folgneri	FOLGNER'S WHITEBEAM	(T)
Sorbus intermedia	SWEDISH WHITEBEAM	(T)
Sorbus latifolia	BROAD-LEAVED WHITEBEAM	(T)
Sorbus latifolia	SERVICE TREE OF FONTAINEBLEAU	(T)
Sorbus minima	LEAST WHITEBEAM	(T)
Sorbus mougeotii	PYRENEAN WHITEBEAM	(T)
Sorbus reducta	CREEPING MOUNTAIN ASH	(S)
Sorbus reducta	PYGMY ROWAN	(S)
Sorbus thuringiaca	BASTARD SERVICE TREE	(T)
Sorbus torminalis	WILD SERVICE TREE	(T)
Sorghatrum avenaceum	INDIAN GRASS	(G)
Sorghum almum	JOHNSON GRASS	(G)
Sorghum halepense	GREAT MILLET	(G)
Sorghum halepense	JOHNSON GRASS	(G)
Sorghum saccharatum	CHINESE SUGAR MAPLE	(G)
Sorghum vulgare	BROOM-CORN	(G)
Sorghum vulgare	MILLET	(G)

Know Your Common Plant Names

Botanical	Common	Type
Sorghum vulgare	SORGHUM	(G)
Sorghum vulgare durra	DURRA	(G)
Sparaxis	WANDFLOWER	(BB)
Sparaxis tricolor	HARLEQUIN FLOWER	(BB)
Sparganium	BUR REED	(G)
Sparganium angustifolium	FLOATING BUR-REED	(WP)
Sparganium emersum	UNBRANCHED BUR-REED	(WP)
Sparganium erectum	BRANCHED BUR-REED	(WP)
Sparganium minimum	SMALL BUR-REED	(H)
Sparganium ramosum	BUR-REED	(WP)
Sparmannia	HOUSE LIME	(HP)
Sparmannia	INDOOR LINDEN	(HP)
Sparmannia africana	AFRICAN HEMP	(HP)
Sparmannia africana	RUMSLIND TREE	(HP)
Sparmannia africana	ZIMMER LINDEN	(HP)
Spartina alternifolia	SMOOTH CORD GRASS	(G)
Spartina anglica	COMMON CORD-GRASS	(G)
Spartina pectinata	CORD GRASS	(G)
Spartina x townsendii	RICE GRASS	(G)
Spartium junceum	SPANISH BROOM	(S)
Spartium junceun	WEAVER'S BROOM	(S)
Spartocytisus nubigenus	TENERIFE BROOM	(S)
Spathelia simplex	MAY POLE	(S)
Spathelia simplex	MOUNTAIN GREEN	(S)
Spathiphyllum floribundum	SNOW FLOWER	(TH)
Spathiphyllum wallisii	PEACE LILY	(HP)
Spathodea camanulata	FOUNTAIN TREE	(TT)
Spathodea campanulata	AFRICAN TULIP TREE	(TT)
Spathodea campanulata	TULIPAN	(TT)
Spathoden campanulata	FLAME OF THE FOREST	(TT)
Spergula arvensis	CORN SPURREY	(A)
Spergularia marina	SEA SPURREY	(H)
Spergularia media	GREATER SAND SPURREY	(H)
Spergularia rubra	RED SPURREY	(H)
Spergularia rubra	SAND SPURREY	(H)
Spergularia rubra	SAND-SPURREY	(H)
Spergularia rupicola	ROCK SPURREY	(H)
Sphaeralcea	GLOBE MALLOW	(A)
Sphagnum cymbifolium	SPHAGNUM MOSS	(MS)
Spigelia	WORM GRASS	(G)
Spigelia marilandica	INDIAN PINK	(BB)
Spigelia marilandica	MARYLAND PINK ROOT	(BB)
Spigelia marilandica	WORM GRASS	(H)
Spigelia marilandiea	PINK-ROOT	(H)
Spigelia marylandica	PINK ROOT	(H)
Spinacia oleracea	SPINACH	(V)
Spiraea douglasii	HARDHACK	(S)

Botanical	Common	Type
Spiraea nipponica tosaensis	'SNOWMOUND'	(S)
Spiraea salicifolia	BRIDEWORT	(S)
Spiraea tomentosa	HARDHACK	(S)
Spiraea tomentosa	STEEPLEBUSH	(S)
Spiraea x arguta	BRIDAL WREATH	(S)
Spiraea x arguta	FOAM-OF-MAY	(S)
Spiraea x arguta	GARLAND WREATH	(S)
Spiranthes	LADIES' TRESSES	(
Spiranthes aestivalis	SUMMER LADY'S TRESSES	(O)
Spiranthes spiralis	AUTUMN LADY'S TRESSES	(O)
Spirnea bumalda 'Gold Flame'	GOLD FLAME	(S)
Spirodela polyrhiza	GREAT DUCKWEED	(WP)
Spirodela polyrhiza	GREATER DUCKWEED	(WP)
Spondias	MOMBIN	(B)
Spondias cytheria	AMBARELLA	(TT)
Spondias dulcis	OTAHEITE APPLE	(T)
Spondias lutea	GOLDEN APPLE	(T)
Spondias lutea	JAMAICA PLUM	(T)
Spondias lutea	YELLOW MOMBIN	(TT)
Spondias mombin	HOG PLUM	(H)
Spondias mombin	YELLOW MOMBIN .	(T)
Spondias purpurea	RED MOMBIN	(TT)
Spraguea multiceps	PUSSY PAWS	(A)
Sprekelia	JACOBEAN LILY	(HP)
Sprekelia formosissima	AZTEC LILY	(BB)
Stachys	HEDGE-NETTLE	(H)
Stachys	WOUNDWORT	(H)
Stachys affinis	CHINESE ARTICHOKE	(H)
Stachys arvensi	FIELD WOUNDWORT	(H)
Stachys arvensis	CORN WOUNDWORT	(H)
Stachys betonica	BETONY	(H)
Stachys byzantina	LAMB'S EAR Bunnys ears	(H)
Stachys byzantina	LAMB'S LUGS	(H)
Stachys byzantina	LAMB'S TONGUE	(H)
Stachys byzantina	SOW'S EAR	(H)
Stachys byzantina	WOOLLY WOUNDWORT	(H)
Stachys germanica	DOWNY WOUNDWORT	(H)
Stachys officinalis	BETONY	(H)
Stachys officinalis	BISHOP'S WORT	(H)
Stachys palustris	MARSH WOUNDWORT	(H)
Stachys recta	YELLOW WOUNDWORT	(H)
Stachys sylvatica	HEDGE WOUNDWORT	(H)
Stachys sylvatica	WOOD WOUNDWORT	(H)
Stallaria neglecta	GREAT CHICKWEED	(H)
Stangeria criopus	HOTTENTOT'S HEAD	(H)
Stapelia	CARRION FLOWER	(H)
Stapelia	CARRION FLOWERS	(HP)

Botanical	Common	Type
Stapelia gigantea	GIANT STAPELIA	(HP)
Stapelia gigantea	GIANT TOAD FLOWER	(HP)
Stapelia gigantea	ZULU GIANT	(HP)
Stapelia variegata	TOAD PLANT	(HP)
Staphylea	BLADDERNUT	(S)
Staphylea pinnata	ANTHONY NUT	(S)
Stellaria	STITCHWORT	(H)
Stellaria alsine	BOG STITCHWORT	(A)
Stellaria graminea	LESSER STITCHWORT	(H)
Stellaria holostea	GREATER STITCHWORT	(H)
Stellaria media	CHICKWEED	(A)
Stellaria media	COMMON CHICKWEED	(H)
Stellaria neglecta	GREATER CHICKWEED	(H)
Stellaria nemorum	WOOD STITCHWORT	(H)
Stellaria pallida	LESSER CHICKWEED	(H)
Stellaria palustris	MARSH STITCHWORT	(H)
Stelloria uliginosa	BOG STITCHWORT	(H)
Stenocarpus sinuatus	FIREWHEEL TREE	(HP)
Stenocarpus sinuatus	QUEENSLAND FIREWHEEL TREE	(TT)
Stenocarpus sinuatus	WHEEL OF FIRE	(HP)
Stenotaphrum secundatum	BUFFALO GRASS	(HP)
Stenotaphrum secundatum	SHORE GRASS	(G)
Stenotaphrum secundatum	ST. AUGUSTINE GRASS	(G)
Stephanotis	MADAGASCAR JASMINE	(HP)
Stephanotis floribunda	WAX FLOWER	(HP)
Sterculia acerfolia	FLAME TREE	(TT)
Sterculia rupestris	QUEENSLAND BOTTLE TREE	(TT)
Sternbergia	LILY OF THE FIELD	(BB)
Sternbergia	LILY-OF-THE-FIELD	(BB)
Sternbergia lutea	YELLOW STAR FLOWER	(BB)
Stetsonia coryne	TOOTHPICK CACTUS	(CS)
Stewartia	DECIDUOUS CAMELLIA	(ST)
Stewartia pseudocamellia	JAPANESE STEWARTIA	(T)
Stewartia sinensis	CHINESE STEWARTIA	(S/T)
Stigmaphyllon	GOLDEN VINE	(G)
Stillingia sylvatica	QUEEN'S DELIGHT	(H)
Stillingia sylvatica	YAWROOT	(H)
Stipa	SPEAR GRASS	(G)
Stipa arundinacea	PHEASANT GRASS	(G)
Stipa arundinacea	PHEASANT TAIL GRASS	(G)
Stipa gigantea	GOLDEN OATS	(G)
Stipa pennata	FEATHER GRASS	(G)
Stipa pulcherrima	GOLDEN FEATHER-GRASS	(G)
Stipa tenacissima	ESPARTO GRASS	(G)
Stizolobium	VELVET-BEAN	(CL)
Stokesia laevis	STOKE'S ASTER	(H)
Stratiotes aloides	WATER ALOE	(WP)

Botanical	Common	Type
Stratiotes aloides	WATER SOLDIER	(WP)
Strelitzia nicolai	WILD BANANA	(HP)
Strelitzia reginae	BIRD OF PARADISE FLOWER	(HP)
Strelitzia reginae	CRANE FLOWER	(HP)
Strelitzia reginae	CRANE LILY	(HP)
Strenbergia lutea	WINTER DAFFODIL	(BB)
Streptocarpus	CAPE PRIMROSE	(HP)
Streptocarpus saxorum	FALSE AFRICAN VIOLET	(HP)
Streptopus	TWISTED STALK	(H)
Streptopus amlexifolius	STREPTOPUS	(S)
Streptosolen jamesonii	MARMALADE BUSH	(HP)
Striga	WITCHWEED	(H)
Strobilanthes	CONE-HEAD	(C)
Strobilanthes	MEXICAN PETUNIA	(HP)
Strobilanthes dyerianus	PERSIAN SHIELD	(H)
Strychnos ignatii	IGNATIUS BEAN	(TS)
Strychnos nux vomica	STRYCHNINE	(TT)
Strychnos nux-vomica	NUX VOMICA	(TT)
Strychnos toxifera	CURARE	(TS)
Stylidium graminifolium	TRIGGER PLANT	(H)
Stylidium macranthum	CRAB CLAWS	(H)
Stylidium scandens	CLIMBING TRIGGER PLANT	(CL)
Stylomecon heterophylla	BLOOD-DROP	(H)
Stylomecon heterophylla	WIND POPPY	(H)
Stylophorum diphyllum	CELANDINE POPPY	(H)
Styrax	SNOWBELL TREE	(T)
Styrax americana	AMERICAN STORAX	(T)
Styrax benzoin	BENZOIN	(TT)
Styrax japonica	JAPANESE SNOWBELL	(S/T)
Styrax obassia	BIG-LEAF STORAX	(S/T)
Styrax officinalis	STORAX	(ST)
Suaeda maritima	ANNUAL SEA-BLITE	(H)
Suaeda maritima	SEABLITE	(A)
Suaeda vera	SHABBY SEABLITE	(H)
Suaeda vera	SHRUBBY SEA-BLITE	(S)
Subularia aquatica	AWLWORT	(WP)
Sucissa pratensis	DEVIL'S BIT SCABIOUS	(H)
Suillus bovinus	JERSEY COW BOLETE	(FU)
Suillus luteus	SLIPPERY JACK	(FU)
Sulidago	AARON'S ROD	(H)
Sutherlandia frutescens	CANCER BUSH	(S)
Swainsona	SWAINSON PEA	(S)
Swainsonia	DARLING RIVER PEA	(H)
Swertia chirata	CHIRETTA	(HB)
Swertia perennis	MARSH FELWORT	(H)
Swietenia macrophylla	MAHOGANY	(TT)
Symphoricarpos albus	SNOWBERRY	(S)

Know Your Common Plant Names

Botanical	Common	Type
Symphoricarpos occidentalis	WOLFBERRY	(S)
Symphoricarpos orbiculatus	CORAL BERRY	(S)
Symphoricarpos orbiculatus	INDIAN CURRANT	(S)
Symphytum caucasicum	BLUE COMFREY	(H)
Symphytum grandiflorum	DWARF COMFREY	(H)
Symphytum officinale	BONESET	(H)
Symphytum officinale	BRUISEWORT	(H)
Symphytum officinale	COMFREY	(H)
Symphytum officinale	COMMON COMFREY	(H)
Symphytum officinale	KNITBONE	(H)
Symphytum orientale	WHITE COMFREY	(H)
Symphytum tuberosum	TUBEROUS COMFREY	(H)
Symphytum x uplandicum	RUSSIAN COMFREY	(H)
Symplocarpus foetidus	MEADOW CABBAGE	(H)
Symplocarpus foetidus	POLECAT WEED	(H)
Symplocarpus foetidus	SKUNK CABBAGE	(H)
Symplocarpus foetidus	SKUNK WEED	(H)
Symplocos paniculata	ASIATIC SWEETLEAF	(T)
Symplocos paniculata	SAPPHINE BERRY	(T)
Symplocos tinctoria	HORSE SUGAR	(T)
Symplocos tinctoria	SWEETLEAF	(T)
Synadenium grantii	AFRICAN MILKBUSH	(TS)
Syncarpia glomulifera	TURPENTINE TREE	(TT)
Syngonium angustatum	ARROWHEAD VINE	(HP)
Syngonium auritum	FIVE FINGERS	(HP)
Syngonium podophyllum	ARROWHEAD PLANT	(HP)
Syngonium podophyllum	ARROWHEAD VINE	(HP)
Syngonium podophyllum	GOOSEFOOT PLANT	(HP)
Synsepalum dulciferum	MIRACULOUS BERRY	(TS)
Syringa	LILAC	(ST)
Syringa amurensis	AMUR LILAC	(S)
Syringa chinensis	ROUEN LILAC	(S)
Syringa emodi	HIMALAYAN LILAC	(S)
Syringa josikaea	HUNGARIAN LILAC	(S)
Syringa meyeri 'Palibin'	KOREAN LILAC	(S)
Syringa microphylla 'Superba'	DAPHNE LILAC	(S)
Syringa persica	PERSIAN LILAC	(S)
Syringa swegiflexa	PINK PEARL LILAC	(S)
Syringa vulgaris	COMMON LILAC	(ST)
Syringa x chinensis	CHINESE LILAC	(S)
Syringa yunnanensis	YUNNAN LILAC	(S)
Tabebuia	ARAGUANEY	(TS)
Tabebuia	GOLD TREE	(TS)
Tabebuia	WEST INDIAN BOXWOOD	(TT)
Tabebuia chrysantha	GOLDEN TRUMPET-TREE	(TT)
Tabebuia flavescens	GREEN EBONY	(TT)
Tabebuia pentaphylla	PINK POUI	(TT)

Botanical	Common	Type
Tabebuia pentaphylla	PINK TECOMA	(TT)
Tabebuia rosea	PINK TRUMPET-TREE	(TT)
Tabebuia serratifolia	APAMATA	(TT)
Tabebuia serratifolia	YELLOW POUI	(TT)
Tabernaemontana coronaria	ADAM'S APPLE	(S)
Tabernaemontana coronaria	CRAPE JASMINE	(S)
Tabernaemontana coronaria	NERO'S CROWN	(S)
Tacca chantrieri	BAT FLOWER	(H)
Tacca chantrieri	CAT'S WHISKERS	(HP)
Tacca chantrieri	DEVIL FLOWER	(HP)
Tacca integrifolia	BAT PLANT	(HP)
Tacca nivea	CAT'S HEAD PLANT	(H)
Tacca nivea	DEVIL'S WHISKER PLANT	(H)
Tacca oceanica	TAHITI ARROWROOT	(TS)
Tacitus bellus	CHIHUAHUA FLOWER	(TS)
Taenitis blechnoides	FILLET FERN	(FN)
Taenitis blechnoides	RIBBON FERN	(FN)
Tagetes erecta	AFRICAN MARIGOLD	(A)
Tagetes patula	FRENCH MARIGOLD	(A)
Tagetes signata	TAGETES	(A)
Tagetes tenuifolia	SIGNET MARIGOLD	(A)
Talinum	FAMEFLOWER	(H)
Tamarindus indica	TAMARIND	(T)
Tamarix	TAMARISK	(S)
Tamarix gallica	FRENCH TAMARISK	(S)
Tamarix gallica mannifera	MANNA	(S)
Tamatix gallica	SALT CEDAR	(S)
Tamus	BRYONY	(CL)
Tamus communis	BLACK BRYONY	(CL)
Tanacetum cinerarii folium	PYRETHRUM	(H)
Tanacetum cinerariifolium	DALMATIAN PELLITORY	(H)
Tanacetum cinerariifolium	DALMATIAN PYRETHRUM	(H)
Tanacetum coccineum	FEVERFEW	(F)
Tanacetum coccineum	PAINTED DAISY	(H)
Tanacetum coccineum	PERSIAN PELLITORY	(H)
Tanacetum coccineum	PYRETHRUM	(H)T
Tanacetum densum amani	PRINCE OF WALES FEATHERS	(R)
Tanacetum parthenium	BACHELORS BUTTONS	(HB)
Tanacetum parthenium	FEVERFEW	(HB)
Tanacetum parthenium 'Aureum'	GOLDEN FEATHER	(H)
Tanacetum parthenium 'Aureum'	GOLDEN FEVER FEW	(H)
Tanacetum vulgare	BUTTONS	(H)
Tanacetum vulgare	TANSY	(HB)
Tanakaea radicans	JAPANESE FOAM FLOWER	(S)
Taratacum officianale	PRIEST'S CROWN	(H)
Taraxacum	PISS-THE-BED	(H)
Taraxacum erythrospermum	LESSER DANDELION	(H)

Botanical	Common	Type
Taraxacum laevicatum	LESSER DANDELION	(H)
Taraxacum officinale	DANDELION	(H)
Taraxacum officinale	FAIRY CLOCK	(H)
Taraxacum officinale	LION'S TEETH	(H)
Taraxacum officinale	PEE IN THE BED	(H)
Taraxacum officinale	SWINES SNOUT	(H)
Taxodium	SWAMP CYPRESS	(C)
Taxodium	YEW CYPRESS	(C)
Taxodium ascendens	POND CYPRESS	(C)
Taxodium distichum	BALD CYPRESS	(C)
Taxodium distichum	DECIDUOUS CYPRESS	(C)
Taxodium distichum 'Pendens'	WEEPING SWAMP CYPRESS	(C)
Taxodium mucronatum	AHUEHUETE	(C)
Taxodium mucronatum	MEXICAN SWAMP CYPRESS	(C)
Taxus	YEW	(C)
Taxus bacc. 'dovastoniana'	WEST FELTON YEW	(C)
Taxus baccata	COMMON YEW	(C)
Taxus Baccata	ENGLISH YEW	(C)
Taxus baccata 'Aurea'	GOLDEN YEW	(C)
Taxus baccata 'Aureovariegata'	GOLDEN IRISH YEW	(C)
Taxus baccata 'Fastigiata'	IRISH YEW	(C)
Taxus baccata 'Fructo-luteo'	YELLOW-BERRIED YEW	(C)
Taxus brevifolia	CALIFORNIAN YEW	(C)
Taxus brevifolia	PACIFIC YEW	(C)
Taxus brevifolia	WESTERN YEW	(C)
Taxus canadensis	CANADIAN YEW	(C)
Taxus chinensis	CHINESE YEW	(C)
Taxus cuspidata	JAPANESE YEW	(C)
Taxus media	ANGLO-JAPANESE YEW	(C)
Taxus media 'Hicksii'	HICK'S YEW	(C)
Tecoma stans	YELLOW BELLS	(TT)
Tecoma stans	YELLOW BIGNONIA	(TT)
Tecoma stans	YELLOW ELDER	(TT)
Tecoma stans	YELLOW TRUMPET-TREE	(TT)
Tecomaria capensis	CAPE HONEYSUCKLE	(CL)
Tecophilaea cyanocrocus	CHILEAN CROCUS	(BB)
Tectona grandis	TEAK	(TT)
Teesdalia nudicaulis	SHEPHERD'S CRESS	(A)
Teesdalia nudicaulis	SHEPHERDS CRESS	(H)
Telekia speciosa	LARGE YELLOW OX-EYE	(H)
Telfairia occidentalis	OYSTER NUTS	(TS)
Tellima	FALSE ALUM ROOT	(H)
Tellima grandiflora	FRINGE CUPS	(H)
Tellima grandiflora	FRINGECUPS	(H)
Telopea	WARRATAH	(ST)
Telopea oreades	GIPPSLAND WARATAH	(S/T)
Telopea truncata	TASMANIAN WARATAH	(T)

Know Your Common Plant Names

Botanical	Common	Type
Templetonia retusa	BULLOCK BUSH	(S)
Templetonia retusa	CORAL BUSH	(S)
Terminalia alata	INDIAN LAUREL	(TS)
Terminalia catappa	INDIAN ALMOND	(T)
Terminalia catappa	OLIVE BARK TREE	(TT)
Terminalia ivorensis	IDIGBO	(TS)
Terminalia superba	AFARA	(TS)
Testudinaria elephantipes	ELEPHANT'S FOOT	(F)
Testudinaria elephantipes	HOTTENTOT BREAD	(F)
Testudinaria elephantipes	TORTOISE PLANT	(F)
Tetracentron sinense	SPUR LEAF	(ST)
Tetraclinis articulata	ALERCE	(C)
Tetradymia	HORSEBRUSH	(H)
Tetragonia expansa	NEW ZEALAND SPINACH	(V)
Tetragonolobus maritimus	DRAGON'S TEETH	(H)
Tetranema mexicana	MEXICAN FOXGLOVE	(H)
Tetrapananax papyrifera	RICE-PAPER TREE	(T.T)
Tetrastigma voinieranum	CHESTNUT VINE	(NP)
Tetrastigma voinieranum	LIZARD PLANT	(HP)
Teucrium	GERMANDER	(HS)
Teucrium chamaedrys	GROUND OAK	(H)
Teucrium chamaedrys	WALL GERMANDER	(H)
Teucrium fruiticans	SHRUBBY GERMANDER	(S)
Teucrium marum	CAT THYME	(H)
Teucrium montanum	ALPINE PENNYROYAL	(H)
Teucrium montanum	MOUNTAIN GERMANDER	(H)
Teucrium scordium	WATER GERMANDER	(H)
Teucrium scorodonia	WOOD SAGE	(H)
Teucrium scorodonia	WOODSAGE	(HB)
Thalictrum	MEADOW RUE	(H)
Thalictrum alpinum	ALPINE MEADOW RUE	(H)
Thalictrum flavum	COMMON MEADOW RUE	(H)
Thalictrum flavum	YELLOW MEADOW-RUE	(H)
Thalictrum minus	LESSER MEADOW-RUE	(H)
Thamnocalamus spathaceus	MURIEL BAMBOO	(G)
Thelocactus bicolor	GLORY OF TEXAS	(CS)
Thelocactus bicolor	TEXAS PRIDE	(CS)
Thelygonum cynocrambe	DOG'S CABBAGE	(H)
Thelymitra	WOMAN'S CAP ORCHID	(O)
Thelypteris hexagonoptera	BROAD BEECH FERN	(FN)
Thelypteris oreopteris	MOUNTAIN BUCKLER FERN	(FN)
Thelypteris palustris	MARSH FERN	(FN)
Theobroma cacao	CACAO	(F)
Theobroma cacao	CHOCOLATE TREE	(TT)
Theobroma cacao	COCOA	(FT)
Thermopsis caroliniana	CAROLINA LUPIN	(H)
Thesium alpinum	ALPINE BASTARD TOADFLAX	(H)

Know Your Common Plant Names

Botanical	Common	Type
Thesium humifusum	BASTARD TOADFLAX	(H)
Thespesia populnea	BHENDI TREE	(TT)
Thespesia populnea	MAHOE	(T)
Thespesia populnea	PORTIA OIL NUT	(S)
Thespesia populnea	PORTIA TREE	(TT)
Thevetia peruviana	YELLOW OLEANDER	(TS)
Thlaspi	PENNYCRESS	(R)
Thlaspi alliaceum	GARLIC PENNYCRESS	(H)
Thlaspi aplestre	ALPINE PENNY CRESS	(H)
Thlaspi arvense	FIELD PENNYCRESS	(H)
Thlaspi perfoliatum	PERFOLIATE PENNYCRESS	(H)
Thrinax	THATCH PALM	(P)
Thrinax argentea	BROOM PALM	(P)
Thuja	ARBOR-VITAE	(C)
Thuja occidentalis	YELLOW CEDAR	(C)
Thuja plicata	WESTERN ARBOR-VITAE	(C)
Thuja standishii	JAPANESE ARBOR-VITAE	(C)
Thuja standishii	JAPANESE THUJA	(C)
Thujopsis	BROAD-LEAVED ARBORVITAE	(C)
Thujopsis	FALSE ARBORVITAE	(C)
Thujopsis dolobrata	HIBA	(C)
Thunbergia alata	BLACK-EYED SUSAN	(CL)
Thunbergia alata	CLOCK VINE	(A)
Thunbergia grandiflora	BENGAL CLOCKVINE	(TCL
Thunbergia grandiflora	BENGAL TRUMPET	(TCL)
Thunbergia grandiflora	BLUE TRUMPET VINE	(TCL)
Thunbergia grandiflora	CLOCK VINE	(CL)
Thunbergia grandiflora	SKY VINE	(TCL)
Thuya occidentalis	AMERICAN ARBOR-VITAE	(C)
Thuya occidentalis	NORTHERN WHITE CEDAR	(C)
Thuya occidentalis	WHITE CEDAR	(C)
Thuya orientalis	CHINESE ARBOR-VITAE	(C)
Thuya plicata	WESTERN RED CEDAR	(C)
Thymelaea passerina	ANNUAL THYMELAEA	(A)
Thymophylla tenuiloba	DAHLBERG DAISY	(H)
Thymophylla tenuiloba	GOLDEN FLEECE	(H)
Thymus	THYME	(HB)
Thymus citriodorus	LEMON THYME	(R)
Thymus herba-barona	CARAWAY THYME	(R)
Thymus praecox	HAIRY THYME	(H)
Thymus pulegioides	LARGE THYME	(H)
Thymus serpyllum	BRECKLAND THYME	(H)
Thymus serpyllum	CREEPING THYME	(HB)
Thymus serpyllum	WILD THYME	(R)
Thymus vulgaris	COMMON THYME	(HB)
Thymus vulgaris	GARDEN THYME	(S)
Thysanotus multiflorus	FRINGE LILY	(H)

Botanical	Common	Type
Tiarella	FALSE MITREWORT	(H)
Tiarella	FOAM FLOWER	(H)
Tiarella cordifolia	COOLWORT	(H)
Tibouchina urvilleana	GLORY BUSH	(HP)
Tibouchina urvilleana	PRINCESS FLOWER	(HP)
Tibouchina urvilleana	PURPLE GLORY TREE	(HP)
Tigridia	MEXICAN SHELL FLOWER	(BB)
Tigridia	TIGER FLOWER	(BB)
Tigridia paronia	PEACOCK TIGER FLOWER	(BB)
Tilia	LIME	(T)
Tilia	LINDEN	(T)
Tilia americana	AMERICAN BASSWOOD	(T)
Tilia americana	AMERICAN LIME	(T)
Tilia americana	BASSWOOD	(T)
Tilia cordata	SMALL-LEAVED LIME	(T)
Tilia euchlora	CRIMEAN LIME	(T)
Tilia europaea 'Pallida'	ROYAL LIME	(T)
Tilia heterophylla	WHITE BASSWOOD	(T)
Tilia japonica	JAPANESE LINDEN	(T)
Tilia monogolica	MONGOLIAN LIME	(T)
Tilia oliveri	OLIVER'S LIME	(T)
Tilia petiolaris	PENDANT SILVER LIME	(T)
Tllia petiolaris	WEEPING SILVER LIME	(T)
Tilia platyphyllos	LARGE-LEAVED LIME	(T)
Tilia platyphyllos 'Rubra'	RED-TWIGGED LIME	(T)
Tilia tomentosa	SILVER LIME	(T)
Tilia x euchlora	CAUCASIAN LIME	(T)
Tilia x europaea	COMMON LIME	(T)
Tilia x europaea	EUROPEAN LINDEN	(T)
Tillandsia cyanea	PINK QUILL	(H)
Tillandsia lindenii	BLUE FLOWERED TORCH	(H)
Tillandsia usneoides	GREYBEARD	(HP)
Tillandsia usneoides	SPANISH MOSS	(HP)
Tipuana tipu	PRIDE OF BOLIVIA	(TT)
Tipuana tipu	TIPA TREE	(TT)
Tithonia rotundifolia	MEXICAN SUNFLOWER	(H)
Toddalia asiatica	LOPEZ ROOT	(H)
Tofieldia calyculata	ALPINE ASPHODEL	(H)
Tofieldia calyculata	GERMAN ASPHODEL	(H)
Tofieldia glutinosa	WESTERN FALSE-ASPHODEL	(H)
Tofieldia pusilla	SCOTTISH ASPHODEL	(H)
Tolmiea menziesii	MOTHER OF THOUSANDS	(HP)
Tolmiea menziesii	MOTHER-OF-THOUSANDS	(HP)
Tolmiea menziesii	PIGGY-BACK PLANT	(HP)
Tolmiea menziesii	YOUTH-ON-AGE	(HP)
Toona odorata	SPANISH CEDAR	(T)
Toona odorata	WEST INDIAN CEDAR	(TT)

Know Your Common Plant Names

Botanical	Common	Type
Toona sinensis	CHINESE CEDAR	(T)
Toona sinensis	TOON	(T)
Tordylium maximum	HARTWORT	(H)
Torenia fourneri	WISHBONE FLOWER	(H)
Torilis japonica	HEDGE PARSLEY	(H)
Torilis nodosa	KNOTTED HEDGE PARSLEY	(H)
Torraya nucifera	JAPANESE MUTMEG	(C)
Torreya californica	CALIFORNIAN NUT MEG	(C)
Torreya nucifera	JAPANESE TORREYA	(C)
Torreya taxifolia	FOETID YEW	(C)
Torreya taxifolia	STINKING CEDAR	(C)
Torreya taxifolia	YEW-LEAVED TORREYA	(C)
Tozzia alpina	TOZZIA	(H)
Trachelium caeruleum	BLUE THROATWORT	(H)
Trachelium coeruleum	THROATWORT	(H)
Trachelospermum	CHINESE JASMINE	(CL)
Trachelospermum jasminoides	STAR JASMINE	(CL)
Trachycarpus fortunei	CHUSAN PALM	(P)
Trachycarpus fortunei	WINDMILL PALM	(P)
Trachystemon orientalis	ABRAHAM, ISAAC & JACOB	(H)
Tradescantia	SPIDERWORT	(H)
Tradescantia	TRINITY FLOWER	(H)
Tradescantia	WIDOW TEARS	(H)
Tradescantia blossfeldiana	FLOWERING INCH PLANT	(HP)
Tradescantia fluminensis	WANDERING JEW	(HP)
Tradescantia navicularis	CHAIN PLANT	(HP)
Tradescantia sillamontana	WHITE VELVET	(HP)
Tradescantia spathacea	MOSES IN THE CRADLE	(HP)
Tradescantia spathacea	THREE-MEN-IN-A-BOAT	(HP)
Tradescantia stathacea	BOAT LILY	(HP)
Tradescantia zebrina	WANDERING JEW	(HP)
Tragopogon porrifolius	OYSTER PLANT	(V)
Tragopogon porrifolius	SALSIFY	(V)
Tragopogon porrifolius	VEGETABLE OYSTER	(V)
Tragopogon pratensis	JACK-GO-TO-BED-AT-NOON	(H)
Tragopogon pratensis	YELLOW GOATSBEARD	(H)
Trapa natans	JESUITS NUT	(WP)
Trapa natans	WATER CHESTNUT	(WP)
Traunsteinera globosa	ROUND-HEADED ORCHID	(O)
Trautvetteria carolinensis	FALSE BUGBANE	(H)
Treculia africana	AFRICAN BREADFRUIT	(TF)
Trichocereus spachianus	GOLDEN COLUMN	(CS)
Trichocereus spachianus	WHITE TORCH CACTUS	(CS)
Tricholaena rosea	NATAL GRASS	(G)
Tricholaena rosea	RUBY GRASS	(G)
Tricholoma gambosum	ST. GEORGES MUSHROOM	(FU)
Tricholoma sulphureum	GAS TAR FUNGUS	(FU)

Know Your Common Plant Names

Botanical	Common	Type
Tricholomopsis rutilans	PLUM AND CUSTARD	(FU)
Tricholomopsis rutilans	PLUMS AND CUSTARD	(FU)
Trichomanes speciosum	KILLARNEY FERN	(FN)
Trichosanthes	SERPENT GOURD	(S)
Trichosanthes anguina	SNAKE GOURD	(H)
Trichosanthes anguine	SNAKEGOURD	(H)
Trichosanthes cucumerina anguina	SNAKE GOURD	(F)
Trichostema	BASTARD PENNYROYAL	(H)
Trichostema	BLUECURLS	(A)
Trichostema lanatum	BLUE CURLS	(H)
Trichostema lanatum	RAMERO	(S)
Trichostema lanatum	WOOLLY BLUE-CURLS	(S)
Tricyrtis	JAPANESE TOAD-LILY	(H)
Tricyrtis	TOAD LILY	(H)
Trientalis	STAR-FLOWER	(H)
Trientalis europaea	CHICKWEED WINTERGREEN	(H)
Trientalis europaea	STAR FLOWER	(H)
Trifolium	CLOVER	(H)
Trifolium	TREFOIL	(H)
Trifolium alpinum	ALPINE CLOVER	(H)
Trifolium arvense	HARE'S FOOT CLOVER	(H)
Trifolium badium	BROWN CLOVER	(H)
Trifolium campestre	HOP TREFOIL	(H)
Trifolium dubium	LESSER TREFOIL	(H)
Trifolium dubium	LESSER YELLOW TREFOIL	(H)
Trifolium dubium	SUCKLING CLOVER	(H)
Trifolium fragiferum	STRAWBERRY CLOVER	(H)
Trifolium glomeratum	CLUSTERED CLOVER	(H)
Trifolium hybridum	ALSIKE CLOVER	(H)
Trifolium incarnatum	CRIMSON CLOVER	(H)
Trifolium medium	ZIGZAG CLOVER	(H)
Trifolium micranthum	SLENDER TREFOIL	(H)
Trifolium ochroleucum	SULPHUR CLOVER	(H)
Trifolium ornithopodioides	FENUGREEK	(V)
Trifolium pratense	RED CLOVER	(H)
Trifolium repens	DUTCH CLOVER	(H)
Trifolium repens	WHITE CLOVER	(H)
Trifolium rubens	RED TREFOIL	(H)
Trifolium scabrum	ROUGH CLOVER	(H)
Trifolium squamosum	SEA CLOVER	(H)
Trifolium striatum	SOFT CLOVER	(H)
Trifolium strictum	UPRIGHT CLOVER	(H)
Trifolium subterraneum	SUBTERRANEAN CLOVER	(H)
Triglochia palustris	SEA ARROW-GRASS	(G)
Triglochin maritima	SEA ARROW-GRASS	(A/H)
Trigonella foenum-graecum	CLASSICAL FENUGREEK	(H)
Trigonella foenum-graecum	FENUGREEK	(H)

Know Your Common Plant Names

Botanical	Common	Type
Trigonella foenum-graecum	GREEK HAY SEED	(H)
Trillium	BETHROOT	(H)
Trillium	BIRTHROOT	(H)
Trillium	TRINITY FLOWER	(H)
Trillium	WAKE ROBIN	(H)
Trillium	WOOD LILY	(H)
Trillium erectum	BETH ROOT	(H)
Trillium erectum	BIRTH-ROOT	(H)
Trillium erectum	GROUND LILY	(H)
Trillium erectum	INDIAN SHAMROCK	(H)
Trillium erectum	LAMB'S QUARTERS	(H)
Trillium erectum	STINKING BENJAMIN	(H)
Trillium grandiflorum	AMERICAN WOOD LILY	(H)
Trillium nivale	DWARF WHITE WOOD LILY	(H)
Trillium nivale	SNOW TRILLIUM	(H)
Trillium sessile	TOADSHADE	(H)
Trillium undulatum	PAINTED TRILLIUM	(H)
Trillium undulatum	PAINTED WOOD-LILY	(H)
Trinia glauca	HONEYWORT	(H)
Triosteum	HORSE GENTIAN	(H)
Triphasia trifolia	LIME BERRY	(H)
Triplochiton scleroxylon	OBECHE	(TT)
Trisetum flavescens	YELLOW OAT GRASS	(G)
Tristania	BRISBANE BOX	(B)
Tristania conferta	BRISBANE BOX	(TT)
Tristania conferta	BRUSH BOX	(S)
Tristania conferta	BRUSHBOX TREE	(TT)
Tristania laurina	KANOOKA	(S)
Triteleia	SPRING STAR-FLOWER	(BB)
Triticum	WHEAT	(VG)
Triticum aestivum	BREAD WHEAT	(G)
Triticum durum	DURUM WHEAT	(G)
Triticum durum	HARD WHEAT	(G)
Tritonia	BLAZING STAR	(BB)
Trollius	GLOBE FLOWER	(H)
Trollius europaeus	BOULE D'OR	(H)
Trollius europaeus	EUROPEAN GLOBE FLOWER	(H)
Tropacolum	INDIAN CRESS	(H)
Tropaealum speciosum	FLAME CREEPER	(CL)
Tropaeolum majus	INDIAN CRESS	(H)
Tropaeolum majus	NASTURTIUM	(A)
Tropaeolum peregrinum	CANARY CREEPER	(CL)
Tropaeolum speciosum	FLAME FLOWER	(CL)
Tropaeolum speciosum	FLAME NASTURTIUM	(CL)
Tropaeolum speciosum	SCOTCH CREEPER	(CL)
Tsuga	HEMLOCK	(C)
Tsuga canadensis	CANADA PITCH	(C)

Know Your Common Plant Names

Botanical	Common	Type
Tsuga canadensis	CANADIAN HEMLOCK	(C)
Tsuga canadensis	EASTERN HEMLOCK	(C)
Tsuga caroliniana	CAROLINA HEMLOCK	(C)
Tsuga chinensis	CHINESE HEMLOCK	(C)
Tsuga diversifolia	NORTHERN JAPANESE HEMLOCK	(C)
Tsuga dumosa	HIMALAYAN HEMLOCK	(C)
Tsuga heterophylla	WESTERN HEMLOCK	(C)
Tsuga mertensiana	MOUNTAIN HEMLOCK	(C)
Tsuga sieboldii	JAPANESE HEMLOCK	(C)
Tsuga sieboldii	SOUTHERN JAPANESE HEMLOCK	(C)
Tsuga x jeffreyi	JEFFREYS HYBRID HEMLOCK	(C)
Tuber aestivum	TRUFFLE	(FU)
Tuber magnatum	PIEDMONT TRUFFLE	(FU)
Tuber melanosporum	PERIGORD TRUFFLE	(FU)
Tuberaria guttata	SPOTTED ROCKROSE	(R)
Tulbaghia fragrans	SWEET GARLIC	(HP)
Tulbaghia violacea	SOCIETY GARLIC	(HP)
Tulipa	TULIP	(BB)
Tulipa acuminata	HORNED TULIP	(BB)
Tulipa clusiana	LADY TULIP	(BB)
Tulipa kaufmanniana	WATER-LILY TULIP	(BB)
Tulipa occulus-solis	PERSIAN SUN'S EYE	(BB)
Tulipa sylvestris	WILD TULIP	(BB)
Tunica	SAND PINK	(H)
Turnera aphrodisiaca	MEXICAN DAMIANA	(S)
Turnera diffusa	DAMIANA	(S)
Turnera ulmifolia	SAGE ROSE	(TS)
Turnera ulmifolia	WEST INDIAN HOLLY	(TS)
Turpinia occidentalis	CASSADA WOOD	(TT)
Turpinia occidentalis	CASSAVA WOOD	(TT)
Tussilago farfara	ASS'S FOOT	(H)
Tussilago farfara	COLT'S FOOT	(H)
Tussilago farfara	COUGHWORT	(H)
Tylecodon reticulata	BARBED-WIRE PLANT	(CS)
Typha	CAT TAIL	(G)
Typha angustifolia	LESSER BULRUSH	(WP)
Typha elephanta	ELEPHANT GRASS	(G)
Typha latifolia	BULRUSH REEDMACE	(H)
Typha latifolia	REED MACE	(G)
Typha minima	LEAST BULRUSH	(WP)
Tytonia	WATER BALSAM	(WP)
Ugni molinae	MURTILLO	(T)
Ugni molinae	UNI	(T)
Ugnia molinae	CHILEAN GUAVA	(T)
Ulex	FURZE	(S)
Ulex	GORSE	(S)
Ulex europaeus	COMMON GORSE	(S)

Know Your Common Plant Names

Botanical	Common	Type
Ulex europaeus	PRICKLY BROOM	(S)
Ulex europaeus	WHIN	(S)
Ulex europaeus 'Strictus'	IRISH GORSE	(S)
Ulex europeaus 'Plenus'	DOUBLE FLOWERED GORSE	(S)
Ulex minor	DWARF GORSE	(S)
Ulex minor	SMALL FURZE	(S)
Ulmus	ELM	(T)
Ulmus americana	AMERICAN ELM	(T)
Ulmus americana	WHITE ELM	(T)
Ulmus angustifolia cornubiensis	CORNISH ELM	(T)
Ulmus carpinifolia	EUROPEAN FIELD ELM	(T)
Ulmus carpinifolia	SMOOTH-LEAVED ELM	(T)
Ulmus crassifolia	CEDAR ELM	(T)
Ulmus davidiana japonica	JAPANESE ELM	(T)
Ulmus fulva	SWEET ELM	(T)
Ulmus glabra	SCOTCH ELM	(T)
Ulmus glabra	WYCH ELM	(T)
Ulmus glabra 'Camperdowmii''	CAMPERDOWN ELM	(T)
Ulmus glabra 'Camperdownii'	WEEPING ELM	(T)
Ulmus glabra 'Horizontalis'	WEEPING WYCH ELM	(T)
Ulmus laevis	EUROPEAN WHITE ELM	(T)
Ulmus mexicana	MEXICAN ELM	(T)
Ulmus minor sarniensis	JERSEY ELM	(T)
Ulmus minor 'Sarniensis'	WHEATLEY ELM	(T)
Ulmus parviflora	CHINESE ELM	(T)
Ulmus procera	ENGLISH ELM	(T)
Ulmus rubra	INDIAN ELM	(T)
Ulmus rubra	MOOSE ELM	(T)
Ulmus rubra	RED ELM	(T)
Ulmus rubra	SLIPPERY ELM	(T)
Ulmus thomasii	CORK ELM	(T)
Ulmus thomasii	ROCK ELM	(T)
Ulmus vegeta	CHICHESTER ELM	(T)
Ulmus x hollandica	DUTCH ELM	(T)
Ulmus x hollandica 'Belgica'	BELGIAN ELM	(CL)
Ulmus x sarniensis 'Dicksonii'	DICKSON'S GOLDEN ELM	(T)
Ulmus xvegeta	HUNTINGDON ELM	(T)
Ulva lactuca	GREEN LAVER	(SW)
Ulva lactuca	SEA LETTUCE	(SW)
Umbellularia californica	CALIFORNIA SASSAFRAS	(S)
Umbellularia californica	CALIFORNIAN BAY	(S)
Umbellularia californica	CALIFORNIAN LAUREL	(ST)
Umbellularia californica	OREGON MYRTLE	(S)
Umbelluria californica	HEADACHE TREE	(S.T)
Umbilicus rupestris	PENNYWORT	(H)
Umbilicus rupestris	WALL-PENNYWORT	(H)
Umbilicus ruprestris	KIDNEYWORT	(H)

Know Your Common Plant Names

Botanical	Common	Type
Ungnadia speciosa	MEXICAN BUCKEYE	(T)
Ungnadia speciosa	SPANISH BUCKEYE	(T)
Uragoga ipecacuanha	IPECACUANHA	(TS)
Urceolina	URN FLOWER	(H)
Urera baccifera	COW-ITCH	(H)
Urginea maritima	CRUSADER'S SPEARS	(BB)
Urginea maritima	RED SQUILL	(BB)
Urginea maritima	SEA ONION	(BB)
Urginea maritima	SEA SQUILL	(BB)
Urginea maritima	WHITE SQUILL	(BB)
Ursinia	JEWEL OF THE VELDT	(H)
Urtica	NETTLE	(HA)
Urtica canadensis	KENTUCKY HEMP	(H)
Urtica dioica	STINGING NETTLE	(H)
Urtica urens	SMALL NETTLE	(H)
Urtica urentissima	DEVIL'S LEAF	(H)
Utricularia	BLADDERWORT	(H)
Utricularia minor	LESSER BLADDERWORT	(H)
Utricularia vulgaris	COMMON BLADDERWORT	(H)
Uvularia	BELLWORT	(H)
Uvularia	THROATWORT	(H)
Uvularia grandiflora	MERRY BELLS	(H)
Vaccaria hispanica	COW BASIL	(H)
Vaccaria pyramidata	COWHERB	(H)
Vaccineum arboreum	FARKLEBERRY	(S)
Vaccineum arctostaphylos	CAUCASIAN WHORTLEBERRY	(S)
Vaccineum myrtillus	BILBERRY	(F)
Vaccineum myrtillus	HUCKLEBERRY	(F)
Vaccineum myrtillus	WHORTLEBERRY	(F)
Vaccineum ovatum	BOX BLUEBERRY	(S)
Vaccineum padifolium	MADEIRA WHORTLEBERRY	(S)
Vaccineum stamineum	DEERBERRY	(S)
Vaccineum uliginosum	BOG WHORTLEBERRY	(S)
Vaccinium angustifolium	LOW-BUSH BLUEBERRY	(S)
Vaccinium caespitosum	DWARF BILBERRY	(S)
Vaccinium canadense	SOUR-TOP	(S)
Vaccinium canadense	VELVET LEAF	(S)
Vaccinium corymbosum	BLUEBERRY	(F)
Vaccinium corymbosum	HIGH-BUSH BLUEBERRY	(F)
Vaccinium corymbosum	SWAMP BLUEBERRY	(F)
Vaccinium hirsutum	HAIRY HUCKLEBERRY	(S)
Vaccinium macrocarpum	AMERICAN CRANBERRY	(S)
Vaccinlum myrsinites	EVERGREEN BLUEBERRY	(S)
Vaccinium myrtillus	BLAEBERRY	(F)
Vaccinium myrtillus	WHINBERRY	(S)
Vaccinium oxycoccos	CRANBERRY	(F)
Vaccinium parvifolium	RED BILBERRY	(S)

Know Your Common Plant Names

Botanical	Common	Type
Vaccinium parvifolium	RED HUCKLEBERRY	(S)
Vaccinium uliginosum	BOG BILBERRY	(S)
Vaccinium virgatum	RABBITEYE BLUEBERRY	(S)
Vaccinium vitis-idaea	COWBERRY	(S)
Vaccinium vitis-idaea	RED BILBERRY	(S)
Valeriana	SETWALL	(H)
Valeriana	VALERIAN	(H)
Valeriana dioica	MARSH VALERIAN	(H)
Valeriana montana	MOUNTAIN VALERIAN	(H)
Valeriana officinalis	PHU	(H)
Valeriana pyrenaica	HEART-LEAVED VALERIAN	(H)
Valeriana pyrenaica	PYRENEAN VALERIAN	(H)
Valeriana walichii	INDIAN VALERIAN	(H)
Valerianella locusta	LAMB'S LETTUCE	(V)
Valerianella olitoria	CORN SALAD	(V)
Vallisneria spiralis	EEL GRASS	(G/WP)
Vallisneria spiralis	TAPE GRASS	(CWP)
Vancouveria	INSIDE-OUT FLOWER	(H)
Vancouveria hexandra	AMERICAN BARRENWORT	(H)
Vancouveria planipetala	REDWOOD IVY	(H)
Vangueria esculenta	FOREST WILD MEDLAR	(S)
Vanilla planifolia	VANILLA	(O)
Varatrum viride	GREEN FALSE HELLEBORE	(H)
Veitchia merrillii	CHRISTMAS PALM	(P)
Veitchia merrillii	MANILA PALM	(P)
Veltheimia viridiflora	FOREST LILY	(BB)
Venidium	MONARCH OF THE VELDT	(A)
Venidium fastuosum	CAPE DAISY	(A)
Venidium fastuosum	NAMAQUALAND DAISY	(H)
Veratrum	FALSE HELLEBORE	(H)
Veratrum album	WHITE FALSE HELLEBORE	(H)
Veratrum nigrum	BLACK FALSE HELLEBORE	(H)
Veratrum sabadilla	SABADILLA	(H)
Veratrum viride	AMERICAN HELLEBORE	(H)
Veratrum viride	GREEN HELLEBORE	(H)
Veratrum viride	INDIAN POKE	(H)
Veratrum viride	SWAMP HELLEBONE	(H)
Verbascum	MULLEIN	(H)
Verbascum blattaria	MOTH MULLEIN	(H)
Verbascum lychnitis	WHITE MULLEIN	(H)
Verbascum nigrum	DARK MULLEIN	(H)
Verbascum phlomoides	ORANGE MULLEIN	(H)
Verbascum phoeniceum	PURPLE MULLEIN	(H)
Verbascum pulverulentum	HOARY MULLEIN	(H)
Verbascum thapsus	AARON'S ROD	(H)
Verbascum thapsus	ADAM'S FLANNEL	(H)
Verbascum thapsus	CANDLEWICK	(H)

Know Your Common Plant Names

Botanical	Common	Type
Verbascum thapsus	COMMON MULLEIN	(H)
Verbascum thapsus	FLANNEL PLANT	(H)
Verbascum thapsus	HAG'S TAPER	(H)
Verbascum thapsus	JACOB'S STAFF	(H)
Verbascum thapsus	JUPITER'S STAFF	(H)
Verbascum thapsus	LADY'S FOXGLOVE	(H)
Verbascum thapsus	RAG PAPER	(H)
Verbascum thapsus	SHEPHERD'S CLUB	(H)
Verbascum thapsus	WHITE MULLEIN	(H)
Verbascum virgatum	TWIGGY MULLEIN	(H)
Verbascus thapsus	PETER'S STAFF	(H)
Verbascus thapsus	VELVET DOCK	(H)
Verbena hastata	BLUE VERVAIN	(H)
Verbena hastata	SIMPLER'S JOY	(H)
Verbena jamaicensis	JAMAICA VERVAIN	(TH)
Verbena officinalis	VERVAIN	(H)
Verbena tridens	MATA NEGRA	(H)
Verbena x hybrida	FLORIST'S VERBENA	(H)
Verbena x hybrida	ROSE VERVAIN	(H)
Verbenna officinalis	HERB OF THE CROSS	(H)
Veronica	SPEEDWELL	(H)
Veronica agrestis	FIELD SPEEDWELL	(H)
Veronica alpina	ALPINE SPEEDWELL	(H)
Veronica anagallis	WATER SPEEDWELL	(WP)
Veronica anagallis-aquatica	BLUE WATER SPEEDWELL	(WP)
Veronica anagallis-aquatica	WATER SPEEDWELL	(WP)
Veronica arvensis	WALL SPEEDWELL	(H)
Veronica austriaca	LARGE SPEEDWELL	(H)
Veronica beccabunga	BROOKLIME	(H)
Veronica beccabunga	COW CRESS	(H)
Veronica beccabunga	LIMPWORT	(H)
Veronica beccabunga	WATER PIMPERNEL	(H)
Veronica chamaedrys	BIRD'S EYE	(H)
Veronica chamaedrys	GERMANDER SPEEDWELL	(H)
Veronica filiformis	ROUND-LEAVED SPEEDWELL	(H)
Veronica fruticans	ROCK SPEEDWELL	(H)
Veronica hederifolia	IVY-LEAVED SPEEDWELL	(H)
Veronica montana	MOUNTAIN SPEEDWELL	(H)
Veronica montana	WOOD SPEEDWELL	(H)
Veronica officinalis	BIRD'S EYE	(H)
Veronica officinalis	COMMON SPEEDWELL	(H)
Veronica officinalis	HEATH SPEEDWELL	(H)
Veronica peregrina	AMERICAN SPEEDWELL	(H)
Veronica perfoliata	DIGGER'S SPEEDWELL	(H)
Veronica persica	BUXBAUM'S SPEEDWELL	(H)
Veronica persica	PERSIAN SPEEDWELL	(A)
Veronica prostrata	ROCKERY SPEEDWELL	(R)

Botanical	Common	Type
Veronica repens	CORSICAN SPEEDWELL	(H)
Veronica scutellata	MARSH SPEEDWELL	(H)
Veronica serpyllifolia	THYME-LEAVED SPEEDWELL	(H)
Veronica spicata	SPIKED SPEEDWELL	(H)
Veronica verna	SPRING SPEEDWELL	(H)
Veronicastrum virginicum	BLACK ROOT	(H)
Veronicastrum virginicum	CULVER'S ROOT	(H)
Verononia	IRON WEED	(H)
Verticordia	FEATHER FLOWER	(S)
Verticordia	JUNIPER MYRTLE	(S)
Verticordia	JUNIPER-MYRTLE	(S)
Vesicaria	BLADDER PEA	(H)
Vestia foetida	HUEVIL	(H)
Viburnham prunifolium	SWEET VIBURNAM	(S)
Viburnum acerifolium	DOCKMACKIE	(S)
Viburnum cassinoides	WITHE-ROD	(S)
Viburnum dentatum	ARROWWOOD	(S)
Viburnum dentatum	SOUTHERN ARROW-WOOD	(S)
Viburnum dilatatum	LINDEN VIBURNUM	(S)
Viburnum japonicum	JAPANESE VIBURNUM	(S)
Viburnum lantana	MEAL TREE	(S)
Viburnum lantana	WAYFARING TREE	(S)
Viburnum lantanoides	AMERICAN WAYFARING TREE	(S)
Viburnum lantanoides	HOBBLE BUSH	(S)
Viburnum lantanoides	WITCH HOBBLE	(S)
Viburnum lantanoides	WITCH-HOBBLE	(S)
Viburnum lentago	NANNY-BERRY	(S)
Viburnum lentago	SHEEPBERRY	(S)
Viburnum macrocephalum	CHINESE SNOWBALL	(S)
Viburnum nudum	SMOOTH WITHE ROD	(S)
Viburnum odoratissimum	SWEET VIBURNUM	(S)
Viburnum opulus	CRAMPBARK	(S)
Viburnum opulus	EUROPEAN CRANBERRY BUSH	(S)
Viburnum opulus	GUELDER ROSE	(S)
Viburnum opulus	RED ELDER	(S)
Viburnum opulus	WATER ELDER	(S)
Viburnum opulus 'Sterile'	SNOWBALL TREE	(S)
Viburnum pauciflorum	MOOSEBERRY	(S)
Viburnum plicatum	JAPANESE SNOWBALL	(S)
Viburnum plicatum tomentosum	LACE-CUP VIBURNUM	(S)
Viburnum prunifolium	BLACK HAW	(S)
Viburnum prunifolium	STAG BUSH	(S)
Viburnum rufidulum	SOUTHERN BLACK HAW	(S)
Viburnum setigerum	TEA VIBURNUM	(S)
Viburnum tinus	LAURUSTINUS	(S)
Viburnum trilobum	CRANBERRY BUSH	(S)
Vicia	VETCH	(H)

Botanical	Common	Type
Vicia argentea	SILVERY VETCH	(H)
Vicia bithynica	BITHYNIAN VETCH	(H)
Vicia cracca	TUFTED VETCH	(H)
Vicia faba	BROAD BEAN	(V)
Vicia faba	HORSE BEAN	(V)
Vicia gigantea	LARGE VETCH	(H)
Vicia hirsuta	HAIRY TARE	(H)
Vicia lathyroides	SPRING VETCH	(H)
Vicia laxiflora	SLENDER TARE	(H)
Vicia lutea	YELLOW VETCH	(H)
Vicia orobus	WOOD BITTER VETCH	(H)
Vicia sativa	COMMON VETCH	(H)
Vicia sativa	TARE	(V)
Vicia sepium	BUSH VETCH	(H)
Vicia sylvatica	WOOD VETCH	(H)
Vicia tetrasperma	SMOOTH TARE	(H)
Vicia villosa	FODDER VETCH	(H)
Victoria amazonica	QUEEN VICTORIA WATERLILY	(WP)
Victoria amazonica	ROYAL WATER LILY	(WP)
Victoria amazonica	VICTORIA WATER LILY	(WP)
Vigna caracalla	SNAILFLOWER	(CL)
Vigna sinensis	COW PEA	(TS)
Vigna sinensis	COWPEA	(TS)
Vigna sinensis cylindrica	CATJANG	(TS)
Vigna unguiculata	COW PEA	(H)
Villaresia mucronata	NARANJILLO	(S)
Villarsia calthifolia	MARSH FLOWER	(H)
Viminaria juncea	GOLDEN SPRAY	(H)
Vinca	PERIWINKLE	(S)
Vinca	TRAILING MYRTLE	(S)
Vinca major	GREATER PERIWINKLE	(S)
Vinca major 'Variegata'	VARIEGATED MAJOR PERIWINKLE	(S)
Vinca minor	LESSER PERIWINKLE	(S)
Vinca minor	RUNNING MYRTLE	(H)
Vincetoxicum hirundinaria	SWALLOW-WORT	(H)
Viola	VIOLET	(H)
Viola arvensis	FIELD PANSY	(H)
Viola biflora	YELLOW WOOD VIOLET	(H)
Viola calcarata	SPURRED VIOLET	(H)
Viola canina	DOG VIOLET	(R)
Viola cornuta	HORNED PANSY	(H)
Viola hederacea	AUSTRALIAN VIOLET	(H)
Viola hederacea	NEW HOLLAND VIOLET	(H)
Viola hirta	HAIRY VIOLET	(H)
Viola hispida	ROUEN PANSY	(H)
Viola lactea	PALE DOG-VIOLET	(H)
Viola lutea	MOUNTAIN PANSY	(H)

Know Your Common Plant Names

Botanical	Common	Type
Viola lutea	MOUNTAIN VIOLET	(H)
Viola nigra	BOWLE'S BLACK VIOLET	(H)
Viola odorata	SWEET VIOLET	(H)
Viola odorata sp.	PARMA VIOLET	(H)
Viola palustris	BOG VIOLET	(H)
Viola (pansy)	LOVE-IN-IDLENESS	(H)
Viola pedata	BIRD'S FOOT VIOLET	(H)
Viola reichenbachiana	EARLY DOG VIOLET	(H)
Viola riviniana	COMMON DOG VIOLET	(H)
Viola riviniana	COMMON VIOLET	(H)
Viola rothomagensis	ROVEN VIOLET	(H)
Viola rupestris	TEESDALE VIOLET	(H)
Viola stagnina	FEN VIOLET	(H)
Viola tricolor	HEARTSEASE	(H)
Viola tricolor	HERB TRINITY	(H)
Viola tricolor	JACK JUMP UP AND KISS ME	(H)
Viola tricolor	KISS HER IN THE BUTTERY	(H)
Viola tricolor	LOVING IDOL	(H)
Viola tricolor	PANSY	(H)
Viola tricolor	TRICOLOR PANSY	(H)
Viola tricolor	WILD PANSY	(H)
Viola x wittrockiana	GARDEN PANSY	(H)
Viscaria oculenta	VISCARIA	(H)
Viscum album	MISTLETOE	(PE)
Vitex agnus-castus	CHASTE TREE	(S)
Vitex agnus-castus	MONK'S PEPPER TREE	(S)
Vitis	GRAPE	(CL.F)
Vitis	VINE	(CL)
Vitis aestivalis	SUMMER GRAPE	(F)
Vitis candicans	MUSTANG GRAPE	(F)
Vitis coignettiae	CRIMSON-GLORY VINE	(CL)
Vitis labrusca	FOX GRAPE	(CL)
Vitis labrusca	NORTHERN FOX GRAPE	(F)
Vitis riparia	RIVERBANK GRAPE	(FCCL
Vitis rotundifolia	MUSCADINE	(F)
Vitis rupestris	BUSH GRAPE	(F)
Vitis vinifera	COMMON GRAPE VINE	(F)
Vitis vinifera 'alpiifolia'	PARSLEY VINE	(CL)
Vitis vinifera 'Incana'	DUSTY MILLER GRAPE	(CL)
Vitis vinifera 'Purpurea'	PURPLE-LEAVED VINE	(CL)
Vitis vinifera 'Purpurea'	TEINTURIER GRAPE	(CL)
Voandzeia subterranea	BOMBARRA GROUND NUT	(TS)
Vriesea hieroglyphica splendens	FLAMING SWORD	(HP)
Vriesea hieroglyphica splendens	KING OF BROMELIADS	(HP)
Vriesia carinata	PAINTED FEATHER	(HP)
Vulpia ambigua	BEARDED FESCUE	(G)
Vulpia bromoides	SQUIRRELTAIL FESCUE	(G)

Know Your Common Plant Names

Botanical	Common	Type
Vulpia fasciculata	DUNE FESCUE	(G)
Vulpia unilateralis	MAT-GRASS FESCUE	(G)
Vulpoia myuros	RATSTAIL FESCUE	(G)
Wahlenbergia	BELLFLOWER	(H)
Wahlenbergia	TUFTED HAREBELL	(H)
Wahlenbergia hederacea	IVY-LEAVED BELLFLOWER	(H)
Wahlenbergia hederacea	IVY-LEAVED HAREBELL	(H)
Waldsteinia	BARREN STRAWBERRY	(H)
Warszewiczia coccinea	CHACONIA	(TS)
Warszewiczia coccinea	WATER WELL TREE	(TS)
Warszewiczia coccinea	WILD POINSETTIA	(TS)
Washingtonia	WASHINGTON PALM	(P)
Washingtonia filifera	DESERT FAN PALM	(P)
Washingtonia filifera	PETTICOAT PALM	(P)
Washingtonia robusta	MEXICAN FAN PALM	(P)
Washingtonia robusta	THREAD PALM	(P)
Watsonia	BUGLE LILY	(BB)
Weigela	WEIGELA	(S)
Weigela florida 'Foliis purpureis'	PURPLE WEIGELA	(S)
Weinmannia racemosa	KAMAHI	(S)
Weinmannia racemosa	TOWAI	(S)
Westringia	AUSTRALIAN ROSEMARY	(S)
Westringia fruticosa	AUSTRALIAN ROSEMARY	(S)
Widdringtonia	AFRICAN CYPRESS	(C)
Widdringtonia cupressoides	SAPRAE WOOD	(C)
Widdringtonia cupressoides	SAPREE WOOD	(C)
Widdringtonia juniperoides	CLANWILLIAM CEDAR	(C)
Widdringtonia schwarzii	WILLOWMORE CEDAR	(C)
Widdringtonia whytei	MILANJI CEDAR	(C)
Widdrintonia cupressoides	MOUNTAIN CYPRESS	(C)
Wigginsia vorwerkiana	COLOMBIAN BALL CACTUS	(CS)
Wilcoxia poselgeri	DAHLIA CACTUS	C S
Wilcoxia poselgeri	PENCIL CACTUS	(CS)
Wildringtonia	CYPRESS PINE	(C)
Wisteria	WISTERIA	(CL)
Wisteria floribunda	JAPANESE WISTERIA	(CL)
Wisteria sinensis	CHINESE WISTERIA	(CL)
Wisteria venusta	SILKY WISTERIA	(CL)
Withania somnifera	ASHWAGANDHA	(H)
Withania somnifera	KUTHMITHI	(H)
Woodwardia	CHAIN FERN	(FN)
Worsleya	BLUE AMARYLLIS	(BB)
Worsleya procera	EMPRESS OF BRAZIL	(TS)
Wyethia helenioides	MULE'S EAR DAISY	(S)
X Citrofortunella microcarpa	CALAMONDIN	(F)
x Citroncirus webberi	CITRANGE	(F)
x Fatschedera lizei	IVY TREE	(S)

Know Your Common Plant Names

Botanical	Common	Type
X Fatshedera lizei	ARALIA-IVY	(S)
X Pardancanda	CANDY LILIES	(BB)
Xanthium echinatum	STINKING COCKLEBUR	(H)
Xanthium spinosum	COCKLEBUR	(H)
Xanthium spinosum	SPINY COCKLEBUR	(H)
Xanthium strumarium	ROUGH COCKLEBUR	(H)
Xanthorrhea	BLACKBOY	(S)
Xanthorrhea	BOTANY BAY GUM	(S)
Xanthorrhoea	BLACK-BOY	(S)
Xanthorrhoea	GRASS TREE	(S)
Xanthorrhoea	GRASS-TREES	(S/T)
Xanthorrhoea arborea	BOTANY BAY GUM	(T)
Xanthorrhoea preissii	BLACK BOY	(T)
Xanthorrhoea spp	GRASS TREES	(S)(T)
Xanthorrniza simplicissima	YELLOW-ROOT	(S)
Xanthosoma	TANIER	(H)
Xanthosoma sagittifolium	YAUTIA	(F)
Xanthoxylum clava-herculis	CLUB OF HERCULES	(S)
Xeranthemum	COMMON IMMORTELLE	(A)
Xeranthemum	IMMORTELLE	(H)
Xerophyllum	TURKEY BEARD	(H)
Xerophyllum	TURKEY'S BEARD	(H)
Xerophyllum tenax	BEARGRASS	(G)
Ximenia americana	HOG PLUM	(TT)
Ximenia americana	TALLOW WOOD	(TT)
Xylopia aethiopica	GUINEA PEPPER	(TS)
Yucca aloifolia	DAGGER PLANT	(S)
Yucca aloifolia	SPANISH BAYONET	(HP)
Yucca aloifolia	SPANISH DAGGER	(HP)
Yucca baccata	WILD DATE	(S)
Yucca brevifolia	JOSHUA TREE	(S)
Yucca elata	SOAPTREE YUCCA	(S)
Yucca elephantipes	SPINELESS YUCCA	(S)
Yucca filamentosa	SILK GRASS	(S)
Yucca filamentosa	SPOONLEAF YUCCA	(S)
Yucca gloriosa	ADAM'S NEEDLE	(S)
Yucca whipplei	OUR LORD'S CANDLE	(S)
Zannichellia palustris	HORNED PONDWEED	(WP)
Zantedeschia	ARUM LILY	(H)
Zantedeschia	RICHARDIA	(WP)
Zantedeschia aethiopica	PIG LILY	(H)
Zantedeschia aethiopica	TRUMPET LILY	(H)
Zantedeschia albomaculata	SPOTTED ARUM	(H)
Zantedeschia albomaculata	SPOTTED CALLA	(H)
Zantedeschia elliottiana	GOLDEN CALLA	(H)
Zantedeschia rehmannii	PINK ARUM	(H)
Zantedeschia rehmannii	PINK CALLA	(H)

Know Your Common Plant Names

Botanical	Common	Type
Zantedeshia	CALLA LILY	(H)
Zanthoxylum	YELLOWWOOD	(S/T)
Zanthoxylum americanum	TOOTHACHE TREE	(S)
Zanthoxylum flavum	WEST INDIAN SILKWOOD	(TT)
Zanthoxylum piperitum	JAPAN PEPPER	(S/T)
Zanthozylum americanum	PRICKLY ASH	(S)
Zauschneria californica	CALIFORNIAN FUCHSIA	(R)
Zauschneria californica	HUMMING BIRD'S TRUMPET	(R)
Zea japonica	ORNAMENTAL CORN	(H)
Zea japonica	ORNAMENTAL MAIZE	(A)
Zea mays	CORN	(V)
Zea mays	CORN SILK	(G)
Zea mays	CORN-ON-THE-COB	(V)
Zea mays	INDIAN CORN	(V)
Zea mays	MAIZE	(V)
Zea mays	SWEET CORN	(V)
Zea mays everta	POP CORN	(V)
Zelkova abelicea	CRETAN ZELKOVA	(T)
Zelkova carpinifolia	CAUCASIAN ELM	(T)
Zelkova serrata	JAPANESE ZELKOVA	(T)
Zelkova serrata	KEAKI	(T)
Zelkova sinica	CHINESE ZELKOVA	(T)
Zelkova verschaffeltii	CUT-LEAF ZELKOVA	(T)
Zephyranthes	FLOWER-OF-THE-WEST-WIND	(BB)
Zephyranthes	RAIN LILY	(BB)
Zephyranthes	ZEPHYR LILY	(BB)
Zephyranthes atamasco	ATAMASCO LILY	(BB)
Zephyranthes candida	FLOWER OF THE WESTERN WIND	(BB)
Zieria smithii	SANDFLY BUSH	(S)
Zigadenus	DEATH CAMAS	(S)
Zingibar cassumunar	BENGAL ROOT	(HB)
Zingiber officinale	GINGER	(HB)
Zinnia elegans	YOUTH AND OLD AGE	(A)
Zizania aquatica	CANADIAN WILD RICE	(WP)
Zizania aquatica	WATER OATS	(G)
Zizania aquatica	WILD RICE	(WP)
Zizania caducifolia	MANCHURIAN WILD RICE	(F)
Ziziphus zizyphus	JUJUBE	(F)
Zizyphus jujuba	CHINESE DATE	(S)
Zizyphus lotus	LOTUS FRUIT	(F)
Zizythis mucronata	BUFFALO THORN	(TS)
Zostera	EEL GRASS	(G/WP)
Zostera	TAPEGRASS	(G)
Zostera angustifolia	NARROW-LEAVED EEL-GRASS	(WP)
Zostera angustifolia	NARROW-LEAVED GRASS-WRACK	(WP)
Zostera marina	COMMON EEL-GRASS	(WP)
Zostera marina	COMMON GRASS-WRACK	(WP)

Know Your Common Plant Names

Botanical	Common	Type
Zostera noltii	DWARF EEL-GRASS	(WP)
Zostera noltii	DWARF GRASS-WRACK	(WP)
Zoysia matrella	MANILA GRASS	(G)
Zoysia tenuifolia	KOREAN GRASS	(G)
Zoysia tenuifolia	MASCARENE GRASS	(G)
Zoyzia japonica	KOREAN LAWN GRASS	(G)

Key To Plant Type

A	-	Annual
B	-	Biennial
BB	-	Bulb or Corm
C	-	Conifer
CL	-	Climber
CS	-	Cactus
FU	-	Fungi
F	-	Fruit
FN	-	Fern
G	-	Grass or Bamboo
H	-	Herbaceous Perennial
HB	-	Herb
HP	-	House Plant
MB	-	Moss
O	-	Orchid
P	-	Palm
PE	-	Parasite
R	-	Rockery or Alpine Plant
S	-	Shrub
ST	-	Shrub or Tree
SW	-	Sea Weed
T	-	Tree
TCL	-	Tropical Climber
TH	-	Tropical Herb
TS	-	Tropical Shrub
TT	-	Tropical Tree
V	-	Vegetable
WP	-	Water Plant

Pseudonyms

Many historical psuedonyms are used in day to day business and we have included a large number in this section. The listing of the "most recent and accepted" are thought to be nomenclaturally correct at time of print.

Many historical names remain in use by commercial and private gardeners for many years before slowly changing to the most recent and accepted name.

Know Your Common Plant Names

Historical Pseudonyms	Most Recent Accepted Naming
Abelia rupestris	Abelia x grandiflora
Abies fabri	Abies delavayi delavayi
Abies lasiocarpa 'Glauca'	Abies concolor 'Violacea'
Abies nobilis	Abies procera
Abies sutchuenensis	Abies fargesii
Abutilon globosum	Abutilon x hybridum
Abutilon striatum	Abutilon pictum
Acacia julibrissin	Albizia julibrissin
Acacia paradoxa	Acacia armata angustifolia
Acaena affinis	Acaena adscendens
Acaena caerulea	Acaena caesiiglauca
Acaena glaucophylla	Acaena magellanica
Acaena microphylla 'Glauca'	Acaena caesiiglauca
Acaena 'Pewter'	Acaena 'Blue Haze'
Acaena sanguisorbae	Acaena anserinifolia
Acanthopanax	Eleutherococcus
Acanthopanax ricinifolius	Kalopanax pictus
Acanthus longifolius	Acanthus balcanicus
Acanthus longifolius	Acanthus hungaricus
Acer colchicum	Acer cappadocicum
Acer coriaceifolium	Acer cinnamomifolium
Acer creticum	Acer sempervirens
Acer dasycarpum	Acer saccharinum
Acer forrestii	Acer pectinatum forrestii
Acer fulvescens	Acer longipes
Acer ginnala	Acer tataricum ginnala
Acer grosseri	Acer davidii grosseri
Acer jap. 'Laciniatum'	Acer japonicum aconitifolium
Acer japonicum 'Aureum'	Acer shirasawanum 'Aureum'
Acer laetum	Acer cappadocicum
Acer laxiflorum	Acer pectinatum laxiflorum
Acer lobelii	Acer cappadocicum lobelii
Acer maximowiczii	Acer pectinatum maximowiczii
Acer neglectum	Acer x zoeschense
Acer nikoense	Acer maximowicziana
Acer orientale	Acer sempervirens
Acer palmatum 'Heptalobum Elegans Purpreum'	Acer palmatum 'Hessei'
Acer palmatum 'Ribesifolium'	Acer palmatum 'Shishigashira'
Acer palmatum 'Senkaki'	Acer palmatum 'Sango-Kaku'
Acer palmatum 'Senkaki'	Acer palmatum 'Sangokaku'
Acer palmatum 'Shishio Improved'	Acer palmatum 'Improved Chishio'
Acer pictum	Acer mono
Acer pictum colchicum	Acer cappadocicum
Acer platanoides 'Dissectum'	Acer platanoides "Palmatifidum"
Acer saccharinum 'Fastigiatum'	Acer saccharinum 'Pyramidale'
Acer striatum	Acer pensylvanicum
Acer tetramerum	Acer stachyophyllum

Know Your Common Plant Names

Historical Pseudonyms	Most Recent Accepted Naming
Acer trifidum	Acer buergeranum
Aceriphyllum rossii	Mukdenia rossii
Achillea argentea	Tanacetum argentea
Achimenes coccinea	Achimenes erecta
Achnatherum	Stipa
Achras zapota	Manilkara zapota
Acidanthera bicolor	Gladiolus callianthus
Acidanthera murielae	Gladiolus callianthus
Acokanthera spectabilis	Acokanthera oblongifolia
Aconitum anglicum	Aconitum napellus anglicum
Aconitum cilicicum	Eranthis hyemalis
Aconitum fischeri	Aconitum carmichaelii
Aconitum hyemalis	Eranthis hyemalis
Aconitum orientale	Aconitum lycoctonum vulparia
Aconitum septentrionale	Aconitum lycoctonum lycoctonum
Aconitum vulparia	Aconitum lycoctonum vulparia
Aconogonum	Polygonum
Acroclinium	Helipterum
Acroclinium roseum	Helipterum roseum
Actaea pachypoda	Actaea alba
Actaea spicata rubra	Actaea erythrocarpa
Actinella scaposa	Hymenoxys scaposa
Actinidia chinensis	Actinidia deliciosa
Adhatoda duvernoia	Duvernoia adhatodoides
Adhatoda vasica	Justicia adhatoda
Adiantum cuneatum	Adiantum raddianum
Aechmea caerulea	Aechmea lueddemanniana
Aechmea rhodocyanea	Aechmea fasciata
Aegle sepiaria	Poncirus trifoliata
Aeonium x domesticum	Aichryson x domesticum
Aeschynanthus splendens	Aeschynanthus speciosus
Aesculus hippocastanum 'Florepleno'	Aesculus hippocastanum 'Baumannii'
Aesculus mutabilis 'Rosea Nana'	Aesculus mutabilis 'Induta'
Aesculus octandra	Aesculus flava
Aesculus splendens	Aesculus pavia
Aethionema graecum	Aethionema saxatile
Aethionema pulchellum	Aethionema grandiflorum
Aganthaea coelestis	Felicia amelloides
Agapanthus umbellatus	Agapanthus africanus
Agapanthus umbellatus	Agapanthus campanulatus
Agapanthus umbellatus	Agapanthus praecox orientalis
Agave avellanidens	Agave sebastiana
Ageratum mexicanum	Ageratum houstonianum
Aglaonema roebelinii	Aglaonema crispum
Agropyron glaucum	Elymus hispidus
Agropyron magellanicum	Elymus magellanicus
Agropyron pubiflorum	Elymus magellanicus

Know Your Common Plant Names

Historical Pseudonyms	Most Recent Accepted Naming
Agropyron repens	Elymus repens
Agrostemma coeli-rosa	Silene coeli-rosa
Agrostemma coronaria	Lychnis coronaria
Agrostis alba	Agrostis stolonifera
Agrostis nigra	Agrostis gigantea
Agrostis vulgaris	Agrostis tenuis
Aichryson dichotomum	Aichryson laxum
Ailanthus glandulosa	Ailanthus altissima
Ajuga metallica	Ajuga pyramidalis
Albizia lophantha	Albizia distachya
Alchemilla arvensis	Aphanes arvensis
Alisma natans	Luronium natans
Alisma ranunculoides	Baldellia ranunculoides
Allium albopilosum	Allium christophii
Allium azureum	Allium .caeruleum
Allium cowanii	Allium neapolitanum
Allium elatum	Allium macleanii
Allium kansuense	Allium sikkimense
Allium nuttallii	Allium drummondii
Allium ostrowskianum	Allium oreophilum
Allium siculum	Nectaroscordum siculum
Allium splendens	Allium stellerianum
Alnus oregona	Alnus rubra
Alnus rugosa	Alnus serrulata
Alnus serrulata	Alnus rugosa
Alnus sitchensis	Alnus sinuata
Aloe barbadensis	Aloe vera
Alopecurus fulvus	Alopecurus aequalis
Aloysia citriodora	Aloysia triphylla
Alpinia nutans	Alpinia zerumbet
Alpinia speciosa	Alpinia zerumbet
Alsobia dianthiflora	Episcia dianthiflora
Alstroemeria aurantiaca	Alstroemeria aurea
Alstroemeria gayana	Alstroemeria pelegrina
Alstroemeria pulchella	Alstroemeria psittacina
Althaea frutex	Hibiscus syriacus
Althaea rosea	Alcea rosea
Alyssum calycinum	Alyssum alyssoides
Alyssum 'Goldkugel'	Alyssum 'Gold Ball'
Alyssum maritimum	Lobularia maritima
Alyssum saxatile	Aurinia saxatilis
Alyssum spinosum	Ptilotrichum spinosum
Amana edulis	Tulipa edulis
Amaranthus albus	Amaranthusgraecizans
Amaranthus hypochondriacus	Amaranthus hybridus erythostachys
Ambrosia mexicana	Chenopodium botrys
Amelanchier canadensis	Amelanchier lamarckii

Historical Pseudonyms	Most Recent Accepted Naming
Amelanchier x grandiflora	Amelanchier lamarckii
Ameranchier laevis	Ameranchier lamarckii
Ammophila arundinacea	Ammophila arenaria
Amomum cardamomum	Amomum compactum
Amomyrtus luma	Myrceugenia exserta
Ampelopsis henryana	Parthenocissus henryana
Ampelopsis tricuspidata 'Veitchii'	Parthenocissus tricuspidata 'Veitchii'
Amsonia salicifolia	Amsonia tabernaemontana
Anacharis densa	Egeria densa
Ananas sativus	Ananas comosus
Anaphalis yedoensis	Anaphalis cinnamomea
Anchusa italica	Anchusa azurea
Anchusa myosotidiflora	Brunnera macrophylla
Anchusa sempervirens	Pentaglottis sempervirens
Andromeda arborea	Oxydendrum arboreum
Andromeda floribunda	Pieris floribunda
Andromeda formosa	Pieris formosa
Andromeda japonica	Pieris japonica
Andromeda lucida	Lyonia lucida
Andromeda paniculata	Lyonia higustrina
Andromeda tetragona	Cassiope tetragona
Androsace imbricata	Androsace vandellii
Androsace limprichtii	Androsace sarmentosa watkinsii
Androsace sarmentosa yunnanensis	Androsace mollis
Andryala lanata	Hieracium lanatum
Anemone japonica	Anemone x hybrida
Anemone pulsatilla	Pulsatilla vulgaris
Anemone vernalis	Pulsatilla vernalis
Anemone x hybrida 'Alba'	Anemone x hybrida 'Honorine Joubert'
Anemone x seemannii	Anemone x lipsiensis
Anisantha sterilis	Bromus sterilis
Annona triloba	Asimina triloba
Anoiganthus	Cyrtanthus
Anthemis frutescens	Argyranthemum frutescens
Anthemis nobilis	Chamaemelum nobile
Anthemis rudolphiana	Anthemis marschalliana
Antholyza coccinea	Crocosmia paniculata
Antholyza paniculata	Crocosmia paniculata
Anthriscus vulgaris	Anthriscus caucalis
Antirrhinum asarina	Asarina procumbens
Antirrhinum orontium	Misopates orontium
Apios tuberosa	Apios americana
Aquilegia ecalcarata	Semiaquilegia ecalcarata
Arabis albida	Arabis caucasica
Aralia japonica	Fatsia japonica
Aralia sieboldii	Fatsia japonica
Araucaria excelsa	Araucaria heterophylla

Know Your Common Plant Names

Historical Pseudonyms	Most Recent Accepted Naming
Araucaria imbricata	Araucaria araucana
Arbutus procera	Arbutus menziesii
Arbutus x hybrida	Arbutus andrachnoides
Arctium majus	Arctium lappa
Arctostaphylos alpina	Arctous alpinus
Ardisia crenulata	Ardisia crenata
Areca lutescens	Chrysalidocarpus lutescens
Arenaria caespitosa	Minuartia verna
Arenaria pinifolia	Minuartia circassica
Arenaria rubella	Minuartia rubella
Arenaria tenuifolia	Minuartia hybrida
Arenaria trinervia	Moehringia trinervia
Arenaria verna	Minuartia verna
Arisaema atrorubens	Arisaema triphyllum
Arisaema japonicum	Arisaema serratum
Aristolochia macrophylla	Aristolochia durior
Aristolochia sipho	Aristolochia durior
Aristotelia macqui	Aristotelia chilensis
Aristotelia racemosa	Aristotelia serrata
Armeria caespitosa	Armeria juniperifolia
Armeria latifolia	Armeria pseudarmeria
Armillaria caligata	Tricholoma caligatum
Armillaria mellea	Armillariella melka
Armillaria mucida	Oudemansiella mucida
Aronia floribunda	Aronia prunifolia
Arrhenatherum avenaceum	Arrhenatherum elatius
Artemisia gnaphalodes	Artemisia ludoviciana
Artemisia lanata	Artemisia caucasica
Artemisia purshiana	Artemisia ludoviciana
Arum cornutum	Sauromatum venosum
Arum dracunculus	Dracunculus vulgaris
Arum italicum 'Pictum'	Arum italicum 'Marmoratum'
Aruncus plumosus	Aruncus dioicus
Aruncus sylvester	Aruncus dioicus
Arundinaria auricoma	Pleioblastus viridistriatus
Arundinaria fastuosa	Semiarundinaria fastuosa
Arundinaria fortunei	Pleioblastus variegatus
Arundinaria humilis	Pleioblastus humilis
Arundinaria japonica	Pseudosasa japonica
Arundinaria marmorea	Chimonobambusa marmorea
Arundinaria nitida	Sinarundinaria nitida
Arundinaria palmata	Sasa palmata
Arundinaria pumila	Pleioblastus humilis 'Pumilus'
Arundinaria pygmaea	Pleioblastus pygmaeus
Arundinaria quadrangularis	Chimonobambusa quadrangularis
Arundinaria simonii	Pleioblastus simonii
Arundinaria variegata	Pleioblastus variegatus

Know Your Common Plant Names

Historical Pseudonyms	Most Recent Accepted Naming
Arundinaria veitchii	Sasa veitchii
Arundinaria viridistriata	Pleioblastus auricoma
Asparagus plumosus	Asparagus setaceus
Asparagus sprengeri	Asparagus densiflorus
Asperula odorata	Galium odoratum
Asphodelus cerasiferus	Asphodelus ramosus
Asphodelus luteus	Asphodeline lutea
Asplenium alternans	Ceterach dalhousiae
Asplenium rhizophyllum	Camptosorus rhizophyllus
Asplenium scolopendrium	Phyllitis scolopendrium
Asplenium viviparum	Asplenium daucifolium
Aster acris	Aster sedifolius
Aster amelloides	Felicia amelloides
Aster capensis 'Variegata'	Felicia amelloides 'Variegated'
Aster coelestis	Felicia amelloides
Aster hybridus luteus	x Solidaster luteus
Aster rotundifolius 'Variegatus'	Felicia amelloides 'Variegated'
Aster yunnanensis	Aster tongolensis
Astrantia major 'Margery Fish'	Astrantia major 'Shaggy'
Astrantia major 'Variegata'	Astrantia major 'Sunningdale Variegated'
Atragene alpina	Clematis alpina
Atriplex portulacoides	Halimione portulacoides
Atropa mandragora	Mandragora officinarum
Aucuba japonica 'Maculata'	Aucuba japonica 'Variegata'
Austrocedrus	Libocedrus
Austrocedrus chilensis	Libocedrus chilensis
Avena candida	Helictotrichon sempervirens
Avena pratensis	Helictotrichon pratense
Avena pubescens	Helictotrichon pubescens
Azalea albrechtii	Rhododendron albrechtii
Azalea arborescens	Rhododendron arborescens
Azalea atlanticum	Rhododendron atlanticum
Azalea calendulaceum	Rhododendron calendulaceum
Azalea canescens	Rhododendron canescens
Azalea indica	Rhododendron indicum
Azalea kiusiana	Rhododendron kiusianum
Azalea ledifolia	Rhododendron mucronatum
Azalea mollis	Rhododendron japonicum
Azalea nipponica	Rhododendron nipponicum
Azalea nudiflora	Rhododendron nudiflorum
Azalea obtusa	Rhododendron obtusum
Azalea occidentalis	Rhododendron occidentale
Azalea oldhamii	Rhododendron oldhamii
Azalea pontica	Rhododendron luteum
Azalea procumbens	Loiseleuria procumbens
Azalea prunifolia	Rhododendron prunifolium
Azalea reticulata	Rhododendron reticulatum

Know Your Common Plant Names

Historical Pseudonyms	Most Recent Accepted Naming
Azalea rosea	Rhododendron roseum
Azalea schlippenbachii	Rhododendron schlippenbachii
Azalea viscosa	Rhododendron viscosum
Azorina	Campanula
Bambusa glaucescens	Bambusa multiplex
Barbacenia elegans	Vellozia elegans
Bartonia aurea	Mentzelia lindleyi
Bartsia odontites	Odontites verna
Bartsia viscosa	Parentucellia viscosa
Bauhinia galpinii	Bauhinia punctata
Begonia glaucophylla	Begonia limmingheiana
Begonia grandis alba	Begonia evansiana alba
Begonia haageana	Begonia scharffii
Begonia nigramarga	Begonia bowerae 'Nigramarga'
Beloperone guttata	Justicia brandegeeana
Benthamia fragifera	Cornus capitata
Benthamia japonica	Cornus kousa
Benthamidia florida	Cornus florida
Benthamidia nuttallii	Cornus nuttallii
Benzoin aestivale	Lindera benzoin
Berberis acuminata	Berberis veitchii
Berberis aquifolium	Mahonia aquifolium
Berberis buxifolia 'Nana'	Berberis buxifolia 'Pygmaea'
Berberis candidula 'Amstelveen'	Berberis frikartii 'Amstelveen'
Berberis caroli Hoanghensis	Berberis vernae
Berberis coriacea	Berberis glaucocarpa
Berberis dictyophylla 'Albicaulis'	Berberis dictyophylla
Berberis dulcis 'Nana'	Berberis buxifolia 'Pygmaea'
Berberis gagnepainii 'Purpurea'	Berberis x interposita 'wallich's Purple'
Berberis Knightii	Berberis manipurana
Berberis thunbergii 'Atroqurpurea Superba'	Berberis x ottawensis 'Purpurea'
Bergenia delavayi	Bergenia purpurascens
Bergenia 'Evening Glow'	Bergenia 'Abendglut'
Bergenia 'Morgenrote'	Bergenia 'Morning Red'
Bergenia 'Schneekonigin'	Bergenia 'Snow Queen'
Bergenia 'Silberlicht'	Bergenia 'Silverlight'
Beta maritima	Beta vulgaris
Betonica officinalis	Stachys officinalis
Betula jacquemontii	Betula utilis jacquemontii
Betula lutea	Betula alleghaniensis
Betula mandshurica	Betula platyphylla
Betula pendula 'Dalecarlica'	Betula pendula 'Laciniata'
Betula verrucosa	Betula pendula
Bidens atrosanguinea	Cosmos atrosanguineus
Bigelowia graveolens	Chrysothamnus graveolens
Bignonia grandiflora	Campsis grandiflora
Bignonia jasminoides	Pandorea jasminoides

Know Your Common Plant Names

Historical Pseudonyms	Most Recent Accepted Naming
Bignonia pandorana	Pandorea pandorana
Bignonia radicans	Campsis radicans
Bignonia stans	Tecoma stans
Bignonia unguis-cati	Macfadyena unguis-cati
Bilderdykia	Fallopia
Bilderdykia baldschuanica	Fallopia baldschuanicum
Biota orientalis	Thuja orientalis
Blechnum corcoradense	Blechnum brasiliense
Blechnum magellanicum	Blechnum tabulare
Bocconia	Macleaya
Bolax glebaria	Azorella trifurcata
Boletus elegans	Suillus grevillei
Boletus granulatus	Suillus granulatus
Boletus luteus	Suillus luteus
Boletus variegatus	Suillus variegatus
Bombax	Ceiba
Botryostege bracteata	Elliottia bracteata
Boussingaultia baselloides	Anredera cordifolia
Boussingaultia baselloides	Anredera cordifolia
Bouteloua oligostachya	Bouteloua gracilis
Bouvardia triphylla	Bouvardia ternifolia
Brassaia	Schefflera
Brassica adpressa	Hirschfeldia incana
Brassica arvensis	Sinapis arvensis
Brassica hirta	Sinapis alba
Brassica japonica	Brassica juncea crispifolia
Brassica nigra	Sinapis nigra
Bravoa	Polianthes
Bravoa geminiflora	Polianthes geminiflora
Breynia nivosa	Breynia disticha
Brodiaca laxa	Triteleia laxa
Brodiaea congesta	Dichelostemma congestum
Brodiaea hyacinthina	Triteleia hyacinthina
Brodiaea ixioides	Triteleia ixioides
Brodiaea peduncularis	Triteleia peduncularis
Bromus giganteus	Festuca gigantea
Bromus pratense	Bromus commutatus
Browningia hertlingianus	Azureocereus hertlingianus
Brunfelsia calycina	Brunfelsia pauciflora
Brunnera macrophylla 'Variegata'	Brunnera macrophylla 'Dawson's White'
Brunsdonna parkeri	Amarygia parkeri
Brunsdonna parkeri	x Amarygia parkeri
Bryophyllum daigremontianum	Kalanchoe daigremontiana
Bryophyllum tubiflorum	Kalanchoe tubiflora
Buddleia	Buddleja
Buddleia davidii 'Nanho Blue'	Buddleja davidii 'Petite Indigo'
Buddleia davidii 'Nanho Purple'	Buddleja davidii 'Petite Plum'

Know Your Common Plant Names

Historical Pseudonyms	Most Recent Accepted Naming
Buddleia nicodemia	Buddleja madagascariensis
Buddleia paniculata	Buddleja crispa
Buddleia variabilis	Buddleja. davidii
Bupthalmum speciosum	Telekia speciosa
Buxus japonica 'Nana'	Buxus microphylla
Buxus sempervirens "Japonica Aurea'	Buxus sempervirens 'Latifolia Maculata'
Buxus sempervirens 'Silver Variegated'	Buxus sempervirens 'Elegantissima'
Caladium x hortulanum	Caladium bicolor
Calamintha acinos	Acinos arvensis
Calamintha alpina	Acinos alpinus
Calanthe bicolor	Calanthe discolor flava
Calanthe sieboldii	Calanthe striata
Calathea lancifolia	Calanthe insignis
Calathea oppenheimiana	Ctenanthe oppenheimiana
Calceolaria acutifolia	Calceolaria polyrrhiza
Calceolaria violacea	Jovellana violacea
Calla aethiopica	Zantedeschia aethiopica
Callicarpa giraldiana	Callicarpa bodinieri giraldii
Callicarpa koreana	Callicarpadichotoma
Callicarpa purpurea	Callicarpa dichotoma
Callistemon lanceolatus	Callistemon citrinus
Callistemon paludosus	Callistemon sieberi
Callistemon speciosus	Callistemon glaucus
Calluna vulgaris 'Snowball'	Calluna vulgaris 'My Dream'
Calonyction aculeatum	Ipomoea alba
Calycanthus praecox	Chimonanthus praecox
Calyptridium umbellatum	Spraguea umbellata
Calystegia sylvestris	Calystegia silvatica
Calytrix alpestris	Lhotzkya alpestris
Camassia esculenta	Camassia quamash
Camassia fraseri	Camassia scilloides
Camellia japonica 'Lady Clare'	Camellia 'Akashi-gata'
Camellia japonica 'Victor Emmanuel'	Camellia japonica 'Blood of China'
Camellia thea	Camellia sinensis
Campanula allionii	Campanula alpestris
Campanula muralis	Campanula portenschlagiana
Campanula planiflora	Campanula persicifolia
Campanula pusilla	Campanula cochleariifolia
Campanula rhomboidalis	Campanula rapunculoides
Campanula vidalii	Azorina vidalii
Campsis chinensis	Campsis grandiflora
Canarina campanula	Canarina canariensis
Candollea cuneiformis	Hibbertia cuneiformis
Cantua dependens	Cantua buxifolia
Caragana frutescens	Caragana frutex
Caragana pygmaea	Caragana aurantiaca
Cardamine latifolia	Cardamine raphanifolia

Know Your Common Plant Names

Historical Pseudonyms	Most Recent Accepted Naming
Cardamine sylvatica	Cardamine flexuosa
Carduus palustris	Cirsium palustre
Carduus pratensis	Cirsium dissectum
Carex canescens	Carex curta
Carex contigua	Carex spicata
Carex fortunei 'Variegata'	Carex morrowii 'Variegata'
Carex fusca	Carex buxbaumii
Carex goodenowii	Carex nigra
Carex gracilis	Carex acuta
Carex hetodes	Carex laevigata
Carex hornschuchiana	Carex hostiana
Carex hudsonii	Carex elata
Carex incurva	Carex maritima
Carex lagopina	Carex lachenalii
Carex morrowii 'Evergold'	Carex oshimensis 'Evergold'
Carex paradoxa	Carex appropinquata
Carex praecox	Carex caryophylla
Carex pulla	Carex saxatilis
Carex rigida	Carex bigelowii
Carex stellulata	Carex echinata
Carex stricta 'Bowles' Golden'	Carex elata 'Aurea'
Carex vulpina	Carex otrubae
Carissa spectabilis	Acokanthera oblongifolia
Carpinus betulus 'Pyramidalis'	Carpinus betulus 'Fastigiata'
Carum bulbocastanum	Bunium bulbocastanum
Carum petroselinum	Petroselinum crispum
Carum segetum	Petroselinum segetum
Carya alba	Carya ovata
Carya amara	Carya cordiformis
Carya pecan	Carya illinoensis
Carya porcina	Carya glabra
Carya sulcata	Carya laciniosa
Caryopteris mastacanthus	Caryopteris incana
Caryopteris tangutica	Caryopteris incana
Cassandra	Chamaedaphne
Castanea americana	Castanea dentata
Castanea vesca	Castanea sativa
Castanopsis chrysophylla	Chrysolepis chrysophylla
Casuarina stricta	Allocasuarina verticillata
Catalpa kaempferi	Catalpa ovata
Catalpa x hybrida	Catalpa x erubescens
Caucalis anthriscus	Torilis japonica
Cedrela	Toona
Cedronella mexicana	Agastache mexicana
Cedrus atlantica	Cedrus libani atlantica
Celastrus articulatus	Celastrus orbiculatus
Celtis mississippiensis	Celtis laevigata

Know Your Common Plant Names

Historical Pseudonyms	Most Recent Accepted Naming
Centaurea candidissima	Centaurea rutifolia
Centaurea gymnocarpa	Centaurea cineraria cineraria
Cephalaria tatarica	Cephalaria gigantea
Ceratostigma larpentae	Ceratostigma plumbaginoides
Cercocarpus parvifolius	Cercocarpus montanus
Cestrum purpureum	Cestrum elegans
Chaenomeles lagenaria	Chaenomeles speciosa
Chaenomeles maulei	Chaenomeles japonica
Chaenomeles sinensis	Pseudocydonia sinensis
Chaenomeles speciosa 'Apple Blossom'	Chaenomeles speciosa 'Moerloosii'
Chaenomeles speciosa 'Choshan'	Chaenomeles x superba 'Yaegaki'
Chamaecyparis lawsoniana 'Lanei'	Chamaecyparis lawsoniana 'Lane'
Chamaenerium angustifolium	Epilobium angustifolium
Chamaepericlymenum canadense	Cornus canadensis
Chamaerops excelsa	Trachycarpus fortunei
Chamaespartium sagittale	Genista sagittalis
Cheiranthus rupestris	Erysimum pulchellum
Cheiranthus scoparius	Erysimum scoparium
Cheiranthus sempervirens	Erysimum sempervirens
Cheiranthus x allionii	Erysimum hieraciifolium
Chelone barbata	Penstemon barbatus
Chiastophyllum simplicifolium	Chiastophyllum oppositifolium
Chimonanthus fragrans	Chimonanthus praecox
Chiogenes hispidula	Gaultheria hispida
Chionodoxa gigantea	Chionodoxa luciliae
Chionodoxa luciliae	Chionodoxa forbesii
Chrysanthemum alpina	Leucanthemopsis alpina
Chrysanthemum balsamita	Balsamita major
Chrysanthemum cinerariifolium	Tanacetum cinerariifolium
Chrysanthemum coccineum	Tanacetum coccineum
Chrysanthemum frutescens	Argyranthemum frutescens
Chrysanthemum haradjani	Tanacetum haradjani
Chrysanthemum hosmariense	Chrysanthemopsis hosmariense
Chrysanthemum leucanthemum	Leucanthemum vulgare
Chrysanthemum macrophyllum	Tanacetum macrophyllum
Chrysanthemum maximum	Leucanthemum maximum
Chrysanthemum maximum	Leucanthemum x superbum
Chrysanthemum parthenium	Tanacetum parthenium
Chrysanthemum ptarmicifolium	Tanacetum ptarmaciflorum
Chrysanthemum roseum	Tanacetum coccineum
Chrysanthemum rubellum	Dendranthema rubella
Chrysanthemum tricolor	Chrysanthemum carinatum
Chrysanthemum uliginosum	Leucanthemella serotina
Cineraria	Senecio cruentus
Cineraria maritima	Senecio bicolor cineraria
Cirsium diacantha	Ptilostemon diacantha
Cissis voinieranum	Tetrastigma voinieranum

Know Your Common Plant Names

Historical Pseudonyms	Most Recent Accepted Naming
Cistus algarvensis	Halimium ocymoides
Cistus crispus	Cistus x pulverulentus
Cistus crispus 'Sunset'	Cistusx pulverulentus 'Sunset'
Cistus formosus	Halimium lasianthum
Cistus halimiifolius	Halimium halimiifolium
Cistus ingwerseniana	x Halimiocistus ingwersenii
Cistus lasianthus	Halimium lasianthum
Cistus ocymoides	Halimium ocymoides
Cistus sahucii	x Halimiocistus sahucii
Cistus wintonensis	x Halimiocistus Wintonensis
Citrofortunella mitis	x Citrofortunella microcarpa
Citrus mitis	x Citrofortunella microcarpa
Citrus trifoliata	Poncirus trifoliata
Cladrastis amurensis	Maackia amurensis
Cladrastis tinctoria	Cladrastis lutea
Clarkia unguiculata	Clarkia elegans
Claytonia australasica	Neopaxia australasica
Clematis 'Bill Mackenzie'	Clematis tangutica 'Bill Machenzie'
Clematis calycina	Clematis cirrhosa balearica
Clematis chrysocoma sericea	Clematis montana sericea
Clematis chrysocoma spooneri	Clematis montana sericea
Clematis flammula 'Rubra Marginata'	Clematis x triternata 'Rubromarginata'
Clematis macropetala 'White Moth'	Clematis alpina 'White Moth'
Clematis montana 'Spooneri'	Clematis montana sericea
Clematis 'Mrs Robert Brydon'	Clematis jouiniana 'Mrs Robert Brydon'
Clematis nutans	Clematis rehderana
Clematis orientalis	Clematis tibetana vernayi
Clematis orientalis 'Bill Mackenzie'	Clematis tangutica 'Bill Mackenzie'
Clematis orientalis 'Orange Peel'	Clematis tibetana vernayi
Clematis orientalis 'Sherriffii'	Clematis tibetana vernayi L & S 13342
Clematis 'Ramona'	Clematis 'Hybrida sieboldiana'
Clematis spooneri	Clematis montana sericea
Clematis tangutica 'Aureolin'	Clematis 'Aureolin'
Cleome spinosa	Cleome hassleriana
Clerodendrum foetidum	Clerodendrum bungei
Clethra canescens	Clethra barbinervis
Clianthus dampieri	Clianthus formosus
Clinopodium grandiflorum	Calamintha grandiflora
Clintonia udensis	Clintonia alpina
Clitocybe gigantea	Leucopaxillus giganteus
Clitocybe olearia	Omphalotus olearius
Cochlearia armoracia	Armoracia rusticana
Cocos capitata	Butia capitata
Cocos chilensis	Jubaea chilensis
Cocos plumosa	Arecastrum romanzoffianum
Codonopsis vinciflora	Codonopsis convolvulacea
Colchicum chalcedonicum	Colchicum lingulatum

Know Your Common Plant Names

Historical Pseudonyms	Most Recent Accepted Naming
Colletia armata	Colletia hystrix
Colletia cruciata	Colletia paradoxa
Collybia radicata	Oudemansiella radicata
Collybia tenacella	Strobilurus tenacellus
Colvolvulus major	Ipomoea purpurea
Comptonia asplenifolia	Comptonia peregrina
Consolida ambigua	Consolida ajacis
Convallaria japonica	Ophiopogon jaburan
Convolvulus mauritanicus	Convolvulus sabatius
Convolvulus minor	Convolvulus tricolor
Convolvulus purpureus	Ipomoea purpurea
Corchorus japonicus	Kerria japonica
Cordyline terminalis	Cordyline fruticosa
Cornus alba 'Barcocks Form'	Cornus alba sibirica 'Albo marginata'
Cornus alba 'Westonbirt'	Cornus alba 'Sibirica'
Cornus alternifolia variegata	Cornus alternifolia 'Argentea'
Cornus florida 'Tricolor'	Cornus florida 'Welchii'
Cornus 'Kelsey's Dwarf'	Cornus stolonifera kelseyi
Cornus mas 'Tricolor'	Cornus mas ' 'Elegantissima'
Cornus paniculata	Cornus racemosa
Cornus sericea	Cornus stolonifera
Correa speciosa	Correa reflexa
Cortaderia argentea	Cortaderia selloana
Cortaderia selloana 'Gold Band'	Cortaderia selloana 'Aureo-lineata'
Corydalis solida	Corydalis bulbosa
Corylopsis platypetala	Corylopsis sinensis calvescens
Corylopsis veitchiana	Corylopsis sinensis calvescens veitchiana
Corylopsis willmottiae	Corylopsis sinensis sinensis
Corylus avellana laciniata	Corylus avellana 'Heterophylla'
Corylus avellana purpurea	Corylus avellana 'Fuscorubra'
Corynabutilon vitifolium	Abutilon vitifolium
Corypha australis	Livistona australis
Cotinus americanus	Cotinus obovatus
Cotinus coggygria 'Rubrifolius'	Cory coggygria 'Foliis purpureis'
Cotoneaster adpressus praecox	Cotoneaster nanshan
Cotoneaster conspicuus 'Decorus'	Cotoneaster conspicuus
Cotoneaster horizontalis 'Major'	Cotoneaster horizontalis 'Robustus'
Cotoneaster humifusus	Cotoneaster dammeri
Cotoneaster 'Hybridus Pendulus'	Cotoneaster x watereri 'Pendulus'
Cotoneaster melanotrichus	Cotoneaster microphyllos cochleatus
Cotoneaster rotundifolius	Cotoneaster distichus
Cotoneaster vulgaris	Cotoneaster integerrimus
Cotula atrata	Leptinella atrata
Cotula lineariloba	Leptinella pyrethrifolia linearifolia
Cotula pectinata	Leptinella pectinata
Cotula potentilloides	Leptinella potentillina
Cotula pyrethrifolia	Leptinella pyrethrifolia

Know Your Common Plant Names

Historical Pseudonyms	Most Recent Accepted Naming
Cotula reptans	Leptinella scariosa
Cotula rotundata	Leptinella rotundata
Cotula scariosa	Leptinella scariosa
Cotula sericea	Leptinella pectinata sericea
Cotula squalida	Leptinella squalida
Cotyledon chrysantha	Rosularia pallida
Cotyledon oppositifolia	Chiastophyllum oppositifolium
Cotyledon reticulata	Tylecodon reticulata
Cotyledon simplicifolia	Chiastophyllum oppositifolium
Cotyledon umbilicus-veneris	Umbilicus rupestris
Cowania mexicana	Cowaniastansburyana
Crassula argentea	Crassula ovata
Crassula ovata	Crassula portulacea
Crassula portulacea	Crassula . ovata
Crassula sediformis	Sedum crassularia
Crataegus calpodendron	Crataegus tomentosa
Crataegus carrierei	Crataegus x lavallei 'Carrierei'
Crataegus korolkowii	Crataegus wattiana
Crataegus laevigata 'Coccinea Plena'	Crataegus laevigata 'Paul's Scarlet'
Crataegus monogyna 'Praecox'	Crataegus monogyna 'Biflora'
Crataegus orientalis	Crataegus laciniata
Crataegus oxyacantha	Crataegus laevigata
Crataegus prunifolia	Crataegus persimilis 'Prunifolia'
Cremanthodium	Ligularia
Crindonna corsii	Amarcrinum memoria-corsii
Crinitaria	Aster
Crinitaria linosyris	Aster linosyris
Crinodonna corsii	x Amarcrinum memoria-corsii
Crinum capense	Crinum bulbispermum
Crocosmia rosea	Tritonia rubrolucens
Crocus susianus	Crocus angustifolius
Crocus suterianus	Crocus olivieri olivieri
Crocus zonatus	Crocus kotschyanus kotschyanus
Crossandra undulifolia	Crossandra infunddibuliformis
Crucianella stylosa	Phuopsis stylosa
Cryptomeria japonica 'Lobbii Nana'	Cryptomeria japonica 'Nana'
Cryptomeria japonica 'Sekkwa-sugi'	Cryptomeria japonica 'Cristata'
Cunninghamia sinensis	Cunninghamia lanceolata
Cuphea platycentra	Cuphea ignea
Cupressus funebris	Chamaecyparis funebris
Cupressus glabra	Cupressus arizonica
Curtonus paniculatus	Crocosmia paniculata
Cyathea smithii	Hemitelia smithii
Cyathodes colensoi	Styphelia colensoi
Cyathodes fraseri	Leucopogon fraseri
Cyclamen europaeum	Cyclamen purpurascens
Cyclamen ibericum	Cyclamen coum caucasicum

Know Your Common Plant Names

Historical Pseudonyms	Most Recent Accepted Naming
Cyclamen latifolium	Cyclamen persicum
Cyclamen neapolitanum	Cyclamen hederifolium
Cyclobothra lutea	Calochortus barbatus
Cydonia japonica	Chaenomeles japonica
Cydonia vulgaris	Cydonia oblonga
Cyperus alternifolius	Cyperus involucratus
Cyperus diffusus	Cyperus albostriatus
Cyperus vegetus	Cyperus eragrostis
Cyrtanthus parviflorus	Cyrtanthus brachyscyphus
Cyrtanthus speciosus	Cyrtanthus purpureus
Cyrtomium	Phanerophlebia
Cytisus adamii	x Laburnocytisus adamii
Cytisus albus	Cytisus multiflorus
Cytisus battandieri	Argyrocytisus batttandieri
Cytisus nigrescens	Lembotropis nigricans
Cytisus racemosus	Cytisus x spachianus
Cytisus ramentaceus	Petteria ramentacea
Cytisus x praecox 'Canary Bird'	Cytisus x praecox 'Gold Speer'
Daboecia cantabrica	Menziesia polifolia
Dacrydium bidwillii	Halocarpus bidwillii
Dacrydium franklinii	Lagarostrobos franklinii
Daphne andina	Ovidia andina
Daphne collina neapolitana	Daphne x neapolitana
Daphne repestris	Daphne petraea
Daphne xburkwoodii 'Variegata'	Daphne x burkwoodii 'Carol Mackie'
Dasylirion gracile	Dasylirion acrotrichum
Datura cornigera	Brugmansia cornigera
Datura metaloides	Datura inoxia
Datura rosea	Brugmansia x insignis
Datura sanguinea	Brugmansia sanguinea
Datura suaveolens	Brugmansia suaveolens
Datura versicolor	Brugmansia versicolor
Datura x candida	Brugmansia x candida
Davallia bullata	Davallia mariesii
Delphinium ajacis	Consolida ajacis
Delphinium ajacis	Consolida ambigua
Delphinium consolida	Consolida ajacis
Dentaria bulbifera	Cardamine bulbifera
Dentaria digitata	Cardamine pentaphyllos
Dentaria enneaphylla	Cardamine enneaphyllos
Dentaria pentaphylla	Cardamine pentaphyllos
Dentaria pinnata	Cardamine heptaphylla
Dentaria polyphylla	Cardamine kitaibelii
Desmodium penduliflorum	Lespedeza thunbergii
Deutzia crenata	Deutzia scabra
Deutzia gracilis 'Carminea'	Deutzia x rosea 'Carminea'
Dianthus caesius	Dianthus gratianopolitanus

Historical Pseudonyms	Most Recent Accepted Naming
Dianthus neglectus	Dianthus pavonius
Diascia felthamii	Diascia fetcaniensis
Diascia flanaganii	Diascia stachyoides
Dictamnus fraxinella	Dictamnus albus purpureus
Didiscus caeruleus	Trachymene caerulea
Didymosperma caudata	Arenga caudata
Diervilla middendorffiana	Weigela middendorffiana
Digitalis ambigua	Digitalis grandiflora
Digitalis canariensis	Isoplexis canariensis
Digitalis lamarckii	Digitalis lanata
Dimorphotheca annua	Dimorphotheca pluvialis
Dimorphotheca barberae	Osteospermum jucundum
Diosphaera asperuloides	Trachelium asperuloides
Diplacus glutinosus	Mimulus aurantiacus
Diplazium japonicum	Lunathyrium japonicum
Diplopappus chrysophyllus	Cassinia fulvida
Dipsacus sylvestris	Dipsacus fullonum
Dipteracanthus	Ruellia
Diuranthera major	Chlorophytum majus
Dizygotheca	Schefflera
Dodecatheon cusickii	Dodecatheon pulchellum
Dodecatheon pauciflorum	Dodecatheon pulchellum
Dodecatheon radicatum	Dodecatheon. pulchellum
Dolichos lablab	Lablab purpureus
Dombeya mastersii	Dombeya burgessiae
Doronicum caucasicum	Doronicum orientale
Doronicum cordatum	Doronicum columnae
Doronicum cordatum	Doronicum pardalianches
Doronicum 'Harpur Crewe'	Doronicum plantagineum 'Excelsum'
Dorycnium hirsutum	Lotus hirsutus
Douglasia vitaliana	Vitaliana primuliflora
Doxantha capreolata	Bignonia capreolata
Doxantha unguis-cati	Macfadyena unguis-cati
Draba aizoon	Draba lasiocarpa
Dracaena australis	Cordyline australis
Dracaena godseffiana	Dracaena surculosa surculosa
Dracaena indivisa	Cordyline indivisa
Dracocephalum virginicum	Physostegia virginiana
Drejerella guttata	Justicia brandegeana
Drepanostachyum aristatum	Thamnocalmus aristatus
Drimys aromatica	Tasmannia aromatica
Drimys colorata	Pseudowintera colorata
Drimys lanceolata	Tasmannia aromatica
Duchesnea indica 'Variegata'	Duchesnea indica 'Harlequin'
Duranta plumieri	Duranta repens
Echeveria nigra	Echeveria affinis
Echinopanax horridus	Oplopanax horridus

Know Your Common Plant Names

Historical Pseudonyms	Most Recent Accepted Naming
Echinops ritro 'Blue Ball'	Echinops bannaticus 'Blue Globe'
Echinopsis aurea	Lobivia aurea
Echioides longiflorum	Arnebia pulchra
Echium violaceum	Echium plantagineum
Edgeworthia papyrifera	Edgeworthia chrysantha
Edwardsia chilensis	Sophora macrocarpa
Edwardsia microphylla	Sophora microphylla
Ehretia acuminata	Ehretia ovalifolia
Ehretia thyrsifolia	Ehretia ovalifolia
Elaeagnus argentea	Elaeagnus commutata
Elaeagnus pungens 'Aureo Variegata'	Elaeagnus pungens 'Maculata'
Elodea crispa	Lagarosiphon major
Elymus arenarius	Leymus arenarius
Elymus glaucus	Elymus hispidus
Emilia flammea	Emilia javanica
Endymion	Hyacinthoides
Enkianthus japonicus	Enkianthus perulatus
Epilobium rosmarinifolium	Epilobium dodonaei
Epimedium macranthum	Epimedium grandiflorum
Eremurus bungei	Eremurus stenophyllus stenophyllus
Erica corsica	Erica terminalis
Erica herbacea	Erica carnea
Erica hibernica	Erica erigena
Erica mediterranea	Erica erigena
Erica stricta	Erica terminalis
Erica x darleyensis 'Silberschmelze'	Erica x darleyensis 'Molten Silver'
Erica x praegeri	Erica x stuartii
Erigeron aureus	Haplopappus brandegeei
Erigeron canadensis	Conyza canadensis
Erigeron mucronatus	Erigeron karvinskianus
Erinacea pungens	Erinacea anthyllis
Erodium balearicum	Erodium x variabile 'Album'
Erodium chamaedrioides	Erodium reichardii
Erodium daucoides	Erodium castellanum
Erodium hymenodes	Erodium trifolium
Erodium macradenum	Erodium glandulosum
Erodium supracanum	Erodiumrupestre
Erodium tordilioides	Erodium gruinum
Erpetion reniforme	Viola hederacea
Eryngium bromeliifolium	Eryngium agavifolium
Eryngium pandanifolium	Eryngium decaisneanum
Eryngium paniculatum	Eryngium eburneum
Erysimum pumilum	Erysimum helveticum
Erysimum rupestre	Erysimum pulchellum
Escallonia organensis	Escallonia laevis
Escallonia phillipiana	Escallonia virgata
Escallonia punctata	Escallonia rubra

Know Your Common Plant Names

Historical Pseudonyms	Most Recent Accepted Naming
Escallonia rubra 'Pygmaea'	Escallonia rubra 'Woodside'
Eucalyptus pauciflora nana	Eucalyptus gregsoniana
Eucalyptus simmondsii	Eucalyptus nitida
Eucalyptus stuartiana	Eucalyptus ovata
Eucharis amazonica	Eucharis grandiflora
Eucomis punctata	Eucomis comosa
Eucomis undulata	Eucomis autumnalis
Eucryphia pinnatifolia	Eucryphia glutinosa
Eugenia australis	Syzgium paniculatum
Eugenia paniculata	Syzgium paniculatum
Eunomia	Aethionema
Euodia	Tetradium
Euonymus nanus koopmannii	Euonymus nanus turkestanicus
Euonymus radicans	Euonymus fortunei radicans
Euonymus sachalinensis	Euonymus planipes
Euonymus yedoensis	Euonymus hamiltonianus sieboldianus
Eupatorium ageratoides	Eupatorium rugosum
Eupatorium ageratoides	Eupatorium rugosum
Eupatorium micranthum	Eupatorium ligustrinum
Eupatorium urticifolium	Eupatorium rugosum
Eupatorium weinmannianum	Eupatorium ligustrinum
Euphorbia amygdaloides purpurea	Euphorbia amygdaloides rubra
Euphorbia biglandulosa	Euphorbia rigida
Euphorbia epithymoides	Euphorbia polychroma
Euphorbia robbiae	Euphorbia amygdaloides robbiae
Euptelea franchatii	Euptelea pleiosperma
Eurya fortunei	Cleyera fortunei
Eurya japonica 'Variegata'	Cleyera fortunei
Euryops evansii	Euryops acraeus
Eustoma russellianum	Eustoma grandiflorum
Exochorda albertii	Exochorda korolkowii
Fagopyrum sagittatum	Fagopyrum esculentum
Fagus americana	Fagus grandifolia
Fagus ferruginea	Fagus grandifolia
Fagus sylvatica 'Fastigiata'	Fagus sylvatica 'Dawyck'
Fagus sylvatica heterophylla	Fagus sylvatica 'Asplenifolia'
Fagus sylvatica 'Quercifolia'	Fagus sylvatica laciniata
Fagus sylvatica 'Roseomarginata'	Fagus sylvatica 'Purpurea Tricolor'
Fallopia aubertii	Fallopia baldschuanicum
Farfugium japonicum	Ligularia tussilaginea
Farsetia clypeata	Fibigia clypeata
Fatsia papyrifera	Tetrapanax papyriferus
Feijoa	Acca
Felicia capensis 'Variegata'	Felicia amelloides 'Variegated'
Ferraria undulata	Ferraria crispa
Ferula 'Giant Bronze'	Foeniculum vulgare 'Giant Bronze'
Festuca ambigua	Vulpia ambigua

Know Your Common Plant Names

Historical Pseudonyms	Most Recent Accepted Naming
Festuca caesia	Festuca glauca
Festuca capillata	Festuca tenuifolia
Festuca myuros	Vulpia myuros
Festuca sciuroides	Vulpia bromides
Festuca silvatica	Festuca altissima
Ficus australis	Ficus rubiginosa
Ficus diversifolia	Ficus deltoidea
Ficus pandurata	Ficus lyrata
Ficus radicans	Ficus sagittata
Ficus repens	Ficus pumila
Ficus retusa	Ficus microcarpa
Filipendula hexapetala	Filipendula vulgaris
Firmiana platanifolia	Firmiana simplex
Fragaria elatior	Fragaria moschata
Fragaria indica	Duchesnea indica
Francoa appendiculata	Francoa sonchifolia
Frangula alnus	Rhamnus frangula
Fraxinus alba	Fraxinus americana
Fraxinus excelsior 'Aurea'	Fraxinus excelsior 'Jaspidea'
Fraxinus excelsior 'Monophylla'	Fraxinus excelsior 'Diversifolia'
Fraxinus mariesii	Fraxinus sieboldiana
Fraxinus oxycarpa 'Raywood'	Fraxinus rotundifolia 'Raywood'
Fraxinus pubescens	Fraxinus pensylvanica
Fremontia	Fremontodendron
Fritillaria citrina	Fritillaria bithynica
Fritillaria hispanica	Fritillaria lusitanica
Fritillaria nigra	Fritillaria pyrenaica
Fritillaria rubra major	Fritillaria imperialis 'Maxima'
Fritillaria tenella	Fritillaria orientalis
Fuchsia magellanica 'Alba Variegata'	Fuchsia magellanica 'Sharpitor'
Fumana procumbens	Fumana nudifolia
Fumaria lutea	Corydalis lutea
Funkia	Hosta
Furcraea gigantea	Furcraea foetida
Gaillardia aristata	Gaillardia x grandiflora
Galanthus latifolius	Galanthus ikariae
Galax aphylla	Galax urceolata
Galeobdolon luteum	Lamium galeobdolon
Galium cruciata	Cruciata laevines
Galium mollugo	Galium album
Gardenia florida	Gardenia jasminoides
Gardenia grandiflora	Gardenia jasminoides
Gaultheria ovalifolia	Gaultheria fragrantissima
Gazania splendens	Gazania rigens
Gelsemium nitidum	Gelsemium sempervirens
Genista dalmatica	Genista sylvestris
Genista spathulata	Genista lydia

Know Your Common Plant Names

Historical Pseudonyms	Most Recent Accepted Naming
Gentiana amarella	Gentianella amarella
Gentiana campestris	Gentianella campestris
Gentiana crinita	Gentianopsis crinita
Gentiana excisa	Gentiana acaulis
Gentiana kochiana	Gentiana acaulis
Gentiana ochroleuca	Gentiana villosa
Gentiana purdomii	Gentiana gracilipes
Geranium aconitifolium	Geranium rivulare
Geranium armenum	Geranium psilostemon
Geranium grandiflorum	Geranium himalayense
Geranium grandiflorum alpinum	Geranium himalayense 'Gravetye'
Geranium phaeum rectum album	Geranium clarkii 'Kashmir White'
Geranium punctatum	Geranium x monacense
Geranium rectum 'Album'	Geranium clarkei 'Kashmir White'
Geranium sanguineum lancastriense	Geranium sanguineum striatum
Geranium versicolor	Geranium striatum
Gesneria cardinalis	Sinningia cardinalis
Geum chiloense	Geum quellyon
Geum japonicum	Geum macrophyllum
Ginkgo biloba 'Autumn Gold'	Ginkgo biloba 'Saratoga'
Gladiolus grandis	Gladiolus liliaceus
Gladiolus murielae	Gladiolus callianthus
Gladiolus segetum	Gladiolus italicus
Glaucium phoenicum	Glaucium corniculatum
Gleditsia triacanthos "Inermis	Gleditsia triacanthos 'Sunburst'
Gleditsia triacanthos 'Pendula'	Gleditsia triacanthos 'Bujoti'
Globularia bellidifolia	Globularia meridionalis
Globularia nana	Globularia repens
Globularia pygmaea	Globularia meridionalis
Gloriosa carsonii	Gloriosa superba
Gloriosa lutea	Gloriosa superba superba
Gloriosa rothschildiana	Gloriosa superba
Glyceria aquatica	Glyceria maxima
Glyceria aquatica 'Variegata'	Glyceria maxima 'Variegata'
Glyceria maritima	Puccinellia maritima
Glycine	Wisteria
Gnaphalium 'Fairy Gold'	Helichrysum thianschanicum 'GoldKind'
Godetia	Clarkia
Gordonia alatamaha	Franklinia alatamaha
Gordonia anomala	Gordonia axillaris
Grindelia speciosa	Grindelia chiloensis
Grindelia speciosa	Grindelia chiloensis
Gunera scabra	Gunera tinctoria
Gunnera chilensis	Gunnera tinctoria
Guzmania tricolor	Guzmania monostachya
Gymnocladus canadensis	Gymnocladus dioica
Gynerium argenteum	Cortaderia selloana

Know Your Common Plant Names

Historical Pseudonyms	Most Recent Accepted Naming
Gynura sarmentosa	Gynura aurantiaca 'Purple Passion'
Gypsophila dubia	Gypsophila repens 'Dubia'
Habenaria bifolia	Platanthera bifolia
Habenaria chlorantha	Platanthera chlorantha
Habenaria conopsea	Gymnadenia conopsea
Haemanthus kalbreyeri	Scadoxus multiflora multiflora
Haemanthus Katherinae 'King Albert'	Scadoxus multiflorus Katherinae
Haemanthus natalensis	Scadoxus puniceus
Halesia carolina	Halesia tetraptera
Halimium formosum	Halimium lasianthum
Halimium libanotis	Halimium commutatum
Halimium wintonensis	x Halimiocistus wintonensis
Hamamelis chinensis	Loropetalum chinense
Hamamelis x intermedia 'Copper Beauty'	Hamamelis x intermedia 'Jelena'
Hamatocactus hamatacanthus	Ferocactus hamatacanthus
Hamatocactus setispinus	Ferocactus setispinus
Harrimanella	Cassiope
Hartia sinensis	Stewartia pteropetiolata
Hebe anomala	Hebe odora 'Anomala'
Hebe 'Carl Teschner'	Hebe 'Youngii'
Hebe catarractae	Parahebe catarractae
Hebe darwiniana	Hebe glaucophylla
Hebe elliptica 'Variegata'	Hebe x franciscana ' Variegata'
Hebe lyallii	Parahebe lyalli
Hebe 'Margery Fish'	Hebe 'Primley Gem'
Hebe 'Royal Purple'	Hebe 'Alicia Amherst'
Hebe 'Ruddigore'	Hebe 'La Seduisante'
Hebe 'Sussex Carpet'	Hebe albicans 'Sussex Carpet'
Hebe 'Veitchii'	Hebe 'Alicia Amherst'
Hedera algeriensis 'Gloire de Marengo'	Hederacanariensis 'Gloire de Marengo'
Hedera canariensis 'Variegata'	Hedera canariensis 'Gloire de Marengo'
Hedera colchica 'Dentata Aurea'	Hedera colchica 'Dentata Variegata'
Hedera colchica 'Paddy's Pride'	Hedera colchica 'Sulphur Heart'
Hedera helix 'Oro di Bogliasco'	Hedera helix 'Goldheart'
Hedera helix 'Silver Queen'	Hedera helix 'Tricolor'
Hedychium acuminatum	Hedychium spicatum
Heimerliodendron brunonianum	Pisonia umbellifera
Heimia salicifolia	Heimia myrtifolia
Helianthemum chamaecistus	Helianthemum nummularium
Helianthemum globulariifolium	Tuberaria globulariifolia
Helianthemum guttatum	Tuberaria guttata
Helianthemum umbellatum	Halimium umbellatum
Helianthemum vulgare	Helianthemum nummularium
Helianthus orgyalis	Helianthus salicifolius
Helianthus rigidus	Helianthus lactiflorus
Helianthus scaberrimus	Helianthus lactiflorus
Helichrysum angustifolium	Helichrysum italicum

Know Your Common Plant Names

Historical Pseudonyms	Most Recent Accepted Naming
Helichrysum ericoides	Dolicothrix ericoides
Helichrysum lanatum	Helichrysum thianshanicum
Helichrysum marginatum	Helichrysum milfordiae
Helichrysum microphyllum	Plecostachys serpyllifolia
Helichrysum petiolare 'Aureum'	Helichrysum petiolare 'Limelight'
Helichrysum petiolatum	Helichrysum petiolare
Helichrysum serotinum	Helichrysum italicum serotinum
Helichrysum trilineatum	Helichrysum splendidum
Helichrysum tumidum	Helichrysum selago
Heliosperma alpestris	Silene alpestris
Heliotropium peruvianum	Heliotropium arborescens
Helleborus corsicus	Helleborus argutifolius
Helleborus lividus corsicus	Helleborus argutifolius
Helxine	Soleirolia
Hemerocallis flava	Hemerocallis lilio-asphodelus
Hemigraphis colorata	Hemigraphis alternata
Hepatica triloba	Hepaticanobilis
Heptapleurum	Schefflera
Heptapleurum arboricola	Schefflera arboricola
Hesperoyucca whipplei	Yucca whipplei
Hetia	Othonna
Heuchera 'Coral Bells'	Heuchera sanguinea
Hibbertia volubilis	Hibbertia scandens
Hibiscus esculentus	Abelmoschus esculentus
Hibiscus huegeli	Alyogyne huegeli
Hibiscus syriacus 'Caeruleus Plenus'	Hibiscus syriacus 'Ardens'
Hibiscus syriacus 'Elegantissimus'	Hibiscus syriacus 'Lady Stanley'
Hibiscus syriacus 'Oiseau Bleu'	Hibiscus syriacus 'Blue Bird'
Hidalgoa ternata	Hidalgoa wercklei
Hieracium brunneocroceum	Hieracium aurantiacum carpathicola
Hippeastrum striatum	Hippeastrum rutilum
Hoheria microphylla	Hoheria angustifolia
Hoheria populnea lanceolata	Hoheria sexstylosa
Hordeum europaeum	Hordelymus europaeus
Hosackia glabra	Lotus scoparius
Hosta albomarginata	Hosta sieboldii
Hosta fortunei 'Aureo-Maculata'	Hosta fortunei albopicta
Hosta fortunei 'Obscura Marginata	Hosta fortunei 'Aureo-Marginata'
Hosta 'Thomas Hogg'	Hosta undulata albomarginata
Hyacinthus amethystinus	Brimeura amethystina
Hyacinthus azureus	Muscari azureum
Hyacinthus comosum 'Plumosum'	Muscari comosum 'Plumosum'
Hydrangea cinerea	Hydrangea arborescens discolor
Hydrangea integerrima	Hydrangea serratifolia
Hydrangea scandens	Hydrangea petiolaris
Hydrangea serrata 'Acuminata'	Hydrangea serrata 'Blue Bird'
Hydrangea serrata 'Preziosa'	Hydrangea 'Preziosa'

Know Your Common Plant Names

Historical Pseudonyms	Most Recent Accepted Naming
Hydrangea tilifolia	Hydrangea petiolaris
Hydrangea villosa	Hydrangea aspera villosa
Hygrophorus brevisporus	Hygrocybe brevispora
Hygrophorus conicus	Hygrocybe conica
Hygrophorus miniatus	Hygrocybe miniata
Hygrophorus psittacinus	Hygrocybe psittacina
Hygrophorus puniceus	Hygrocybe punicea
Hygrophorus spadiceus	Hygrocybe spadicea
Hygrophorus virgineus	Camarophyllus virgineus
Hypercium androsaemum 'Variegatum'	Hypercium androsaemum 'Gladys' Brabazon'
Hypericum elatum	Hypericum x inodorum
Hypericum grandiflorum	Hypericum kouytchense
Hypericum patulum forrestii	Hypericum forrestii
Hypericum patulum grandiflorum	Hypericum kouytchense
Hypericum patulum henryi	Hypericum pseudohenryi
Hypericum patulum 'Hidcote'	Hypericum 'Hidcote'
Hypericum patulum 'Sungold'	Hypericum kouytchense
Hypericum persistens	Hypericum x inodorum
Hypericum polyphyllum	Hypericum olympicum minus
Hypericum reptans	Hypericum olympicum minus
Hypericum x moseranum 'Variegatum'	Hypericum x moseranum 'Tricolor'
Hypholoma velutinum	Lacrymaria velutina
Hypocyrta nummularia	Alloplectus nummularia
Hypocyrta radicans	Nematanthus gregarius
Hypoestes sanguinolenta	Hypoestes phyllostachya
Hypoxis stellata	Hypoxis capensis
Iberis commutata	Iberis sempervirens
Ilex aquifolium 'Argentea Medio-Picta'	Ilex aquifolium 'Silver Milkboy'
Ilex aquifolium 'Argentea Regina'	Ilex aquifolium 'Silver Queen'
Ilex aquifolium 'Aurea Medio-Picta'	Ilex aquifolium ' 'Golden Milkboy'
Ilex aquifolium 'Aurea-regina'	Ilex aquifolium 'Golden Queen'
Ilex aquifolium 'Bicolor'	Ilex aquifolium 'Aurifodina'
Ilex aquifolium 'Fructo-luteo'	Ilex aquifolium ' 'Bacciflava'
Ilex aquifolium 'Muricata'	Ilex aquifolium 'Aurifodina'
Ilex aquifolium 'Polycarpa'	Ilex x altaclarensis 'J C'
Ilex aquifolium 'Silver Sentinel'	Ilex x altaclarensis 'Belgica Aurea'
Ilex cassina	Ilex vomitoria
Ilex folium 'Bicolor	Ilex aguifolium 'Aurifodina'
Ilex maderensis	Ilex perado
Ilex xaltaclavensis 'Silver Sentinel'	Ilex xaltaclarensis 'Belgica Aurea'
Impatiens fulva	Impatiens capensis
Impatiens holstii	Impatiens walleriana
Impatiens roylei	Impatiens glandulifera
Indigofera gerardiana	Indigofera heterantha
Indigofera incarnata	Indigofera decora
Inula glandulosa	Inula orientalis
Inula squarrosa	Inula conyza

Know Your Common Plant Names

Historical Pseudonyms	Most Recent Accepted Naming
Ipomoea bona-nox	Ipomoea alba
Ipomoea rubrocaerulea	Convolvulus tricolor
Ipomoea tuberosa	Merremia tuberosa
Ipomoea versicolor	Mina lobata
Iris pallida dalmatica	Iris pallida pallida
Iris stylosa	Iris unguicularis
Iris thunbergii	Iris sanguinea
Iris tuberosa	Hermodactylus tuberosus
Iris xiphioides	Iris latifolia
Ismene	Hymenocallis
Ismene calathina	Hymenocallis narcissiflora
Isocoma	Haplopappus
Isopyrum ohwianum	Isopyrum nipponicum sarmentosum
Ixiolirion montanum	Ixiolirion tataricum
Ixiolirion pallasii	Ixiolirion tataricum
Jacaranda ovalifolia	Jacarandamimosifolia
Jacobinia	Justicia
Jacobinia spicigera	Justicia spicigera
Jasione perennis	Jasione laevis
Jasminum ferreri	Jasminum humile
Jasminum officinale 'Aureovariegatum'	Jasminum officinale 'Aureum'
Jasminum officinale 'Variegatum'	Jasminum officinale 'Argenteo Variegatum'
Jasminum primulinum	Jasminum mesnyi
Jasminum reevesianum	Jasminum humile 'Revolutum'
Jubaea spectabilis	Jubaea chilensis
Juglans rupestris	Juglans microcarpa
Juglans sieboldiana	Juglans ailantifolia
Juncus communis	Juncus effusus
Juncus conglomeratus	Juncus subuliflorus
Juncus glaucus	Juncus inflexus
Juncus macer	Juncus tenuis
Juniperus litoralis	Juniperus conferta
Justicia pauciflora	Justicia rizzinii
Justicia pohliana	Justicia carnea
Kalmia glauca	Kalmia polifolia
Kalopanax ricinifolius	Kalopanax pictus
Kalopanax septemlobus	Kalopanax pictus
Kentia belmoreana	Howea belmoreana
Kentia canterburyana	Hedyscepe canterburyana
Kentranthus	Centranthus
Kerria japonica 'Variegata'	Kerria japonica 'Picta'
Kitchingia uniflora	Kalanchoe uniflora
Kleinia articulata	Senecio articulatus
Kniphofia galpinii	Kniphofia triangularis
Laburnum adamii	x Laburnocytisus adamii
Laburnum vulgare	Laburnum anagyroides
Lachenalia pendula	Lachenaliabulbifera

Know Your Common Plant Names

Historical Pseudonyms	Most Recent Accepted Naming
Lactarius plumbeus	Lactarius turpis
Lactuca alpina	Cicerbita alpina
Lactuca macrophylla	Cicerbita macrophylla
Lactuca muralis	Mycelis muralis
Lamiastrum	Lamium
Lamium maculatum 'Shell Pink'	Lamium maculatum roseum
Lampranthus edulis	Carpobrotus edulis
Lampranthus lehmanii	Delosperma behmanii
Lampranthus pallidus	Delosperma pallidum
Lantana delicatissima	Lantana montevidensis
Lantana sellowiana	Lantana montividensis
Lapeirousia cruenta	Anomatheca laxa
Lapeirousia grandiflora	Anomatheca grandiflora
Lapeirousia laxa	Anomatheca laxa
Larix europaea	Larix decidua
Larix leptolepis	Larix kaempferi
Larix thibetica	Larix potaninii
Lasiagrostis splendens	Stipa splendens
Lasiandra macrantha	Tibouchina semidecandra
Latania borbonica	Livistona chinensis
Lathyrus maritimus	Lathyrus japonicus
Laurelia aromatica	Laurelia serrata
Laurus benzoin	Lindera benzoin
Laurus canariensis	Laurus azorica
Lavandula angustifolia 'Nana Atropurpurea'	Lavandula angustifolia 'Hidcote'
Lavandula officinalis	Lavandula angustifolia
Lavandula spica	Lavandula angustifolia
Lavatera cachemirica	Lavatera cachemiriana
Lavatera olbia 'Variegata'	Lavatera olbia 'Wembdon Variegated'
Ledum buxifolium	Leiophyllum buxifolium
Ledum latifolium	Ledum groenlandicum
Leonotis leonurus	Leonotis oxymifolia
Leontice alberti	Gymnospermium albertii
Leontodon leysseri	Leontodon taraxacoides
Leontopodium tataricum	Leontopodium discolor
Leopoldia comosa	Muscari comosum
Lepidium draba	Cardaria draba
Lepiota lenticularis	Limacella guttata
Lepiota procera	Macrolepiota procera
Lepiota puellaris	Macrolepiota puellaris
Lepiota rhacodes	Macrolepiota rhacodes
Leptospermum cunninghamii	Leptospermum lanigerum
Leptospermum ericoides	Kunzea ericoides
Leptospermum humifusum	Leptospermum rupestre
Leptospermum phylicoides	Kunzea ericoides
Leptospermum prostratum	Leptospermum rupestre
Leptospermum pubescens	Leptospermum lanigerum

Know Your Common Plant Names

Historical Pseudonyms	Most Recent Accepted Naming
Leptospermum rodwayanum	Leptospermum grandiflorum
Lespedeza sieboldii	Lespedeza thunbergii
Leucanthemopsis hosmariensis	Chrysanthemopsis hosmariense
Leucanthemum hosmariense	Chrysanthemopsis hosmariense
Leucothoe catesbaei	Leucothoe walteri
Leucothoe fontanesiana	Leucothoe walteri
Libertia chilensis	Libertia formosa
Libocedrus decurrens	Calocedrus decurrens
Libonia floribunda	Justicia rizzinii
Ligularia clivorum	Ligularia dentata
Ligustrum ibota	Ligustrum obtusifolium
Ligustrum ionandrum	Ligustrum delavayanum
Ligustrum japonicum 'Coriaceum'	Ligustrum japonicum 'Rotundifolium'
Lilium tigrinum	Lilium lancifolium
Limonia trifoliata	Poncirus trifoliata
Linaria cymbalaria	Cymbalaria muralis
Linaria elatine	Kickxia elatine
Linaria minor	Chaenorhinum minus
Linaria origanifolia	Chaenorhinum origanifolium
Linaria pallida	Cymbalaria pallida
Linaria pilosa	Cymbalaria pilosa
Lindera triloba	Lindera obtusiloba
Lippia chamaedrifolia	Verbena peruviana
Lippia citriodora	Aloysia triphylla
Liriope graminifolia	Liriope muscari
Liriope hyacinthifolia	Reineckea carnea
Lisianthus russellianus	Eustoma grandiflorum
Lithospermum diffusum	Lithodora diffusa
Lithospermum doerfleri	Moltkia doerfleri
Lithospermum oleifolium	Lithodora oleifolia
Lithospermum purpureocaeruleum	Buglossoides purpureocaerulea
Litsea glauca	Neolitsea sericea
Lobivia pygmaea	Rebutia pygmaea
Lochroma tubulosum	Lochroma cyaneum
Lolium italicum	Lolium multiflorum
Lomaria alpina	Blechnum penna-marina alpinum
Lomaria gibbum	Blechnum gibbum
Lomaria magellanica	Blechnum magellanicum
Lomatia longifolia	Lomatia myricoides
Lomatia obliqua	Lomatia hirsuta
Lonicera flexuosa	Lonicera j. repens
Lonicera grata	Lonicera x americana
Lonicera involucrata	Lonicera ledebourii
Lonicera italica	Lonicera x americana
Lonicera japonica flexuosa	Lonicera japonica repens
Lonicera ledebourii	Lonicera involucrata
Lonicera syringantha	Lonicera rupicola syringantha

Know Your Common Plant Names

Historical Pseudonyms	Most Recent Accepted Naming
Lonicera yunnanensis	Lonicera nitida 'Elegant'
Lunaria biennis	Lunaria annua
Luzula maxima	Luzula sylvatica
Lychnis alba	Silene alba
Lychnis dioica	Silene dioica
Lychnis githago	Agrostemma githago
Lycium chinense	Lycium barbarum
Lycium malimifolium	Lycium barbarum
Lycium vulgare	Lycium barbarum
Machilus	Persea
Machilus ichangensis	Persea ichangensis
Maclura aurantiaca	Maclura pomifera
Macrodiervilla middendorffiana	Weigela middendorffiana
Macropiper crocatum	Piper ornatum
Macroplectrum sesquipedale	Angraecum sesquipedale
Magnolia conspicua	Magnolia denudata
Magnolia glauca	Magnolia virginiana
Magnolia heptapeta	Magnolia denudata
Magnolia hypoleuca	Magnolia obovata
Magnolia insignis	Manglietia insignis
Magnolia nicholsoniana	Magnolia wilsonii
Magnolia parviflora	Magnolia sieboldii
Magnolia quinquepeta	Magnolia liliiflora
Mahoberberis illicifolia	Mahoberberis neubertii
Mahonia eutriphylla	Mahonia trifolia
Mahonia fascicularis	Mahonia x wagneri 'Pinnacle'
Mahonia schiedeana	Mahonia trifolia
Mahonia toluacensis	Mahonia aquifolium 'Heterophylla'
Mahonica aquifolium 'Moseri'	Mahonia x wagneri 'Woseri'
Malus 'Kaido'	Malus x micromalus
Malus sieboldii	Malus toringo
Malus theifera	Malus hupehensis
Malva bicolor	Lavatera maritima
Malvastrum capensis	Anisodontea capensis
Malvastrum hypomadarum	Anisodontea hypomadarum
Manetta bicolor	Manetta inflata
Marasmiellus ramealis	Marasmius ramealis
Marasmius dryophilus	Collybia dryophila
Marasmius foetidus	Micromphale foetidum
Marasmius perforans	Micromphale perforans
Marasmius peronatus	Collybia peronata
Marginatocereus marginatus	Lemaireocereus marginatus
Margyricarpus setosus	Margyricarpus pinnatus
Marsdenia erecta	Cionura erecta
Martynia louisiana	Martynia annua
Mascarena	Hyophorba
Matricaria chamomilla	Matricaria recutita

Know Your Common Plant Names

Historical Pseudonyms	Most Recent Accepted Naming
Matricaria eximia	Tanacetum parthenium
Maurandya	Asarina
Maytenus chilensis	Maytenus boaria
Meconopsis baileyi	Meconopsis betonicifolia
Meconopsis wallichii	Meconopsis napaulensis
Medicago maculata	Medicago arabica
Megasea	Bergenia
Melandrium elisabethae	Silene elisabethae
Melandrium noctiflorum	Silene noctiflora
Melandrium rubrum	Silene dioica
Melica montana	Melica nutans
Melilotus arvensis	Melilotus officinalis
Melilotus officinalis	Melilotus altissima
Meliosma pendens	Meliosma dillenifolia flexuosa
Mentha citrata	Mentha x gentilis
Mentha 'Eau de Cologne'	Mentha x piperita citrata
Mentha x rotundifolia 'Variegata'	Mentha suaveolens 'Variegata'
Menziesia alba	Daboecia cantabrica alba
Menziesia polifolia	Daboecia cantabrica
Merendera bulbocodium	Merendera montana
Mertensia virginica	Mertensia pulmonarioides
Mesembryanthemum 'Basutoland'	Delosperma nubigenum
Mesembryanthemum brownii	Lampranthus brownii
Mesembryanthemum criniflorum	Dorotheanthus bellidiformis
Mesembryanthemum ornatalum	Delosperma ornatalum
Metrosideros lucida	Metrosideros umbellata
Metrosideros tomentosa	Metrosideros excelsa
Michelia excelsa	Michelia doltsopa
Microglossa albescens	Aster albescens
Micromeria corsica	Acinos corsicus
Mimulus glutinosus	Mimulus aurantiacus
Mimulus langsdorfii	Mimulus guttatus
Minuartia verna aurea	Sagina subulata 'Aurea'
Modiolastrum	Malvastrum
Molinia altissima	Molinia caerulea arundinacea
Montbretia	Crocosmia
Montia australasica	Neopaxia australasica
Montia parvifolia	Claytonia parvifolia
Montia perfoliata	Claytonia perfoliata
Montia sibirica	Claytonia sibirica
Moraea iridioides	Dietes iridioides
Morisia hypogaea	Morisia monanthos
Morus papyrifera	Broussonetia papyrifera
Muehlenbeckia complexa 'Nana'	Muehlenbeckia axillaris
Mucidula mucida	Oudemansiella mucida
Musa ensete	Ensete ventricosum
Muscari moschatum	Muscari muscarimi

Know Your Common Plant Names

Historical Pseudonyms	Most Recent Accepted Naming
Muscari pallens	Muscari armeniacum
Muscari racemosum	Muscari neglectum
Muscari tubergenianum	Muscari aucheri
Muscarimia macrocarpum	Muscari macrocarpum
Myoporum perforatum	Myoporum laetum
Myosotis rupicola	Myosotis alpestris
Myosotis scorpioides	Myosotis palustris
Myrica carolinensis	Myricacerifera
Myriophyllum proserpinacoides	Myriophyllum aquaticum
Myrtus apiculata	Luma apiculata
Myrtus bullata	Lophomyrtus bullata
Myrtus chequen	Luma chequen
Myrtus communis 'Jenny Reitenbach'	Myrtus communis tarentina
Myrtus lechleriana	Myrceugenia exserta
Myrtus luma	Luma apiculata
Myrtus nummularia	Myrteola nummularia
Myrtus obcordata	Lophomyrtus obcordata
Myrtus 'Traversii'	Lophomyrtus 'Traversii'
Myrtus ugni	Ugni molinae
Myrtus x ralphii	Lophomyrtus x ralphii
Myxocybe radicosum	Hebeloma radicosa
Naegelia cinnabarina	Smithiantha cinnabarina
Naegelia zebrina	Smithiantha zebrina
Naematoloma fasciculare	Hypholoma fasciculare
Narcissus lobularis	Narcissus pseudonarcissus 'Lobularis'
Narcissus 'Old Pheasant's Eye'	Narcissus poeticus recurvus
Narcissus triandus albus	Narcissus triandus triandus
Nasturtium amphibium	Rorippa amphibia
Nasturtium palustre	Rorippa palustris
Neanthe bella	Chamaedorea elegans
Neillia longiracemosa	Neillia thibetica
Neillia opulifolia	Physocarpus opulifolius
Nematanthus radicans	Nematanthus gregarius
Nemesia foetens	Nemesia fruticans
Nemophila insignis	Nemophila menziesii
Nepeta glechoma	Glechoma hederacea
Nepeta hederacea	Glechoma hederacea
Nephthytis	Syngonium
Nephthytis triphylla	Syngonium podophyllum
Nerine crispa	Nerine undulata
Nicodemia	Buddleia
Nicotiana affinis	Nicotiana alata
Nidularium flandria	Neoregelia carolinae 'Flandria'
Nierembergia rivularis	Nierembergia repens
Nolina recurvata	Beaucarnea recurvata
Nolina tuberculata	Beaucarnea recurvata
Nomocharis mairei	Nomocharis pardanthina

Know Your Common Plant Names

Historical Pseudonyms

Most Recent Accepted Naming

Historical Pseudonyms	Most Recent Accepted Naming
Nothofagus procera	NNothofagus nervosum
Nothopanax davidii	Pseudopanax davidii
Nuttallia cerasiformis	Oemleria cerasiformis
Nyssa multiflora	Nyssa sylvatica
Oakesiella sessilifolia	Uvularia sessilifolia
Ochna multiflora	Ochna serrulata
Oenothera glaber	Oenothera biennis
Oenothera macrocarpa	Oenothera missouriensis
Oenothera pumila	Oenothera perennis
Oenothera taraxacifolia	Oenothera acaulis
Olea excelsa	Notelaea excelsa
Olea excelsa	Picconia excelsa
Olea fragrans	Osmanthus fragrans
Olearia dentata	Olearia macrodonta
Olearia gunniana	Olearia phlogopappa
Olearia subrepanda	Olearia phlogopappa subrepanda
Olearia x scilloniensis	Olearia stellulata
Onixotis	Dipidax
Onobrychis sativa	Onobrychis viciifolia
Ononis campestris	Ononis spinosa
Onopordon	Onopordum
Onopordum arabicum	Onopordum nervosum
Ophiopogon 'Black Dragon'	Ophiopogon planiscapus nigrescens
Ophiopogon graminifolius	Liriope muscari
Ophrys aranifera	Ophrys sphegodes
Ophrys fuciflora	Ophrys holoserica
Ophrys speculum	Ophrys vernixia
Orchis foliosa	Dactylorhiza foliosa
Orchis hircina	Himantoglossum hircinum
Orchis maculata	Dactylorhiza maculata
Orchis maderensis	Dactylorhiza foliosa
Orchis majalis	Dactylorhiza majalis
Orchis musifera	Orchis insectifera
Orchis pyramidalis	Anacamptis pyramidalis
Oreocereus celsianus	Borzicactus celsianus
Ornithogallum oligophyllum	Ornithogallum balansae
Orobus luteus	Lathyrus luteus
Orobus niger	Lathyrus niger
Orobus tuberosus	Lathyrus montanus
Orphanidesia gaultherioides	Epigaea gaultherioides
Oscularia	Lampranthus
Osmanthus aquifolium	Osmanthus heterophyllus
Osmanthus aquifolius	Osmanthus heterophyllus
Osmanthus forrestii	Osmanthus yunnanensis
Osmanthus illicifolius	Osmanthus heterophyllus
Osmarea burkwoodii	Osmanthus x burkwoodii
Osmaronia cerasiformis	Oemleria cerasiformis

Know Your Common Plant Names

Historical Pseudonyms	Most Recent Accepted Naming
Osteospermum barberae	Osteospermum jucundum
Ostrya vulgaris	Ostryacarpinifolia
Othonnopsis	Othonna
Oxalis cernua	Oxalis pes-caprae
Oxalis deppei	Oxalis tetraphylla
Oxalis depressa	Oxalis inops
Oxalis inops	Oxalis depressa
Oxalis speciosa	Oxalis purpurea
Oxycoccus macrocarpus	Vaccinium macrocarpon
Oxycoccus palustris	Vaccinium oxycoccos
Oxypetalum caeruleum	Tweedia caerulea
Ozothamnus	Helichrysum
Pachistima	Paxistima
Paeonia albiflora	Paeonia lactiflora
Paeonia arborea	Paeonia suffruticosa
Paeonia lutea	Paeonia delavayi lutea
Paeonia lutea ludlowii	Paeonia delavayi ludlowii
Paeonia moutan	Paeonia suffruticosa
Paliurus aculeatus	Paliurus spina-christi
Panax arboreum	Pseudopanax arboreus
Pandorea ricasoliana	Podranea ricasoliana
Panicum variegatum	Oplismenus hirtellus 'Variegatus'
Panicum viride	Setaria viridis
Panus tigrinus	Lentinus tigrinus
Parabenzoin	Lindera
Parasyringa sempervirens	Ligustrum sempervirens
Parietaria officinalis	Parietaria judaica
Paulownia imperialis	Paulownia tomentosa
Pellionia repens	Pellioniadaveauana
Peltandra virginica	Peltandra undulata
Peltiphyllum peltatum	Darmera peltata
Pennisetum compressum	Pennisetum alopecuroides
Pennisetum longistylum	Pennisetum villosum
Pennisetum ruppellii	Pennisetum setaceum
Penstemon arizonicus	Penstemon whippleanus
Penstemon caeruleus	Penstemon angustifolius
Penstemon cristatus	Penstemon erianthorus
Penstemon diffusus	Penstemon serrulatus
Penstemon fendleri	Penstemon nitidus
Penstemon pulchellus	Penstemon campanulatus
Penstemon scouleri	Penstemon fruticosus scouleri
Pentas carnea	Pentas lanceolata
Peperomia hederifolia	Peperomia griseo-argentea
Peperomia pulchella	Peperomia verticilliata
Peperomia resediflora	Peperomia fraseri
Peperomia sandersii	Peperomia argyreia
Peperomia serpens	Peperomia scandens

Know Your Common Plant Names

Historical Pseudonyms	Most Recent Accepted Naming
Peperomia tithymaloides	Peperomia magnoliifolia
Perilla nankinensis	Perilla frutescens
Pernettya	Gaultheria
Phaedranthus buccinatorius	Distictis buccinatoria
Pharbitis	Ipomoea
Philesia buxifolia	Philesia magellanica
Phillyrea decora	Osmanthus decorus
Phillyrea media	Phillyrea latifolia
Philodendron andreanum	Philodendron melanochrysum
Philodendron elegans	Philodendron angustisectum
Philodendron epipremnum	Epipremnum pinnatum
Philodendron laciniatum	Philodendron pedatum
Philodendron panduriforma	Philodendron bipennifolium
Philodendron sodiroi	Philodendron ornatum
Phleum nodosum	Phleum bertolonii
Phlomis samia	Phlomis russeliana
Phlomis viscosa	Phlomis russeliana
Phlox amoena	Phlox x procumbens
Pholiota cylindracea	Agrocybe cylindracea
Pholiota mutabilis	Galerina mutabilis
Phormium colensoi	Phormium cookianum
Photina glabra 'Pink Lady'	Photina glabra 'Parfait'
Photinia arbutifolia	Heteromeles arbutifolia
Photinia glabra 'Roseamarginata'	Photina glabra 'Parfait'
Photinia glabra 'Variegata'	Photina glabra 'Parfait'
Phragmites communis	Phragmites australis
Phygelius aequalis alba	Phygelius aequalis 'Yellow Trumpet'
Phygelius aequalis 'Aureus'	Phygelius aequalis 'Yellow Trumpet'
Phygelius aequalis 'Cream Trumpet'	Phygelius aequalls 'Yellow Trumpet'
Phyllanthus nivosus	Breynia disticha
Phyllodoce taxifolia	Phyllodoce coerulea
Phyteuma comosum	Physoplexis comosa
Phytolacca clarigera	Phytolacca polyandra
Phytolacca decandra	Phytolacca americana
Picea excelsa	Picea abies
Picrasma ailanthoides	Picrasma quassioides
Pieris nana	Arcterica nana
Pilosella aurantiaca	Hieracium aurantiacum
Pinus austriaca	Pinus nigra nigra
Pinus excelsa	Pinus wallichiana
Pinus griffithii	Pinus wallichiana
Pinus leucodermis	Pinus heldreichii leucodermis
Pinus montana	Pinus mugo
Pinus mughus	Pinus mugo
Pinus nigra laricio	Pinus nigra maritima
Piptanthus laburnifolius	Piptanthus nepalensis
Pittosporum nigricans	Pittosporum tenuifolium

Know Your Common Plant Names

Historical Pseudonyms	Most Recent Accepted Naming
Plagianthus lyallii	Hoheria lyallii
Plagiorhegma dubia	Jeffersonia dubia
Platanus x hispanica	Platanus x acerifolia
Platycerium albicorne	Platycerium bifurcatum
Platycerium grande	Platycerium suberbum
Pleioblastus viridistriatus	Pleioblastus auricoma
Pleomele reflexa	Dracaena reflexa
Plumbago capensis	Plumbago auriculata
Plumbago larpentae	Ceratostigma plumbaginoides
Plumbago rosea	Plumbago indica
Podocarpus andinus	Prumnopitys andina
Podocarpus chilinus	Prumnopitys salignus
Podocarpus dacrydioides	Dacrycarpus dacrydioides
Podocarpus ferrugineus	Prumnopitys ferruginea
Podocarpus spicatus	Prumnopitys taxifolia
Podophyllum emodi	Podophyllum hexandrum
Podophyllum hexandurm	Podophyllum emodi
Poinciana gilliesii	Caesalpinia gilliesii
Poinsettia	Euphorbia pulcherrima
Polygonatum commutatum	Polygonatum biflorum
Polygonatum giganteum	Polygonatum biflorum
Polygonatum latifolium	Polygonatum hirtum
Polygonatum multiflorum	Polygonatum x hybridum
Polygonatum officinale	Polygonatum odoratum
Polygonatum pumilum	Polygonatum falcatum
Polygonum affinis	Persicaria affinis
Polygonum amplexicaulis	Persicaria amplexicaulis
Polygonum aubertii	Fallopia baldschuanica
Polygonum baldschuanicum	Fallopia baldschuanica
Polygonum bistorta	Persicaria bistorta
Polygonum campanulata	Persicaria campanulatum
Polygonum cuspidatum	Fallopia japonica
Polygonum emodi	Persicaria emodi
Polygonum milletii	Persicaria milletii
Polygonum polystachyum	Persicaria wallichii
Polygonum reynoutria	Fallopia japonica compacta
Polygonum virginiana	Persicaria virginiana
Polypodium aureum	Phlebodium aureum
Populus alba bolleana	Populus alba 'Pyramidalis'
Populus nigra 'Pyramidalis'	Populus nigraitalica
Populus tacamahaca	Populus balsamifera
Populus 'Van Geertii'	Populus 'Serotina Aurea'
Populus x canadensis	Populus x euroamerica
Potamogeton flabellatus	Potamogeton pectinatus
Potamogeton heterophyllus	Potamogeton gramineus
Potamogeton oblongus	Potamogeton polygonifolius
Potamogeton panormitanus	Potamogeton pusillus

Know Your Common Plant Names

Historical Pseudonyms	Most Recent Accepted Naming
Potamogeton rufescens	Potamogeton alpinus
Potamogeton zosteraefolius	Potamogeton compressus
Potentilla ambigua	Potentilla cuneata
Potentilla 'Arbuscula'	Potentilla 'Elizabeth'
Potentilla fragiformis	Potentilla megalantha
Potentilla 'Maanelys'	Potentilla 'Moonlight'
Potentilla Mandschurica	Potentilla 'Manchu'
Potentilla 'Sandvedana'	Potentilla 'Sandved'
Potentilla ternata	Potentilla aurea chrysocraspeda
Potentilla tommasiniana	Potentilla cinerea
Potentilla tormentilla	Potentilla erecta
Potentilla verna	Potentilla tabernaemontani
Potentilla villosa	Potentilla crantzii
Poterium	Sanguisorba
Poterium sanguisorba	Sanguisorba minor
Prinos verticilliata	Ilex verticilliata
Prostranthera sieberi	Prostrantheramelissifolia parvifolia
Protea mellifera	Protearepens
Prunella incisa	Prunella vulgaris
Prunus amygdalus	Prunus dulcis
Prunus 'Benifugen'	Prunus 'Fugenzo'
Prunus 'Cheal's Weeping'	Prunus Kiku Shidare Zakura'
Prunus communis	Prunus dulcis
Prunus domestica institia	Prunus institia
Prunus 'Kojima'	Prunus 'Shirotae'
Prunus 'Korean Hill'	Prunus serrulata pubescens
Prunus laurocerasus 'Marbled White'	Prunus laurocerasus'Castlewellan'
Prunus laurocerasus 'Variegata'	Prunus laurocerasus'Castlewellan'
Prunus mandshurica	Prunus armeniaca mandshurica
Prunus 'Mount Fuji'	Prunus'Shirotae'
Prunus mume 'Beni-shidon'	Prunus mume 'Beni-shidare'
Prunus 'Okumiyako'	Prunus Shogetsu'
Prunus padus grandiflora	Prunus padus'Watereri'
Prunus pissardii	Prunuscerasifera 'Pissardii'
Prunus 'Pissardii Nigra'	Prunus cerasifera 'Nigra'
Prunus 'Sekiyama'	Prunus 'Kanzan'
Prunus serrulata albida	Prunus 'Shirotae'
Prunus serrulata 'Erecta'	Prunus 'Amanogawa'
Prunus serrulata grandiflora	Prunus'Ukon'
Prunus serrulata 'Grandiflora'	Prunus 'Ukon'
Prunus serrulata 'Longipes'	Prunus 'Shogetsu'
Prunus serrulata tricolor	Prunus' Gioiko'
Prunus 'Shimidsu-Zakura'	Prunus 'Shogetsu'
Prunus spinosa 'Rosea'	Prunus cerasifera 'Rosea'
Prunus tibetica	Prunus serrula
Prunus triloba multiplex	Prunus triloba
Prunus x yedoensis 'Perpendens'	Prunus x yeodensis 'Shidara-Yoshino'

Know Your Common Plant Names

Historical Pseudonyms	Most Recent Accepted Naming
Prunus x yeodensis pendula	Prunus x yeodensis 'Shidare-Yoshino'
Psalliota arvensis	Agaricus arvensis
Psalliota campestris	Agaricus campestris
Psalliota silvicola	Agaricus silvicola
Pseudolarix fortunei	Pseudolarix kaempferi
Pseudomuscari azureum	Muscari azureum
Pseudotsuga taxifolia	Pseudotsuga menziesii
Pterocephalus parnassi	Pterocephalus perennis perennis
Pueraria thunbergiana	Pueraria lobata
Pulmonaria 'Highdown'	Pulmonaria 'Lewis Palmer'
Puschkinia libanotica	Puschkiniascilloides
Pyracantha gibbsii	Pyracantha atalantioides
Pyracantha 'Golden Sun'	Pyracantha 'Soleil d'Or'
Pyracantha 'Orange Giant'	Pyracantha 'Kazan'
Pyrethrum	Tanacetum
Pyrethrum roseum	Tanacetum ptarmiciflorum
Pyrus malus	Malus
Pyrus pyraster	Pyrus communis
Quamoclit coccinea	Ipomoea coccinea
Quamoclit lobata	Mina lobata
Quamoclit pinnata	Ipomoea quamoclit
Quercus aegilops	Quercus ithaburensis macrolepis
Quercus aquatica	Quercus nigra
Quercus bambusifolia	Quercus myrsinifolia
Quercus borealis	Quercus rubra
Quercus conferta	Quercus frainetto
Quercus densiflora	Lithocarpus densiflorus
Quercus glabra	Lithocarpus glabra
Quercus henryi	Lithocarpus henryi
Quercus lusitanica	Quercus fruticosa
Quercus macedonica	Quercus trojana
Quercus mirbeckii	Quercus canariensis
Quercus pedunculata	Q.Quercus
Quercus robur 'Filicifolia'	Quercus x rosacea 'Filicifolia'
Quercus serrata	Quercus acutissima
Quercus sessilifolia	Quercus petraea
Quercus tinctoria	Quercus velutina
Quercus toza	Quercus pyrenaica
Quercus vibrayeana	Quercus myrsinifolia
Ramonda pyrenaica	Ramonda myconi
Ranunculus heterophyllus	Ranunculus aquatilis
Ranunculus speciosus 'Flora Plena'	Ranunculus constantinopolitanus 'Plenus'
Raoulia lutescens	Raoulia australis
Raoulia x loganii	x Leucoraoulia loganii
Raphiolepis japonica	Raphiolepis umbellata
Rehmannia angulata	Rehmannia elata
Reinwardtia trigyna	Reinwardtia indica

Know Your Common Plant Names

Historical Pseudonyms	Most Recent Accepted Naming
Reynoutria	Fallopia
Rhamnus alaternus 'Variegata'	Rhamnus alaternus 'Argenteovariegata'
Rhaphithamnus cyanocarpus	Rhaphithamnus spinosus
Rheum palmatum 'Atropurpureum'	Rheum palmatum 'Atrosanguineum'
Rhinanthus major	Rhinanthus serotinus
Rhipsalis clavata	Hatiora clavata
Rhodanthe manglesii	Helipterum manglesii
Rhodocactus grandifolius	Pereskia grandifolia
Rhodochiton volubile	Rhodochiton atrosanguineum
Rhododendron argenteum	Rhododendron grande
Rhododendron californicum	Rhododendron macrophyllum
Rhododendron cantabile	Rhododendron russatum
Rhododendron charidotes	Rhododendron chameunum
Rhododendron croceum	Rhododendron wardii
Rhododendron cyclium	Rhododendron callimorphum
Rhododendron deleiense	Rhododendron tethropeplum
Rhododendron kingianum	Rhododendron zeylanicum
Rhododendron ledoides	Rhododendron trichostomum
Rhododendron muliense	Rhododendron chryseum
Rhododendron muliense	Rhododendron chryseum
Rhododendron niphargum	Rhododendron uvariifolium
Rhododendron obovatum	Rhododendron lepidotum
Rhododendron pentamerum	Rhododendron degronianum
Rhododendron primulinum	Rhododendron flavidum
Rhododendron riparium	Rhododendron calostrotum
Rhododendron silvaticum	Rhododendron lanigerum
Rhododendron sphaeranthum	Rhododendron trichostomum
Rhododendron tsusiophyllum	Tsusiophyllum tanakae
Rhododendron villosum	Rhododendron tricanthum
Rhodora canadensis	Rhododendron canadense
Rhodostachys bicolor	Fascicularia bicolor
Rhodotypos kerrioides	Rhodotypos scandens
Rhoeo	Tradescantia
Rhoicissus rhomboidea	Cissus rhombifolia
Rhus canadensis	Rhus aromatica
Rhus cotinoides	Cotinus obovatus
Rhus cotinus	Cotinus coggygria
Rhus javanica	Rhus chinensis
Rhus osbeckii	Rhus chinensis
Rhus toxicodendron	Rhus radicans
Rhus x hybrida	Rhus x pulvinata
Rhynchelytrum roseum	Rhynchelytrum repens
Rhyncospermum jasminoides	Trachelospermum jasminoides
Ribes aureum	Ribes odoratum
Ribes fuchsioides	Ribes speciosum
Ribes grossularia	Ribes uva-crispa
Robinia glutinosa	Robinia viscosa

Know Your Common Plant Names

Historical Pseudonyms	Most Recent Accepted Naming
Robinia pseudoacacia 'Fastigiata'	Robinia pseudoacacia 'Pyramidalis'
Robinia pseudoacacia 'Inermis'	Robinia pseudoacacia 'Umbraculifera'
Rochea	Crassula
Rodgersia tabularis	Astilboides tabularis
Romneya x hybrida 'White Cloud'	Romneya coulteri 'White Cloud'
Rooksbya euphorbioides	Lemaireocactus euphorbioides
Rorippa nasturtium-aquaticum	Nasturtium officinale
Rosa 'Alfred de Dalmas'	Rose 'Mousselline'
Rosa alpina	Rosa pendulina
Rosa 'Amelia'	Rosa 'Celsiana'
Rosa anemonoides	Rosa 'Anemone'
Rosa anemonoides ramona	Rosa 'Ramona'
Rosa 'Apothecary's Rose'	Rosa gallica officinalis
Rosa 'Auscot'	Rosa 'Abraham Darby'
Rosa 'Ausmary'	Rosa 'Mary Rose'
Rosa 'Ausmas'	Rosa 'Graham Thomas'
Rosa 'Ausroyal'	Rosa 'WIlliam Shakespeare'
Rosa 'Austrian Copper'	Rosa foetida 'Bicolor'
Rosa 'Austrian Yellow'	Rosa foetida
Rosa 'Autumn Fire'	Rosa 'Herbstfeuer'
Rosa 'Baby Crimson'	Rosa 'Perle d'Alcanada
Rosa 'Bad Nauheim'	Rosa 'National Trust'
Rosa 'Belle de Londres'	Rosa 'Compassion'
Rosa 'Belle des Jardins'	Rosa centifolia 'Variegata'
Rosa 'Bluenette'	Rosa 'Blue Peter'
Rosa 'Bouquet de la Mariee'	Rosa 'Aimee Vibert'
Rosa californica 'Plena'	Rosa nutkana 'Plena'
Rosa 'Canary Bird'	Rosa xanthina spontanea 'Canary Bird'
Rosa canina 'Abbotswood'	Rosa 'Abbotswood'
Rosa canina 'Andersonii'	Rosa 'Andersonii'
Rosa 'Chapeau de Napolean'	Rosa centifolia 'Cristata'
Rosa chinensis 'Mutabilis'	Rosa x odorata 'Mutabilis'
Rosa cinnamomea	Rosa majalis
Rosa 'Cocdestin'	Rosa 'Remember Me'
Rosa 'Coeur D'Amour'	Rosa 'Red Devil'
Rosa 'Common Moss'	Rosa x centifolia 'Muscosa'
Rosa 'Cottage Maid'	Rosa centifolia 'Variegata'
Rosa 'Crested Moss'	Rosa centifolia 'Cristata'
Rosa 'Cuisse de Nymphe'	Rosa 'Great Maiden's Blush'
Rosa 'Daily Mail'	Rosa 'Madame Edouard Herriot'
Rosa 'Dicbar'	Rosa 'Memento'
Rosa 'Dicdance'	Rosa 'Bright Smile'
Rosa 'Dicdivine'	Rosa 'Pot O' Gold'
Rosa 'Dicfire'	Rosa 'Beautiful Britain'
Rosa 'Dicgrow'	Rosa 'Peek A Boo'
Rosa 'Dicinfra'	Rosa 'Disco Dancer'
Rosa 'Dicjana'	Rosa 'Peaudouce'

Know Your Common Plant Names

Historical Pseudonyms	Most Recent Accepted Naming
Rosa 'Dicjeep'	Rosa 'Lou Turner'
Rosa 'Dicjem'	Rosa 'Freedom'
Rosa 'Dicjubell'	Rosa 'Lovely Lady'
Rosa 'Dickerfuffle'	Rosa 'Wishing'
Rosa 'Dickooky'	Rosa 'Tall Story'
Rosa 'Diclittle'	Rosa 'Little Women'
Rosa 'Diclulu'	Rosa 'Gentle Touch'
Rosa 'Dicmagic'	Rosa 'Sweet Magic'
Rosa 'Dicmicky'	Rosa 'Buttons'
Rosa 'Duftwolke'	Rosa 'Fragrant Cloud'
Rosa 'Duftzauber '84'	Rosa 'Royal William'
Rosa 'Empress Josephine'	Rosa x francofurtana
Rosa 'Estrellita de Oro'	Rosa 'Baby Gold Star'
Rosa 'Etendard'	Rosa 'Red New Dawn'
Rosa fargesii	Rosa moyesii 'Fargesii'
Rosa farreri	Rosa elegantula
Rosa farreri persetosa	Rosa elegantula 'Persetosa'
Rosa 'Flaming Peace'	Rosa 'Kronenbourg'
Rosa 'Flower Girl'	Rosa 'Sea Pearl'
Rosa 'For You'	Rosa 'Para Ti'
Rosa 'Frau Dagmar Hartopp'	Rosa 'Fru Dagmar Hastrup'
Rosa 'Frau Dagmar Hastrup'	Rosa "Fru Dagmar Hastrup'
Rosa 'Freisia'	Rosa 'Korresia'
Rosa 'Frohsinn'	Rosa 'Joyfulness'
Rosa 'Frygran'	Rosa 'Johnnie Walker'
Rosa 'Fryjasso'	Rosa 'Inner Wheel'
Rosa 'Gipsy Boy'	Rosa 'Ziguenerknabe'
Rosa 'Golden Rambler'	Rosa 'Alister Stella Gray'
Rosa 'Golden Scepter'	Rosa 'Spek's Yellow'
Rosa 'Golden Wave'	Rosa 'Dr. A.J. Verhage'
Rosa 'Harcomp'	Rosa 'Highfield'
Rosa 'Harkaramel'	Rosa 'Anne Harkness'
Rosa 'Harlaylong'	Rosa 'Fairyland'
Rosa 'Harlightly'	Rosa 'Princess Michael of Kent'
Rosa 'Harmantelle'	Rosa 'Mountbatten'
Rosa 'Harprocrustes'	Rosa 'Clarissa'
Rosa 'Harquanna'	Rosa 'Breath of Life'
Rosa 'Harqueterwife'	Rosa 'Paul Shirville;
Rosa 'Harregale'	Rosa 'Cardinal Hume'
Rosa 'Harrison's Yellow'	Rosa x harisonii
Rosa 'Harroony'	Rosa 'Amber Queen'
Rosa 'Harrowbond'	Rosa 'Rosemary Harkness'
Rosa 'Harsherry'	Rosa 'Sheila's Perfume'
Rosa 'Hartanna'	Rosa 'Princess Alice'
Rosa 'Haruseful'	Rosa 'Armada'
Rosa 'Harwanna'	Rosa 'Jacqueline du Pre'
Rosa holodonta	Rosa moyesii rosea

Know Your Common Plant Names

Historical Pseudonyms	Most Recent Accepted Naming
Rosa horrida	Rosa biebersteinii
Rosa 'Interall'	Rosa 'Rosy Cushion'
Rosa 'Intercell'	Rosa 'Red Blanket'
Rosa 'Interfour'	Rosa 'Petit Four'
Rosa 'Interrob'	Rosa 'Robin Redbreast'
Rosa 'Intersmart'	Rosa 'Smarty'
Rosa 'Irish Beauty'	Rosa 'Elizabeth of Glamis'
Rosa 'Irish Gold'	Rosa 'Grandpa Dickson'
Rosa 'Irish Wonder'	Rosa "Evelyn Fison"
Rosa 'Isle of Man'	Rosa 'Manx Queen'
Rosa 'Josephine Wheatcroft'	Rosa 'Rosina'
Rosa 'Julia's Rose'	Rosa 'Julia'
Rosa 'Kazanlik'	Rosa damascena 'Trigintipetala'
Rosa 'Kiftsgate'	Rosa filipes 'Kiftsgate'
Rosa 'Konigen der Rosen'	Rosa 'Colour Wonder'
Rosa 'Korbelma'	Rosa 'Simba'
Rosa 'Korblue'	Rosa 'Shocking Blue'
Rosa 'Kordapt'	Rosa 'Pheasant'
Rosa 'Korgund'	Rosa 'Loving Memory'
Rosa 'Korimro'	Rosa 'Grouse'
Rosa 'Korlech'	Rosa 'Intrigue'
Rosa 'Korlift'	Rosa 'Congratulations'
Rosa 'Kormalda'	Rosa 'Keepsake'
Rosa 'Korpean'	Rosa 'The Times Rose'
Rosa 'Korred'	Rosa 'Ace of Hearts'
Rosa 'Korweiso'	Rosa 'Hannah Gordon'
Rosa 'Korwierien'	Rosa 'Partridge'
Rosa 'Korzuan'	Rosa 'Royal William'
Rosa 'La Reine Victoria'	Rosa 'Reine Victoria'
Rosa 'Lanken'	Rosa 'Felicity Kendal'
Rosa 'Leggab'	Rosa 'Pearl Drift'
Rosa lucida	Rosa virginiana
Rosa 'Maccarpe'	Rosa 'Snow Carpet'
Rosa 'Macfreego'	Rosa 'Penelope Keith'
Rosa 'Macgem'	Rosa 'Benson and Hedges Gold'
Rosa 'Macrat'	Rosa 'Priscilla Burton'
Rosa 'Macrexy'	Rosa 'Sexy Rexy'
Rosa 'Macshana'	Rosa 'Benson and Hedges Special'
Rosa 'Macspash'	Rosa 'Sue Lawley'
Rosa 'Mactru'	Rosa 'Trumpeter'
Rosa 'Macyou'	Rosa 'Regensberg'
Rosa 'Mainzer Fastnacht'	Rosa 'Blue Moon'
Rosa 'Marquisa Boccella'	Rosa 'Jacques Cartier'
Rosa 'Max Graf'	Rosa x jacksonii 'Max Graf'
Rosa 'Megalii'	Rosa 'Starina'
Rosa 'Meibeluxen'	Rosa 'Fiona'
Rosa 'Meiblam'	Rosa 'Yorkshire Sunblaze'

Know Your Common Plant Names

Historical Pseudonyms	Most Recent Accepted Naming
Rosa 'Meiburenae'	Rosa 'Swany'
Rosa 'Meidanover'	Rosa 'Colibre 79'
Rosa 'Meidomoncae'	Rosa 'Bonica'
Rosa 'Meigekanu'	Rosa 'La Sevillana'
Rosa 'Meijidiro'	Rosa 'Pink Sunblaze'
Rosa 'Meijiktar'	Rosa 'Orange Sunblaze'
Rosa 'Meillucca'	Rosa 'Darling Flame'
Rosa 'Meinatac'	Rosa 'Susan Hampshire'
Rosa 'Meiranovi'	Rosa 'Candy Rose'
Rosa 'Meitrisical'	Rosa 'Yellow Sunblaze'
Rosa microphylla	Rosa roxburghii
Rosa 'Mme A. Meilland'	Rosa 'Peace'
Rosa 'Mme Hebert'	Rosa 'President de Seze'
Rosa multiflora watsoniana	Rosa watsoniana
Rosa mundi	Rosa gallica 'Versicolor'
Rosa namothamnus	Rosa webbiana microphylla
Rosa 'Ocarina'	Rosa 'Angela Rippon'
Rosa 'Ocaru'	Rosa 'Angela Rippon'
Rosa 'Old Pink Moss'	Rosa centifolia 'Muscosa'
Rosa omeiensis pteracantha	Rosa sericea pteracantha
Rosa 'Opa Potschke'	Rosa 'Precious Platinum'
Rosa 'Peahaze'	Rosa 'Geraldine'
Rosa 'Peamight'	Rosa 'Leaping Salmon'
Rosa 'Persian Yellow'	Rosa foetida 'Persiana'
Rosa 'Pink Nevada'	Rosa 'Marguerite Hilling'
Rosa polyantha	Rosa multiflora
Rosa polygantha grandiflora	Rosa gentiliana
Rosa pomifera	Rosa villosa
Rosa pomifera 'Duplex'	Rosa 'Wolley-Dod'
Rosa 'Poulbells'	Rosa 'Pink Bells'
Rosa 'Poulman'	Rosa 'Ingrid Bergman'
Rosa 'Poulred'	Rosa 'Red Bells'
Rosa 'Poulwhite'	Rosa 'White Bells'
Rosa 'Pour Toi'	Rosa 'Para Ti'
Rosa 'Prolifera de Redoute'	Rosa 'Duchesse de Montebello'
Rosa 'Prominent'	Rosa 'Korp'
Rosa 'Quatre Saisons'	Rosa x damasceona semperflorens
Rosa 'Queen of Denmark'	Rosa 'Konigin Von Danemark'
Rosa 'Red Grootendorst'	Rosa 'F.J. Grootendorst'
Rosa 'Red Star'	Rosa 'Precious Platinum'
Rosa 'Rouge Eblouissante'	Rosa 'Assemblage des Beautes'
Rosa 'Royal Dane'	Rosa 'Troika'
Rosa rubiginosa	Rosa eglanteria
Rosa rubra	Rosa gallica
Rosa rubrifolia	Rosa glauca
Rosa 'Rubrotincta'	Rosa 'Hebe's Lip'
Rosa 'Ruiblun'	Rosa 'Blue Peter'

Know Your Common Plant Names

Historical Pseudonyms	Most Recent Accepted Naming
Rosa 'Saint Mark's rose'	Rosa 'Rose d'Amour'
Rosa sancta	Rosa richardii
Rosa 'Scarlet Fire'	Rosa 'Scharlachglut'
Rosa 'Scarlet Pimpernel'	Rosa 'Scarlet Gem'
Rosa 'Schneewittchen'	Rosa 'Iceberg'
Rosa 'Schwanensee'	Rosa 'Swan Lake'
Rosa 'Seven Sisters Rose'	Rosa multiflora 'Grevillei'
Rosa 'Skyrocket'	Rosa Wilhelm
Rosa 'Snow Queen'	Rosa 'Frau Karl Druschki'
Rosa 'Sonia'	Rosa 'Sweet Promise'
Rosa 'Sonia Meilland'	Rosa 'Sweet Promise'
Rosa 'Spanish Beauty'	Rosa 'Mme Gregoire Staechlin'
Rosa spinosissima	Rosa pimpinellifolia
Rosa 'Susan Ann'	Rosa 'Southampton'
Rosa 'Taniolokip'	Rosa 'Piccolo'
Rosa 'Tanky'	Rosa 'Whisky Mac'
Rosa 'Tanlarpost'	Rosa 'Polar Star'
Rosa 'Tanrowis'	Rosa 'Wimi'
Rosa 'Tapis d'Orient'	Rosa 'Yesterday'
Rosa 'The Optimist'	Rosa 'Sweet Repose'
Rosa 'Tipo Ideale'	Rosa x odorata 'Mutabilis'
Rosa triphylla	Rosa anemoniflora
Rosa 'Tropicana'	Rosa 'Super Star'
Rosa 'Village Maid'	Rosa centifolia 'Variegata'
Rosa 'Ville de Chine'	Rosa 'Chinatown'
Rosa Villosa 'Duplex'	Rosa 'Wolley-Dod'
Rosa 'Violet Blue'	Rosa 'Veilchenblau'
Rosa 'Viridiflora'	Rosa x odorata 'Viridiflora'
Rosa 'White Knight'	Rosa 'Message'
Rosa 'White Rose of York'	Rosa 'Alba Semiplena'
Rosa x pruhoniciana	Rosa 'Hillieri'
Rosa 'York and Lancaster'	Rosa x damascana versicolor
Rosa'Mattwyt'	Rosa 'Tynwald'
Roscoea capitata	Roscoea scillifolia
Rose 'Ziguenerknabe'	Rose 'Gipsy Boy'
Rosmarinus angustifolius	Rosmarinus officinalis angustissimus
Rosmarinus officinalis fastigiatus	Rosmarinus officinalis 'Miss Jessup's Upright'
Rosmarinus officinalis prostratus	Rosmarinus officinalis x lavandulaceus
Rosmarinus officinalis 'Variegatus'	Rosmarinus officinalis aureus
Rosularia crassipes	Rhodiola crassipes
Rosularia pallida	Rosularia chrysantha
Rubus fockeanus	Rubus calycinoides
Rubus giraldianus	Rubus cockburnianus
Rubus nutans	Rubus nepalensis
Rubus nutkanus	Rubus parviflorus
Rubus veitchii	Rubus thibetanus
Rudbeckia echinacea purpurea	Echinacea purpurea

Know Your Common Plant Names

Historical Pseudonyms	Most Recent Accepted Naming
Rudbeckia newmannii	Rudbeckia fulgida speciosa
Rudbeckia purpurea	Echinacea purpurea
Ruellia amoena	Ruellia graecizans
Rumex acetosa	Rumex rugosus
Ruscus racemosus	Danae racemosa
Russelia juncea	Russelia equisetiformis
Ruta prostrata	Ruta chalepensis
Sagina glabra 'Aurea'	Sagina subulata 'Aurea'
Sagittaria japonica	Sagittaria sagittifolia
Salisburia adiantifolia	Ginkgo biloba
Salix adenophylla	Salix syrticola
Salix alba argentea	Salix alba sericea
Salix alba 'Chermesina'	Salix alba 'Britzensis'
Salix alba 'Splendens'	Salix alba sericea
Salix amygdalina	Salix triandra
Salix arbutifolia	Chosenia arbutifolia
Salix babylonica 'Annularis'	Salix babylonica 'Crispa'
Salix caprea pendula (f)	Salix caprea 'Weeping Sally'
Salix caprea pendula (m)	Salix caprea 'Kilmarnock'
Salix 'Chrysocoma'	Salix x sepulcralis chrysocoma
Salix cordata	Salix syrticola
Salix daphnoides acutifolia	Salix acutifolia
Salix daphnoides 'Latifolia'	Salix daphnoides 'Aglaia'
Salix 'Elegantissima'	Salix pendula 'Blanda'
Salix 'Fuiri-Koriyanagi'	Salix integra 'Hakuro-Nishiki'
Salix 'Golden Curls'	Salix 'Erythroflexuosa'
Salix 'Hagensis'	Salix 'The Hague'
Salix incana	Salix elaeagnos
Salix integra 'Albomaculata'	Salix integra 'Hakuro-Nishiki'
Salix Kurome	Salix gracilistyla melanostachys
Salix lanata 'Stuartii'	Salix 'Stuartii'
Salix matsudana	Salix babylonica pekinensis
Salix medemii	Salix aegyptiaca
Salix melanostachys	Salix gracilistyla melanostachys
Salix myrsinites 'Jacquiniana'	Salix alpina
Salix nepalensis	Salix lindleyana
Salix nigricans	Salix myrsinifolia
Salix occidentalis	Salix humilis
Salix purpurea 'Eugenei'	Salix 'Eugenei'
Salix purpurea 'Gracilis'	Salix purpurea 'Nana'
Salix rosmarinifolia	Salix elaeagnos
Salix sachalinensis 'Sekka'	Salix udensis 'Sekka'
Salix setsuka	Salix udensis 'Sekka'
Salix tristis	Salix humilis
Salix vitellina 'Pendula'	Salix alba 'Tristis'
Salvia buchananii	Salix bacheriana
Salvia grahamii	Salvia microphylla

Know Your Common Plant Names

Historical Pseudonyms	Most Recent Accepted Naming
Salvia haematodes	Salvia pratensis Haematodes Group
Salvia hispanica	Salvia lavandulifolia
Salvia horminum	Salvia viridis
Salvia officinalis 'Variegata'	Salvia officinalis 'Icterina'
Sambucus glauca	Sambucus caerulea
Sambucus nigra 'Albomarginata'	Sambucus nigra 'Marginata'
Sambucus nigra 'Heterophylla'	Sambucus nigra 'Linearis'
Sambucus nigra 'Purpurea'	Sambucus nigra 'Guincho Purple'
Santolina chamaecyparisssus corsica	Santolina chamaecyparisssus nana
Santolina incana	Santolina chamaecyparissus
Santolina neapolitana	Santolina pinnata neapolitana
Santolina virens	Santolina rosmarinifolia rosmarinifolia
Saponaria officinalis 'Variegata'	Saponaria officinalis 'Dazzler'
Sarcococca orientalis	Sarcococca hookeriana digyna
Sarmienta repens	Sarmienta scandens
Sarothamnus scoparius	Cytisus scoparius
Sasa borealis	Sasamorpha borealis
Sasa tessellata	Indocalamus tessellatus
Sassafras officinale	Sassafras albidum
Sauromatum guttatum	Sauromatum venosum
Saxifraga aizoon	Saxifraga paniculata
Saxifraga 'Baldensis'	Saxifraga paniculata baldensis
Saxifraga luteoviridis	Saxifraga corymbosa
Saxifraga sarmentosa	Saxifraga stolonifera
Saxifraga x pectinata	Saxifraga x fritschiana
Scabiosa alpina	Cephalaria alpina
Scabiosa arvensis	Knautia arvensis
Scabiosa gigantea	Cephalaria gigantea
Scabiosa parnassi	Pterocephalus perennis
Scabiosa pterocephala	Pterocephalus perennis
Scabiosa rumelica	Knautia macedonica
Scabiosa succisa	Succisa pratensis
Scabiosa tatarica	Cephalaria gigantea
Schisandra grandiflora rubriflora	Schisandra rubriflora
Schizocentron elegans	Heterocentron elegans
Schizocodon	Shortia
Schizophragma viburnoides	Pileostegia viburnoides
Schlumbergera gaertneri	Rhipsalidopsis gaertneri
Schoenoplectus lacustris	Scirpus lacustris
Scilla adlamii	Ledebouria cooperi
Scilla campanulata	Hyacinthoides hispanica
Scilla chinensis	Scilla scilloides
Scilla non-scripta	Hyacinthoides non-scripta
Scilla nutans	Hyacinthoides non-scripta
Scilla ovalifolia	Ledebouria ovalifolia
Scilla tubergeniana	Scilla mischtschenkoana
Scilla violacea	Ledebouria socialis

Know Your Common Plant Names

Historical Pseudonyms	Most Recent Accepted Naming
Scindapsus aureus	Epipremnum aureum
Scolymus cardunculus	Cynara cardunculus
Scrophularia aquatica	Scrophularia auriculata
Scutellaria canescens	Scutellaria incana
Sedum albescens	Sedum reflexum
Sedum altissimum	Sedum sediforma
Sedum anopetalum	Sedum ochroleucum
Sedum athoum	Sedum album
Sedum batesii	Villadia hemsleyana
Sedum cyaneum	Sedum ewarsii homophyllum
Sedum floriferum	Sedum kamtschaticum
Sedum heterodontum	Rhodiola heterodonta
Sedum maximum	Sedum telephium maximum
Sedum primuloides	Rhodiola primuloides
Sedum purpureum	Sedum telephium
Sedum rhodiola	Rhodiola rosea
Sedum rosea	Rhodiola rosea
Sedum rupestre	Sedum forsterianum
Sedum spurium album	Sedum oppositifolium
Seemannia	Gloxinia
Selaginella emmeliana	Selaginella pallescens
Semiaquilegia simulatrix	Semiaquilegia ecalcarata
Semiarundinaria nitida	Sinarundinaria nitida
Sempervivella alba	Rosularia seaoides alba
Sempervivum arachnoideum	Sempervivum arachnoideum tomentosum
Sempervivum arvernense	Sempervivum tectorum
Sempervivum 'Aureum'	Greenovia aurea
Sempervivum hirtum	Jovibarba hirta
Sempervivum schlehanii	Sempervivum marmoreum
Sempervivum soboliferum	Jovibarba sobolifera
Senebiera didyma	Coronopus didymus
Senecio compactus	Brachyglottis compacta
Senecio greyi	Brachyglottis greyi
Senecio laxifolius	Brachyglottis laxifolia
Senecio monroi	Brachyglottis monroi
Senecio przewalskii	Ligularia przewalskii
Senecio reinoldii	Brachyglottis rotundifolia
Senecio 'Sunshine'	Brachyglottis 'Sunshine'
Sequoia gigantea	Sequoiadendron giganteum
Serissa japonica	Serissa foetida
Serratula shawii	Serratula seoanii
Setcreasea	Tradescantia
Setcreasea striata	Callisia elegans
Silene coeli-rosa	Viscaria elegans
Silene maritima	Silene vulgaris maritima
Silene schafta 'Abbotswood'	Lychnis x walkeri 'Abbotswood Rose'
Silene x arkwrightii	Lychnis x arkwrightii

Know Your Common Plant Names

Historical Pseudonyms	Most Recent Accepted Naming
Sinapis nigra	Brassica nigra
Siphonosmanthus delavayi	Osmanthus delavayi
Sisymbrium alliaria	Alliaria petiolata
Sisymbrium sophia	Descurainia sophia
Sisymbrium thalianum	Arabidopsis thaliana
Sisyrinchium brachypus	Sisyrinchium californicum
Sisyrinchium cuspidatum	Sisyrinchium arenarium
Sisyrinchium grandiflorum	Sisyrinchium douglasii
Sisyrinchium macounii	Sisyrinchium idahoense
Sisyrinchium odoratissimum	Phaiophleps biflora
Sisyrinchium scabrum	Sisyrinchium chilense
Sisyrinchium striatum variegatum	Sisyrinchium striatum 'Aunt May'
Sium erectum	Berula erecta
Skimmia fortunei	Skimmia reevesiana
Skimmia japonica 'Alba'	Skimmia japonica 'Fructo'albo'
Skimmia japonica 'Foremanii'	Skimmia x rogersii
Solanum crispum autumnale	Solanum crispum 'Glasnevin'
Solidago brachystachys	Solidago cutleri
Solidago hybrida	x Solidaster luteus
Solidago 'Lemore'	x Solidaster luteus 'Lemore'
Solidaster hybridus	Solidaster luteus
Solidaster hybridus	x Solidaster luteus
Sollya fusiformis	Sollya heterophylla
Sophora viciifolia	Sophora davidii
Sorbaria lindleyana	Sorbaria tomentosa
Sorbus americana erecta	Sorbus decora
Sorbus aria 'Decaisneana'	Sorbus aria 'Majestica'
Sorbus aria 'Mitchellii'	Sorbus thibetica 'John Mitchell'
Sorbus aucuparia 'Dulcis laciniata'	Sorbus aucuparia 'Beissneri'
Sorbus aucuparia pluripinnata	Sorbus scalaris
Sorbus aucuparia 'Xanthocarpa'	Sorbus aucuparia. 'Fructo Luteo'
Sorbus 'Embley'	Sorbus commixta 'Embley'
Sorbus hupehensis 'Rosea'	Sorbus hupehensis obtusa
Sorbus 'Mitchellii'	Sorbus thibetica 'John Mitchell'
Sorbus reflexipetala	Sorbus commixta
Sparganium natans	Sorbus angustifolium
Sparganium ramosum	Sparganium erectum
Sparganium simplex	Sparganium emersum
Spartina stricta	Spartina maritima
Spartocytisus nubigenus	Spartocytisus supranubius
Specularia hybrida	Legousia hybrida
Speirantha gardenii	Speirantha convallarioides
Spergula vulgaris	Spergula arvensis
Sphacele chamaedryoides	Lepechinia chamaedryoides
Spiraea aitchinsonii	Sorbaria aitchisonii
Spiraea albiflora	Spiraea japonica 'Albiflora'
Spiraea arborea	Sorbaria arborea

Know Your Common Plant Names

Historical Pseudonyms	Most Recent Accepted Naming
Spiraea 'Arguta Compacta'	Spiraea x cinerea
Spiraea ariifolius	Holodiscus discolor
Spiraea bracteata	Spiraea nipponica
Spiraea callosa 'Alba'	Spiraea japonica 'Albiflora'
Spiraea crispifolia	Spiraea japonica 'Bullata'
Spiraea discolor	Holodiscus discolor
Spiraea filipendula	Filipendula vulgaris
Spiraea hendersoni	Petrophytum hendersonii
Spiraea laevigata	Sibiraea laevigata
Spiraea menziesii 'Triumphans'	Spiraea x billiardii 'Triumphans'
Spiraea opulifolia	Physocarpus opulifolius
Spiraea palmata	Filipendula palmata
Spiraea 'Snowmound'	Spiraea nipponica tosaensis
Spiraea ulmaria	Filipendula ulmaria
Spiraea venusa	Filipendula rubra 'Venusta Magnifica'
Spiraea x bumalda	Spiraea japonica
Stachys betonica	Stachys officinalis
Stachys grandiflora	Stachys macrantha
Stachys lanata	Stachys byzantina
Stachys olympica	Stachys byzantina
Stachys spicata	Stachys macrantha
Stachyurus japonicus	Stachyurus praecox
Statice	Limonium
Statice limonium	Limonium vulgare
Statice suworowii	Psylliostachys suworowii
Stauntonia latifolia	Holboellia latifolia
Stenolobium stans	Tecoma stans
Stenomesson coccineum	Stenomesson variegatum
Stenomesson incarnatum	Stenomesson variegatum
Stephanandra incisa 'Prostrata'	Stephanandra incisa 'Crispa'
Stereulia acerifolia	Brachychiton acerifolius
Stewartia koreana	Stewartia pseudocamellia koreana
Stewartia pentagyna	Stewartia ovata
Stipa lasiagrostis	Stipa calamagrostis
Strangweia spicata	Bellevalia hyacinthoides
Stranvaesia davidiana	Photinia davidiana
Streptanthera elegans	Sparaxis elegans
Stuartia	Stewartia
Submatucana aurantiaca	Borzicactus aurantiacus
Suttonia australis	Myrsine australis
Suttonia nummularia	Myrsine nummularia
Swida alba	Cornus alba
Swida alternifolia	Cornus alternifolia
Swida amomum	Cornus amomum
Swida baileyi	Cornus baileyi
Swida controversa	Cornus controversa
Swida sanguinea	Cornus sanguinea

Know Your Common Plant Names

Historical Pseudonyms	Most Recent Accepted Naming
Symphoricarpos racemosus	Symphoricarpos albus
Symphoricarpos rivularis	Symphoricarpos albus laevigatus
Symphoricarpos vulgaris	Symphoricarpos orbiculatus
Symphytum grandiflorum	Symphytum ibericum
Symphytum ibericum 'Variegatum'	Symphytum 'Goldsmith'
Symphytum peregrinum	Symphytum x uplandicum
Symplocos crataegoides	Symplocos paniculata
Syringa afghanica	Syringa x protolaciniata
Syringa amurensis	Syringa reticulata mandschurica
Syringa palabiniana	Syringa meyeri 'Palibin'
Syringa persica laciniata	Syringa laciniata
Syringa 'Souvenir de Louis Spaeth'	Syringa 'Andenken an Ludwig Spath'
Syringa velutina	Syringa patula
Tabebuia donnell-smithii	Cybistax donnell-smithii
Tacitus bellus	Graptopetalum bellum
Tacsonia umbilicata	Passiflora umbilicata
Tacsonia van-volxemii	Passiflora antioquiensis
Tagetes tenuifolia	Tagetes signata
Tamarix germanica	Myricaria germanica
Tamarix pentandra	Tamarix ramosissima
Tamarix tetrandra 'Purpurea'	Tamarix perviflora
Tanacetum balsamita	Balsamita major
Taraxacum erythrospermum	Taraxacum laevigatum
Tasmannia lanceolata	Tasmannia aromatica
Taxus baccata 'Xanthocarpa'	Taxus baccata 'Lutea'
Taxus baccata'Fructoluteo'	Taxus baccata 'Lutea'
Tecoma australis	Pandorea pandorana
Tecoma radicans	Campsis radicans
Telesonix jamesii	Boykinia jamesii
Tellima grandiflora 'Purpurea'	Tellima grandiflora rubra
Testudinaria elephantipes	Dioscorea elephantipes
Tetranema mexicanum	Tetranema roseum
Teucrium latifolium	Teucrium fruticans
Teucrium rosmarinifolium	Teucrium creticum
Thalictrum adiantifolium	Thalictrum minus adiantifolium
Thalictrum coreanum	Thalictrum ichangense
Thalictrum dipterocarpum	Thalictrum delavayi
Thalictrum speciosissimum	Thalictrum flavum glaucum
Thamnocalamus falcatus	Drepanostachyum falcatum
Thamnocalamus falconeri	Drepanostachyum falconeri
Thamnocalamus tessellatus	Indocalamus tessellatus
Thelypteris phegopteris	Phegopteris connectilis
Thermopsis caroliniana	Thermopsis villosa
Thermopsis lanceolata	Thermopsis lupinoides
Thevetia neriifolia	Thevetia peruviana
Thlaspi macrophyllum	Pachyphragma macrophyllum
Thuja dolabrata	Thujopsis dolobrata

Know Your Common Plant Names

Historical Pseudonyms	Most Recent Accepted Naming
Thuja lobbii	Thuja plicata
Thuya	Thuja
Thymus 'Anderson's Gold'	Thymus x citriodorus 'Bertram Anderson'
Thymus drucei	Thymus praecox arcticus
Thymus 'E.B. Anderson'	Thymus x citriodorus 'Bertram Anderson'
Thymus lanuginosus	Thymus pseudolanuginosus
Thymus montanus	Thymus pulegioides
Thymus 'Silver Posy'	Thymus x citriodorus 'Variegatus'
Tiarella collina	Tiarella wherryi
Tilia alba	Tilia tomentosa
Tilia argentea	Tilia tomentosa
Tilia grandifolia	Tilia platyphyllos
Tilia parvifolia	Tilia cordata
Tilia platyphyllos 'Corallina'	Tilia platyphyllos 'Rubra'
Tilia platyphyllos erecta	Tilia platyphyllos 'Fastigiata'
Tilia x vulgaris	Tilia x europaea
Tolmiea 'Goldsplash'	Tolmiea menziesii 'Taff's Gold'
Tolmiea menziesii 'Variegata'	Tolmiea menziesii 'Taff's Gold'
Tovara	Persicaria
Trachelospermum japonicum	Trachelospermum majus
Tradescantia albiflora	Tradescantia fluminensis
Tradescantia blossfeldiana	Tradescantia cerinthoides
Tradescantia pexata	Tradescantia sillamontana
Tradescantia velutina	Tradescantia sillamontana
Tradescantia virginiana	Tradescantia x andersoniana
Tragopogon roseus	Tragopogon ruber
Tricholoma carneum	Calocybe carnea
Tricholoma crista	Melanoleuca strictipes
Tricholoma equestre	Tricholoma flavovirens
Tricholoma georgii	Calocybe gambosa
Tricholoma glaucocona	Lepista glaucocona
Tricholoma ionides	Calocybe ionides
Tricholoma nudum	Lepista nuda
Tricuspidaria lanceolata	Crinodendron hookerianum
Tricyrtis stolonifera	Tricyrtis formosana
Trifolium repens 'Tetraphyllum purpureum'	Trifolium repens 'Purpurascens Quadrifolium'
Trigonella ornithopodioides	Trifolium ornithopodioides
Trillium nervosum	Trillium catesbyi
Triodia decumbens	Sieglingia decumbens
Tripetaleia	Elliottia
Tripleurospermum maritimum	Matricaria maritima
Triteleia uniflora	Ipheion uniflorum
Trollius ledebourii	Trollius chinensis
Tsuga menziesii	Pseudotsuga menziesii
Tulipa aitchisonii	Tulipa clusiana
Tulipa eichleri	Tulipa undulatifolia
Tulipa persica	Tulipa celsiana

Know Your Common Plant Names

Historical Pseudonyms	Most Recent Accepted Naming
Tulipa polychroma	Tulipa biflora
Tulipa whittallii	Tulipa orphanidea
Tulipa wilsonima	Tulipa montana
Tunica 'Rosette'	Petrorhagia saxifraga 'Rosette'
Tunica saxifraga	Petrorhagia saxifraga
Typha stenophylla	Typha laxmannii
Ulex nanus	Ulex minor
Ulmus campestris	Ulmus procera
Ulmus carpinifolia 'Cornubiensis'	Ulmus angustifolia cornubiensis
Ulmus chinensis	Ulmus parvifolia
Ulmus fulva	Ulmus rubra
Ulmus glabra 'Horizontalis'	Ulmus glabra 'Pendula'
Ulmus montana	Ulmus glabra
Ulmus nitens	Ulmus carpinifolia
Ulmus sieboldii	Ulmus parvifolia
Ulmus stricta	Ulmus angustifolia cornubiensis
Ulmus x hollandica 'Wredei'	Ulmus 'Dampieri Aurea'
Ulmus x sarniensis 'Aurea'	Ulmus x sarniensis 'Dicksonii'
Uniola latifolia	Chasmanthium latifolium
Urcelina miniata	Urcelina peruviana
Ursinia chrysanthemoides 'Carl'	Euryops c. 'Carl'
Uvularia pudica	Uvularia caroliniana
Vaccinium maderense	Vaccinium padifolium
Valerianella olitoria	Valerianella locusta
Vallota	Cyrtanthus
Veltheimia undulata	Veltheimia bracteata
Veltheimia viridifolia	Veltheimia bracteata
Venidium	Arctotis
Venidium hirsutum	Arctotis hirsuta
Verbascum 'Broussa'	Verbascum bombyciferum
Verbascum longifolium pannosum	Verbascum olympicum
Verbascum thapsiforme	Verbascum densiflorum
Verbena alpina	Verbena tenera maonettii
Verbena bonariensis	Verbena patagonica
Verbena chamaedrifolia	Verbena peruviana
Verbena chamaedrioides	Verbena peruviana
Verbena 'Pink Bouquet'	Verbena 'Silver Anne'
Verbena pulchella	Verbena tenera
Verbena venosa	Verbena rigida
Veronica austriaca dubia	Veronica prostrata
Veronica buxbaumii	Veronica persica
Veronica candida	Veronica spicata incana
Veronica incana	Veronica spicata incana
Veronica lyallii	Parahebe lyallii
Veronica perfoliata	Parahebe perfoliata
Veronica rupestris	Veronica prostrata
Veronica saxatilis	Veronica fruticans

Know Your Common Plant Names

Historical Pseudonyms	Most Recent Accepted Naming
Veronica selleri	Veronica wormskjoldii
Veronica (Shrubby)	Hebe
Veronica teucrium	Veronica austriaca teucrium
Veronica virginica	Veronicastrum virginicum
Vestia lycoides	Vestia foetida
Viburnum alnifolium	Viburnum lantanoides
Viburnum coriaceum	Viburnum cylindricum
Viburnum fragrans	Viburnum farreri
Viburnum lentago 'Pink Beauty'	Viburnum nudum
Viburnum macrophyllum	Viburnum japonicum
Viburnum opulus "Fructo-luteo'	Viburnum opulus 'Xanthocarpum'
Viburnum opulus 'Sterile'	Viburnum opulus 'Roseum'
Viburnum plicatum 'Watanabe'	Viburnum plicatum 'Nanum Semperflorens'
Viburnum theiferum	Viburnum setigerum
Viburnum tomentosum	Viburnum plicatum tomentosum
Vicia angustifolia	Vicia sativa nigra
Vicia gracilis	Vicia tenuissima
Victoria regia	Victoria amazonica
Villaresia mucronata	Citronella mucronata
Vinca major 'Elegantissima'	Vinca major 'Variegata'
Vinca major 'Surrey Marble'	Vinca major 'Maculata'
Vinca minor 'Bowle's Variety'	Vinca major 'La Grave'
Vinca minor 'Caerulea Plena'	Vinca major 'Azurea Flora Pleno'
Vinca minor 'Double Burgundy'	Vinca major 'Multiplex'
Vinca minor 'Purpurea'	Vinca major atropurpurea
Viola albanica	Viola magellensis
Viola arenaria rosea	Viola rupestris rosea
Viola bosniaca	Viola elegantula
Viola cucullata	Viola oblique
Viola heterophylla epirota	Viola bertoloni
Viola sylvestris	Viola reichenbachiana
Viola velutina	Viola gracilis
Viscaria alpina	Lychnis alpina
Viscaria elegans	Silene coeli-rosa
Viscaria vulgaris	Lychnis viscaria
Vitis arborea	Ampelopsis arborea
Vitis brevipedunculata	Ampelopsis brevipedunculata
Vitis henryana	Parthenocissus henryana
Vitis inconstans 'Veitchii'	Parthenocissus tricuspidata 'Veitchii'
Vitis quinquefolia	Parthenocissus quinquefolia
Vitis rhombifolia	Cissus rhombifolia
Vitis vinifera 'Apiifolia'	Vitis vinifera 'Ciotat'
Vitis vinifera 'Brandt'	Vitis vinifera 'Brandt'
Volvaria bombycina	Volvariella bombycina
Vriesia botafogoensis	Vriesia saundersii
Wahlenbergia pumilio	Edraianthus pumilio
Wahlenbergia tasmanica	Wahlenbergia saxicola

Know Your Common Plant Names

Historical Pseudonyms	Most Recent Accepted Naming
Waldsteinia trifolia	Waldsteinia ternata
Watsonia angusta	Watsonia fulgens
Watsonia ardernei	Watsonia meriana
Wattakaka	Dregea
Welwitschia bainesii	Welwitschia mirabilis
Westringia rosmariniformis	Westringia fruticosa
Widdringtonia nodiflora	Widdringtonia cupressoides
Wilcoxia albiflora	Echinocereus leucanthus
Wilcoxia schmollii	Echinocereus schmollii
Wistaria	Wisteria
Wisteria 'Black Dragon'	Wisteria 'Kokkuryu'
Wisteria brachybotrys	Wisteria venusta
Wisteria floribunda 'Macrobotrys'	Wisteria floribunda 'Multijuga'
Worsleya procera	Worsleya rayneri
Xanthorrhiza apiifolia	Xanthorrhiza simplicissima
Xanthosoma lindenii	Caladium lindenii
Yucca angustifolia	Yucca glauca
Yucca filamentosa 'Bright Edge'	Yuccaflaccida 'Bright Edge'
Yucca guatemalensis	Yucca elephantipes
Yucca parviflora	Hesperaloe parviflora
Zantedeschia melanoleuca	Zantedeschia albo-maculata
Zauschneria californica 'Glasnevin'	Epilobium canum 'Dublin'
Zauschneria californica latifolia	Epilobium canum latifolium
Zauschneria microphylla	Epilobium canum
Zauschneria villosa	Epilobium canum mexicanum
Zebrina pendula	Tradescantia zebrina
Zebrina tabulaemontana	Tradescantea tabulaemontana
Zelkova acuminata	Zelkova serrata
Zelkova crenata	Zelkova carpinifolia
Zelkova cretica	Zelkova abelicea
Zelkova keaki	Zelkova serrata
Zenobia speciosa	Zenobia pulverulenta
Zephyranthes carinata	Zephyranthes grandiflora
Zephyranthes robusta	Habranthus robustus
Zerna erecta	Bromus erectus
Zerna ramosa	Bromus ramosus
Zizyphus jujuba	Ziziphus zizyphus
Zygocactus truncatus	Schlumbergera truncata

Translations

To be nomenclaturally correct the name in the original language should be used but in some cases the English language translation has been adopted for ease of use.

Language Key:
DH   –   Dutch
DK   –   Danish
FR   –   French
GN   –   German
JA   –   Japanese
LN   –   Latin
Sioux   –   Sioux (Red Indian)

Know Your Common Plant Names

Normally Used Name	Alternatively Used Name	Translated Language
Abies koreana 'Silberlocke'	Abies koreana 'silver curl'	GN
Acaena inermis 'Kupferteppich'	Acaena inermis 'Copper Carpet'	GN
Achillea 'Apfelblute'	Achillea 'Apple Blossom'	GN
Achillea 'Lachsschonheit'	Achillea 'Salmon Beauty'	GN
Achillea ptarmica 'Boule de Niege'	Achillea ptarmica 'Snowball'	FR
Achillea 'Schwefelblute'	Achillea 'Flowers of Sulphur'	GN
Achillea 'Unschuld'	Achillea 'Innocence'	GN
Ajuga reptans 'Braunherz'	Ajuga reptans 'Brown Heart'	GN
Alyssum 'Bergold'	Alyssum Mountain Gold	GN
Alyssum 'Goldkugel'	Alyssum 'Gold Ball'	GN
Anaphalis 'Neuschnee'	Anaphalis 'New Snow'	GN
Anaphalis 'Sommerschnee'	Anaphalis 'Summer Snow'	GN
Anemone x hybrida 'Königin Charlotte'	Anemone x hybrida 'Queen Charlotte'	GN
Anemone x hybrida 'Wirbelwind'	Anemone x hybrida 'Whirlwind'	GN
Arabis 'Fruhlingszauber'	Arabis 'Spring Charm'	GN
Arabis 'Schnechaube'	Arabis 'Snowcap'	GN
Armeria martima 'Düsseldorfer Stolz'	Armeria martima 'Dusseldorf Pride'	GN
Aster amellus 'Lac de Geneve'	Aster amellus 'Lake Geneva'	FR
Aster 'Herbstschnee'	Aster 'Autumn Snow'	GN
Aster 'Schneekissen'	Aster 'Snow Cushion'	GN
Aster 'Veilchen Konigin'	Aster 'Violet Queen'	GN
Aster x frikartii 'Mönch'	Aster x frikarti 'Monk'	GN
Astilbe 'Brautschleier'	Astilbe 'Bridal Veil'	GN
Astilbe 'Fever'	Astilbe 'Fire'	GN
Astilbe 'Germania'	Astilbe 'Deutschland'	GN
Astilbe 'Glut'	Astilbe 'Glow'	GN
Astilbe 'Irrlicht'	Astilbe 'Will o' the Wisp'	GN
Astilbe 'Koln'	Astilbe 'Cologne'	GN
Astilbe 'Straussenfeder'	Astilbe 'Ostrich Plume'	GN
Astilbe 'Weisse Gloria'	Astilbe 'White Gloria'	GN
Bellis perennis 'Bunter Teppich'	Bellis perennis 'Variegated Carpet'	GN
Berberis thunbergii 'Kobold'	Berberis thunbergii 'Goblin'	GN
Bergenia 'Abendglocken'	Bergenia 'Evening Bell'	GN
Bergenia 'Evening Glow'	Bergenia 'Abendglut'	GN
Bergenia 'Morgenrote'	Bergenia 'Morning Red'	GN
Bergenia 'Schneekonigin'	Bergenia 'Snow Queen'	GN
Bergenia 'Silberlicht'	Bergenia 'Silverlight'	GN
Campanula carpatica 'Blaue Clips'	Campanula carpatica 'Blue Clips'	GN
Campanula 'Schneekrone'	Campanula 'Crown of Snow'	GN
Castanea sativa 'Marron de Lyon'	Castanea sativa 'Chestnut of Lyon'	FR
Ceanothus 'Gloire de Versailles'	Ceanothus 'Glory of Versailles'	FR
Clematis 'Etoile de Paris'	Clematis 'Star of Paris'	FR
Clematis 'Etoile Rose'	Clematis 'Rose Star'	FR
Clematis 'Etoile Violette'	Clematis 'Violet Star'	FR
Clematis 'Perle d''Azur'	Clematis 'Azure Pearl'	FR
Clematis 'Ville de Lyon'	Clematis 'City of Lyon'	FR

Normally Used Name	Alternatively Used Name	Translated Language
Coreopsis 'Goldfink'	Coreopsis 'Goldfinch'	GN
Coreopsis 'Sonnenkind'	Coreopsis 'Baby Sun'	GN
Corylus maxima 'Red Zellernut'	Corylus maxima 'Red Filbert'	DH
Corylus maxima 'Witpit Lambertsnoot'	Corylus maxima 'White Filbert'	DH
Cotoneaster 'Cornubia'	Cotoneaster 'Cornwall'	LN
Cotoneaster salicifolius 'Herbstfeuer'	Cotoneaster salicifolius 'Autumn Fire'	GN
Cotoneaster salicifolius 'Parkteppich	Cotoneaster salicifolius 'Park Carpet'	GN
Cytisus 'Rote Favorit'	Cytisus 'Red Favourite'	GN
Deschampsia cespitosa 'Bronze-schleier'	Deschampsia cespitosa 'Bronze Veil'	GN
Deschampsia cespitosa 'Goldschleier'	Deschampsia cespitosa 'Gold Veil'	GN
Deschampsia cespitosa 'Goldstrub'	Deschampsia cespitosa 'Gold Dust'	GN
Deschampsia cespitosa 'Goldtau'	Deschampsia cespitosa 'Golden Dew'	GN
Doronicum 'Fruhlingspracht'	Doronicum 'Spring Beauty'	GN
Erigeron 'Dunkelste Aller'	Erigeron 'Darkest of All'	GN
Erigeron 'Rotes Meer'	Erigeron 'Red Sea'	GN
Erigeron 'Schwarzes Meer'	Erigeron 'Black Sea'	GN
Festuca glauca 'Blaufuchs'	Festuca glauca 'Blue Fox'	GN
Festuca glauca 'Blausilber'	Festuca glauca 'Blue Silver'	GN
Festuca glauca 'Meerblau'	Festuca glauca 'Sea Blue'	GN
Festuca Valesinca 'Silbersee'	Festuca Valesinca 'Silver Sea'	GN
Forsythia 'Goldzauber'	Forsythia 'Gold Charm'	GN
Gaillardia 'Kobold'	Gaillardia 'Goblin'	GN
Gypsophila 'Rosenschieier'	Gypsophila 'Rosy Veil'	GN
Gypsophila 'Schneeflocke'	Gypsophila 'Snowflake'	GN
Hamamelis x intermedia 'Feuerzauber'	Hamamelis x intermedia 'Magic Fire'	GN
Helenium 'Goldene Jugend'	Helenium 'Golden Youth'	GN
Helichrysum 'Schweffellicht'	Helichrysum 'Sulphur Light'	GN
Heliopsis 'Goldgrunherz'	Heliopsis 'Goldgreen heart'	GN
Heliopsis 'Hohlspiegel'	Heliopsis 'Concave mirror'	GN
Heliopsis 'Sommersonne'	Heliopsis 'Summer Sun'	GN
Hibiscus syriacus 'Oiseau Bleu'	Hibiscus syriacus 'Blue Bird'	GN
Hyacinthus 'Sneeuwwitje'	Hyacinthus 'Snow White'	GN
Hydrangea 'Blauer Prinz'	Hydrangea'Blue Prince'	GN
Hydrangea macrophylla 'Soeur Therésé'	Hydrangea macrophylla 'Sister Therese'	FR
Hydrangea 'Nidersachsen'	Hydrangea 'Lower Saxony'	GN
Iberis 'Weisser Zwerg'	Iberis 'Little Gem'	GN
Lamium galeobdolon 'Silberteppich'	Lamium galeobdolon 'Silver Carpet'	GN
Lathyrus latifolius 'Weisse Perle'	Lathyrus latifolius 'White Pearl'	GN
Liatris spicata 'Kobold'	Liatris spicata 'Goblin'	GN
Linum perenne 'Blau Saphir'	Linum perenne 'Blue Sapphire'	GN
Lythrum salicaria 'Feverkerze'	Lythrum salicaria 'Firecandle'	GN
Mahonia aquifolium 'Smaragd'	Mahonia aquifolium 'Emerald'	GN
Monarda 'Blaustrumpf'	Monarda 'Blue Stocking'	GN
Monarda 'Prarienacht'	Monarda Prairie Night'	GN
Monarda 'Schneewittchen'	Monarda 'Snow Maiden'	GN
Oenothera 'Feververkeri'	Oenothera 'Fireworks'	GN

Normally Used Name	Alternatively Used Name	Translated Language
Oenothera 'Fevererverkeri'	Oenothera 'Fireworks'	GN
Oenothera 'Hoheslicht'	Oenothera 'Highlight'	GN
Papaver orientale 'Turkenlaiis'	Papaver orientale 'Turkish Delight'	GN
Pernettya mucronata 'Parcelmoer'	Pernettya mucronata 'Mother of Pearl'	GN
Pernettya mucronata 'Sneeuwwitje'	Pernettya mucronata 'Snow White'	GN
Philadelphus 'Albatre'	Philadelphus 'Alabaster'	FR
Philadelphus 'Beauclerk'	Philadelphus 'Good Scholar'	FR
Philadelphus 'Belle Etoile'	Philadelphus 'Beautiful Star'	FR
Philadelphus 'Boule de Argent'	Philadelphus 'Ball of Silver'	FR
Philadelphus 'Bouquet Blanc'	Philadelphus 'White Bouquet'	FR
Philadelphus 'Conquete'	Philadelphus 'Conquest'	FR
Philadelphus 'Coupe d'Argent'	Philadelphus 'Cup of Silver'	FR
Philadelphus 'Manteau d'Hermine'	Philadelphus 'Coat of Ermine'	FR
Philadelphus 'Silverregen'	Philadelphus Silver Showers'	GN
Philadelphus 'Voie Lactee'	Philadelphus 'Milky Way'	FR
Phlox douglas 'Lilakönigin'	Phlox douglas 'Lilac Queen'	GN
Populus alba 'Raket'	Populus alba 'Rocket'	GN
Potentilla 'Goldrausch'	Potentilla 'Goldrush'	GN
Potentilla 'Goldteppich'	Potentilla 'Gold Carpet'	GN
Prunella 'Little Red Riding Hood'	Prunella 'Rotkappchen'	GN
Prunus 'Amanogawa'	Prunus 'Milky Way'	JA
Prunus 'Cistena'	Prunus 'Baby'	SIOUX
Prunus 'Fugenzo'	Prunus 'Goddess on a White Elephant'	JA
Prunus 'Jo-nioi'	Prunus 'Supreme Fragrance'	JA
Prunus 'Kiku Shidare'	Prunus 'Weeping Chrysanthemum'	JA
Prunus 'Shirofugen'	Prunus 'White Goddess'	JA
Prunus 'Shirotae'	Prunus 'Snow White'	JA
Prunus 'Shirotae'	Prunus 'Snowflake'	JA
Prunus 'Shogetsu'	Prunus 'Moon Hanging Low by a Pine'	JA
Prunus 'Ukon'	Prunus 'Yellowish'	JA
Pulmonaria sccharata 'Fruhlingshimmel'	Pulmonia saccharata 'Spring Sky'	GN
Robinia 'Casque Rouge'	Robinia 'Red Helmet'	FR
Rosa 'Assemblage des Beautés'	Rosa 'Assembly of Beauties'	FR
Rosa 'Chapeau de Napoleon'	Rosa 'Hat of Napoleon'	FR
Rosa 'Coupe D' Hebe	Rosa 'Cup of Hebe'	FR
Rosa 'Danse du Feu'	Rosa 'Dance of Fire'	FR
Rosa 'Devil de Paul Fontaine'	Rosa 'Death of Paul Fontaine'	FR
Rosa 'Du Mâitre d'Ecole'	Rosa 'The Schoolmaster'	FR
Rosa 'Düsterlohe'	Rosa 'Dark Flame'	GN
Rosa 'Etoile d'Hollande'	Rosa 'Star of Holland'	FR
Rosa 'Etude'	Rosa 'Study'	FR
Rosa 'Fruhlingsanfang'	Rosa 'Spring's Beginning'	GN
Rosa 'Fruhlingsanfang'	Rosa 'Spring's Beginning'	GN
Rosa 'Fruhlingsduft'	Rosa 'Spring's Fragrance'	GN
Rosa 'Fruhlingsduft'	Rosa 'Spring's Fragrance'	GN
Rosa 'Fruhlingsgold'	Rosa 'Spring's Gold'	GN

Know Your Common Plant Names

Normally Used Name	Alternatively Used Name	Translated Language
Rosa 'Fruhlingsgold'	Rosa 'Spring's Gold'	GN
Rosa 'Fruhlingsmorgen'	Rosa 'Spring's Morning'	GN
Rosa 'Fruhlingsmorgen'	Rosa 'Spring's Morning'	GN
Rosa 'Fruhlingstag'	Rosa 'Spring's Day'	GN
Rosa 'Fruhlingstag'	Rosa 'Spring's Day'	GN
Rosa 'Fruhlingszauber'	Rosa 'Spring's Charm'	GN
Rosa 'Fruhlingszauber'	Rosa 'Spring's Charm'	GN
Rosa 'Gros Chou d'Hollande'	Rosa 'Large Cabbage of Holland'	FR
Rosa 'Herzog von Windsor'	Rosa 'Duke of Windsor'	GN
Rosa 'Königin Von Dänemark'	Rosa 'Queen of Denmark'	GR
Rosa 'Konigin Von Danemark'	Rosa 'Queen of Denmark'	GN
Rosa 'Königliche Hoheit'	Rosa 'Royal Highness'	GN
Rosa 'La Réve'	Rosa 'The Dream'	FR
Rosa 'Lafter'	Rosa 'Laughter'	GN
Rosa 'Licherloh'	Rosa 'Light Flame'	FR
Rosa 'Lykkefund'	Rosa 'Lucky Find'	DK
Rosa 'Mousseline'	Rosa 'Muslin'	FR
Rosa 'München'	Rosa 'Munich'	GN
Rosa 'Nuage Parfume'	Rosa 'Fragrant Cloud'	FR
Rosa 'Oeillet Parfait'	Rosa 'Perfect Carnations'	FR
Rosa 'Perle d'Or'	Rosa 'Pearl of Gold'	FR
Rosa 'Pour Toi'	Rosa 'Para Ti'	FR
Rosa 'Quatre Saisons'	Rosa 'Four Seasons'	FR
Rosa 'Quatre saisons Blanc Mousseux'	Rosa 'Four Seasons White Moss'	FR
Rosa 'Raubritter'	Rosa 'Robber Knight'	FR
Rosa 'Reine des Violettes'	Rosa 'Queen of Violets'	FR
Rosa 'Ritter Von Barmstede'	Rosa 'Knight of Barmstede'	GN
Rosa 'Rose du Roi à fleur Pourpre'	Rosa 'King of Purple Flowered Roses'	FR
Rosa 'Rosenwunder'	Rosa 'Rose Wonder'	FR
Rosa 'Ruhm Von Steinfurth'	Rosa 'Glory of Steinfurth'	GN
Rosa 'Scharlachglut'	Rosa 'Scarlet Fire'	GN
Rosa 'Scharlachglut'	Rosa 'Scarlet Fire'	GN
Rosa 'Schneelicht'	Rosa 'Snow Light'	GN
Rosa 'Schneezwerg'	Rosa 'Snow Dwarf'	GN
Rosa 'Schwanensee'	Rosa 'Swan Lake'	GN
Rosa 'Soleil d'Or'	Rosa 'Golden Sun'	FR
Rosa 'Sonnenlicht'	Rosa 'Sunlight'	FR
Rosa 'Surpasse Tout'	Rosa 'Surprise All'	FR
Rosa 'Veilchenblau'	Rosa 'Violet Blue'	GN
Rosa 'Ville de Chine'	Rosa 'Chinatown'	FR
Rosa 'Violet Blue'	Rosa 'Veilchenblau'	GN
Rosa 'Zitronenfalter'	Rosa 'Lemon Butterfly'	GN
Rosa 'Zwergkönig'	Rosa 'Dwarf King'	GN
Rose 'Ziguenerknabe'	Rose. 'Gipsy Boy'	GN
Salvia x superba 'Blauhugel'	Salvia x superba 'Blue Hill'	GN
Salvia x superba 'Blaukonigin'	Salvia x superba 'Blue Queen'	GN

Know Your Common Plant Names

Normally Used Name	Alternatively Used Name	Translated Language
Salvia x superba 'Mainacht'	Salvia x superba 'May Night'	GN
Salvia x superba 'Ostfriesland'	Salvia x superba 'East Friesland'	GN
Sedum spurium 'Purpurteppich'	Sedum spurium 'Purple Carpet'	GN
Sedum spurium 'Schorbuser Blut'	Sedum spurium 'Dragon's Blood'	GN
Thuja occidentalis 'Smaragd'	Thuja occidentalis 'Emerald'	GN
Thuya occidentalis 'Danica'	Thuya occidentalis 'Denmark'	LN
Viburnum x hillieri 'Winton'	Viburnum x hillieri 'Winchester'	LN